Ordinary Differential Equations

INTRODUCTIONS TO HIGHER MATHEMATICS

A series of brief expository texts designed for use in upper undergraduate courses and in the early years of graduate study.

BIRKHOFF, G. and ROTA, G. *Ordinary Differential Equations*

HILLE, E. *Analytic Function Theory, Volume I*

HILLE, E. *Analytic Function Theory, Volume II*

KEMENY, J. G. and SNELL, J. L.
Mathematical Models in the Social Sciences

PRAGER, W. *Introduction to Mechanics of Continua*

ORDINARY DIFFERENTIAL EQUATIONS

GARRETT BIRKHOFF
Harvard University

GIAN-CARLO ROTA
Massachusetts Institute of Technology

GINN AND COMPANY

Boston New York Chicago Atlanta Dallas Palo Alto Toronto

Library of Congress Catalog Card Number: 61–15025

Preface

The theory of differential equations is distinguished for the wealth of its ideas and methods. Although this richness makes the subject attractive as a field of research, it has frequently been the cause of confusion on the part of the student. For many students the transition from the elementary theory of differential equations to the study of advanced methods and techniques has been too abrupt. One of the chief purposes of the present text is to fill this gap.

We present what seem to us to be the most important key ideas of the subject in their simplest context, often that of second-order equations. We have deliberately avoided the systematic elaboration of these key ideas, feeling that this is often best done by the student himself. After one has grasped the underlying methods, one of the best ways to develop technique is to generalize (say, to higher-order equations or systems) by one's own efforts.

The exposition presupposes primarily a knowledge of the advanced calculus, and some experience with the formal manipulation of elementary differential equations. Beyond this, only an acquaintance with vectors, matrices, and elementary complex functions is assumed in most of the book. Familiarity with the concepts of pole and branch point is assumed in Chapter IX, and in Chapter XI Euclidean vector spaces are used freely.

The book falls broadly into three parts. Chapters I through IV constitute a review of material to which, presumably, the student has already been exposed in elementary courses. This has a twofold purpose: to fill the inevitable gaps in the student's knowledge of the beginnings of the subject, and to give a rigorous presentation of the material. This first part covers elementary methods of integration of first-order, second-order linear, and n-th order linear constant-coefficient differential equations. Besides reviewing elementary methods, it includes rigorous discussions of comparison theorems and the method of majorants. Finally, a brief introduction is given to the concepts of transfer function and Nyquist diagram, and their relation to the Laplace transform. Although widely used for many years in electrical engineering, these concepts seem not to have previously found their way into textbooks on differential equations.

Chapters V through VIII deal with systems of nonlinear differential equations. Chapter V includes theorems of existence, uniqueness, and continuity, both in the small and in the large, and introduces the perturbation equations. Chapter VI treats plane autonomous systems, including the classification of nondegenerate critical points, and introduces the important notion of stability and Liapunov's method, which is then applied to some of the simpler types of nonlinear oscillations. Chapters VII and VIII provide a brief survey of the theory of effective numerical integration.

Finally, Chapters IX through XI are devoted to the study of second-order linear differential equations. Chapter IX develops the theory of regular singular points, with applications to some important special functions. Chapter X is devoted to Sturm-Liouville theory and related asymptotic formulas, for both finite and infinite intervals. Chapter XI establishes the completeness of the eigenfunctions of regular Sturm-Liouville systems, without assuming the Lebesgue integral.

Throughout the book, the properties of various important special functions—notably Bessel functions, hypergeometric functions, and the more common orthogonal polynomials—are derived from their defining differential equations and boundary conditions. We have thought in this way both to illustrate the theory of ordinary differential equations and to show its power.

This textbook can be used either in a one-term survey course, or as a leisurely one-year course. In a one-term course, one would normally omit starred sections. Or one might try to cover thoroughly a selection of chapters, developing each in full. Thus, one might cover Chapters I–III, V and VI, and IX–XI—or, in a more elementary course, Chapters I–VIII.

In a year's course, the book can be used as an introduction to more advanced and systematic treatments, such as are found in the well-known treatises of Cesari, Coddington and Levinson, Ince, and Niemytskii and Stepanoff. Another possibility is to use the book as a continuation of an elementary text on differential equations.

This text contains several hundred exercises of varying difficulty, which in all cases should be an important part of the course. The most difficult exercises are starred.

It is a pleasure to extend our thanks to John Barrett, Fred Brauer, Thomas Brown, Lamberto Cesari, Abol Ghaffari, Norman Levinson, Robert Lynch, Laurence Markus, and Frank Stewart for their comments, criticisms, and help in eliminating errors. We also thank John Freeman, Nicholas Metas, Richard Moroney, David Morrison, Norton Starr, Fred Van Vleck, John Wells, and Michael Wilber for assistance in proofreading.

We are also grateful for expert typing by Judith Bowers, Peggy Ericson, Laura Schlesinger, and especially Ellen Burns, who prepared not only the final version, but three preliminary editions of course notes. Finally, we wish to thank Priscilla England for her careful editorial work, and the College Department of Ginn and Company for their continuous cooperation during three years of book preparation.

Cambridge, Massachusetts

Garrett Birkhoff
Gian-Carlo Rota

Table of Contents

CHAPTER I.	First-order Differential Equations	3
CHAPTER II.	Second-order Linear Equations	25
CHAPTER III.	Power Series Solutions	49
CHAPTER IV.	Linear Equations with Constant Coefficients	73
CHAPTER V.	Existence and Uniqueness Theorems	99
CHAPTER VI.	Plane Autonomous Systems	129
CHAPTER VII.	Approximate Solutions	161
CHAPTER VIII.	Efficient Numerical Integration	184
CHAPTER IX.	Regular Singular Points	213
CHAPTER X.	Sturm-Liouville Systems	247
CHAPTER XI.	Expansions in Eigenfunctions	286

Ordinary Differential Equations

1-1
1-2
1-3
1-4
1-5
1-9
1-10
1-11
2-3
3-1
3-2
3-5
3-6
3-8
3-9
3-10
4-1
4-2
4-3
4-4

CHAPTER I

First-order Differential Equations

1. Introduction. A *differential equation* is an equation between the derivatives of a function, its values, and known quantities. Because the laws of physics are most simply and naturally formulated as differential equations (or DE's, as we shall write for short), the latter have been studied by the greatest mathematicians and mathematical physicists since the time of Newton.

Ordinary differential equations are DE's whose unknowns are functions of a single variable; they arise most commonly in the study of dynamical systems and electrical networks. They are much easier to treat than partial differential equations, whose unknown functions depend on two or more independent variables.

Ordinary DE's are classified according to their order. The *order* of a DE is defined as the largest positive integer n, for which an n-th derivative occurs in the equation. This chapter will be restricted to *real first-order* DE's of the form

$$\phi(x,y,y') = 0. \tag{1}$$

Given the function ϕ of three real variables, the problem is to determine all real functions $y = f(x)$ which satisfy the DE, that is, all solutions of (1) in the following sense.

DEFINITION. *A* solution *of* (1) *is a differentiable function $f(x)$ such that $\phi(x,f(x),f'(x)) = 0$, for all x in the interval where $f(x)$ is defined.*

EXAMPLE 1. In the first-order DE

$$x + yy' = 0, \tag{2}$$

the function ϕ is a polynomial function $\phi(x,y,z) = x + yz$ of the three variables involved. The solutions of (2) can be found by considering the identity $d(x^2 + y^2)/dx = 2(x + yy')$. From this identity, one sees that $x^2 + y^2 = C$ is a constant if $y = f(x)$ is any solution of (2).

The equation $x^2 + y^2 = C$ defines y *implicitly* as a two-valued function of x, for any positive constant C. Solving for y, we get *two* solutions, the (single-valued†) functions $y = \pm\sqrt{C - x^2}$, for each positive constant C.

†In this book, the word "function" will always mean single-valued function, unless the contrary is expressly specified.

The *graphs* of these solutions, the so-called *solution curves*, form two families of semicircles, which fill the upper half-plane $y > 0$ and the lower half-plane $y < 0$, respectively.

On the x-axis, where $y = 0$, the DE (2) implies $x = 0$. Hence the DE has no solutions which cross the x-axis, except possibly at the origin. This fact is easily overlooked, because the solution curves *appear* to cross the x-axis to form full circles, as in Figure I-1. However, these circles have infinite slope where they cross the x-axis; hence y' does not exist there and the DE (2) is *not* satisfied.

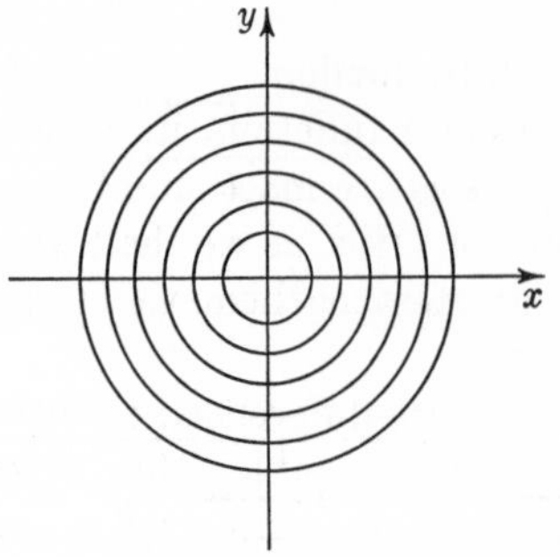

Figure I-1.
Integral Curves of $x + yy' = 0$

The preceding difficulty also arises if one tries to solve the DE (2) for y'. Dividing through by y, one gets $y' = -x/y$, an equation which cannot be satisfied if $y = 0$. The preceding difficulty is thus avoided if one restricts attention to regions where the DE (1) is normal, in the following sense.

DEFINITION. *A* normal *first-order DE is one of the form*

(3) $$y' = F(x,y).$$

In the normal form $y' = -x/y$ of the DE (2), the function $F(x,y)$ is continuous in the upper half-plane $y > 0$, and in the lower half-plane where $y < 0$; it is undefined on the x-axis.

2. Fundamental Theorem of the Calculus. The most familiar class of differential equations consists of the first-order normal DE's of the form

(4) $$y' = g(x).$$

The solutions of such DE's are described by the Fundamental Theorem of the Calculus, which reads as follows.

FUNDAMENTAL THEOREM OF THE CALCULUS. *Let the function $g(x)$ in the DE (4) be continuous in the interval $a \leqq x \leqq b$. Given a number c, there is one and only one solution $f(x)$ of the DE (4) in the interval such that $f(a) = c$. This solution is given by the definite integral*

(5) $$f(x) = c + \int_a^x g(t)dt, \qquad c = f(a).$$

This basic result serves as a model of rigorous formulation in several respects. First, it specifies the region under consideration, as a vertical strip $a \leqq x \leqq b$ in the (x,y)-plane. Second, it describes in precise terms the class of functions $g(x)$ considered. And third, it asserts the *existence* and *uniqueness* of a solution, given the "initial condition" $f(a) = c$.

It will be recalled that the definite integral

$$(5') \qquad \int_a^x g(t)dt = \lim_{\max \Delta t_k \to 0} \sum g(t_k)\,\Delta t_k, \quad \Delta t_k = t_k - t_{k-1}$$

is defined for each fixed x as a limit of Riemann sums; it is not necessary to find a formal expression for the indefinite integral $\int g(x)dx$ in order to give a meaning to the definite integral $\int_a^x g(t)dt$, provided only that $g(t)$ is continuous. Such functions as the *error function* $\operatorname{erf} x = (2/\sqrt{\pi})\int_0^x e^{-t^2}dt$ and the *sine integral function* $\operatorname{SI}(x) = \int_x^\infty [(\sin t)/t]dt$ are indeed commonly *defined* as definite integrals; cf. Ch. III, § 1.

To formulate and prove analogous theorems for more general first-order normal DE's we need some technical concepts. We define a *domain*† as a nonempty *open connected* set. A function $\phi = \phi(x_1,\cdots,x_r)$ is said to be *of class* $\mathcal{C}^n$ in a domain D, when all its derivatives $\partial\phi/\partial x_i$, $\partial^2\phi/\partial x_i\partial x_j, \cdots$ of orders $1, \cdots, n$ exist and are continuous in D. One writes this condition in symbols as $\phi \in \mathcal{C}^n$ in D, or $\phi \in \mathcal{C}^n(D)$. When ϕ is merely assumed to be continuous in D, one writes $\phi \in \mathcal{C}$ in D, or $\phi \in \mathcal{C}(D)$.

Intervals appear so frequently in analysis that they are referred to by a special notation. Thus, the *closed* interval $a \leqq x \leqq b$, which is not a domain (why not?) is denoted by $[a,b]$, the *open* interval $a < x < b$ by (a,b), the positive semi-axis $0 \leqq x < +\infty$ by $[0, +\infty)$, and so on. Generally, a round bracket indicates that the endpoint adjacent to it is excluded from the interval, and a square bracket that the adjacent endpoint is included.

Given $F(x,y)$, the notation $F \in \mathcal{C}^2[1,+\infty)$ thus means that F is twice continuously differentiable in the *closed* domain including the vertical line $x = 1$ and all points to the right of it in the (x,y)-plane. Likewise $F \in \mathcal{C}[0,1]$ means that F is continuous in the vertical strip $0 \leqq x \leqq 1$. Where there is any question of just what domain is referred to below, the domain will be described in words as well as in symbols.

There are a number of obvious facts about the differentiability of solutions of DE's. Such facts about differentiability will be used below without special comment where they are irrelevant to the main idea of a proof. For instance, if $g \in \mathcal{C}^n(a,b)$, and $y = f(x)$ is any solution of the DE $y' = g(x)$, then $y \in \mathcal{C}^{n+1}(a,b)$. Again, if $\phi \in \mathcal{C}^n$ and $\psi \in \mathcal{C}^n$ in a domain D, and $F(u,v) \in \mathcal{C}^n$ in the entire (u,v)-plane, then $G(x,y) = F(\phi(x,y),\psi(x,y)) \in \mathcal{C}^n(D)$.

†Some authors say *region* where we say domain. We will call the closure of a domain a *closed domain*.

3. Normal and regular curve families. Closely related to the concepts of a normal first-order DE (3) and a first-order DE (1) are the concepts of a normal curve family and a regular curve family, respectively. These are defined as follows.

DEFINITION. *In a domain D of the (x,y)-plane, a* normal curve family *is a family of curves defined by an equation $y=f(x,C)$ with f of class $\mathcal{C}^1$ and $\partial f/\partial C > 0$. A* regular curve family *is a family of curves such that; (i) one and only one curve of the family passes through each point of D, (ii) each curve of the family has a tangent at every point, and (iii) the tangent direction is a continuous function of position.*

To avoid ambiguity, one must distinguish systematically between *explicit* (single-valued) functions $y=f(x)$, *implicit* functions defined by equations such as $u(x,y)=C$, and functions defined *parametrically* by equation-pairs $x=\xi(t)$, $y=\eta(t)$. Though we shall reserve the word *function* for explicit functions, equations and equation-pairs also define single-valued functions locally. This follows from the Implicit Function Theorem,† which we now state for functions of two variables.

IMPLICIT FUNCTION THEOREM. *Let $u(x,y)$ be a function of class $\mathcal{C}^n$, for some $n \geqq 1$. Let $u(x_0,y_0)=C$, and let $\partial u(x_0,y_0)/\partial y \neq 0$. Then there exists a unique single-valued function $f(x)$ of class $\mathcal{C}^n$ in some open interval (a,b) containing x_0, such that $y_0=f(x_0)$ and $u(x,f(x))=C$ for all x in (a,b).*

THEOREM 1. *Any normal curve family is regular. The curves of any regular curve family having nowhere vertical tangents are all solution curves of the same normal DE $y'=F(x,y)$ with continuous F.*

Proof. By the Implicit Function Theorem, the condition $\partial f/\partial C > 0$ implies that there is one and only one curve $y=f(x,C(x_0,y_0))$ passing through each point (x_0,y_0) of the domain. The condition that $\partial f/\partial x$ is continuous means that the slope of the tangent to the curve passing through (x,y) varies continuously with the point (x,y). Hence any normal curve family is regular in its domain of definition.

The second statement is little more than a restatement in analytical terms of the definition of a regular curve family, but it gives a suggestive idea of the geometrical meaning of (3).

Clearly, the graphs of the solutions $y=c+f(x)$ of the DE (4) form a normal curve family in the vertical strip $a \leqq x \leqq b$, with $\partial y/\partial c=1$. They are all obtained from the particular solution curve $y=f(x)$ by vertical translation. This is apparent in Figure I-2, which shows the solutions of the DE $y'=e^{-x^2}$.

†Courant, Vol. 2, p. 114; Widder, p. 55. Here and below, page references to authors refer to the books listed in the selected Bibliography on pp. 311–312.

The preceding distinction is illustrated by Example 1. The solution curves $y = \sqrt{C - x^2}$ $(C > 0)$ form a normal curve family in the upper half-plane, while the graphs of the solutions $y = -\sqrt{-C - x^2}$ $(C < 0)$ form a normal curve family in the domain $y < 0$. The circles $x^2 + y^2 = C$ $(C > 0)$ form a regular curve family in the plane with the origin deleted (the "punctured plane"). This regular curve family is, however, not normal.

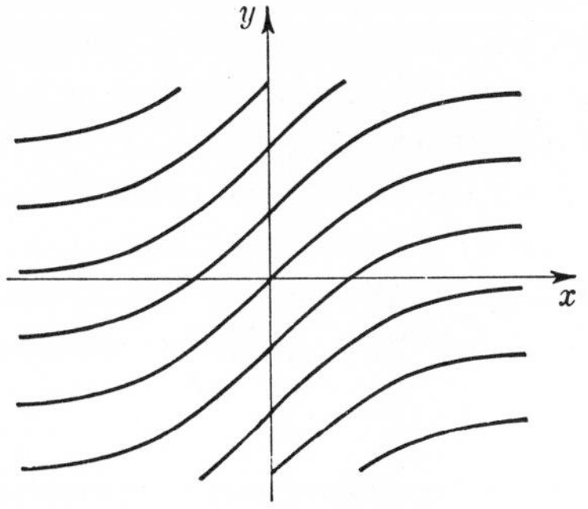

Figure I-2.

Solution Curves of $y' = e^{-x^2}$

One of our main objects will be to generalize Theorem 1 to wider classes of DE's. We will show that, if $F \in \mathcal{C}^1$ in a domain D (in symbols, if $F \in \mathcal{C}^1(D)$), then the graphs of the solutions of $y' = F(x,y)$ form a normal curve family in D. Moreover, if M and N are continuously differentiable in a domain D, then the graphs of the parametrically defined solutions of $M(x,y)dx/dt + N(x,y)dy/dt = 0$ form a regular curve family in the domain consisting of D with the "critical points" where $M = N = 0$ deleted.

However, these general results will not be proved until Ch. V, § 12, and Ch. VI, § 2, respectively. For the present, in order to give precise formulations and proofs, we will have to content ourselves with much less sweeping conclusions.

4. Exact differentials. A differential $Mdx + Ndy$ $(M,N \in \mathcal{C})$ is called *exact* in a domain D, when the line integral

$$\int_\Gamma M(x,y)dx + N(x,y)dy \tag{6}$$

is the same for all paths of integration Γ in D which have the same end-points. It is shown in the calculus† that $Mdx + Ndy$ is exact if and only if there exists a continuously differentiable function $u(x,y)$ such that $M = \partial u/\partial x$ and $N = \partial u/\partial y$, that is, such that the total differential $du = (\partial u/\partial x)dx + (\partial u/\partial y)dy$ is $Mdx + Ndy$. *For continuously differentiable* M, N, a necessary condition for $Mdx + Ndy$ to be exact is that M and N satisfy the partial DE $\partial M/\partial y = \partial N/\partial x$; if D is simply connected, this condition is also sufficient.

We now consider first-order DE's of the form

$$\phi(x,y,y') = M(x,y) + N(x,y)y' = 0, \tag{7}$$

with M, $N \in \mathcal{C}$ in a domain D. Dividing by N, we obtain the algebraically

†Courant, Vol. 2, p. 352; Widder, p. 251.

equivalent normal form

$$(7') \qquad y' = F(x,y) = -M(x,y)/N(x,y),$$

except on the closed set where N vanishes, i.e., where $\partial\phi/\partial y' = 0$. This set (the x-axis in Example 1) divides the domain D into a number of *subdomains*, in each of which the normal form (7′) is equivalent to (7).

It is often stated that the solutions of the DE (7) are the contour lines $u(x,y) = C$, whenever $Mdx + Ndy = du$ is an exact differential. But as Example 1 shows, this is not true. To describe the precise relation between the solutions of the DE (7) and the contour lines $u(x,y) = C$, we make the following definitions.

DEFINITION. *An integral of the DE (7) is a function $u(x,y) \in \mathcal{C}^1$ which is constant whenever $y = f(x)$ is a solution of (7) (on all solution curves). When u is an integral of (7), the contour lines $u(x,y) =$ constant are called* integral curves, *in any domain where* grad $u = (\partial u/\partial x, \partial u/\partial y)$ *is nonvanishing.*

THEOREM 2. *If $M(x,y)dx + N(x,y)dy$ is an exact differential du in a domain D, then the contour lines $u(x,y) = C$ are integral curves of (7), for any constant C. These contour lines form a regular curve family in the domain D^*, consisting of D with the* critical points *where $M = N = 0$ (i.e., where* grad $u = 0$) *deleted.*

The proof is immediate, for any continuous M, N. Along any solution curve $y = f(x)$,

$$du/dx = \partial u/\partial x + y' \, \partial u/\partial y = M(x,y) + N(x,y)y' = 0.$$

The regularity of the family of contour lines follows directly from the Implicit Function Theorem. They form a normal family in any subdomain where N does not vanish.

EXERCISES A

1. Plot the integral curves of the DE $y' = y^2/x^2$. In which regions of the plane do they form a regular curve family? A normal curve family?
2. Find equations describing all solutions of $y' = (x + y)^2$.
3. Find equations describing all solutions of $y' = (2x + y)^{-1}$.
4. Show that if a normal curve family is invariant under horizontal translation, then the curves of the family are the solution curves of a DE of the form $y' = f(y)$.
5. Find all functions $f(x)$ whose definite integral between 0 and any x equals the reciprocal of $f(x)$. (*Hint:* DE is $y' = -y^3$.)
6. For what pairs of positive integers n, r is the function $|x|^n$ of class $\mathcal{C}^r$?
7. In what domains do the level lines $x^3 + 3x^2y + y^3 = c$ form a regular curve family? A normal curve family?
8. Same question for $x^3 - 3x^2y + y^3 = c$.
9. Find all integral curves of $(x^n + y^n)y' - x^{n-1}y = 0$. (*Hint:* Set $u = y/x$.)

*10. Let $f(x)$ and $g(y) \neq 0$ be continuous in the rectangle $a < x < b$, $c < y < d$. Prove that the DE $y' = f(x)g(y)$ has a unique solution through each point of the rectangle.

*11. Show that each solution of Ex. 10 can be continued up to the boundary of the rectangle.

12. Solve the DE $yy' + x = 0$ by the method of separation of variables, deducing rigorously the domains in which the method gives normal families of solutions.

*13. Same question for the DE $y' = xy - xy^3$.

5. Integrating factors. When the differential $Mdx + Ndy$ is not exact, one can often find a function $\mu(x,y)$ such that the product

$$(\mu M)dx + (\mu N)dy = du$$

is an exact differential. The contour lines $u(x,y) = C$ will then again be integral curves of the DE $M(x,y) + N(x,y)y' = 0$ because $du/dx = \mu(M + Ny') = 0$; and segments of these contour lines between points of vertical tangency will be solution curves. Such a function μ is called an integrating factor.

DEFINITION. *An* integrating factor *for a differential* $M(x,y)dx + N(x,y)dy$ *is a nonvanishing function* $\mu(x,y)$ *such that the product* $(\mu M)dx + (\mu N)dy$ *is an exact differential.*

For example, consider the DE $xy' = y$. The differential $xdy - ydx$ which is associated with it is not exact, but it has the integrating factor $1/(x^2 + y^2)$ in the right half-plane $x > 0$. In fact, the function $\theta(x,y)$ defined by the line integral

$$\theta(x,y) = \int_{(1,0)}^{(x,y)} (xdy - ydx)/(x^2 + y^2)$$

is the angle made with the positive x-axis by the vector (x,y). That is, it is just the polar angle θ when the point (x,y) is expressed in polar coordinates. Thus the integral curves of $xy' = y$ in the domain $x > 0$ are the radii $\theta = C$, where $-\pi/2 < \theta < \pi/2$; the solution curves are the same.

Note that the differential $(xdy - ydx)/(x^2 + y^2)$ is not exact in the punctured plane, consisting of the (x,y)-plane with the origin deleted. For, θ changes by 2π in going around the origin. This is possible, even though $\partial[x/(x^2 + y^2)]/\partial x = \partial[-y/(x^2 + y^2)]/\partial y$, because the punctured plane is not a simply connected domain.

EXAMPLE 2. The first-order *linear* DE is

$$a(x)y' + b(x)y + c(x) = 0. \tag{8}$$

It is called *homogeneous* if $c(x) \equiv 0$, and *inhomogeneous* otherwise.

*The more difficult exercises are starred throughout this book.

Let the coefficient-functions a, b, c be continuous. In any interval I where $a(x)$ does not vanish, the linear DE (8) can be reduced to the normal form

$$y' = -p(x)y - q(x), \tag{9}$$

with continuous coefficient-functions $p = b/a$ and $q = c/a$. The Fundamental Theorem of the Calculus (§ 2) implies the existence of an indefinite integral $\int p(x)dx = P(x)$ of class $\mathfrak{C}^1$, such that $P'(x) = p(x)$. Any such $P(x)$ defines a positive continuous integrating factor $e^{P(x)}$ of the normal linear DE (9). For, the expression

$$[e^{P(x)}q(x) + e^{P(x)}p(x)y]dx + e^{P(x)}dy$$

is an exact differential, with the integral

$$u = ye^{P(x)} + \int e^{P(x)}q(x)dx. \tag{10}$$

The existence of the integral on the right side of (10) again follows from the Fundamental Theorem of the Calculus. Formula (10) implies that

$$ye^{\int pdx} + \int [qe^{\int pdx}]dx = C. \tag{10'}$$

By Theorem 2, the contour lines $u(x,y) = C$ are integral curves of (9), where any indefinite integral is chosen in (10). Solving for y, we get for any $x_0 \in I$ the equivalent equation

$$y = Ce^{-P(x)} - e^{-P(x)} \int_{x_0}^{x} e^{P(t)}q(t)dt, \quad P(x) = \int p(t)dt, \tag{11}$$

where C is an arbitrary constant. Namely, we have shown that if $y = f(x)$ is any solution of (9), then the left side of (10′) is constant. Conversely, for any constant C, the function (11) defines a solution of (9). This proves

THEOREM 3. *If $p(x)$ and $q(x)$ are continuous, the solutions of the normal linear DE (9) are the functions (11).*

For this reason, formula (11) is said to define the *general solution* of (9). In formula (11), the right side is a function $y = f(x,C)$ of class $\mathfrak{C}^1$ in any vertical strip $a < x < b$ where the functions p, q are continuous; this follows from the Fundamental Theorem of the Calculus. Moreover, since any power of e is positive, $\partial f/\partial C = e^{-P(x)} > 0$. From this follows the

COROLLARY. Let *$p, q \in \mathfrak{C}$ in any open interval (a,b) of the x-axis. Then the solutions (11) of (9) form a normal curve family in the vertical strip $a < x < b$ in the (x,y)-plane.*

In particular, for any "initial value" y_0, the choice

$$C = e^{P(x_0)}y_0 + \int_{x_0}^{x} e^{P(t)}q(t)dt$$

gives one and only one solution of (9) satisfying the "initial condition" $f(x_0) = y_0$.

Quadrature. In the Fundamental Theorem of the Calculus, if the function g is nonnegative, the definite integral in (5) is the area under the curve $y = g(x)$ in the vertical strip between a and x. For this reason, the integration of (4) is called a *quadrature.* Formula (11) reduces the solution of any first-order linear DE to the performance of a sequence of quadratures. Using Tables of Indefinite Integrals,† the solutions can therefore often be expressed in closed form, in terms of well-known functions whose numerical values have been tabulated ("tabulated functions").

EXERCISES B

1. Find all solutions of the DE $|x| + |y| y' = 0$. In which regions of the plane is the differential on the left side exact?

2. (a) Reduce the *Bernoulli* DE $y' + p(x)y = q(x)y^n$ to a linear first-order DE by the substitution $u = y^{1-n}$. (b) Express its general solution using indefinite integrals.

3. Show that if $\mu(x,y)$ and $\nu(x,y)$ are integrating factors of class $\mathcal{C}^1$ for the same DE $M(x,y) + N(x,y)y' = 0$, with $M, N \in \mathcal{C}^2$, then the quotient $h(x,y) = \mu(x,y)/\nu(x,y)$ is an integral of the DE whenever $\nu(x,y) \neq 0$.

In Exs. 4–7, describe domains in which the solutions of the DE's specified form regular curve families:

4. $y' = \dfrac{y}{x} - \dfrac{x}{\log |x|}$.

5. $y' = \dfrac{y}{x} - \cos(\log |x|)$.

6. $\dfrac{dr}{d\theta} = r^2 \sin \dfrac{1}{r}$ (Polar coordinates).

7. $\dfrac{dr}{d\theta} = 2 \log r$.

6. Linear fractional equation. An important first-order DE is the *linear fractional equation*

$$\frac{dy}{dx} = \frac{cx + dy}{ax + by}, \qquad ad \neq bc, \tag{12}$$

which is the normal form of

$$(ax + by)y' - (cx + dy) = 0. \tag{12'}$$

It is understood that the coefficients a, b, c, d are constants.

The integration of the DE (12) can be reduced to a quadrature by the substitution $y = vx$. This substitution replaces (12) by the DE

$$xv' + v = (c + dv)/(a + bv),$$

in which the variables x and v can be separated. Transposing v, we are led

†See the books by Peirce and Foster and by Dwight listed in the Bibliography. Kamke's book listed there contains an extremely useful catalog of solutions of DE's not of the form $y' = g(x)$. For a bibliography of function tables, see Fletcher, Miller, and Rosenhead.

to the separation of variables

$$\frac{(a+bv)dv}{bv^2+(a-d)v-c}+\frac{dx}{x}=0.$$

Since the integrands are rational functions, this can be integrated in terms of elementary functions. Thus x can be expressed as a function of $v=y/x$:

$$x = CG(y/x), \qquad \text{where}$$
$$G(v) = \exp - \left\{\int [(a+bv)/(bv^2+(a-d)v-c)]dv\right\}. \tag{13}$$

The preceding formulations can be rigorously justified provided $x \neq 0$, $ax+by \neq 0$, and $bv^2+(a-d)v \neq c$. These loci divide the (x,y)-plane into at most eight sectors.

Another good way to obtain solutions of (12) is to introduce polar coordinates, setting $x=r\cos\theta$, $y=r\sin\theta$. If $\psi=\gamma-\theta$ is the angle between the tangent direction γ and the radial direction θ, then

$$\frac{1}{r}\frac{dr}{d\theta}=\cot\psi=\frac{\cot\gamma\cot\theta+1}{\cot\theta-\cot\gamma}$$

Since $\tan\gamma=y'=(cx+dy)/(ax+by)=(c+d\tan\theta)/(a+b\tan\theta)$, the final expression in the preceding equation is equal to

$$[(a+b\tan\theta)\cot\theta+(c+d\tan\theta)]/[(c+d\tan\theta)\cot\theta-(a+b\tan\theta)].$$

Multiplying numerator and denominator by $\sin\theta\cos\theta$, we reduce the linear fractional DE (12) to

$$\frac{1}{r}\frac{dr}{d\theta}=\frac{a\cos^2\theta+(b+c)\sin\theta\cos\theta+d\sin^2\theta}{c\cos^2\theta+(d-a)\sin\theta\cos\theta-b\sin^2\theta}=Q(\theta). \tag{14}$$

This can also be integrated by a quadrature. The solution is

$$r(\theta)=r(0)\exp\left\{\int_0^\theta Q(\theta)d\theta\right\}, \tag{14'}$$

which is well-defined by the Fundamental Theorem of the Calculus as long as the denominator of $Q(\theta)$ does not vanish.

Invariant radii. The radii along which the denominator of $Q(\theta)$ vanishes are those where (12) is equivalent to $d\theta/dr=0$. Hence they are particular solution curves of (12); they are called *invariant radii.* They are the solutions $y=\tau x$, for constant $\tau=\tan\theta$. Therefore they are the radii $y=\tau x$ for which $y'=\tau=(c+d\tau)/(a+b\tau)$, by (12), and so their slopes τ are the roots of the quadratic equation

$$b\tau^2+(a-d)\tau=c. \tag{15}$$

This equation can also be obtained by setting the denominator of (14) equal to zero.

Equation (15) has zero, one, or two roots, according as its discriminant is negative, zero, or positive. This discriminant is

$$\Delta = (a - d)^2 + 4bc = (a + d)^2 - 4(ad - bc). \tag{16}$$

In the sectors between invariant radii, $d\theta/dr$ has constant sign; this fact facilitates the sketching of solution curves. Together with the invariant radii, the solution curves (14′) form a regular curve family in the *punctured plane*, consisting of the (x,y)-plane with the origin deleted.

7. Graphical integration. The simplest way to sketch approximate solution curves of a given first-order normal DE $y' = F(x,y)$ proceeds as follows. Draw a short segment with slope $\lambda_i = F(x_i,y_i) = \tan \theta_i$ through each point (x_i,y_i) of a set of sample points sprinkled fairly densely over the domain of interest. Then draw smooth curves so as to have at every point a slope y' approximately equal to the average of the $F(x_i,y_i)$ at nearby points, weighting the nearest points most heavily (i.e., using graphical interpolation). Methods of doing this systematically are called schemes of *graphical integration.*

The preceding construction also gives a graphical representation of the direction field associated with a given normal first-order DE. This is defined as follows.

DEFINITION. *A* direction field *in a region D of the plane is a function which assigns to every point (x,y) in D a* direction. *Two directions are considered the same if they differ by an integral multiple of* 180°, *or π radians.*

Direction fields are defined by many DE's which are not normal. Thus, for the DE $M(x,y) + N(x,y)y' = 0$ with continuous M and N, one can draw a short segment through points (x_i,y_i) parallel to the vector $(N(x_i,y_i), -M(x_i,y_i))$, through any point not a "critical point" where $M = N = 0$, and proceed as before. Such segments can be vertical, whereas this is impossible for normal DE's.

It is very easy to integrate graphically the linear fractional equation (14), because the direction is constant along each radius $y = vx$, $v =$ constant. One needs only draw segments having the right direction fairly densely on radii spaced at intervals of (say) 30°. After tracing one approximate integral curve through the direction field by the graphical method described above, one can construct others by similarity, taking advantage of the following

Similarity Property. Each solution of the linear fractional DE (12) is transformed into another solution when x and y are both multiplied by the same nonzero constant k. In polar coordinates, if $r = f(\theta)$ is a solution (14), then so is $r = kf(\theta)$. Since the transformation $(x,y) \to (kx,ky)$ is a similarity transformation of the (x,y)-plane for any fixed k, it follows that the solution curves in the sector between any two adjacent invariant lines are all *geometrically similar*. This fact is apparent in the drawings of Figure I-3.

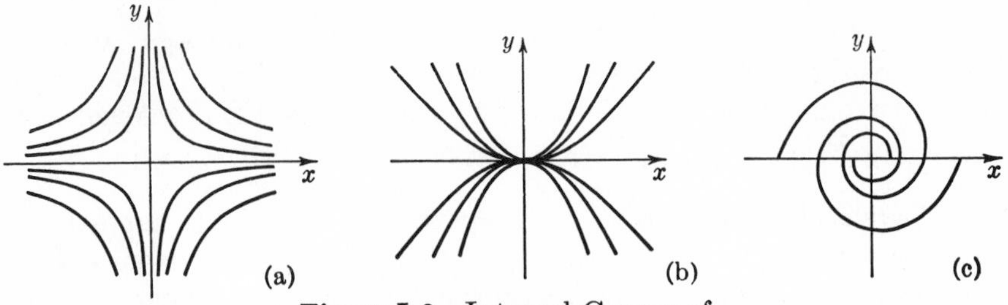

Figure I-3. Integral Curves of

(a) $xy' + y = 0$, (b) $xy' = 2y$, (c) $y' = (3x + y)/(x - 3y)$

EXERCISES C

1. Sketch the integral curves of the DE's in Ex. B4–B7 in the neighborhood of the origin of coordinates.

2. Represent graphically the direction fields of the following linear fractional DE's and sketch typical solution curves:
(a) $y' = -x/2y$, (b) $y' = 1 + y/x$, (c) $y' = (2x + y)/(2x - y)$.

3. (a) Show that the inhomogeneous linear fractional DE

$$(cx + dy + e)dx - (ax + by + f)dy = 0, \quad ad \neq bc,$$

can be reduced to the form (12) by a translation of coordinates.

(b) Using this idea, integrate $(x + y + 1)dx = (2x - y - 1)dy$.

(c) For what constants a, b, c, d, e, f, is the DE exact?

4. Express in closed form all solutions of the following DE's:
(a) $y' = (x^2 - y^2)/(x^2 + y^2)$, (b) $y' = \sin (y/x)$, (c) $xy' = f(y/x)$.

5. Show that the solutions of any homogeneous DE $y' = g(y/x)$ have the Similarity Property described in § 7.

6. Show that the solution curves of $y' = G(x,y)$ cut those of $y' = F(x,y)$ at a constant angle β if and only if $G = (\tau + F)/(1 - \tau F)$, where $\tau = \tan \beta$.

7. Let A, B, C be constants. Show that the coaxial conics $Ax^2 + 2Bxy + Cy^2 = K$, where K is a parameter, satisfy the DE $y' = -(Ax + By)/(Bx + Cy)$.

8. (a) Show that the differential $(ax + by)dy - (cx + dy)dx$ is exact if and only if $a + d = 0$, and that in this case the integral curves form a family of coaxial conics.

(b) Using Exs. 6 and 7, show that if $\tan \beta = (a + d)/(c - b)$, then the curves cutting the solution curves of the linear fractional DE $y' = (cx + dy)/(ax + by)$ at an angle β form a family of coaxial conics.

9. Sketch sample curves of the family of graphs of

$$y = f(x,c) = \begin{cases} -x^2 - c + 1 & c < -1 \\ cx^2 & -1 \leqq c \leqq 1 \\ x^2 + c - 1 & 1 < c. \end{cases}$$

Do the above curves form a normal curve family in the punctured plane, with the origin deleted? Do they form a regular curve family in this domain?

10. (a) Show that the functions in Ex. 9 satisfy the DE

$$(*)\quad y' = F(x,y) = \begin{cases} -2x & \text{if} \quad y < -x^2 \\ 2y/x & \text{if} \quad -x^2 \leqq y \leqq x^2 \\ 2x & \text{if} \quad y > x^2. \end{cases}$$

(b) Is F continuous? Justify your answer.

(c) Find a two-parameter family of curves satisfying (*). (*Hint:* See the discussion of Example 4 below.)

11. For the linear fractional DE (12), show that

$$y'' = (ad - bc)[cx^2 - (a - d)xy - by^2]/(ax + by)^3.$$

Discuss the domains of convexity and concavity of solutions.

12. Find an integrating factor for $y' + 2y/x = a$, and integrate the DE by quadratures.

13. Find all integral curves of $y' = -(2x + y - 1)/(x + 2y - 1)$, and make a sketch of the regular family of these curves. (*Hint:* See Ex. 3c.)

8*. Equations of higher degree.

A first-order polynomial DE of the form

$$(17)\qquad \phi(x,y,y') = y'^n + \sum_{k=1}^{n} M_k(x,y)y'^{\,n-k} = 0$$

is said to be of degree n when it is of degree n considered as a polynomial in y'. For given x,y, it is satisfied by at most n values of y'. This observation leads one to define the *degree* of a first-order DE $\phi(x,y,y') = 0$ generally, as the largest number of values of y' compatible with given values of x and y.

The reduction of a first-order DE of degree $n > 1$ to normal form may be accomplished as follows.

Let ϕ be of class $\mathcal{C}^1$ in a domain D of three-dimensional (x,y,y')-space. The locus $\partial\phi/\partial y' = 0$ is then a closed set, called the *singular locus.* Thus, for the DE $M(x,y) + N(x,y)y' = 0$, the singular locus is the set $N = 0$ where the normal form is undefined. In each subdomain where $\partial\phi/\partial y' \neq 0$, the DE $\phi(x,y,y') = 0$ is equivalent to a set of normal DE's by the Implicit Function Theorem. We illustrate this situation by example.

EXAMPLE 3. Consider Euler's quadratic DE

$$(18)\qquad (1 - x^2)y'^2 = (1 - y^2),$$

for which ϕ is $(1 - x^2)y'^2 - (1 - y^2)$ in (1). In the region of the (x,y)-plane where $(1 - x^2)$ and $(1 - y^2)$ have opposite signs, (18) has no real solution because y'^2 is never negative. In the region where they have the same sign, solving (18) for y' gives the two alternative normal forms

$$(18')\quad y' = \sqrt{\frac{1 - y^2}{1 - x^2}} = F_1(x,y) \text{ and } y' = -\sqrt{\frac{1 - y^2}{1 - x^2}} = F_2(x,y).$$

*Sections marked with a star can be skipped without loss of continuity.

The solutions of these DE's can be found by the method of separation of variables, as follows.

In the square $|x| < 1$, $|y| < 1$, equations (18′) are equivalent to

$$dy/\sqrt{1-y^2} = \pm\, dx/\sqrt{1-x^2}.$$

In the domain $|x| > 1$, $|y| > 1$, they are equivalent to

$$dy/\sqrt{y^2-1} = \pm\, dx/\sqrt{x^2-1}.$$

Taking the indefinite integrals of all terms, we get four families of solutions:

(18a) $$\sin^{-1}y \pm \sin^{-1}x = C \quad \text{on} \quad |x| < 1,\ |y| < 1,$$

and

(18b) $$\cosh^{-1}y \pm \cosh^{-1}x = C \quad \text{on} \quad |x| > 1,\ |y| > 1,$$

where C is an arbitrary constant or *parameter*.

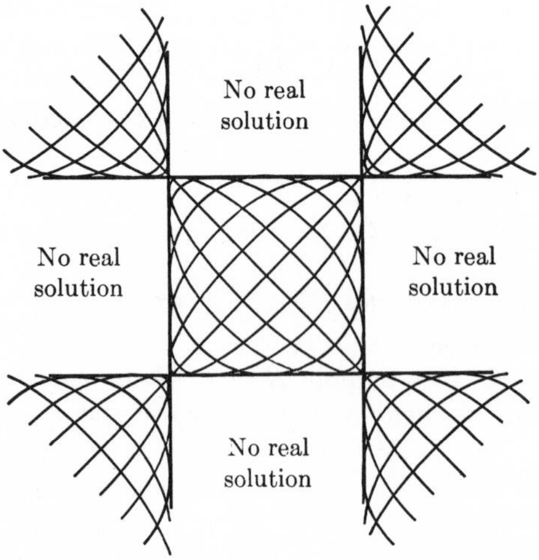

Figure I-4. Integral Curves of Euler's Quadratic DE

Typical solution curves of the DE (18), as given by (18a) and (18b), are sketched in Figure I-4. Two such curves pass through each point (x_0,y_0) in the regions where real solutions exist. The number of curves through each point is equal to the degree of the DE (18), regarded as a polynomial equation expressing the unknown y' implicitly as a function of x and y.

Note that the function $y \equiv 1$, which clearly satisfies the DE (18), is a solution for which $dy/\sqrt{y^2-1}$ and $dy/\sqrt{1-y^2}$ are undefined. Finally, the solutions are exhibited in (18a) and (18b) not as explicit functions

$y = f(x)$ of the independent variable x, but only as implicit functions $u(x,y) = \text{constant}$.

Clairaut equation. Another equation of higher degree is the Clairaut DE

$$y = xy' + h(y'),$$

where h is an arbitrary function. Solutions can be obtained by inspection, as a one-parameter family

$$y = Cx + h(C)$$

of nonparallel straight lines.

For example, if $h(y') = -y'^2/2$, the straight lines so obtained are the tangents to the parabola $y = x^2/2$. This parabola, which is an *envelope* of the straight line solutions, is also a solution since it has the "right" slope at every point. One can also verify analytically that $y = x^2/2$ satisfies the DE $y = xy' - y'^2/2$. The parabola is called a *singular* solution of the Clairaut DE; it is the singular locus where $\partial\phi/\partial y' = 0$ in the given DE.

EXERCISES D

1. Show that the confocal ellipses $x^2/\lambda + y^2/(1+\lambda) = 1$, $0 < \lambda < +\infty$, form a regular curve family in the domain exterior to the interval $-1 \leqq y \leqq 1$ of the y-axis.

2. Show that the ellipses of Ex. 1 satisfy the DE

$$(*) \qquad y'^2 + [(x^2 - y^2 + 1)/xy]y' = 1.$$

3. Show that the hyperbolas $x^2/\lambda + y^2/(1+\lambda) = 1$, $-1 < \lambda < 0$, form a family of curves which satisfy (*) and are orthogonal to the ellipses of Ex. 1. Describe the domain in which the curve family is regular.

4. Show that the tangents to the parabola $y = x^2$ are the lines $y = \lambda^2/4 = \lambda(x - \lambda/2)$. In which domains of the plane, if any, do these lines form a regular curve family?

5. Show that the family of straight lines in Ex. 4 satisfies the Clairaut DE $y = xy' - y'^2/4$. Find a two-parameter family of solutions of this DE. (See the discussion of Example 4 below.)

6. Show that the integral curves of Example 3 are ellipses and hyperbolas with diagonal axes, tangent to four straight lines (the "singular solutions" $y = \pm 1$, $x = \pm 1$), as in Figure I-4.

7. Integrate and find the singular solutions of the DE

$$y'^2 - 2x\sqrt{y}\, y' + 4y\sqrt{y} = 0 \qquad \text{(Boole).}$$

(*Hint*: Reduce to a Clairaut DE by setting $u = \sqrt{y}$.)

*8. Reduce the following DE's to normal form, specifying for each normal form a domain of regularity in (x, y, y'):

(a) $y'^3 + 3xy' = y$,

(b) $2xy(1 + y'^2) - (xy' + y)^2 = 0$, (Abbé Moigno)

(c) $xy^2y'^2 - y^3y' + a^2x = 0$. (Schlömilch)

9. Initial value problem. For any normal first-order differential equation $y' = F(x,y)$, and any "initial" x_0 (think of x as time), the *initial value problem* consists in finding the solution or solutions of the DE, for $x \geqq x_0$, which assume a given initial value $f(x_0) = c$. In geometric language, this amounts to finding the solution curve or curves which issue from the point (x_0,c) in the (x,y)-plane.

When $F(x,y) = g(x)$ depends on x alone, the initial value problem is solved by the Fundamental Theorem of the Calculus (§ 2). Given $x_0 = a$ and $y_0 = c$, the initial value problem for the DE $y' = g(x)$ has one and only one solution, given by the definite integral (5).

The initial value problem is said to be *well-set* in a domain D, when there is one and only one solution $y = f(x,c)$ in D of the given DE, for each given $(x_0,c) \in D$, and when this solution varies continuously with c. To show that the initial value problem is well-set, therefore, requires proving theorems of *existence* (there is a solution), *uniqueness* (there is only one solution), and *continuity* (the solution depends continuously on the initial value). The term *well-set* is applied to boundary value problems for DE's generally. As was pointed out by Hadamard, solutions which do not have the properties specified are useless physically, because no physical measurement is exact. The concept of a well-set initial value problem gives a precise mathematical interpretation of the physical concept of *determinism* (cf. Ch. V, § 5).

From the definition of a normal curve family (§ 3), it follows that the initial value problem is well-set in any domain D where the solution curves constitute a normal curve family. Thus it is well-set for the linear DE $y' + p(x)y = q(x)$, in any vertical strip $a < x < b$ where p and q are continuous. The initial value problem is also well-set for the linear fractional DE (12), in each of the half-planes $ax + by > 0$ and $ax + by < 0$.

For the solutions of a DE to form a normal curve family in a domain D, and hence for the initial value problem to be well-set there, it is sufficient that $F \in \mathcal{C}^1$ in D. But it is not sufficient that $F \in \mathcal{C}$: though the continuity of F implies the existence of at least one solution through every point (cf. Ch. V, § 13), it does not necessarily imply uniqueness, as the following example shows.

EXAMPLE 4. Consider the curve family $y = (x - C)^3$, sketched in Figure I-5. It is regular but not normal: $\partial y/\partial C$ vanishes when $y = 0$, on the x-axis. Moreover, for fixed C,

$$y' = \partial y/\partial x = 3(x - C)^2 = 3y^{2/3}, \tag{19}$$

a DE whose right side is a continuous function of position (x,y). Through every point (x_0,c) of the plane passes just one curve $y = (x - C)^3$ of the family, for which $C = x_0 - c^{1/3}$ depends continuously on (x_0,c). Hence the initial value problem for the DE (19) always has one and only one solution of the form $y = (x - C)^3$. But there are also other solutions.

Thus the function $y = 0$ also satisfies (19). Its graph is the envelope of the curves $y = (x - C)^3$. In addition, for any $\alpha < \beta$, the function defined by the three equations

$$y = \begin{cases} (x-\alpha)^3 & x < \alpha \\ 0 & \alpha \leqq x \leqq \beta \\ (x-\beta)^3 & x > \beta, \end{cases}$$

is a solution of (19). Hence the first-order DE $y' = 3y^{2/3}$ has a *two-parameter* family of solutions, depending on the parameters α and β.

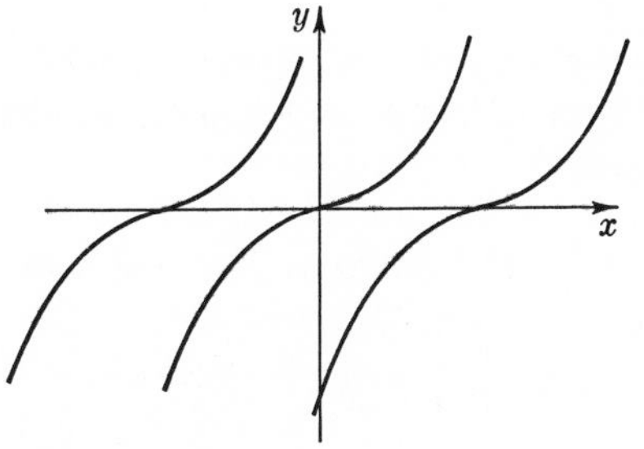

Figure I-5. Solution Curves of $y' = 3y^{2/3}$

10. Uniqueness. We are now ready to show that, under a relatively mild and easily tested condition on the function F, the normal first-order DE $y' = F(x,y)$ admits of only one solution $f(x)$ satisfying a given initial condition $f(a) = c$. In order that the initial value problem have a unique solution, it is not sufficient that the function F be only continuous, as Example 4 shows. However, the following stronger condition implies uniqueness.

DEFINITION. *A function $F(x,y)$ satisfies a Lipschitz condition*† *in a domain D, when, for some finite constant L (Lipschitz constant), it satisfies the inequality*

$$|F(x,y) - F(x,z)| \leqq L\,|y - z|, \tag{20}$$

for all point-pairs (x,y) and (x,z) in D having the same x-coordinate.

The same function F may satisfy Lipschitz conditions with different Lipschitz constants, or no Lipschitz conditions at all, as the domain D under consideration varies. For example, the function $F(x,y) = 3y^{2/3}$ of the *DE* in Example 4 satisfies a Lipschitz condition in any strip $|y| \geqq \epsilon$, $\epsilon > 0$,

†R. Lipschitz, *Bull. Sci. Math.* 10 (1876), p. 149; the idea of the proof is due to Cauchy (1839). See Ince, p. 76, for a historical discussion.

with $L = 2\epsilon^{-1/3}$. More generally, one can prove

LEMMA 1. *Let F be continuously differentiable in any closed convex*† *domain D. Then it satisfies a Lipschitz condition, with $L = \sup_D |\partial F/\partial y|$.*

Proof. The domain being convex, it contains the entire vertical segment joining (x,y) with (x,z). Applying the Law of the Mean to $F(x,\eta)$ on this segment, considered as a function of η, we have

$$|F(x,y) - F(x,z)| = |y - z|\,|\partial F(x,\eta)/\partial y|,$$

for some η between y and z. The inequality (20), with $L = \sup_D |\partial F/\partial y|$, follows.

The case $F(x,y) = g(x)$ of ordinary integration, or "quadrature," is easily identified as the case when $L = 0$. A Lipschitz condition is satisfied even if $g(x)$ is discontinuous.

LEMMA 2. *Let σ be a differentiable function satisfying the differential inequality*

$$\sigma'(x) \leqq K\sigma(x), \qquad a \leqq x \leqq b, \tag{21}$$

where K is a constant. Then

$$\sigma(x) \leqq \sigma(a)e^{K(x-a)} \quad \text{for} \quad a \leqq x \leqq b. \tag{21'}$$

Proof. Multiply both sides of (21) by e^{-Kx} and transpose, getting

$$0 \geqq e^{-Kx}[\sigma'(x) - K\sigma(x)] = \frac{d}{dx}\left\{\sigma(x)e^{-Kx}\right\}.$$

The function $\sigma(x)e^{-Kx}$ thus has a nonpositive derivative, and so is nonincreasing for $a \leqq x \leqq b$. Therefore $\sigma(x)e^{-Kx} \leqq \sigma(a)e^{-Ka}$, q.e.d.

COROLLARY. *If $\sigma(a) = 0$ in Lemma 2 and $\sigma(x) \geqq 0$, then $\sigma(x) \equiv 0$.*

THEOREM 5 (Uniqueness Theorem). *In any domain of the plane where the Lipschitz condition* (20) *is satisfied, at most one solution of the first-order normal DE $y' = F(x,y)$ can pass through each point.*

Proof. It is to be shown that if $y = f(x)$ and $y = g(x)$ both satisfy the DE, and if $f(a) = g(a)$, then $f(x) = g(x)$ as long as the curves defined by these equations stay in the given domain where the Lipschitz condition holds. To prove this, consider the nonnegative function

$$\sigma(x) = [f(x) - g(x)]^2 \geqq 0.$$

†A set of points is called *convex* when it contains, with any two points, the line segment joining them.

The derivative of this function exists and is the function

$$\begin{aligned}\sigma'(x) &= 2[f(x) - g(x)][f'(x) - g'(x)] \\ &= 2[f(x) - g(x)][F(x,f(x)) - F(x,g(x))].\end{aligned}$$

Hence, using the Lipschitz condition (20), we obtain the inequality

$$\sigma'(x) \leqq 2\,|\,f(x) - g(x)\,| \cdot |\,f'(x) - g'(x)\,| \leqq 2L\sigma(x).$$

Under the hypotheses of Theorem 5 we have $\sigma(a) = 0$, and hence by (21′), $\sigma(x)$ being nonnegative, $\sigma(x) \equiv 0$ for $x > a$. A similar argument applies for $x < a$: replacing x by $t = 2a - x$ gives $d\sigma/dt = -d\sigma/dx \leqq 2L\sigma(x)$. Since $f(x) \equiv g(x)$ if $\sigma(x) \equiv 0$, the conclusion of Theorem 5 now follows from the corollary of Lemma 2, with $K = 2L$.

It is important to notice that the Lipschitz condition is a sufficient, but not a necessary condition for the uniqueness of solutions.

Continuity. The continuous dependence of solutions of normal first-order DE's on their initial values, in any domain in which a Lipschitz condition holds, can be proved by an argument similar to that used in proving uniqueness.

THEOREM 6 (Continuity Theorem). *For any given a, and for variable c, consider the value at a fixed point x of the solution $f(x,c)$ of $y' = F(x,y)$ which satisfies $f(a) = c$. Under the hypotheses of Theorem 5, $f(x,c)$ depends continuously on c.*

Proof. As in the proof of Theorem 5, $\sigma'(x) \leqq 2L\sigma(x)$. Hence, by Lemma 2,

$$\sigma(x) \leqq \sigma(a)e^{2L|x-a|}.$$

Referring to the definition of $\sigma(x)$, and taking the square root of both sides, we have

$$|\,f(x) - g(x)\,| \leqq e^{L|x-a|}\,|\,f(a) - g(a)\,|, \tag{22}$$

from which the continuity of $f(x,c)$ is evident. Specifically, (22) implies

$$|\,f(x,c) - f(x,c_1)\,| \leqq \exp(L\,|\,x - a\,|) \cdot |\,c - c_1\,|.$$

EXERCISES E

1. In which domains do the following functions satisfy a Lipschitz condition?

(a) $F(x,t) = 1 + x^2$,
(b) $F(x,t) = 1 + t^2$,
(c) $F(x,t) = 1/(1 + x^2)$,
(d) $F(x,t) = t/(1 + x^2)$,

2. In which domains of the plane does $|\,xy\,|$ satisfy a Lipschitz condition? Find all solutions of $y' = |\,xy\,|$.

3. Same question for $F(x,t) = \begin{cases} 0 \text{ if } t \text{ is rational,} \\ 1 \text{ if } t \text{ is irrational.}\end{cases}$

4. Let f and g be solutions of $y' = F(x,y)$ where F is a continuous function. Show that the functions m and M, defined as $m(x) = \min(f(x), g(x))$ and $M(x) = \max(f(x), g(x))$, satisfy the same DE. (*Hint:* Discuss separately the cases $f(x) = g(x)$, $f(x) < g(x)$, and $f(x) > g(x)$.)

5. Let $\sigma(t)$, positive and of class $\mathcal{C}^1$ for $a \leqq t \leqq a + \epsilon$, satisfy the differential inequality $\sigma'(t) \leqq K\sigma(t)\log\sigma(t)$. Show that $\sigma(t) \leqq \sigma(a)^{\exp[K(t-a)]}$.

6. Let $F(x,y) = y \log(1/y)$ for $0 < y < 1$, $F(y) = 0$ for $y = 0$. Show that $y' = F(x,y)$ has at most one solution satisfying $f(0) = c$ even though F does not satisfy a Lipschitz condition.

7. (*Peano Uniqueness Theorem*). For each fixed x, let $F(x,y)$ be a nonincreasing function of y. Show that, if $f(x)$ and $g(x)$ are two solutions of $y' = F(x,y)$, and $b > a$, then $|f(b) - g(b)| \leqq |f(a) - g(a)|$. Infer a uniqueness theorem.

8. Discuss uniqueness and nonuniqueness for solutions of the DE $y' = -y^{1/3}$. (*Hint:* Use Ex. 7.)

9. (a) Prove a uniqueness theorem for $y' = xy$ on $-\infty < x, y < +\infty$.
(*b) Prove the same result for $y' = y^{2/3} + 1$.

10. (*Generalized Lipschitz condition.*) Let $F \in \mathcal{C}$ satisfy

$$|F(x,y) - F(x,z)| \leqq k(x)|y - z|,$$

identically on the strip $0 < x < a$. Show that, if the improper integral $\int_0^a k(x)dx$ is finite, then $y' = F(x,y)$ has at most one solution satisfying $y(0) = 0$.

*11. Let F be continuous and satisfy

$$|F(x,y) - F(x,z)| \leqq K|y - z|\log(|y - z|^{-1}), \quad \text{for} \quad |y - z| < 1.$$

Show that the solutions of (3) are unique.

*12. Assuming only the *one-sided* Lipschitz condition

$$F(x,y) - F(x,z) \leqq L \cdot (y - z) \quad \text{if} \quad y \geqq z,$$

show that two solutions of the DE $y' = F(x,y)$ which coincide when $x = a$ must coincide for all $x > a$. (*Hint:* Modify the proof of Theorem 5.)

11. Comparison Theorem. Since most DE's cannot be solved in terms of elementary functions, it is important to be able to compare the unknown solutions of one DE with the known solutions of another. It is also often useful to compare functions satisfying the differential inequality

$$f'(x) \leqq F(x,f(x)) \tag{23}$$

with exact solutions of the DE (1). The following theorem gives such a comparison.

THEOREM 7. *Let F satisfy a Lipschitz condition for $x \geqq a$. If the function f satisfies the differential inequality (23) for $x \geqq a$, and if g is a solution of $y' = F(x,y)$ satisfying the initial condition $g(a) = f(a)$, then $f(x) \leqq g(x)$ for $x \geqq a$.*

Proof. Suppose that $f(x_1) > g(x_1)$ for some x_1 in the given interval, and define x_0 to be the largest x in the interval $a \leqq x \leqq x_1$ such that $f(x) \leqq g(x)$. Then $f(x_0) = g(x_0)$. Letting $\sigma(x) = f(x) - g(x)$, we have $\sigma(x) \geqq 0$ for $x_0 \leqq x \leqq x_1$, and for $x_0 \leqq x \leqq x_1$,

$$\begin{aligned}\sigma'(x) = f'(x) - g'(x) &\leqq F(x,f(x)) - F(x,g(x)) \\ &\leqq L(f(x) - g(x)) = L\sigma(x),\end{aligned}$$

where L is the Lipschitz constant for the function F. That is, the function σ satisfies the hypothesis of Lemma 2 of § 10 on $x_0 \leqq x \leqq x_1$, with $K = L$. Hence $\sigma(x) \leqq \sigma(x_0)e^{L(x-x_0)} = 0$, and so σ, being nonnegative, vanishes identically. But this contradicts the hypothesis $f(x_1) > g(x_1)$. We conclude that $f(x) \leqq g(x)$ for all x in the given interval, q.e.d.

Theorem 8 (Comparison Theorem). *Let f and g be solutions of the DE's*

$$y' = F(x,y), \qquad z' = G(x,z), \tag{24}$$

respectively, satisfying the same initial condition $f(a) = g(a)$. Suppose further that F or G satisfies a Lipschitz condition, and that $F(x,y) \leqq G(x,y)$ for all x,y in a given domain. Then $f(x) \leqq g(x)$ for $x > a$.

Proof. Let G satisfy a Lipschitz condition. Since $y' = F(x,y) \leqq G(x,y)$, the functions f and g satisfy the conditions of Theorem 7 with G in place of F. Therefore, the inequality $f(x) \leqq g(x)$ for $x \geqq a$ follows immediately.

If F satisfies a Lipschitz condition, then the functions $u = -f(x)$ and $v = -g(x)$ satisfy the DE's $u' = -F(x,-u)$ and $v' = -G(x,-v) \leqq -F(x,-v)$. Theorem 7, applied to the functions v,u and $H(u,v) = -F(x,-v)$ now yields the inequality $v(x) \leqq u(x)$ for $x \geqq a$, or $g(x) \geqq f(x)$, as asserted.

The inequality $f(x) \leqq g(x)$ in this Comparison Theorem can often be replaced by a strict inequality. Either f and g are identically equal for $a \leqq x \leqq x_1$, or else $f(x_0) < g(x_0)$ for some x_0 in the interval (a,x_1). By the Comparison Theorem, the function $\sigma_1(x) = g(x) - f(x)$ is nonnegative for $a \leqq x \leqq x_1$, and moreover $\sigma_1(x_0) > 0$. Much as in the preceding proof,

$$\begin{aligned}\sigma_1'(x) &= G(x,g(x)) - F(x,f(x)) \\ &\geqq G(x,g(x)) - G(x,f(x)) \geqq -L\sigma_1.\end{aligned}$$

Hence $[e^{Lx}\sigma_1(x)]' = e^{Lx}[\sigma_1' + L\sigma_1] \geqq 0$, whence $e^{Lx}\sigma_1(x)$ is a nondecreasing function on $a \leqq x \leqq x_1$. Consequently

$$\sigma_1(x) \geqq \sigma_1(x_0)e^{-L(x-x_0)} > 0,$$

which gives a strict inequality. This proves

Corollary 1. *In Theorem 7, for any $x_1 > a$, either $f(x_1) < g(x_1)$, or $f(x) \equiv g(x)$ for $a \leqq x \leqq x_1$.*

Theorem 8 can also be sharpened in another way, as follows:

COROLLARY 2. *In Theorem* 8, *assume that F, as well as G, satisfies a Lipschitz condition, and, instead of $f(a) = g(a)$, that $f(a) < g(a)$. Then $f(x) < g(x)$ for $x > a$.*

Proof. The proof will be by contradiction. If we had $f(x) \geqq g(x)$ for some $x > a$, there would be a first $x = x_1 > a$ where $f(x) \geqq g(x)$. The two functions $y = \phi(x) = f(-x)$ and $z = \psi(x) = g(-x)$ satisfy the DE's $y' = -F(-x,y)$ and $z' = -G(-x,z)$, as well as the respective initial conditions $\phi(-x_1) = \psi(-x_1)$. Since $-F(-x,t) \geqq -G(-x,y)$, we can apply Theorem 8 in the interval $[-x_1,-a]$, knowing that the function $-F(-x,y)$ satisfies a Lipschitz condition. We conclude that $\phi(-a) \geqq \psi(-a)$, that is, that $f(a) \geqq g(a)$, a contradiction.

EXERCISES F

1. Let $f(u)$ be continuous and $a + bf(u) \neq 0$ for $p \leqq x \leqq q$. Show that the DE $y' = f(ax + by + c)$ (a, b, c are constants) has a solution passing through every point of the strip $p < ax + by + c < q$.

2. Find all solutions of the DE $y' = | x^3y^3 |$.

3. Show that if M and N are homogeneous functions of the same degree, then (7) has the integrating factor $(xM - yN)^{-1}$ in any simply connected domain where $xM - yN$ does not vanish.

4. Show that (7) has the integrating factor $(M^2 + N^2)^{-1}$ if $M_x = N_y$, $M_y = -N_x$.

5. Let $g(x)$ be continuous for $0 \leqq x < \infty$, $\lim_{x\to\infty} g(x) = b$ and $a > 0$. Show that for every solution $y = f(x)$ of $y' + ay = g(x)$ we have $\lim_{x\to\infty} f(x) = b/a$.

6. Show that if $a < 0$ in Ex. 5, then there exists one and only one solution of the DE such that $\lim_{x\to\infty} f(x) = b/a$.

*7. (*Osgood's Uniqueness Theorem.*) Let $\phi(u)$ be a continuous increasing function defined and positive for $u > 0$, such that $\int_\epsilon^1 du/\phi(u) \to \infty$ as $\epsilon \to 0$. If $| F(x,y) - F(x,z) | < \phi(| y - z |)$, then the solutions of the DE (3) are unique. (*Hint:* Use Ex. E4.)

8. Let F, G, f, g be as in Theorem 8, and $F(x,y) < G(x,y)$. Show that $f(x) < g(x)$ for $x > a$, without assuming that F or G satisfies a Lipschitz condition.

*9. Let $f'(x) < F(x,f(x))$ for $x \geqq a$, and let F be continuous. Show that $f(x) < g(x)$, when g is any solution of (3) such that $f(a) < g(a)$.

In Exs. 10–11, $G(x,u)$ is a nonnegative continuous function, nondecreasing in u for fixed x, such that the DE $u' = G(x,u)$ has a *unique* solution $g(x)$ satisfying $g(0) = 0$.

*10. Let $h \in \mathcal{C}^1$ satisfy $h(0) \leqq 0$ and the differential *inequality* $h'(x) \leqq G(x,h(x))$. Show that $h(x) \leqq g(x)$ for $x > 0$.

*11. Let $G(x,0) = 0$. Show that if F satisfies Kamke's inequality

$$2 | y - z | \cdot | F(x,y) - F(x,z) | \leqq G(x, | y - z |^2),$$

then $y' = F(x,y)$ has at most one solution satisfying $y(0) = c$.

*12. Infer Osgood's Uniqueness Theorem (Ex. 7) from Exs. 10 and 11.

CHAPTER II

Second-order Linear Equations

1. Basic definitions. The most intensively studied class of ordinary differential equations is that of second-order linear DE's, of the form

$$(1) \qquad p_0(x)\frac{d^2u}{dx^2} + p_1(x)\frac{du}{dx} + p_2(x)u = p_3(x).$$

The coefficient-functions $p_i(x)$ $[i = 0, 1, 2, 3]$ are assumed continuous and real-valued on an interval I of the real axis, which may be finite or infinite. The interval I may include one or both of its endpoints, or neither of them. The central problem is to find and describe the unknown functions $u = f(x)$ on I satisfying this equation, the *solutions* of the DE.

Dividing through (1) by the leading coefficient $p_0(x)$, one obtains the *normal form*

$$(1') \qquad \begin{gathered} d^2u/dx^2 + p(x)du/dx + q(x)u = r(x), \\ p = p_1/p_0, \quad q = p_2/p_0, \quad r = p_3/p_0. \end{gathered}$$

This DE is equivalent to (1) so long as $p_0(x) \neq 0$; if $p_0(x_0) = 0$ at some point $x = x_0$, then the functions p and q are not defined at the point x_0. One therefore says that the DE (1) has a *singular point*, or *singularity*, at the point x_0, when $p(x_0) = 0$.

The present chapter will be devoted to second-order linear DE's and the behavior of their solutions. We first observe that, if u and v are any two solutions of the inhomogeneous DE (1), then their difference $u - v$ is a solution of the *homogeneous* second-order linear DE

$$(2) \qquad p_0(x)\frac{d^2u}{dx^2} + p_1(x)\frac{du}{dx} + p_2(x)u = 0.$$

This simple observation has the following result as an immediate consequence.

Lemma 1. *If the function $u(x)$ is any particular solution of the inhomogeneous DE* (1), *then the general solution of* (1) *is obtained by adding to $u(x)$ the general solution of the corresponding homogeneous DE* (2).

The homogeneous DE (2), obtained by dropping from the given inhomogeneous DE the *forcing term* $p_3(x)$, is called the *reduced* equation of (1).

A fundamental property of the homogeneous linear DE (2) is the following *Superposition Principle.* Given two solutions $f_1(x)$ and $f_2(x)$ of (2), and any two constants c_1 and c_2, the function

$$f(x) = c_1 f_1(x) + c_2 f_2(x) \tag{3}$$

is also a solution of (2). This property is characteristic of homogeneous linear equations; the function f is called a *linear combination* of the functions f_1 and f_2 with constant coefficients c_1 and c_2.

Notice that the DE (2) always has the trivial solution $u \equiv 0$. This is true of all homogeneous linear DE's; solutions not vanishing identically are called nontrivial.

EXAMPLE 1. The trigonometric DE $u'' + k^2 u = 0$ has the general solution

$$A \cos k(x - x_1) = c_1 \cos kx + c_2 \sin kx, \tag{4}$$

where $A = (c_1^2 + c_2^2)^{1/2}$ is the *amplitude* and x_1 is the *phase* constant.

EXAMPLE 2. The *Bessel* DE of order† n is the DE

$$u'' + \frac{1}{x} u' + \left(1 - \frac{n^2}{x^2}\right) u = 0. \tag{5}$$

This second-order linear DE has its only singular point at $x = 0$; its solutions will be described in Ch. III, § 4.

The trigonometric and Bessel DE's are commonly written in normal form; the following DE is not.

EXAMPLE 3. The *Legendre* DE is

$$\frac{d}{dx}\left[(1 - x^2)\frac{du}{dx}\right] + n(n + 1)u = 0; \tag{6}$$

its solutions will be described (as power series) in Ch. III, § 2. This DE has singular points at $x = \pm 1$.

There is a basic difference between linear and nonlinear DE's. The singular points of nonlinear DE's can be arbitrary curves in the (x,y)-plane. For example, the DE $(x - y)y' = x + y$ is singular on the line $x = y$. Whereas the singular points of linear DE's correspond to fixed values of x, and hence to vertical lines in the (x,y)-plane. This justifies the following

DEFINITION. *The normal DE* (1′) *is* regular *on an interval I of the x-axis when $p(x)$, $q(x)$, and $r(x)$ are continuous on I. A* solution *of* (1) *is a twice differentiable function $u = f(x)$ which satisfies* (1) *at every point of I.*

It is understood that, when I contains an endpoint, the solution need only have one-sided derivatives there.

In the rest of this chapter, we will be concerned only with second-order linear DE's which are regular in specified intervals. The study of singular points of DE's will be taken up in Chapter IX.

†*Note* that the Bessel DE of "order" n is still a "second-order" DE.

2. Initial value problems. In differential equations arising from physical problems, one is often interested in particular solutions satisfying additional "boundary conditions." Thus one may know the state of a given physical system at some initial time $t = a$, and wish to predict its state at later times. Consider for instance the following mass-spring system.

EXAMPLE 4. Let $u(t)$ be the vertical displacement of a mass m, at time t, from its equilibrium position when suspended on a spring. Then the linear DE with constant coefficients,

$$m\frac{d^2u}{dt^2} = -mp\frac{du}{dt} - mqu, \tag{7}$$

expresses Newton's Third Law of Motion for an elastic restoring force mqu proportional to the displacement from the equilibrium position $u = 0$, and an idealized viscous damping force $mp\,du/dt$.

Physical intuition suggests that it should be possible to predict the motion of the mass at all future times from the law (7), whenever the initial position and velocity are known. These initial conditions amount to prescribing $f(a) = u_0$ and $f'(a) = u_0'$. One then refers to the *initial conditions* $f(a) = u_0$, $f'(a) = u_0'$; the problem of integrating a DE like (1) subject to given initial conditions is called the *initial value problem.*

Thus, physical intuition leads one to conjecture the truth of *existence* and *uniqueness* theorems for the initial value problem for (1), at least in the special case (7). It can be proved that this intuition is justified as regards the initial value problem for regular linear DE's, in intervals free from singular points. However, as will be shown in § 9 below, it is not true for "two-endpoint problems," in which $f(a)$ and $f(b)$ are assumed given at the two endpoints of a given interval $[a,b]$.

The *uniqueness* of solutions of initial value problems for second-order linear DE's will be proved now; *existence* will be proved in Chapter III (for analytic coefficient-functions) and in Chapter V (for continuous coefficient-functions), where the continuous dependence of solutions on their initial values will also be proved. In short, the initial value problem for regular second-order linear DE's is a *well-set* problem.

THEOREM 1 (Uniqueness Theorem). *If p and q are continuous, then at most one solution of (1′) can satisfy given initial conditions $f(a) = c_0$ and $f'(a) = c_1$.*

Proof. Let v and w be any two solutions; their difference $u = v - w$ satisfies (1′) by Lemma 1, with $r(x) = 0$. It also satisfies the initial conditions $u = u' = 0$ when $x = a$. Now consider the nonnegative function $\sigma(x) = u^2 + u'^2$. By definition, $\sigma(0) = 0$. Differentiating, we have since $r(x) = 0$:

$$\begin{aligned}\sigma'(x) &= 2u'(u + u'') = 2u'[u - p(x)u' - q(x)u] \\ &= -2p(x)u'^2 + 2(1 - q(x))uu'.\end{aligned}$$

Since $(u \pm u')^2 \geqq 0$, $|2uu'| \leqq u^2 + u'^2$. Hence

$$2(1 - q(x))uu' \leqq (1 + |q(x)|)(u^2 + u'^2),$$

and

$$\sigma'(x) \leqq [1 + |q(x)|]u^2 + [1 + |q(x)| + |2p(x)|]u'^2.$$

Hence, if $K = 1 + \max(|q(x)| + 2|p(x)|)$, the maximum being taken over any finite closed interval $[a,b]$,

$$\sigma'(x) \leqq K\sigma(x), \qquad K < +\infty.$$

By the Corollary of Lemma 2 of Ch. I, § 10, it follows that $\sigma(x) = 0$ for all x on any interval containing a, on which (1′) holds. Hence $u(x) \equiv 0$ and $v(x) \equiv w(x)$ on the interval, as claimed.

The Uniqueness Theorem just proved implies an important extension of the Superposition Principle stated in § 1.

THEOREM 2. *Let f and g be two solutions of the homogeneous second-order linear DE*

(8) $$u'' + p(x)u' + q(x)u = 0, \qquad p, q \in \mathcal{C}.$$

For some $x = x_0$, let $(f(x_0), f'(x_0))$ and $(g(x_0), g'(x_0))$ be linearly independent vectors. Then every solution of this DE is equal to some linear combination $h(x) = cf(x) + dg(x)$ of f and g, with constant coefficients c, d.

In other words, the *general solution* of the given homogeneous DE (8) is $cf(x) + dg(x)$, where c and d are arbitrary constants.

Proof. By the Superposition Principle (§ 1), any such $h(x)$ satisfies (8). Conversely, suppose the function $h(x)$ satisfies the given DE (8). Then, at the given point x_0, constants c and d can be found such that

$$cf(x_0) + dg(x_0) = h(x_0), \qquad cf'(x_0) + dg'(x_0) = h'(x_0).$$

In fact, the constants c and d are given by Cramer's Rule, as

$$c = (h_0g_0' - g_0h_0')/(f_0g_0' - g_0f_0'), \qquad d = (f_0h_0' - h_0f_0')/(f_0g_0' - g_0f_0'),$$

where we have used the abbreviations $f_0 = f(x_0)$, $f_0' = f'(x_0)$, etc. For this choice of c and d, the function

$$u(x) = h(x) - cf(x) - dg(x)$$

satisfies the given homogeneous DE by the Superposition Principle, and the initial conditions $u(x_0) = u'(x_0) = 0$. Hence, by the Uniqueness Theorem, $u(x)$ is the trivial solution $u(x) \equiv 0$ of the given homogeneous DE. Hence $h = cf + dg$.

Two solutions f and g of a homogeneous linear second-order DE (8) with the property that every other solution can be expressed as a linear combination of them are said to be a *basis of solutions* of the DE.

3. The Wronskian. The question of whether two solutions of a homogeneous linear DE form a basis of solutions is easily settled by examining their Wronskian, a concept which we now define.

DEFINITION. *The* Wronskian *of any two differentiable functions* $f(x)$ *and* $g(x)$ *is*

$$W(f, g; x) = f(x)g'(x) - g(x)f'(x) = \begin{vmatrix} f(x) & f'(x) \\ g(x) & g'(x) \end{vmatrix}. \tag{9}$$

THEOREM 3. *The Wronskian* (9) *of any two solutions of* (8) *satisfies the identity*

$$W(f, g; x) = W(f, g; a)e^{-\int_a^x p(t)dt}. \tag{10}$$

Proof. Differentiating (9), and writing $W(f, g; x) = W(x)$ for short, a direct computation gives $W' = fg'' - gf''$. Substituting for g'' and f'' from (8) and cancelling, we obtain the linear homogeneous first-order DE

$$W'(x) + p(x)W(x) = 0. \tag{11}$$

Equation (10) follows from the first-order homogeneous linear DE (11) by Theorem 3 of Ch. I, § 5.

COROLLARY. *The Wronskian of any two solutions of the homogeneous linear DE* (8) *is identically positive, identically negative, or identically zero.*

We now relate the Wronskian of two functions to the concept of linear independence. In general, a collection of functions $f_1, f_2, \cdots, f_n$ is called *linearly independent* on the interval $a \leqq x \leqq b$ when no linear combination $c_1f_1(x) + c_2f_2(x) + \cdots + c_nf_n(x)$ of the functions gives the identically zero function for $a \leqq x \leqq b$ except the trivial linear combination where all coefficients vanish. Functions which are not linearly independent are called linearly dependent. If f and g are any two linearly dependent functions, then $cf + dg = 0$ for suitable constants c and d, not both zero. Hence $g = -(c/d)f$ or $f = -(d/c)g$: the functions f and g are proportional.

LEMMA. *If* f *and* g *are linearly dependent differentiable functions, then their Wronskian vanishes identically.*

Proof. Suppose that f and g are linearly dependent. Then there are two constants c and d, not both zero, which satisfy the *two* linear equations

$$cf(x) + dg(x) = 0, \qquad cf'(x) + dg'(x) = 0,$$

identically on the interval of interest. Therefore the determinant of the two equations, which is the Wronskian $W(f, g; x)$, vanishes identically.

The interesting fact is that when f and g are both solutions of a second-order linear DE, the *converse* of this lemma is also true:

THEOREM 4. *If f and g are linearly independent solutions of the second-order linear DE* (8), *then their Wronskian never vanishes.*

Proof. Suppose that the Wronskian $W(f,g;x)$ vanished at some point x_1. Then the vectors $(f(x_1),f'(x_1))$ and $(g(x_1),g'(x_1))$ would be linearly dependent, and therefore proportional: $g(x_1) = kf(x_1)$ and $g'(x_1) = kf'(x_1)$ for some constant k. Consider now the function $h(x) = f(x) - kg(x)$. This function is a solution of the DE (8), since it is a linear combination of solutions. It also satisfies the initial conditions $h(x_1) = h'(x_1) = 0$. By the Uniqueness Theorem, this function must vanish identically. Therefore $g(x) = kf(x)$ for all x, contradicting the hypothesis of linear independence of f and g.

Caution. The functions x^3 and $|x|^3$ are linearly independent on $-1 < x < 1$, yet their Wronskian vanishes identically. Hence it is not true for functions in general, that the vanishing of the Wronskian implies linear dependence. It is true for analytic functions, however.

If *one* solution $f(x)$ of the homogeneous linear DE (8) is known, the Wronskian can be used to construct a second, linearly independent solution, as follows. By Theorem 3, this unknown solution satisfies the first-order DE

$$f(x)g'(x) - f'(x)g(x) = W(x) = W(a)e^{-\int_a^x p(t)dt}. \tag{12}$$

This *first-order* linear DE in $g(x)$ can be solved by using the integrating factor $1/f^2(x)$, as in Ch. I, Theorem 3, in any interval where f is nonvanishing. The general solution (in terms of quadratures) is

$$g(x) = f(x)\left\{C + \int_a^x [W(a)e^{-\int_a^s p(t)dt}/f^2(s)]ds\right\}, \tag{13}$$

where a is any point in the interval of x considered, and C is an arbitrary constant of integration (say $C = 0$).

In particular, let f be any nontrivial solution of $u'' + q(x)u = 0$. Then a second, linearly independent solution is given in any interval where f is nonvanishing by the formula

$$g(x) = f(x)\int \frac{dx}{f^2(x)}, \tag{13'}$$

for any indefinite integral of $1/f^2(x)$.

Riccati equation. The homogeneous linear second-order DE (8) can also be reduced to a first-order, *nonlinear* DE by another simple algebraic substitution. Namely, the ratio $v = u'/u$ of the first derivative of any solution of the linear DE (8) to the solution, satisfies the quadratic first-order DE

$$v' + v^2 + p(x)v + q(x) = 0. \tag{14}$$

This is called the Riccati equation associated with (8); its solutions form a one-parameter family. Conversely, if $v(x)$ is any solution of the Riccati equation (14), and if $u' = v(x)u$, then u satisfies (8). Hence the general solution of (8) is

$$u(x) = C \exp \int v(x)dx,$$

where $v(x)$ is the general solution of the associated Riccati equation (14).

The Riccati substitution $v = u'/u$ thus reduces the problem of solving (8) to the integration of a first-order quadratic DE and a quadrature. For instance, the Riccati equation associated with the trigonometric equation $u'' + k^2u = 0$ is $v' + v^2 + k^2 = 0$, whose general solution is $v = \tan k(x_1 - x)$.

EXERCISES A

1. Show that all solutions of (8) have continuous second-order derivatives. Show that this is not true for (1).

2. Find a formula expressing the fourth derivative u^{iv} of any solution u of (8) in terms of u, u', and the derivatives of p and q. What differentiability conditions must be assumed on the coefficients of (8) to justify this formula?

For the solution-pairs of the DE's specified in Exs. 3–5 to follow, (a) calculate the Wronskian, and (b) solve the initial value problem for the DE specified with each of the initial conditions $u(0) = 2$, $u'(0) = 1$, and with $u(0) = 1$, $u'(0) = -1$ (or explain why there is no solution).

3. $f(x) = \cos x$, $g(x) = \sin x$ (solutions of $u'' + u = 0$).
4. $f(x) = e^{-x}$, $g(x) = e^{-3x}$ (solutions of $u'' + 4u' + 3u = 0$).
5. $f(x) = x$, $g(x) = e^x$ (solutions of $u'' + \dfrac{x}{1-x}u' - \dfrac{1}{1-x}u = 0$).
6. Let $f(x)$, $g(x)$, and $h(x)$ be any three solutions of (8). Show that

$$\begin{vmatrix} f & f' & f'' \\ g & g' & g'' \\ h & h' & h'' \end{vmatrix} \equiv 0.$$

7. What is wrong with the following "proof" of Theorem 3: "Let $w(x) = \log W(x)$; then $w'(x) = -p(x)$. Hence $w(x) = w(a) - \int_a^x p(x)dx$, from which (10) follows."

8. Show that, in the linear homogeneous DE (8), the coefficient-functions $p(x)$ and $q(x)$ are determined by any basis of solutions through the formulas

$$p = -\frac{fg'' - gf''}{W(f,g)}, \qquad q = \frac{f'g'' - g'f''}{W(f,g)}.$$

9. Construct second-order linear homogeneous DE's having the following bases of solutions; you may assume the result of Ex. 8:

(a) x, $\sin x$, (c) $\sinh x$, $\sin x$,
(b) x^m, x^n, (d) $\tan x$, $\cot x$.

In each case determine the singular points and possible domains of definition of the DE in normal form.

10. (a) Show that if $p, q \in \mathcal{C}^n$, then every solution of (8) is of class $\mathcal{C}^{n+2}$.
(b) Show that if every solution of (8) is of class $\mathcal{C}^{n+2}$, then $p \in \mathcal{C}^n$ and $q \in \mathcal{C}^n$.

11. The *generalized Riccati* DE is $y' + P(x)y + Q(x)y^2 = R(x)$.
(a) Show that the substitution $y = u'/Qu$ transforms this DE into

$$u'' + [P - (Q'/Q)]u' - QRu = 0.$$

(b) Show that the substitution $y = Ru/u'$ transforms this DE into

$$u'' - [P + (R'/R)u'] - QRu = 0.$$

12. (a) Show that the substitution $y = z/a(x)$ transforms the DE

$$y' + a(x)y^2 + b(x)y + c(x) = 0$$

into the Riccati DE (14), with $p(x) = b - a'/a$ and $q(x) = a(x)c(x)$.
(b) Show that if y is a solution of $y' + a(x)y^2 + b(x)y = c(x)$, then $z = 1/y$ is a solution of $z' + c(x)z^2 - b(x)z = a(x)$.

13. Let $f(x)$, $g(x)$, $h(x)$ be three solutions of the linear third-order DE

$$y''' + p_1(x)y'' + p_2(x)y' + p_3(x)y = 0.$$

Derive a first-order DE satisfied by the determinant

$$w(x) = \begin{vmatrix} f & f' & f'' \\ g & g' & g'' \\ h & h' & h'' \end{vmatrix}.$$

*14. Let $y'' + q(x)y = 0$, where $q(x)$ is "piecewise continuous" (i.e., continuous and bounded except for isolated discontinuities). Define a "solution" of the above DE as a function $f \in \mathcal{C}^1$ which satisfies the DE at all points where $q(x)$ is continuous.
(a) Describe explicitly a basis of solutions for the DE $y'' + q(x)y = 0$, where

$$q(x) = \begin{cases} +1 \text{ when } x > 0 \\ \\ -1 \text{ when } x < 0. \end{cases}$$

(N.B. The preceding function $q(x)$ is commonly denoted sgn x.)
(b) Prove an existence and uniqueness theorem for the initial value problem, and discuss the associated Wronskian.

*15. In Ex. 14, show that the solution has second left- and right-derivatives at every point of discontinuity.

4. Separation and Comparison Theorems. The Wronskian can also be used to derive some properties of the graphs of solutions of the DE (8). The following result, the celebrated Sturm Separation Theorem, describes the relative position of the zeros of solutions. (A *zero* of a function is a point where its graph crosses the x-axis.)

THEOREM 5. *If $f(x)$ and $g(x)$ are linearly independent solutions of the DE (8), then $f(x)$ must vanish between any two successive zeros of $g(x)$, and conversely. In other words, the zeros of $f(x)$ and $g(x)$ occur alternately.*

Proof. If $g(x)$ vanishes at $x = x_i$, then the Wronskian

$$W(f,g;\ x_i) = f(x_i)g'(x_i) \neq 0,$$

since f and g are linearly independent; hence $f(x_i) \neq 0$ and $g'(x_i) \neq 0$ if $g(x_i) = 0$. If x_1 and x_2 are two successive zeros of $g(x)$, then $g'(x_1)$, $g'(x_2)$, $f(x_1)$, and $f(x_2)$ are all nonzero; moreover, the nonzero numbers $g'(x_1)$ and $g'(x_2)$ cannot have the same sign, because if the function is increasing at $x = x_1$ then it must be decreasing at $x = x_2$, and vice-versa. Since $W(f,g;x)$ has constant sign by the Corollary of Theorem 3, it follows that $f(x_1)$ and $f(x_2)$ must also have opposite signs. Therefore $f(x)$ must vanish somewhere between x_1 and x_2.

For instance, applied to the trigonometric DE $u'' + k^2u = 0$, the Sturm Separation Theorem shows that the zeros of $\sin kx$ and $\cos kx$ must alternate, simply because these functions are two linearly independent solutions of the same linear homogeneous DE.

A slight refinement of the same reasoning can be used to prove an even more useful Comparison Theorem, also due to Sturm.

THEOREM 6. *Let $f(x)$ and $g(x)$ be nontrivial solutions of the DE's $u'' + p(x)u = 0$ and $v'' + q(x)v = 0$, respectively, where $p(x) \geqq q(x)$. Then $f(x)$ vanishes at least once between any two zeros of $g(x)$, unless $p(x) \equiv q(x)$ and f is a constant multiple of g.*

Proof. Let x_1 and x_2 be two successive zeros of $g(x)$, so that $g(x_1) = g(x_2) = 0$. Suppose that $f(x)$ failed to vanish in $x_1 < x < x_2$. Replacing f and/or g by their negative, if necessary, we could find solutions f and g positive on $x_1 < x < x_2$. This would make

$$W(f,g;\ x_1) = f(x_1)g'(x_1) \geqq 0$$

and

$$W(f,g;\ x_2) = f(x_2)g'(x_2) \leqq 0.$$

On the other hand, since $f > 0$, $g > 0$, and $p \geqq q$ on $x_1 < x < x_2$,

$$\frac{d}{dx}[W(f,g;\ x)] = fg'' - gf'' = (p - q)fg \geqq 0 \quad \text{on} \quad x_1 < x < x_2.$$

Hence W is nondecreasing, giving a contradiction unless

$$p - q \equiv W(f,g;\ x) \equiv 0.$$

In this event $f \equiv kg$ for some constant k by Theorem 4, completing the proof.

COROLLARY 1. *If $q(x) \leqq 0$, then no nontrivial solution of the DE $u'' + q(x)u = 0$ can have more than one zero.*

The proof is by contradiction. By the Sturm Comparison Theorem, the solution $v \equiv 1$ of the DE $v'' = 0$ would have to vanish at least once between any two zeros of any nontrivial solution of the DE $u'' + q(x)u = 0$.

The preceding results show that the oscillations of the solutions of $u'' + q(x)u = 0$ are largely determined by the sign and magnitude of $q(x)$. When $q(x) \leqq 0$, oscillations are impossible: no solution can change sign more than once. On the other hand, if $q(x) \geqq k^2 > 0$, then any solution of $u'' + q(x)u = 0$ must vanish between any two successive zeros of any solution $A \cos k(x - x_1)$ of the trigonometric DE $u'' + k^2u = 0$, hence in any interval of length π/k.

This result can be applied to solutions of the Bessel DE (5) (e.g., to the Bessel function of order n; see Ch. III, § 4). Substituting $u = v/\sqrt{x}$ into (5), we obtain the equivalent DE

$$v'' + \left[1 - \frac{4n^2 - 1}{4x^2}\right]v = 0, \tag{15}$$

whose solutions vanish when u does (for $x \neq 0$). Applying the Comparison Theorem to (15) and $u'' + u = 0$, we get

COROLLARY 2. *Each interval of length π of the positive x-axis contains at least one zero of any solution of the Bessel DE of order zero, and at most one zero of any nontrivial solution of the Bessel DE of order n if $n > 1/2$.*

The fact that the oscillations of the solutions of $u'' + q(x)u = 0$ depend on the sign of $q(x)$ is illustrated by Figure II-1 and Figure II-2, which depict sample solution curves for the cases $q(x) = k^2$ and $q(x) = -k^2$, respectively.

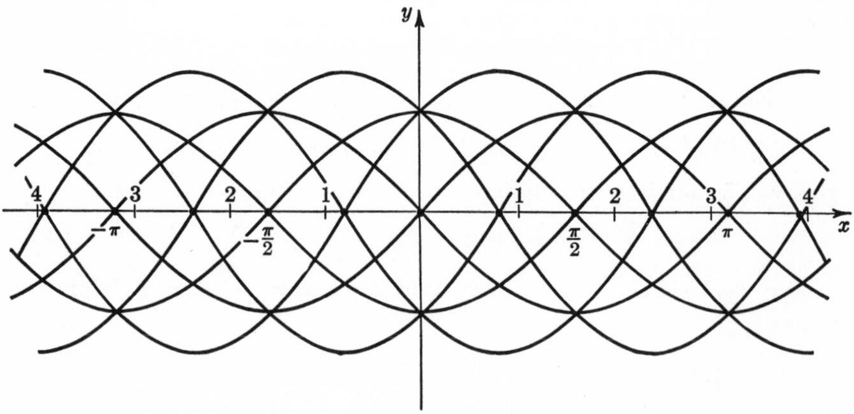

Figure II-1.

Solution Curves of $u'' + k^2u = 0$

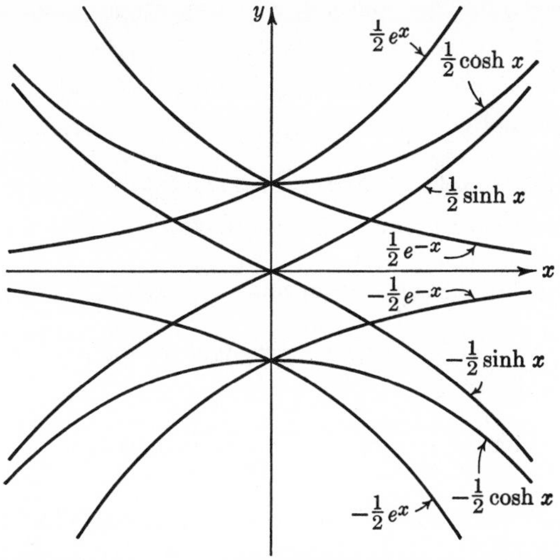

Figure II-2. Solution Curves of $u'' - k^2u = 0$

5. Linear operators. The operation of transforming a given function f into a function g by the rule

$$g = p_0f'' + p_1f' + p_2f$$

(for continuous p_i) is a transformation from one family of functions (in our case, the family $\mathcal{C}^2(I)$ of continuously twice-differentiable functions on a given interval I), to another family of functions (in our case, $\mathcal{C}(I)$). Such a functional transformation is called an *operator*, and is written in operator notation

$$L[f] = p_0f'' + p_1f' + p_2f.$$

In our case, the operator L is *linear*, that is, it satisfies

$$L[cf + dg] = cL[f] + dL[g],$$

for any constants c and d.

The preceding identity generalizes the Superposition Principle of § 1 to inhomogeneous DE's. It may be stated at greater length as follows.

LEMMA 1. *If $u(x)$ is a solution of $L[u] = r(x)$, if $v(x)$ is a solution of $L[u] = s(x)$, and if c, d are constants, then $w = cu(x) + dv(x)$ is a solution of the DE $L[u] = cr(x) + ds(x)$.*

The proof is trivial, but the result describes the most fundamental property of linear operators.

Adjoint operators. The concepts of integrating factor and exact differential, defined for first-order DE's in Ch. I, § 5, can be extended to equations of higher order. We extend them now to second-order *linear* DE's.

DEFINITION. *The second-order homogeneous linear DE*

$$L[u] = p_0(x)u''(x) + p_1(x)u'(x) + p_2(x)u(x) = 0 \tag{16}$$

is said to be exact *if and only if, for all functions* $u \in \mathcal{C}^2$,

$$p_0(x)u'' + p_1(x)u' + p_2(x)u = \frac{d}{dx}[A(x)u' + B(x)u], \tag{16'}$$

for some $A(x), B(x) \in \mathcal{C}^1$. *An* integrating factor *for the DE* (16) *is a function* $v(x)$ *such that* $vL[u] = 0$ *is exact.*

If an integrating factor v can be found, then clearly

$$v(x)[p_0(x)u'' + p_1(x)u' + p_2(x)u] = \frac{d}{dx}[A(x)u' + B(x)u]. \tag{17}$$

Hence the solutions of the homogeneous DE (16) are those of the first-order inhomogeneous linear DE

$$A(x)u' + B(x)u = C, \tag{18}$$

where C is an arbitrary constant. Also, the solutions of the inhomogeneous DE $L[u] = r(x)$ are those of the first-order DE

$$A(x)u' + B(x)u = \int v(x)r(x)dx + C. \tag{18'}$$

The DE's (18) and (18') can be solved by a quadrature (Ch. I, § 5). Hence, if an integrating factor of (16) can be found, we can reduce the solution of $L[u] = r(x)$ to a sequence of quadratures.

Evidently, $L[u] = 0$ is exact if and only if $p_0 = A$, $p_1 = A' + B$, $p_2 = B'$. Hence it is exact if and only if

$$p_2 = B' = (p_1 - A') = p_1' - (p_0')'.$$

This simple calculation proves the following result.

LEMMA 2. *The DE* (16) *is exact if and only if its coefficient-functions satisfy* $p_0'' - p_1' + p_2 = 0$.

COROLLARY. *A function* $v \in \mathcal{C}^2$ *is an integrating factor for the DE* (16) *if and only if it is a solution of the second order-homogeneous linear DE*

$$M[v] = [p_0(x)v]'' - [p_1(x)v]' + p_2(x)v(x) = 0. \tag{19}$$

The operator M is called the *adjoint* of the linear operator L. Equation (19) can be expanded to give

$$p_0v'' + (2p_0' - p_1)v' + (p_0'' - p_1' + p_2)v = 0. \tag{19'}$$

This DE is called the *adjoint equation* of the DE (16).

Thus, whenever a nontrivial solution of the adjoint DE (19) of a given second-order linear DE (16) is known, every solution of the DE $L[u] = r(x)$ can be obtained by quadratures.

6. Lagrange identity. The concept of the adjoint of a linear operator, which originated historically in the search for integrating factors, owes its major importance to the role which it plays in the theory of orthogonal and biorthogonal expansions. We now lay the foundations for this theory.

Substituting into (19), one finds that the adjoint of the adjoint of a given second-order linear DE (16) is again the original DE (16). Another consequence of (19) is the identity

$$vL[u] - uM[v] = (vp_0)u'' - u(p_0v)'' + (vp_1)u' + u(p_1v)'.$$

This can be simplified to give the *Lagrange identity*

$$vL[u] - uM[v] = \frac{d}{dx}[p_0vu' - (p_0v)'u + p_1uv], \tag{20}$$

or

$$\int_a^b \{vL[u] - uM[v]\}dx = \Big[p_0vu' - (p_0v)'u + p_1uv\Big]_{x=a}^{x=b} \tag{20'}$$

The integrand in (20′) is thus an exact differential, the differential of a homogeneous bilinear expression in u, v, and their derivatives.

Self-adjoint equations. Homogeneous linear DE's which coincide with their adjoint are of great importance; they are called *self-adjoint.* For instance, the Legendre DE (6) is self-adjoint. The condition for the second-order DE (16) to be self-adjoint is easily derived. It is necessary by (19′) that $2p_0' - p_1 = p_1$, that is, that $p_0' = p_1$. Since this relation implies $p_0'' - p_1' = 0$, it is also sufficient. This proves the first statement of

THEOREM 7. *The second-order linear DE* (16) *is* self-adjoint *if and only if it has the form*

$$\frac{d}{dx}\left[p(x)\frac{du}{dx}\right] + q(x)u = 0. \tag{21}$$

The DE (16) *can be made self-adjoint by multiplying through by*

$$h(x) = [\exp \int (p_1/p_0)dx]/p_0. \tag{21'}$$

To prove the second statement, first reduce (16) to normal form by dividing through by p_0, and then observe that the DE

$$hu'' + (ph)u' + (qh)u = 0$$

is self-adjoint if and only if $h' = ph$, or $h = \exp(\int pdx)$.

For example, the self-adjoint form of the Bessel DE (5) is

$$(xu')' + [x - (n^2/x)]u = 0.$$

EXERCISES B

1. Show that if $u(x)$ and $v(x)$ are solutions of the self-adjoint DE

$$(pu')' + q(x)u = 0,$$

then $p(x)[uv' - vu']$ is a constant. (Abel's identity.)

2. Reduce the following DE's to self-adjoint form:

(a) $x^2u'' + xu' + u = 0,$
(b) $u'' + u' \tan x = 0.$

3. For each of the following DE's, $y = x^3$ is one solution; find a second, linearly independent solution by quadratures.

(a) $x^2y'' - 4xy' - 2y = 0,$
(b) $xy'' + (x - 2)y' - 3y = 0.$

4. Show that the substitution $y = e^{\int p\, dx/2}u$ replaces (8) by

$$y'' + I(x)y = 0, \quad I(x) = q - p^2/4 - p'/2.$$

*5. Show that two DE's of the form (8) can be transformed into each other by a change of dependent variable of the form $y = v(x)u$ if and only if the function $I(x) = q(x) - p^2(x)/4 - p'(x)/2$ is the same for both DE's. ($I(x)$ is called the *invariant* of the DE.)

6. Reduce the self-adjoint DE $(pu')' + qu = 0$ to normal form, and show that, in the notation of Ex. 5, $I(x) = (p'^2 - 2pp'' + 4pq)/4p^2$.

7. (a) Show that, for the normal form of the Legendre DE $[(1 - x^2)u']' + \lambda u = 0,$

$$I(x) = (1 + \lambda - \lambda x^2)/(1 - x^2)^2. \quad \text{(Use Ex. 6.)}$$

(b) Show that, if $\lambda = n(n + 1)$, then every solution of the Legendre equation has at least $(2n + 1)/\pi$ zeros on $(-1,1)$.

8. Let $u(x)$ be a solution of $u'' = q(x)u$, $q(x) > 0$, such that $u(0)$ and $u'(0)$ are positive. Show that uu' and $u(x)$ are increasing for $x > 0$.

9. Let $h(x)$ be a nonnegative function of class $\mathcal{C}^1$. Show that the change of independent variable $t = \int_a^t h(x)dx$, $u(x) = v(t)$, transforms the DE (8) into $v'' + p_1(t)v' + q_1(t)v = 0$, where $p_1(t) = [p(x)h(x) + h'(x)]/h(x)^2$; $q_1(t) = q(x)/h(x)^2$.

10. (a) Show that the change of independent variable $t = \int | q(x) |^{1/2} dx$, $q \neq 0$, changes the DE (8) into one whose normal form is

$$\frac{d^2u}{dt^2} + \left(\frac{q' + 2pq}{2q^{3/2}}\right)\frac{du}{dt} \pm u = 0. \qquad (*)$$

(b) Show that no other change of independent variable makes $| q | = 1$.

*11. Using Ex. 10, show that the DE (8) is equivalent to a DE with constant coefficients under a change of independent variable if and only if $(q' + 2pq)/q^{3/2}$ is a constant.

*12. By a suitable change of independent variable find the general solution of the DE $(x^3 - x)u'' + u' + n^2x^2u = 0.$

7. Green's functions. The *inhomogeneous* linear second-order DE in normal form

$$L[u] = \frac{d^2u}{dx^2} + p(x)\frac{du}{dx} + q(x)u = r(x), \tag{22}$$

differs from the homogeneous linear DE

$$L[u] = \frac{d^2u}{dx^2} + p(x)\frac{du}{dx} + q(x)u = 0 \tag{22'}$$

by the nonzero function $r(x)$ on the right side. In applications to electrical and dynamical systems the function $r(x)$ is called the *forcing term*. By the Uniqueness Theorem of § 2 and Lemma 1 of § 5, it is clear that the solution $u(x)$ of $L[u] = r(x)$ for given homogeneous initial conditions such as $u(0) = u'(0) = 0$ depends linearly on the forcing term. We will now determine the exact nature of this linear dependence.

Given the inhomogeneous linear DE (22), we will show that there exists an integral operator G:

$$G[r] = \int G(x,\xi)r(\xi)d\xi, \tag{23}$$

such that $G[r] = u$. In fact, one can find a function G which makes $G[r]$ satisfy given homogeneous boundary conditions, provided the latter define a well-set problem.

The kernel $G(x,\xi)$ of equation (23) is then called the Green's function associated with the given boundary value problem. In operator notation, it is defined by the identity $L[G[r]] = r$ (G is a "right-inverse" of the linear operator L), and the given boundary conditions. For initial value problems, the preceding ideas can be generalized to n-th order equations as follows.

DEFINITION. *Let* $L[u] = \frac{d^nu}{dx^n} + p_1(x)\frac{d^{n-1}u}{dx^n} + \cdots + p_n(x)u$ *be an n-th order homogeneous linear differential operator. By the* Green's function *of* $L[u]$ *for the initial value problem at* $x = a$ *is meant a function* $G(x,\xi)$ *such that the function* $u(x)$ *defined by* (23) *satisfies* $L[u] = r(x)$ *for any continuous* $r(x)$, *and satisfies the initial conditions* $u(a) = \cdots = u^{(n-1)}(a) = 0$.

To provide an intuitive basis for the concept of a Green's function, two examples will be described first. In these examples, the independent variable will be denoted by t, and should be thought of as representing time.

EXAMPLE 5. Suppose that money is deposited continuously in a bank account, at a continuously varying rate $r(t)$, and that interest is compounded continuously at a constant rate p ($= 100p\%$ per annum). As a function of time, the amount $u(t)$ in the account satisfies the DE

$$du/dt = pu + r(t).$$

If the account is opened when $t = 0$ and initially has no money: $u(0) = 0$, then one can calculate $u(T)$ at any later time $T > 0$ as follows. Each "infinitesimal" deposit $r(t)dt$, made in the time interval $(t, t + dt)$, increases through compound interest accrued during the time interval from t to T to the amount $e^{p(T-t)}r(t)dt$, that is, by a factor $e^{p(T-t)}$. Hence the account should amount, at time T, to the integral (limit of sums)

$$u(T) = \int_0^T e^{p(T-t)}r(t)dt = e^{pT}\int_0^T e^{-pt}r(t)dt. \tag{24}$$

This plausible reasoning is easily verified. Obviously $u(0) = 0$. Differentiating the product in the final expression of (24), one obtains

$$u'(T) = pe^{pT}\int_0^T e^{-pt}r(t)dt + e^{pT}e^{-pT}r(T) = pu(T) + r(T),$$

where the derivative of the integral is evaluated by the Fundamental Theorem of the Calculus.

EXAMPLE 6. Consider again the motion of a mass m on a spring, as in Example 4. We have (8) with constant coefficients p and q. Suppose that the mass is at rest up to time t_0, and is then given an impulsive (that is, instantaneous) velocity v_0 at time t_0.

The function f describing the position of the mass m as a function of time under such conditions is continuous, but its derivative f' is not defined at t_0, because of the sudden jump in the velocity. However, the left-hand derivative of f at the point t_0 exists and is equal to zero, and the right-hand derivative also exists and is equal to v_0, the impulsive velocity. For $t > 0$, the function f is obtained by solving the constant coefficient DE $u'' + pu' + qu = 0$. If $q > p^2/4$ the roots of the characteristic equation are complex conjugate, and we obtain an oscillatory solution

$$u(t) = \begin{cases} 0 & t < t_0 \\ (v_0/\nu)e^{-\mu(t-t_0)} \sin \nu(t - t_0), & t \geqq t_0, \end{cases}$$

where $\mu = p/2$ and $\nu = \sqrt{q - p^2/4}$.

Now suppose the mass is given a sequence of small velocity-impulses $\Delta v_k = r(t_k)\Delta t$, at successive instants t_0, $t_1 = t_0 + \Delta t, \cdots$; $t_k = t_0 + k\Delta t, \cdots$. Summing the effects of these over the time interval $0 \leqq t \leqq T$, and passing to the limit as $\Delta t \to 0$, we are led to conjecture the formula

$$u(T) = \int_0^T \frac{1}{\nu} e^{-\mu(T-t)} \sin \nu(T - t)r(t)dt. \tag{25}$$

This represents the *forced* oscillation associated with the DE

$$u'' + pu' + qu = r(t), \qquad q > p^2/4, \tag{26}$$

having the forcing term $r(t)$.

8. Variation of parameters. The preceding conjecture can be verified, as a special case of the following general result, valid for second-order linear DE's with variable coefficients.

THEOREM 8. *Let the function $G(t,\tau)$ be defined as follows:*
(i) $G(t,\tau) = 0$, *for* $a \leqq t \leqq \tau$,
(ii) *for each fixed* $\tau \geqq a$, *and all* $t > \tau$, $G(t,\tau)$ *is the solution of the DE* $L[G] = G_{tt} + p(t)G_t + q(t)G = 0$ *which satisfies the initial conditions* $G = 0$ *and* $G_t = 1$, *at* $t = \tau$.
Then G is the Green's function of the operator L for the initial value problem on $t \geqq a$.

Proof. We must prove that, for any continuous function r, the definite integral

$$(27) \qquad u(t) = \int_a^t G(t,\tau)r(\tau)d\tau = \int_\tau^t G(t,\tau)r(\tau)d\tau \qquad \text{(by (}i\text{))},$$

is a solution of the second-order inhomogeneous linear DE (22) which satisfies the initial conditions $u(a) = u'(a) = 0$.

The proof is based on Leibniz' Rule for differentiating definite integrals.† This rule is: For any continuous function $g(t,\tau)$ having a piecewise continuous first derivative,

$$\frac{d}{dt}\int_a^t g(t,\tau)d\tau = g(t,t) + \int_a^t \frac{\partial g}{\partial t}(t,\tau)d\tau.$$

Applying this rule twice to the right side of formula (27) we obtain successively

$$u'(t) = G(t,t)r(t) + \int_a^t G_t(t,\tau)r(\tau)d\tau = \int_a^t G_t(t,\tau)r(\tau)d\tau,$$
$$u''(t) = G_t(t,t)r(t) + \int_a^t G_{tt}(t,\tau)r(\tau)d\tau.$$

By assumption (ii), the last equation simplifies to

$$u''(t) = r(t) + \int_a^t G_{tt}(t,\tau)r(\tau)d\tau.$$

Here the subscripts indicate partial differentiation with respect to t. Thus

$$L[u] = u''(t) + p(t)u'(t) + q(t)u(t)$$
$$= r(t) + \int_a^t [G_{tt}(t,\tau) + p(t)G_t(t,\tau) + q(t)G(t,\tau)]r(\tau)d\tau = r(t), \text{ q.e.d.}$$

The reader can easily verify that the function $\nu^{-1}e^{-\mu(t-\tau)} \sin \nu(t-\tau)$ in (25) satisfies the conditions of Theorem 8, in the special case of Example 6.

To construct the Green's function $G(t,\tau)$ of Theorem 8 explicitly, it suffices to know two linearly independent solutions $f(t)$ and $g(t)$ of the

†Kaplan, *Advanced Calculus*, p. 219.

reduced equation $L[u]=0$. Namely, to compute $G(t,\tau)$ for $t \geqq \tau$, write $G(t,\tau)=c(\tau)f(t)+d(\tau)g(t)$ by Theorem 2. Solving the simultaneous linear equations $G=G_t=0$ at $t=\tau$ specified in condition (ii) of Theorem 8:

$$c(\tau)f(\tau)+d(\tau)g(\tau)=0, \qquad c(\tau)f'(\tau)+d(\tau)g'(\tau)=1,$$

we get the formulas

$$c(\tau)=-g(\tau)/W(f,g;\tau), \qquad d(\tau)=f(\tau)/W(f,g;\tau),$$

where $W(f,g;\tau)=f(\tau)g'(\tau)-g(\tau)f'(\tau)$ is the Wronskian. This gives for the Green's function the formula

$$G(t,\tau)=[f(t)g(\tau)-g(t)f(\tau)]/[f(\tau)g'(\tau)-g(\tau)f'(\tau)].$$

Substituting into (27), we get our final result:

COROLLARY. *The solution of* (22) *for the initial conditions* $u(a)=u'(a)=0$ *is*

$$u(t)=\int_a^t \frac{f(t)g(\tau)-g(t)f(\tau)}{f(\tau)g'(\tau)-g(\tau)f'(\tau)}\, r(\tau)d\tau. \tag{28}$$

In textbooks on the elementary theory of DE's, formula (28) is often derived formally by posing the question: what must $c(\tau)$ and $d(\tau)$ be in order that the function

$$G(t,\tau)=c(\tau)f(t)+d(\tau)g(t),$$

when substituted into (23), should give a solution of the inhomogeneous DE $L[u]=r(t)$? Since $c(\tau)$ and $d(\tau)$ may be regarded as "variable parameters," which vary with τ, formula (28) is said to be obtained by the method of *variation of parameters*.

EXERCISES C

1. Integrate the following DE's by the method of variation of parameters:

(a) $y''-y=x^n$, (c) $y''-qy'+y=2xe^x$,
(b) $y''+y=e^x$, (d) $y''+10y'+25y=\sin x$.

2. Show that the general solution of the inhomogeneous DE $y''+k^2y=R(x)$ is given by $y=\dfrac{1}{k}\displaystyle\int_a^x \sin k(x-t)R(t)dt+c_1\sin kx+c_2\cos kx$.

3. Solve $y''+3y'+2y=x^3$, for the initial conditions $y(0)=y'(0)=0$.

4. Show that any second-order inhomogeneous linear DE which is satisfied by both x^2 and $\sin^2 x$ must have a singular point at the origin.

5. Construct Green's functions for the initial value problem, for the following DE's:

(a) $u''=0$, (b) $u''=u$, (c) $u''+u=0$,

(d) $u''+\dfrac{x}{1+x}u'-\dfrac{1}{1+x}u=0$. (*Hint*: x is a solution.)

6. Find the general solutions of the following inhomogeneous Euler DE's:

(a) $x^2y'' - 2xy' + 2y = x^2 + px + q$,
(b) $x^2y'' + 3xy' + y = R(x)$.

(*Hint:* Any homogeneous Euler DE has a solution of the form x^ν.)

7. (a) Construct a Green's function for the inhomogeneous first-order DE

$$y' = p(x)y + r(x).$$

(b) Interpret in terms of compound interest (cf. Example 5).
(c) Relate to formula (11) of Chapter I.

8. Show that, if $q(t) < 0$, then the Green's function $G(t,\tau)$ of $u_{tt} + q(t)u = 0$ for the initial value problem is positive and convex upwards for $t > \tau$.

9*. Two-endpoint problems. So far, we have considered only boundary conditions of the "initial value" type. That is, in considering solutions of second-order DE's such as $y'' = -p(x)y' - q(x)y$, we have supposed y and y' both given at the same point a. This is natural in many dynamical problems. One is given the initial position and velocity, and a general law relating the acceleration to the instantaneous position and velocity, and then one wishes to determine the subsequent motion from these data, as in Example 4.

In other problems, *two-endpoint* conditions, at points $x = a$ and $x = b$, are more natural. For instance, the DE $y'' = 0$ characterizes straight lines in the plane, and one may be interested in determining the straight line joining two given points (a,c) and (b,d). That is, the problem is to find the solution $y = f(x)$ of the DE $y'' = 0$ which satisfies the *two* endpoint conditions $f(a) = c$ and $f(b) = d$.

Many two-endpoint problems for second-order DE's arise in the calculus of variations; the following example leads to a linear DE.

EXAMPLE 7. For given p, q, $r \in \mathcal{C}^1$, find the curve which minimizes the integral

$$\text{(29)} \qquad \int_a^b \tfrac{1}{2}[p(x)y'^2 + 2q(x)yy' + r(x)y^2]dx = \int_a^b F(x,y,y')dx$$

among all curves joining two given endpoints (a,c) and (b,d). By a classical result of Euler,† the line integral (29) is an extremum (maximum, minimum, or minimax), relative to all curves $y = f(x)$ satisfying $f(a) = c$ and $f(b) = d$, if and only if $f(x)$ satisfies the self-adjoint second-order linear DE

$$\text{(30)} \qquad \frac{d}{dx}\left(\frac{\partial F}{\partial y'}\right) - \left(\frac{\partial F}{\partial y}\right) = (py')' + (q' - r)y = 0.$$

It is natural to ask: under what circumstances does a second-order DE have a unique solution assuming given values $f(a) = c$ and $f(b) = d$ at two

†See for example Courant, Vol. 1, Ch. VII. We will recur to (30) later, in Ch. X.

given points a and $b > a$? This is obviously true in the case $p - r = 1$, $q = 0$ of $y'' = 0$. The following result provides a partial answer to this question.

THEOREM 9. *Let the second-order linear homogeneous DE*

$$p_0(x)u'' + p_1(x)u' + p_2(x)u = 0, \qquad p_0(x) \neq 0, \tag{31}$$

with continuous coefficient-functions have two linearly independent solutions.† *Then it has one and only one solution $u = \phi(x)$ satisfying two given endpoint conditions $\phi(a) = c$, $\phi(b) = d$ if and only if no nontrivial solution satisfies the endpoint conditions*

$$u(a) = u(b) = 0 \tag{31'}$$

Proof. By Theorem 2, the general solution of the DE (31) is the function $u = \alpha f(x) + \beta g(x)$, where f and g are a basis of solutions of the DE (30), and α, β are arbitrary constants. By the elementary theory of linear equations, the equations

$$\alpha f(a) + \beta g(a) = c, \qquad \alpha f(b) + \beta g(b) = d,$$

have one and only one solution-vector (α, β), if and only if the determinant $f(a)g(b) - g(a)f(b) \neq 0$. The alternative $f(a)g(b) = f(b)g(a)$ is however the condition that the *homogeneous* simultaneous linear equations

$$\alpha f(a) + \beta g(a) = \alpha f(b) + \beta g(b) = 0 \tag{32}$$

should have a nontrivial solution $(\alpha, \beta) \neq (0,0)$. This proves Theorem 9.

When the DE (31) has a nontrivial solution satisfying the homogeneous endpoint conditions $\phi(a) = \phi(b) = 0$, the point $(b,0)$ on the x-axis is called a *conjugate point* of the point $(a,0)$ for the given homogeneous linear DE (31) or for a variational problem leading to this DE. In general, such conjugate points exist for DE's whose solutions *oscillate*, but not for those of non-oscillatory type, such as $u'' = q(x)u$, $q(x) > 0$.

Thus, in Example 7, let $p = 1$, $q = 0$, and $r = -k^2 < 0$. Then the general solution of (30) for the initial condition $u(a) = 0$ is $u = A \sin [k(x - a)]$. For $u(b) = 0$ to be compatible with $A \neq 0$, it is necessary and sufficient that $b = a + (n\pi/k)$. The conjugate points of a are spaced periodically. On the other hand the DE $y'' - \lambda y = 0$, corresponding to the choice $p = 1$, $q = 0$, $r = \lambda$ in Example 7, admits no conjugate points if $\lambda = r$ is positive.

10*. Green's functions. We now show that, except in the case that a and b are conjugate points for the reduced equation $L[u] = 0$, the inhomogeneous linear DE (22) can be solved for the boundary conditions

†In Chapter V, it will be shown that this hypothesis is unnecessary; a basis of solutions always exists.

$u(a) = u(b) = 0$, by constructing an appropriate Green's function $G(x,\xi)$ on the square $a \leqq x,\ \xi \leqq b$, and setting

$$u(x) = \int_a^b G(x,\xi)r(\xi)d\xi = G[r]. \tag{33}$$

Note that G is an *integral operator* whose kernel is the Green's function $G(x,\xi)$.

The existence of a Green's function for a typical two-endpoint problem is suggested by simple physical considerations, as follows.

EXAMPLE 8. Consider a nearly horizontal taut string under constant tension T, supporting a continuously distributed load $w(x)$ per unit length. If $y(x)$ denotes the vertical displacement of the string, then the load $w(x)\,\Delta x$ supported by the string in the interval $(x_0, x_0 + \Delta x)$ is in equilibrium with the net vertical component of tension forces, which is

$$T\{y'(x_0 + \Delta x) - y'(x_0)\}$$

in the nearly horizontal ("small amplitude") approximation.† Dividing through by Δx and letting $\Delta x \downarrow 0$, we get $Ty''(x) = w(x)$.

The displacement $y(x)$ depends linearly on the load, by the Lemma of § 5. This suggests that we consider the load as the sum of point-concentrated loads $w_i = w(\xi_i)\Delta\xi_i$ at isolated points. For each such concentrated load, the taut string consists of two straight segments, the slope jumping by w_i/T at ξ_i. Thus, if the string extends from 0 to 1, the vertical displacement is

$$w_i G(x,\xi_i) = \begin{cases} \epsilon_i(\xi_i - 1)x, & 0 < x \leqq \xi_i, \\ \epsilon_i\xi_i(x - 1), & \xi_i \leqq x \leqq 1, \end{cases}$$

where ϵ_i is set equal to w_i/T in order to give a jump in slope of w_i/T at the point $x = \xi_i$. Passing to the limit as the $\Delta\xi_i \downarrow 0$, we are led to guess that

$$y(x) = \int_0^1 G(x,\xi)w(\xi)d\xi, \text{ where } G(x,\xi) = \begin{cases} (\xi - 1)x/T & 0 \leqq x \leqq \xi \\ \xi(x - 1)/T & \xi \leqq x \leqq 1. \end{cases}$$

These heuristic considerations suggest that the Green's function $G(x,\xi)$ is determined by the following conditions: it satisfies $L[G] = 0$ for each fixed ξ in the intervals $a \leqq x \leqq \xi$ and $\xi \leqq x \leqq b$; it is continuous across the principal diagonal $x = \xi$ of the square $a \leqq x,\ \xi \leqq b$ over which G is defined; its derivative $\partial G/\partial x$ jumps by $1/p_0(x)$ across this diagonal. That is, let $f(x)$ and $g(x)$ be any nontrivial solutions of $L[u] = 0$ which satisfy

†For a more thorough discussion, see J. L. Synge and B. A. Griffith, *Principles of Mechanics*, McGraw-Hill, 1949, p. 99.

$f(a) = 0$, $g(b) = 0$, respectively. The conjecture is that

$$G(x,\xi) = \begin{cases} \epsilon(\xi)f(x)g(\xi), & a \leqq x \leqq \xi, \\ \epsilon(\xi)f(\xi)g(x), & \xi \leqq x \leqq b, \end{cases}$$

where the factor $\epsilon(\xi)$ above is chosen to give $\partial G/\partial x$ a jump of $1/p_0(x)$ across $x = \xi$:

$$\frac{\partial G}{\partial x}(\xi^+,\xi) - \frac{\partial G}{\partial x}(\xi^-,\xi) = \epsilon(\xi)\{f(\xi)g'(\xi) - g(\xi)f'(\xi)\} = 1/p_0(\xi).$$

We are therefore led to try the kernel

$$G(x,\xi) = \begin{cases} f(x)g(\xi)/p_0(\xi)W(\xi), & a \leqq x \leqq \xi, \\ f(\xi)g(x)/p_0(\xi)W(\xi), & \xi \leqq x \leqq b, \end{cases} \tag{34}$$

where $W = fg' - gf'$ is the Wronskian of f and g.

THEOREM 10. *For any continuous function $r(x)$ on $[a,b]$, the function $u(x)$ defined by (33) and (34) is the solution of the DE (22) which satisfies the boundary conditions $u(a) = u(b) = 0$, provided there is no nontrivial solution of (22′) satisfying the same boundary conditions.*

The proof is similar to that of Theorem 8; the existence of two linearly independent solutions of (22′) is again assumed. Rewriting (33) in the form

$$u(x) = \int_a^x G(x,\xi)r(\xi)d\xi + \int_x^b G(x,\xi)r(\xi)d\xi,$$

and differentiating by Leibniz' Rule, we have

$$u'(x) = \int_a^x G_x(x,\xi)r(\xi)d\xi + \int_x^b G_x(x,\xi)r(\xi)d\xi.$$

The endpoint contributions cancel, since $G(x,\xi)$ is continuous for $x = \xi$. Differentiating again,

$$u''(x) = \int_a^x G_{xx}(x,\xi)r(\xi)d\xi + G_x(x,x^-)r(x^-) + \int_x^b G_{xx}(x,\xi)r(\xi)d\xi - G_x(x,x^+)r(x^+),$$

where $f(x^+)$ signifies the limit of $f(\xi)$ as ξ approaches x from above, and $f(x^-)$ the limit as ξ approaches x from below. The two terms corresponding to the contributions from the endpoints come from the sides $\xi < x$ and $\xi > x$ of the diagonal; since r is continuous, $r(x^-) = r(x^+)$, and their difference is $[G_x(x^+,x) - G_x(x^-,x)]r(x)$, which equals $r(x)/p_0(x)$ by (34). Simplifying, we obtain

$$u''(x) = \int_a^b G_{xx}(x,\xi)r(\xi)d\xi + r(x)/p_0(x).$$

From this identity we can calculate $L[u]$. It is

$$L[u] = \int_a^b L[G(x,\xi)]r(\xi)d\xi + r(x) = r(x),$$

since $L[G(x,\xi)] \equiv 0$. Here the operator L acts on the variable x in $G(x,\xi)$; though G is not in $\mathcal{C}^2$, the expression $L[G]$ is meaningful for one-sided derivatives and the above can be justified. This gives the identity (33).

Since $G(x,\xi)$, as a function of x, satisfies the boundary conditions $u(a) = u(b) = 0$, it follows from (33), by differentiating under the integral sign, that u satisfies the same boundary conditions. This completes the proof of the theorem.

EXERCISES D

In Exs. 1–3, (a) construct Green's functions for the two-endpoint problem defined by the DE specified, and the boundary conditions $u(0) = u(1) = 0$, and (b) solve for $r(x) = x^2$:

1. $u'' - u = r(x)$.
2. $u'' + 4u = r(x)$.
3. $u'' - \dfrac{4x}{2x-1}u' + \dfrac{4}{2x-1} = r(x)$.

In Exs. 4–6, find the conjugate points nearest to $x = 0$ for the DE specified:

4. $u'' + 2u' + 10u = 0$.
5. $(x^2 - x + 1)u'' + (1 - 2x)u' + 2u = 0$. (*Hint:* Look for polynomial solutions.)
*6. $u_{tt} - u_t + e^{2t}u = 0$. (*Hint:* Use Ex. B10.)
7. (a) Show that, for two-endpoint problems containing no pairs of conjugate points, the Green's function is always negative.

(b) Show that, if $q(x) < 0$, then the Green's function for $u'' + q(x)u = 0$ in the two-endpoint problem is always negative and convex (concave downwards), with negative slope if $x < \xi$ and positive slope if $x > \xi$.

ADDITIONAL EXERCISES

1. Show that the ratio $v = f/g$ of any two linearly independent solutions of the DE $u'' + q(x)u = 0$ is a solution of the third-order nonlinear DE

$$(*) \qquad S[v] = \frac{v'''}{v'} - \frac{3}{2}\left(\frac{v''}{v'}\right)^2 = 2q(x).$$

2. The *Schwarzian* $S[v]$ of a function $v(x)$ being defined by (*), show that $S[(av + b)/(cv + d)] = S[v]$ for any four constants a, b, c, d with $ad \neq bc$.

*3. Prove that, if v_0, v_1, v_2, v_3 are any four distinct solutions of the Riccati DE, their cross-ratio is constant: $(v_0 - v_1)(v_3 - v_2)/(v_0 - v_2)(v_3 - v_1) = c$.

4. Find the general solutions of the following inhomogeneous Euler DE's:

(a) $x^2y'' - 2xy' + 2y = x^2 + px + q$,

(b) $x^2y'' + 3xy' + y = R(x)$.

5. (a) Show that if f and g satisfy $u'' + q(x)u = 0$, then the product $fg = y$ satisfies $2yy'' = (y')^2 - 4y^2q(x) + c$ for some constant c.

*(b) Express the general solution of the latter DE for given c, in terms of f and g, assuming $W(f,g) \neq 0$.

(c) As an application, solve $2xy'' = (y')^2 - (x + 1)^{-2}y^2 + 1$.

6. Show that, if u is the general solution of the DE (1) of the text, and $W_{ij} = p_i p_j' - p_i' p_j$, then $v = u'$ is the general solution of:

$$p_0 p_2 v'' + (p_1 p_2 - W_{02})v' + (p_2{}^2 - W_{12})v = W_{23}.$$

7. (a) Show that the Riccati equation $y' = 1 + x^2 + y^2$ has no solution on the interval $(0,\pi)$.

(b) Show that the Riccati equation $y' = 1 + y^2 - x^2$ has a solution on the interval $(-\infty, +\infty)$.

8. In $u''(x) = p(x)u'(x) + q(x)u(x)$, let $p(x) > p_0$ and $q(x) > q_0$, where p_0, q_0 are positive constants. Prove that if $u(0) > 0$ and $u'(0) > 0$, then there exists a positive A such that $u(x) > A \exp(p_0 x)$ for all $x > 0$. (*Hint:* Apply the Comparison Theorem of Ch. I to the Riccati equation.)

9. For the DE $u'' + (B/x^2)u = 0$, show that every solution has infinitely many zeros on $(1,+\infty)$ if $B > 1/4$, and a finite number if $B < 1/4$. (*Hint:* The DE is an Euler DE.)

10. For the DE $u'' + q(x)u = 0$, show that every solution has a finite number of zeros on $(1,+\infty)$ if $q(x) < 1/4x^2$, and infinitely many if $q(x) > B/x^2$, where $B > 1/4$.

*11. For the DE $u'' + q(x)u = 0$, show that every solution has infinitely many zeros on $(1,+\infty)$ if $\int_1^\infty \left[xq(x) - \frac{1}{4x}\right]dx = +\infty$.

*12. Show that, if $p,q \in \mathcal{C}^2$ and $I(0) \neq 0$, one can transform the DE (8) to the form $d^2z/d\xi^2 = 0$ in some neighborhood of the y-axis by transformations of the form $z = f(x)y$ and $d\xi = h(x)dx$. (*Hint:* Use Exs. B4, B5, B10 to transform a basis of solutions to $y_1 = 1$, $y_2 = \xi$.)

CHAPTER III

Power Series Solutions

1. Introduction. In Chapters I and II, we have shown how to construct solutions of various special types of DE's using the Fundamental Theorem of the Calculus—that is, how to reduce the integration of these DE's to one or more quadratures. The devices used lead to formulas expressing the general solution explicitly, in terms of the integration symbol $\int$. However, a much more fundamental approach is to think of the solutions of a given DE as *defined* by this DE and appropriate initial conditions or other boundary conditions. The validity of this approach depends, of course, on theorems of existence, uniqueness and continuity to be proved in Chapter V.

From now on, we will usually adopt this viewpoint; it is inevitable. Even in the integral calculus, many functions "cannot be integrated" in terms of elementary functions. Thus, such expressions as

$$(1) \qquad \int \frac{\sin x}{x}\,dx, \quad \int \frac{e^{-x}}{x}\,dx, \quad \text{and} \quad \int \frac{dx}{\sqrt{(1-x^2)(1-k^2x^2)}}$$

are conspicuously missing from Tables of Integrals. The Fundamental Theorem of the Calculus, which guarantees the existence and uniqueness of integrals of continuous functions, provides a way out of the difficulty (cf. Ch. I, § 2). One simply *defines* such higher transcendental functions by the formulas

$$(2) \qquad \begin{gathered} \mathrm{SI}(x) = \int_x^\infty \frac{\sin \xi}{\xi}\,d\xi, \quad \mathrm{EI}(x) = \int_x^\infty \frac{e^{-\xi}}{\xi}\,d\xi \\ \int_0^x \frac{d\xi}{\sqrt{(1-\xi^2)(1-k^2\xi^2)}} = F(k, \arcsin x), \end{gathered}$$

By the Fundamental Theorem of the Calculus, these formulas define differentiable functions whose values can be computed (though inefficiently, see Chapters VII and VIII) as limits of Riemann sums.

This is also a good way to treat the logarithmic function.† One can

†See for example Courant, Vol. 1, pp. 167–178.

define $\log_e x = \ln x$ as the definite integral (limit of Riemann sums):

$$\ln x = \int_1^x \frac{dt}{t} = \lim_{n\to\infty} \sum_{k=1}^{n} \frac{1}{n + k(x-1)}. \tag{3}$$

From this definition, using the Fundamental Theorem of the Calculus, one can derive all the properties of logarithms.

Just as $\ln x$ can be defined as a solution of the DE $y' = 1/x$ satisfying $y(1) = 0$, so the inverse function e^x can be defined as the solution of the DE $y' = y$ satisfying the initial condition $y(0) = 1$, and its fundamental properties can be derived from this definition.

In the present chapter, we will first show how various *analytic* functions can be effectively defined as solutions of second-order linear homogeneous DE's

$$u'' + p(x)u' + q(x)u = 0, \tag{4}$$

with *analytic* coefficient-functions

$$p(x) = p_0 + p_1x + p_2x^2 + \cdots, \quad q(x) = q_0 + q_1x + q_2x^2 + \cdots. \tag{5}$$

These functions include many of the special functions most commonly used in applied mathematics.

We will then give a similar construction for the solutions of normal first-order DE's of the form $y' = F(x,y)$, where

$$F(x,y) = b_{00} + b_{10}x + b_{01}y + b_{20}x^2 + b_{11}xy + b_{02}y^2 + \cdots \tag{5'}$$

is also assumed to be analytic.

In summary, restricting our attention to *analytic* functions, we will develop in this chapter the basic idea stated above: That *DE's and appropriate boundary conditions constitute one of the best ways of defining new functions*, and that the properties of these functions can often be best derived directly from a study of the defining DE.

2. Method of Undetermined Coefficients. The class $\mathcal{A}(D)$ of functions *analytic* in a domain D is defined as the class of those functions which can be expanded in a power series around any point of D, which is *convergent* in some neighborhood of that point. By a translation of coordinates, one can reduce the consideration of such power series to power series like (5) and (5′) of § 1, having the origin as the center of expansion.

Most of the special functions commonly used in applied mathematics have simple power series expansions. This is especially true of functions defined as definite integrals. Thus:

$$\mathrm{SI}(x) = \int_x^\infty \sum_{k=0}^{\infty} (-1)^k \frac{\xi^{2k}\,d\xi}{(2k+1)!} = \frac{\pi}{2} - \sum_{k=0}^{\infty} (-1)^k \frac{x^{2k+1}}{(2k+1)^2(2k!)};$$

only the evaluation of the constant term $\pi/2$ poses any difficulty. Expanding the integrand in power series, one gets the first few terms of the series expansion for the elliptic integral

$$F(k, \sin^{-1} x) = \int_0^x (1 - \xi^2)^{-1/2}(1 - k^2\xi^2)^{-1/2}d\xi$$
$$= x + (1 + k^2)x^3/6 + (3 + 2k^2 + 3k^4)x^5/40 - \cdots,$$

with a little more effort.

Likewise, consider the exponential function e^x, defined as the solution of $y' = y$ and the initial condition $y(0) = 1$. Differentiating this DE n times we get $y^{(n+1)} = y^{(n)}$. Substitution into Taylor's formula then gives the familiar exponential series $e^x = \sum_{k=0}^{\infty} x^k/(k!)$.

We now give some simple applications of the same principle to some special functions familiar in applied mathematics, defined as solutions of second-order linear homogeneous DE's (4) with analytic coefficient-functions.

To express such solutions in the form of power series, one writes down the solution in the form of a power series $u = a_0 + a_1x + a_2x^2 + \cdots$ with undetermined coefficients a_k, substitutes into the DE, differentiates term by term, and equates to zero the coefficients of each power x^k of x. This is called the Method of Undetermined Coefficients.

To apply this method, one must assume that p and q are analytic near the origin. This means that they can be expanded into power series

$$(5) \qquad p(x) = p_0 + p_1x + p_2x^2 + \cdots, \quad q(x) = q_0 + q_1x + q_2x^2 + \cdots,$$

convergent for sufficiently small x.

To compute the solution, form the trial series

$$(6) \qquad u = a_0 + a_1x + a_2x^2 + a_3x^3 + \cdots = \sum_{k=0}^{\infty} a_kx^k.$$

Term-by-term differentiation gives

$$u'' = 2a_2 + 6a_3x + 12a_4x^2 + \cdots + (n+1)(n+2)a_{n+2}x^n + \cdots$$
$$pu' = p_0a_1 + (2p_0a_2 + p_1a_1)x + \cdots + \left[\sum_{k=0}^{n} (n+1-k)p_ka_{n+1-k}\right]x^n + \cdots$$
$$qu = q_0a_0 + (q_0a_1 + q_1a_0)x + \cdots + \left[\sum_{k=0}^{n} q_ka_{n-k}\right]x^n + \cdots.$$

Substituting into (4), and equating the coefficients of $1, x, \cdots, x^{n-1}, \cdots$ to zero, we get successively

$$a_2 = -(p_0a_1 + q_0a_0)/2, \quad a_3 = -(2p_0a_2 + p_1a_1 + q_0a_1 + q_1a_0)/6,$$

and so on. The general equation is

$$(7) \quad a_{n+1} = -\left[\sum_{k=0}^{n-1} (n-k)p_ka_{n-k} + \sum_{k=0}^{n-1} q_ka_{n-1-k}\right] \Big/ n(n+1), \quad n \geqq 2.$$

Given $a_0 = f(0)$ and $a_1 = f'(0)$, a unique power series is determined by (7) which formally satisfies the DE (4). We have proved

THEOREM 1. *Given a linear homogeneous second-order DE* (4) *with analytic coefficient-functions* (5), *there exists a unique power series* (6) *which formally satisfies the DE, for each choice of* a_0 *and* a_1.

Caution. We have not stated or proved that the formal power series (6) represents a function. To see the need for proving this, consider the DE $x^2u' = u - x$, which has the everywhere *divergent* formal power series solution

$$x + x^2 + (2!)x^3 + (3!)x^4 + \cdots + (n-1)!x^n + \cdots.$$

The *convergence* of the power series (6) to an *analytic function*, for normal second-order linear DE's (4), will be proved in § 6. First we treat some special cases, in which convergence is easily verified.

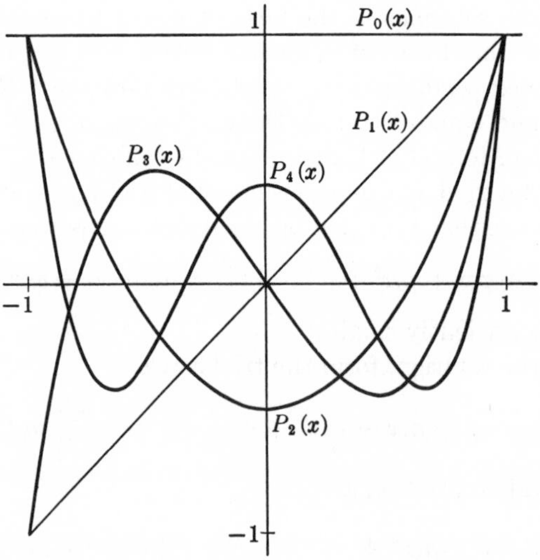

Figure III-1. Graphs of $P_n(x)$—Legendre Polynomials

EXAMPLE 1. The Legendre DE (Ch. II, § 1) is usually written

$$\frac{d}{dx}\left[(1 - x^2)\frac{du}{dx}\right] + \lambda u = 0, \tag{8}$$

where λ is a parameter.

Substituting the series (6) into the linear DE (8), and equating to zero the coefficients of $1 = x^0$, x, x^2, $\cdots$, we get an infinite system of linear equations

$$0 = 2a_2 + \lambda a_0 = 6a_3 + (\lambda - 2)a_1 = 12a_4 + (\lambda - 6)a_2 = \cdots.$$

The k-th equation of this system is the *recurrence relation*

(8′) $$a_{k+2} = [k(k+1) - \lambda]a_k/(k+1)(k+2).$$

This relation defines for each λ two nontrivial solutions, one consisting of *even* powers of x and the other of *odd* powers of x. These solutions are power series whose *radius of convergence* is unity by the Ratio Test,† unless $\lambda = n(n+1)$ for some nonnegative integer n. In this event there is a polynomial solution which is an even function if n is even and an odd function if n is odd. These polynomial solutions are the *Legendre polynomials* $P_n(x)$.

Graphs of the Legendre polynomials $P_0(x), \cdots, P_4(x)$ are shown in Figure III-1. Note how the number of their oscillations increases with $\lambda = n(n+1)$, as predicted by the Sturm Comparison Theorem.

EXAMPLE 2. The Hermite DE is

(9) $$u'' - 2xu' + \lambda u = 0.$$

Applying the Method of Undetermined Coefficients to (9), one gets the recursion formula

(9′) $$a_{k+2} = (2k - \lambda)a_k/(k+1)(k+2),$$

which again gives for each λ one power series in the even powers x^{2k} of x, and another in the odd powers x^{2k+1}. These power series are convergent for all x; if $\lambda = 2n$ is a nonnegative even integer, one series is a polynomial of degree n, the *Hermite polynomial* $H_n(x)$.

3*. Sine and cosine functions. To emphasize the idea that the properties of solutions of DE's can be derived from the DE's themselves, we now study the *trigonometric* DE

(10) $$y'' + y = 0.$$

The general solution of this DE is $y = a \cos x + b \sin x$ where a and b are arbitrary constants, and the functions $\cos x$ and $\sin x$ are defined geometrically.

We shall now pretend that we do not know this, and show that all properties of the trigonometric functions $\sin x$ and $\cos x$ can be deduced analytically from the trigonometric DE (10), and the initial conditions which they satisfy. In this spirit, we *define* the functions $C(x)$ and $S(x)$ as the solutions of the DE (10) satisfying the initial conditions $C(0) = 1$, $C'(0) = 0$ and $S(0) = 0$, $S'(0) = 1$, respectively. The Method of Undetermined Coefficients of § 2 gives for these functions the familiar power series expansions

(11) $$C(x) = 1 - \frac{x^2}{2!} + \frac{x^4}{4!} - \cdots, \quad S(x) = x - \frac{x^3}{3!} + \frac{x^5}{5!} - \cdots,$$

whose convergence for all x follows by the Ratio Test.

†Courant, Vol. 1, p. 378; Widder, p. 242.

Differentiation of (10) gives the DE $y''' + y' = 0$. Therefore the function $C'(x)$ is also a solution of the DE (10); moreover, since this function satisfies the initial conditions $C'(0) = 0$ and $C''(0) = -C(0) = -1$, it follows from the Uniqueness Theorem (Ch. II, Thm. 1) that $C'(x) = -S(x)$. This proves the differentiation rule for the cosine function. A similar computation gives $S'(x) = C(x)$.

The Wronskian of the functions $S(x)$ and $C(x)$ can be computed from these two formulas; it is $W(S,C; x) = S(x)^2 + C(x)^2$. From Theorem 3 of Chapter II, $W(S,C; x) \equiv S(0)^2 + C(0)^2 = 1$ follows. This proves the familiar trigonometric formula $\sin^2 x + \cos^2 x = 1$.

Again, by Theorem 2 of Chapter II, every solution of the DE (10) is a linear combination of the functions S and C. We now use this fact to derive the addition formula for the sine function:

$$\sin (a + x) = \cos a \sin x + \sin a \cos x.$$

First, by the chain rule for differentiating composite functions, the function $S(a + x)$ is also a solution of the DE (10). Therefore (Ch. II, Thm. 2) this function must be a linear combination of $S(x)$ and $C(x)$:

$$S(a + x) = AS(x) + BC(x).$$

Furthermore, if we write $f(x) = S(a + x)$, then $f(0) = S(a)$ and $f'(0) = C(a)$. But if we differentiate the right side of the equality displayed above, we find that $f(0) = B$ and $f'(0) = A$, and this proves the addition formula. The addition formula for $C(x)$,

$$C(a + x) = C(a)C(x) - S(a)S(x),$$

can be derived similarly.

Finally, the fact that the functions S and C are periodic can be proved from the addition formulas, if one defines $\pi/4$ as the least positive x such that $S(\pi/4) = 1/\sqrt{2}$. Since $S' = C = \sqrt{1 - S^2} \geqq 1/\sqrt{2}$ on any interval $[0,b]$ where $S(x) \leqq 1/\sqrt{2}$, we see that $S(x)$ is increasing and satisfies $S(x) \geqq x/\sqrt{2}$ there. Hence $S(x) \leqq 1/\sqrt{2}$ on $[0,1]$ is impossible, which shows that $\pi/4$ exists in $[0,1]$. Moreover $\pi/4 = S^{-1}(1/\sqrt{2})$, where S^{-1} is the inverse function of S. Since the derivative of S^{-1} is given by $1/S'(x) = 1/\sqrt{1 - S^2}$, this makes $\pi/4 = \int_0^{1/\sqrt{2}} dt/\sqrt{1 - t^2}$. Moreover C cannot change sign until $S^2 = 1 - C^2 = 1$. Hence $\cos (\pi/4) = 1/\sqrt{2} = \sin (\pi/4)$. Consequently, by the addition formulas proved above,

$$\sin \left(\frac{\pi}{4} + x\right) = \frac{1}{\sqrt{2}} (\sin x + \cos x) = \cos \left(\frac{\pi}{4} - x\right).$$

In particular, $\sin(\pi/2) = (2/\sqrt{2})/\sqrt{2} = 1$ and so $\cos(\pi/2) = 0$. Using the addition formulas again, one gets the formulas $\sin(\pi/2 + x) = \sin(\pi/2 - x)$, $\cos(\pi/2 + x) = -\cos(\pi/2 - x)$, $\sin(\pi + x) = -\sin x$, $\cos(\pi + x) = -\cos x$, and finally the periodicity relations $\cos(2\pi + x) = \cos x$, $\sin(2\pi + x) = \sin x$.

EXERCISES A

1. (a) Prove that the Legendre DE has a polynomial solution if and only if $\lambda = n(n+1)$. (b) Prove that every nonpolynomial solution of the Legendre DE has radius of convergence equal to one.

2. Find a recurrence relation like (8′) for the DE $(1 + x^2)y'' = y$, and compute expansions through terms in x^{10} for a basis of solutions.

3. (a) Find power series expansions for a basis of solutions of Airy's DE $u'' + xu = 0$.

(b) Prove that the radius of convergence of both solutions is infinite.

(c) Reduce $u'' + (ax + b)u = 0$ to $d^2u/dt^2 + tu = 0$ by a suitable change of independent variable.

4. Define $\sinh x$ and $\cosh x$ as the solutions of the DE $u'' = u$ which satisfy the initial conditions $u(0) = 0$, $u'(0) = 1$ and $u(0) = 1$, $u'(0) = 0$, respectively. Show that $\sinh x$ has only one real zero and $\cosh x$ has no real zeros. Relate to the Sturm Comparison Theorem.

*5. Using methods like those of § 3, establish the following formulas (cf. Ex. 4):

(a) $\cosh^2 x - \sin^2 x = 1$, (c) $\sinh(-x) = -\sinh x$,

(b) $\cosh(-x) = \cosh x$, (d) $\sinh(x + y) = \sinh x \cosh y + \cosh x \sinh y$,

(e) $\sinh^{-1} x = \ln(x + \sqrt{x^2 + 1})$.

6. Show that $u(x)$ satisfies the Hermite DE (9) if and only if $v = e^{-x^2/2}u$ satisfies $v'' + (\lambda + 1 - x^2)v = 0$.

7. Show that the DE $(Ax^2 + B)u'' + Cxu' + Du = 0$ has a solution which is a polynomial of degree n if and only if $An^2 + (C - A)n + D = 0$.

8. Show that the change of independent variable $x = \cos\theta$ transforms the Legendre DE (8) of the text into $u_{\theta\theta} + (\cot\theta)u_\theta + \lambda u = 0$. What is the self-adjoint form of this equation?

9. In spherical coordinates, the Laplacian of a function $F(r,\theta)$ is

$$\nabla^2 F = F_{rr} + \frac{2}{r}F_r + F_{\theta\theta} + (\cot\theta)F_\theta.$$

Show that $F(r,\theta) = r^n P(\cos\theta)$ satisfies $\nabla^2 F = 0$ if and only if $P(x)$ satisfies the Legendre DE with $\lambda = n(n+1)$.

10. (a) Show that, in spherical coordinates, $U(r,\theta) = (1 - 2r\cos\theta + r^2)^{-1/2}$ satisfies $\nabla^2 U = 0$. (*Hint:* Consider the potential of a charge at (1,0,0).)

(b) Infer that $(1 - 2r\cos\theta + r^2)^{-1/2} = \sum_0^\infty r^n P_n(\cos\theta)$, where $P_n(x)$ is a solution of the Legendre equation (8) with $\lambda = n(n+1)$.

*11. Find conditions on the constants $A, \cdots, F$ necessary and sufficient for the DE $(Ax^2 + Bx + C)u'' + (Dx + E)u' + Fu = 0$ to have a solution which is a polynomial of degree n.

4*. Bessel functions. The Bessel functions of order n can be defined similarly, for $n = 0, 1, 2, \cdots$, as solutions of the Bessel DE of order n,

$$u'' + \frac{1}{x}u' + \left(1 - \frac{n^2}{x^2}\right)u = 0. \tag{12}$$

The coefficients of this DE have a singular point at $x = 0$, and are analytic at all other points (see § 5).

Though the Bessel DE (12) of integral order n has a singular point at the origin, it has a nontrivial analytic solution there. The power series expression for this solution can be computed by the Method of Undetermined Coefficients. For example, when $n = 0$, the DE (12) reduces to

$$(xu')' + xu = 0. \tag{13}$$

Substituting $u = \sum a_k z^k$ into (13), we get the recursion relation $r^2 a_r = -a_{r-2}$. For $a_0 = 1$, $a_1 = 0$, (13) has the analytic solution

$$\begin{aligned} J_0(x) &= 1 - \left(\frac{x}{2}\right)^2 + \left(\frac{x^2}{2\cdot 4}\right)^2 - \left(\frac{x^3}{2\cdot 4\cdot 6}\right)^2 + \cdots, \\ &= 1 - \frac{x^2}{4} + \frac{x^2}{64} - \frac{x^6}{2304} + \cdots + (-1)^r \frac{x^{2r}}{[2^r (r!)]^2} + \cdots. \end{aligned} \tag{14}$$

This series is convergent for all x, by the Ratio Test.

Similar calculations give, for general n, the solution

$$\begin{aligned} J_n(x) = \left(\frac{x}{2}\right)^n \bigg\{ \frac{1}{n!} - \frac{x^2}{4(n+1)!} + \frac{x^4}{32(n+2)!} - \cdots \\ + (-1)^r \left(\frac{x}{2}\right)^{2r} / (r!)(n+r)! + \cdots \bigg\}, \end{aligned} \tag{15}$$

whose coefficients a_r satisfy the recursion relation $2r(n+r)a_r = -a_{r-2}$. The series (15) is also everywhere convergent. Hence the Bessel function of order n is an *entire* function, analytic for all finite x. Graphs of $J_0(x)$ and $J_1(x)$ are shown as Figure III-2.

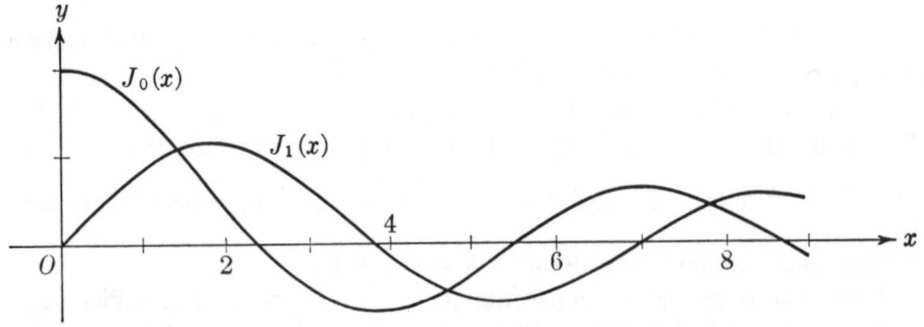

Figure III-2. Bessel Functions $J_0(x)$ and $J_1(x) = -J_0'(x)$

By comparing coefficients, one can easily verify the relations

$$J_1 = -J_0', \quad xJ_2 = J_1 - xJ_1' = 2J_1 - xJ_0, \quad xJ_3 = 2J_2 - xJ_2'.$$

For general n, one can verify likewise the *recursion formulas*

$$xJ_{n+1} = nJ_n - xJ_n' = 2nJ_n - xJ_{n-1}. \tag{16}$$

Clearly, formula (16) defines $J_1, J_2, J_3, \cdots$ recursively from J_0.

One can prove all the properties of the Bessel functions of integral order from (12) and the recursion relations (16). For example, one can obtain such useful formulas as

$$\int xJ_0 dx = xJ_1, \qquad \int xJ_1 dx = -xJ_0 + \int J_0 dx,$$

$$\int xJ_0^2 dx = (x^2/2)(J_0^2 + J_1^2) = (x^2/2)(J_0^2 + J_0'^2).$$

More generally, one can obtain useful expressions representing, in closed form, integrals of arbitrary polynomial functions times Bessel functions and products of Bessel functions. The basic formulas are (16) and

$$\int x^k J_1 dx = -x^k J_0 + k \int x^{k-1} J_0 dx, \tag{17a}$$

$$\int x^k J_0 dx = x^k J_1 - (k-1) \int x^{k-1} J_1 dx, \tag{17b}$$

$$2 \int x^k J_0 J_1 dx = -x^k J_0^2 + k \int x^{k-1} J_0^2 dx, \tag{17c}$$

$$\int x^k (J_0^2 - J_1^2) dx = x^k J_0 J_1 - (k-1) \int x^{k-1} J_0 J_1 dx, \tag{17d}$$

$$\int x^k [(k+1) J_0^2 + (k-1) J_1^2] dx = x^{k+1} (J_0^2 + J_1^2). \tag{17e}$$

Equation (17a) follows from $J_1 = -J_0'$, integrating by parts. To derive (17b), use (13) to get $(x^k J_1)' = x_k J_0 + (k-1)x^{k-1} J_1$. To derive (17c)–(17e), differentiate $x^k J_0^2$, $x^k J_0 J_0'$, and $x^{k+1}(J_0^2 + J_0'^2)$, respectively, and use (13) to eliminate J_0''. The integral $\int J_0 dx$ cannot be reduced further, and so it has been calculated (by numerical integration) and tabulated.†

Important *qualitative* information can also be obtained from a study of the DE (12) which the Bessel functions satisfy. Substituting $u = v/\sqrt{x}$ into (12), we obtain the equivalent DE

$$v'' + \left[1 - \frac{4n^2 - 1}{4x^2}\right] v = 0. \tag{18}$$

The oscillatory behavior of nontrivial solutions of the Bessel DE (12), for large x, can now be shown using the Sturm Comparison Theorem (Ch. II, § 4). This result, when applied to (18), shows that, for large x, the distance between successive zeros of $J_0(x)$ is inferior to π by a small quantity (at

†G. N. Watson, *Bessel Functions*, Ch. VIII. Cambridge. Fletcher, Rosenhead, and Miller is very helpful for locating such tabulations.

most $\pi/8x^2$), while that between successive zeros x_i and x_{i+1} of $J_n(x)$ exceeds π by about $n^2\pi/2x_i^2$, if $n \geqq 1$. Also, since $J_1 = -J_0'$, there is a zero of J_1 between any two successive zeros of J_0.

Setting $\sigma(x) = v^2 + v'^2 = x(J_n^2 + J_n'^2) + J_nJ_n' + J_n^2/4x$, it also follows from (18) that $\sigma'(x) = (4n^2 - 1)vv'/2x^2$. Since $|2vv'| \leqq v^2 + v'^2 = \sigma(x)$, there follows

$$(18') \qquad |\sigma'(x)| \leqq K_n\sigma(x)/x^2, \quad K_n = |n^2 - \tfrac{1}{4}|, \quad \sigma(x) > 0.$$

Using the Comparison Theorem of Ch. I, § 11, we get from (18′)

$$Ae^{-K_n/x} \leqq \sigma(x) = x(J_n^2 + J_n'^2) + J_nJ_n' + J_n^2/4x \leqq Ae^{K_n/x},$$

where $K_n = |n^2 - 1/4|$. For large x, therefore, $\sigma(x)$ must approach a constant A. Clearly, $A/\sqrt{x}$ is the asymptotic *amplitude* of the oscillations of the Bessel functions for large x, since J_n' vanishes at maxima and minima of $J_n(x)$, so that $\sigma(x) = xJ_n^2(x)$ there. Much more precise results about the oscillations of Bessel functions will be proved in Chapter X.

EXERCISES B

1. Verify formula (16).
2. Verify the three formulas displayed below (16).

Establish the following identities for Bessel functions of integral order:

3. $J_n(-x) = (-1)^nJ_n(x)$.

*4. $\left(\dfrac{1}{x}\dfrac{d}{dx}\right)^k (x^nJ_n(x)) = x^{n-k}J_{n-k}(x)$.

*5. $J_{n-1}(x) + J_{n+1}(x) = 2n\,x^{-1}J_n(x)$.

*6. $J_{n-1}(x) - J_{n+1}(x) = 2J_n'(x)$.

7. In polar coordinates, $\nabla^2 u = u_{rr} + r^{-1}u_r + r^{-2}u_{\theta\theta}$. Show that $u = J(r)\sin n\theta$ satisfies $\nabla^2 u + u = 0$ if and only if $J(r)$ satisfies $J_{rr} + r^{-1}J_r + (1 - n^2/r^2)J = 0$.

*8. (a) Show that the real and imaginary parts $\cos(r\sin\theta)$ and $\sin(r\sin\theta)$ of $e^{iy} = e^{ir\sin\theta}$ satisfy $\nabla^2 u + u = 0$.

(b) Show that $e^{iy} = e^{r(t-t^{-1})/2}$, $t = e^{i\theta}$, $y = r\sin\theta$.

(c) Show that the functions $F_n(r)$ in the Laurent series expansion

$$e^{r(t-t^{-1})/2} = \sum_{-\infty}^{\infty} t^nF_n(r)$$

satisfy the Bessel equation of order n. (Use (a) and (b).)

(d) Comparing the coefficients of t^nr^n, prove the identity $e^{r(t-t^{-1})/2} = \sum_{-\infty}^{\infty} t^nJ_n(r)$.

*9. (a) Show that $u(r,\theta,\alpha) = \cos[r\cos(\theta - \alpha)]$ satisfies $\nabla^2 u + u = 0$ for all α, whence so does its average $\dfrac{1}{2\pi}\displaystyle\int_0^{2\pi} u(r,\theta;\alpha)d\alpha = U(r)$.

(b) Prove that $J_0(r) = \dfrac{1}{2\pi}\displaystyle\int_{-\pi}^{\pi} \cos[r\cos\alpha]d\alpha = \dfrac{1}{\pi}\int_0^{\pi}\cos[r\cos\alpha]d\alpha$.

10. (a) Show that the *confluent* hypergeometric function

$$F(a,b;x) = 1 + \frac{a}{c}x + \frac{a(a+1)}{c(c+1)}\frac{x^2}{2!} + \cdots + \frac{a(a+1)\cdots(a+n)}{c(c+1)\cdots(c+n)}\frac{x^n}{n!} + \cdots$$

is a solution of the DE $xF'' + (c - x)F' + aF = 0$.

(b) Show that the preceding function is an entire function.

5. Analytic functions. A function is called *analytic* in a domain D, when it can be expanded in a power series at any point of D, which is *convergent* in some neighborhood of that point. For instance, a real function $p(x)$ of one real variable is analytic in the open interval (x_1,x_2) when, given any x_0 in this interval (i.e., satisfying $x_1 < x_0 < x_2$), there exist coefficients $p_0, p_1, p_2, \cdots$ and a positive number δ such that

$$(19) \qquad p(x) = \sum_{k=0}^{\infty} p_k(x - x_0)^k \quad \text{if} \quad |x - x_0| < \delta, \quad \delta > 0.$$

The numerical values of the coefficients p_k will, of course, depend on x_0.

Likewise, a real function $F(x,y)$ is analytic in a domain D of the real (x,y)-plane when, given $(x_0,y_0) \in D$, there exist constants b_{jk} $(j, k = 0, 1, 2, \cdots)$ and $\delta > 0$ such that

$$F(x,y) = \sum_{j=0}^{\infty}\sum_{k=0}^{\infty} b_{jk}(x - x_0)^j(y - y_0)^k \quad \text{if} \quad |x - x_0| + |y - y_0| < \delta.$$

An example of such a series expansion is the double geometric series

$$G(x,y) = \frac{M}{\left(1 - \frac{x}{H}\right)\left(1 - \frac{y}{K}\right)} = \sum_{j=0}^{\infty}\sum_{k=0}^{\infty} (M/H^jK^k)x^jy^k.$$

This series converges in the rectangle $|x| < H$, $|y| < K$, and defines an analytic function in this rectangle.

Analytic functions of three and more variables are defined similarly.

For analytic functions of one variable, the key concept is that of the radius of convergence. The *radius of convergence* R of the power series (19) is the largest δ such that the series (19) converges whenever $|x - x_0| < \delta$. The radius of convergence of the series (19) is given in terms of its coefficients by Cauchy's formula

$$(20) \qquad 1/R = \lim\sup_{n\to\infty} \sqrt[n]{|p_n|} = \lim_{n\to\infty} \{\sup_{k>n} \sqrt[k]{|p_k|}\}.$$

The series then diverges for all x with $|x - x_0| > R$. The *interval of convergence* of (19) is the interval $(x_0 - R, x_0 + R)$.

In the complex plane, the radius of convergence of the series (19) can still be defined by formula (20). The series (19) is convergent in the *circle of convergence* $|x - x_0| < R$, and divergent if $|x - x_0| > R$; it defines a single-valued analytic (or *holomorphic*) complex function inside its circle of convergence. Analytic complex functions of two or more complex variables can be defined by power series just like real functions, except that the coefficients of the power series may be complex.

Power series can be added, subtracted, multiplied, differentiated, and integrated term-by-term within their interval (circle) of convergence.†

†Courant, Vol. 1, Ch. VIII, Appendix; Widder, pp. 303–306 and 318–320. For a more complete discussion, see K. Knopp, *Theory and Application of Infinite Series*.

A basic property of *linear* DE's with analytic coefficient-functions is the following. Every solution is analytic, with a radius of convergence at least as large as the smaller of the radii of convergence of the coefficient-functions. We first establish this result in an important special case.

EXAMPLE 3. The substitution $\xi = C - x$ reduces the DE

$$u'' + \frac{A}{C-x}u' + \frac{B}{(C-x)^2}u = 0, \quad C > 0, \tag{21}$$

to *Euler's homogeneous DE*

$$\frac{d^2u}{d\xi^2} - \frac{A}{\xi}\frac{du}{d\xi} + \frac{B}{\xi^2}u = 0, \tag{22}$$

to be discussed more fully in Ch. IV, § 2, and in Chapter IX.

To solve (22), try the function $\xi^\nu = (C-x)^\nu$. This satisfies (22) if and only if ν is a root of the *indicial equation* of (22)

$$\nu(\nu - 1) - A\nu + B = 0.$$

When the discriminant $(A+1)^2 - 4B$ is positive, the indicial equation of (22) has two distinct real roots ν_1 and ν_2 of opposite sign. Hence (21) has two linearly independent real solutions, given by the binomial series

$$\left(1 - \frac{x}{C}\right)^\nu = 1 - \nu\left(\frac{x}{C}\right) + \frac{\nu(\nu-1)}{2}\left(\frac{x}{C}\right)^2 - \cdots, \quad |x| < C, \tag{23}$$

with $\nu = \nu_1, \nu_2$. When ν is a nonnegative integer, a polynomial solution is obtained. Otherwise, the radius of convergence of the series is C, the same as that of the power series expansions of the coefficient-functions

$$p(x) = A/(C-x) = (A/C)\left[1 + \sum_{k=1}^{\infty} (x/C)^k\right]$$

and $q(x) = B/(C-x)^2$ of the DE (21).

6. Method of Majorants. If one keeps in mind the results of § 5, one can show quite easily that the formal power series obtained in § 2 has a radius of convergence as large as the smaller of the radii of convergence of the coefficient-functions. To prove this, one uses an ingenious method due to Cauchy, the so-called Method of Majorants.

A power series $\Sigma a_k x^k$ is said to be *majorized* by the series $\Sigma A_k x^k$, if and only if $|a_k| \leqq A_k$ for all $k = 0, 1, 2, 3, \cdots$. By the Comparison Test, the radius of convergence of $\Sigma a_k x^k$ is then at least as large as that of $\Sigma A_k x^k$, and all A_k are positive or zero. We therefore say that the DE

$$u'' = P(x)u' + Q(x)u, \quad P(x) = \Sigma P_k x^k, \quad Q(x) = \Sigma Q_k x^k, \tag{24}$$

majorizes the DE (4) if and only if $P_k \geqq |p_k|$ and $Q_k \geqq |q_k|$, for all k.

In particular, the choice of coefficient-functions

(24′) $$P(x) = \Sigma \mid p_k \mid x^k \quad \text{and} \quad Q(x) = \Sigma \mid q_k \mid x^k$$

in (24) gives a DE which majorizes (4). Moreover by (20), the coefficient-functions (24′) have the same radius of convergence as $p(x)$ and $q(x)$, respectively.

LEMMA. *Let the DE* (24) *majorize the DE* (4), *and let* $\sum_{k=0}^{\infty} c_k x^k$ *be the formal power series solution of* (24) *whose first two coefficients are* $|a_0|$ *and* $|a_1|$. *Then* $c_k \geqq |a_k|$ *for all* k.

This lemma may be thought of as a generalized Comparison Test.

Proof. For the DE of the form (24), the coefficients of formal power series solutions satisfy, by (7) with $p_k = -P_k$, $q_k = -Q_k$:

(7′) $$c_{n+1} = \Big[\sum_{k=0}^{n-1} (n-k)P_k c_{n-k} + \sum_{k=0}^{n-1} Q_k c_{n-k-1}\Big]/n(n+1), \quad n \geqq 1.$$

Hence if $c_0 \geqq |a_0|$, $c_1 \geqq |a_1|, \cdots, c_n \geqq |a_n|$, then $c_{n+1} \geqq |a_{n+1}|$ as stated. This is because a_{n+1} is given for $n \geqq 1$ by a display (7) like (7′) above, with each (positive) term replaced by one having at most as great an absolute value. The lemma follows by induction on n.

Now let x_1 be any number whose absolute value $|x_1| = C$ is smaller than the radius of convergence of both series (5). Then $p_k x_1^k$ and $q_k x_1^k$ are uniformly bounded† in magnitude for all k by some finite constant M. Hence

$$|p_k| \leqq MC^{-k}, \quad |q_k| \leqq MC^{-k}, \quad k = 0, 1, 2, \cdots.$$

This implies that the power series for $p(x)$ and $q(x)$ are majorized by the geometric series

$$M \sum_{k=0}^{\infty} (x/C)^k = MC/(C-x), \quad M > 0, C > 0.$$

This series being majorized in turn by

$$MC^2/(C-x)^2 = M \sum_{k=0}^{\infty} (k+1)(x/C)^k,$$

the DE (4) is majorized by the DE

(25) $$u'' = \frac{MC}{(C-x)} u' + \frac{MC^2}{(C-x)^2} u.$$

But, as in Example 3, one solution of this DE is the function

$$\phi(x) = [1 - (x/C)]^{-\mu}$$

where $-\mu = \nu$ is the negative root of the quadratic indicial equation

$$\nu(\nu - 1) - MC\nu - MC^2 = 0,$$

whose discriminant $(MC+1)^2 + 4MC^2$ is positive. This function $\phi(x)$ has

†Because if a series is convergent, then its n-th term tends to zero as $n \to \infty$.

a power series expansion

$$\phi(x) = \left(1 - \frac{x}{C}\right)^{-\mu} = 1 + \frac{\mu x}{C} + \frac{\mu(\mu+1)x^2}{2C^2} + \cdots \tag{26}$$

convergent for $|x| < C$, as in (23).

Now apply the above lemma. Each solution of (4) is majorized by K times the solution $\phi(x)$ of (25), provided

$$K = \max\{|a_0|, |a_1 C/\mu|\}. \tag{26'}$$

But $K\phi(x)$ has the radius of convergence C. Hence, by the preceding lemma, the radius of convergence of the series (7) is at least $C = |x_1|$. This proves the following

THEOREM 2. *For any choice of a_0 and a_1, the radius of convergence of the power series solution defined by the recursion formula (7) is at least as large as the smaller of the radii of convergence for the series defining the coefficient-functions.*

We now recall (§ 5) that power series can be added, multiplied together, and differentiated term-by-term within their intervals (circles) of convergence. It follows from Theorem 2 that, when applied to power series defined by (7), the three equations displayed in § 2 between formulas (6) and (7) are identities in the common interval of convergence specified. Hence the power series defined by (7) are solutions of (4), and we have proved the following local existence theorem.

THEOREM 3. *Any initial value problem defined by a normal second-order linear homogeneous DE (4) with analytic coefficient-functions and initial conditions $f(0) = a_0$, $f'(0) = a_1$, has an analytic solution near $x = 0$, given by (7).*

EXERCISES C

1. Let $\Sigma\, a_k x^k$ have the radius of convergence R. Show that, for any $r < R$, the series is majorized by $\Sigma\, (m/r^k)x^k$ for some $m > 0$.

2. Using Ex. 1, prove Cauchy's formula (20).

3. Prove that, unless ν is a nonnegative integer, the radius of convergence of the binomial series (23) is C.

4. Using the symbols A, B, C to denote the series $\Sigma a_k x^k$, $\Sigma b_k x^k$, $\Sigma c_k x^k$, and writing $A << B$ to express the statement that series A is majorized by series B, prove the following results:

(a) $A << B$ and $B << C$ imply $A << C$.

(b) $A << B$ and $B << A$ imply $A = B$.

(c) If $A << B$, then the derivative series A': $\Sigma k a_k x^k$ and B': $\Sigma k b_k x^k$ satisfy $A' << B'$.

(d) If $A << B$ and $C << D$, then $A + C << B + D$ and $AC << BD$.

5. Prove that the radius of convergence of $\Sigma a_k x^k$ is unaffected by term-by-term differentiation or integration.

6. (a) Obtain a recursion relation on the coefficients a_k of power series solutions $\Sigma a_k x^k$ of Pearson's DE $y' = (D + Ex)y/(A + Bx + Cx^2)$, $A \neq 0$.

(b) What is the radius of convergence of the solution?

(c) Integrate by quadratures, and compare.

*7. Extend the Method of Majorants of § 6 to prove the convergence of the power series solutions of the inhomogeneous DE $u'' + p(x)u' + q(x)u = r(x)$, when the functions p, q, r are all analytic.

*8. Let the coefficients of $u = \Sigma a_k x^k$ satisfy a recursion relation of the form $a_{k+1}/a_k = P(k)/Q(k+1)$, where P and Q are polynomials without common factors. Show that u must satisfy a DE of the form

$$Q\left(x\frac{d}{dx}\right)[u] = xP\left(x\frac{d}{dx}\right)[u],$$

and conversely.

7. First-order nonlinear DE's. The Method of Undetermined Coefficients and the Method of Majorants can also be applied to any normal analytic *first-order* DE, of the form

$$dy/dx = F(x,y) = \sum_{j=0}^{\infty}\sum_{k=0}^{\infty} b_{jk}x^j y^k. \tag{27}$$

The discussion is however more difficult, since *nonlinear* DE's are concerned. We first treat a simple example.

EXAMPLE 4. The general solution of the DE

$$y' = 1 + y^2 \tag{28}$$

is $y = \tan(x - c)$, since (28) implies

$$x = \int dy/(1 + y^2) = c + \arctan y,$$

where c is an arbitrary constant. We therefore *define* the function $y = \tan x$ as the solution of (28) which satisfies the initial condition $y(0) = 0$, and proceed to derive some of its basic properties from this definition.

Since $1 + y^2$ is positive, $\tan x$ is always increasing. Again, by repeated differentiation, we get the formulas

$$y'' = 2yy' = 2(y + y^3),$$
$$y''' = 2(1 + 3y^2)y' = 2(1 + 3y^2)(1 + y^2),$$

and so on. These formulas show that y'' has the same sign as y: the graph of $y = \tan x$ is concave upwards in the upper half-plane; likewise y''' is always positive.

Again, setting $t = -x$ and $z = -y$, we obtain the formulas

$$dz/dt = dy/dx = 1 + y^2 = 1 + z^2 \quad \text{and} \quad z(0) = 0.$$

Hence $z(t)$ satisfies the initial value problem of Example 4, and so, by the Uniqueness Theorem (Ch. I, Thm. 5) for first-order DE's, $z = \tan t$. This proves that $-\tan(-x) = \tan x$: $\tan x$ is an *odd function*.

Consequently, the Taylor series expansion of $\tan x$ contains only terms of odd order:

$$y = x + a_3x^3 + a_5x^5 + a_7x^7 + a_9x^9 + \cdots.$$

Substituting into the defining DE (28), we get

$$1 + 3a_3x^2 + 5a_5x^4 + 7a_7x^6 + 9a_9x^8 + \cdots$$
$$= 1 + x^2 + 2a_3x^4 + (2a_5 + a_3^2)x^6 + 2(a_7 + a_3a_5)x^8 + \cdots.$$

Equating coefficients of like powers of x, we get

$$3a_3 = 1, \quad 5a_5 = 2a_3, \quad 7a_7 = 2a_5 + a_3^2, \quad 9a_9 = 2a_7 + 2a_3a_5,$$

and so on. Solving recursively, we get the first few terms of the power series expansion for $\tan x$,

$$\tan x = x + \frac{x^3}{3} + \frac{2x^5}{15} + \frac{17}{315}x^7 + \frac{62}{2835}x^9 + \cdots. \tag{29}$$

The radius of convergence of this power series is $\pi/2$, as follows from the formula $\tan x = \sin x/\cos x$ and the results of § 3.

8. Undetermined Coefficients. The preceding Method of Undetermined Coefficients can be applied to analytic first-order DE's generally. For simplicity, we treat the initial condition $y(0) = 0$, to which any initial condition can be reduced by a translation of coordinates.

Namely, we look for a solution of (27) in the power series form

$$y = f(x) = a_1x + a_2x^2 + a_3x^3 + \cdots; \tag{30}$$

the coefficient a_0 vanishes since it is assumed that $f(0) = 0$. Hence

$$y' = a_1 + 2a_2x + 3a_3x^2 + \cdots, \tag{30'}$$

in the interval of convergence. The coefficients a_k can be calculated recursively by substituting these power series into the given equation (27), and equating the coefficients of like powers of x in the resulting expression. Carrying out the steps indicated, we obtain in succession

$$a_1 = b_{00}, \quad 2a_2 = b_{10} + b_{01}a_1, \quad 3a_3 = b_{01}a_2 + b_{20} + b_{11}a_1 + b_{02}a_1^2, \tag{31}$$

and so on. The expression on the right side of each of these equations is a polynomial with positive integral coefficients. Equations (31) can be solved recursively, giving the formulas

$$a_1 = b_{00}, \quad a_2 = (b_{10} + b_{00}b_{01})/2$$
$$a_3 = (b_{20} + b_{11}b_{00} + b_{02}b_{00}^2)/3 + (b_{10}b_{01} + b_{00}b_{01}^2)/6,$$

and so on. When one substitutes the series (30) for y into the series (27) for $F(x,y)$, the coefficient of x^h is a sum of products of factors b_{jk} (with $j+k \leqq h$) times polynomials of degree k in the a_i obtained by raising the series (30) to the k-th power. The coefficient of x^h on the left side of (27) is however $(h+1)a_{h+1}$, by (30′). Equating coefficients of like powers of x, we have therefore

$$(31') \qquad (h+1)a_{h+1} = q_h(b_{00}, \cdots, b_{0h};\ b_{10}, \cdots, b_{1,h-1};\ \cdots, b_{h0};\ a_1, \cdots, a_h),$$

where the coefficients of q_h are positive integers. Substituting for $a_1, \cdots, a_h$ already available formulas, we get

$$(31'') \qquad a_{h+1} = p_h(b_{00}, \cdots, b_{0h};\ b_{10}, \cdots, b_{1,h-1};\ \cdots;\ b_{h0}).$$

The *polynomial* functions p_h have *positive, rational* numbers as coefficients. They are the same, no matter which function $F(x,y)$ is used in (27).

Solving the resulting equation at $x=0$ for $a_{n+1} = y^{(n+1)}/(n+1)!$, we get the following result.

THEOREM 4. *There exists a power series* (30) *which formally satisfies any analytic first-order DE* (27). *The coefficients of this formal power series are polynomial functions of the* b_{hk} *with positive rational coefficients.*

The preceding formulas can also be obtained in another way. Let $y=f(x)$ be the graph of any solution of the DE $y' = F(x,y)$, and let $u(x,y)$ be any function analytic in a domain containing this graph. Differentiating with respect to x along the graph, we get the formula

$$\frac{du}{dx} = \frac{\partial u}{\partial x} + \left(\frac{\partial u}{\partial y}\right)\left(\frac{dy}{dx}\right) = \frac{\partial u}{\partial x} + F\frac{\partial u}{\partial y}.$$

This formula can be differentiated repeatedly, giving the operator identity

$$(32) \qquad \frac{d^n}{dx^n} = \left(\frac{\partial}{\partial x} + F(x,y)\frac{\partial}{\partial y}\right)^n.$$

Applying this identity to the function $F(x,y) = y'$, we get in succession

$$y'' = F_x + FF_y, \quad y''' = F_{xx} + 2FF_{xy} + F^2F_{yy} + F_xF_y + FF_y^2,$$

and so on. The general formula is

$$(32') \qquad y^{(n+1)} = d^{n+1}y/dx^{n+1} = \left(\frac{\partial}{\partial x} + F\frac{\partial}{\partial y}\right)^n [F(x,y)].$$

The right side of (32′), evaluated at $x=y=0$, is a polynomial in the variables b_{jk} with positive integers as coefficients. This is because the operations used in evaluating this expression are addition, multiplication, and differentiation.

EXERCISES D

In Exs. 1–7, calculate the first four terms of the power series expansion of the solutions of the DE indicated, for the initial value $y(0) = 0$.

1. $y' = x + y$.
2. $y' = 1 + x^2y^2$.
3. $y' = g(x) = \Sigma\, b_kx^k$.
4. $y' = g(y) = \Sigma\, b_ky^k$.
5. $y' = xy^2 + yx^2 + 1$.
6. $y' = 1 + y^n$.
7. $y' = \cos \sqrt{y} + 1$.
8. Calculate explicitly the polynomials p_h of Theorem 3 for $h = 4$.
9. Compute the first five polynomials p_h of Theorem 3 when $F(x,y) = b(x)y + c(x)$ in (27).
10. Same question for the Riccati DE $y' + y^2 = b(x)y + c(x)$.
11. Show that the DE $y' = x^2 + y^2$ has a solution of the form $\sum_1^{\infty} a_kx^{4k-1}$, with all $a_k > 0$. For $a_1 = 1$, compute a_2, $a_{,3}$ a_4.
12. From the DE $y' = 1 + y^2$, prove that the coefficient a_{n+1} in the expansion $\tan x = \Sigma\, a_kx^k$, $a_0 = 0$, satisfies $(n + 1)a_{n+1} = \sum_{k=1}^{n-1} a_ka_{n-k}$. (*Hint:* Differentiate y^2 using the binomial expansion of $(uv)^{(n)}$.)
13. Show that if $y' = F(x,y)$, where $F \in \mathcal{C}^3$, then
$$y^{\text{iv}} = F_{xxx} + 3y'F_{xxy} + 3y'^2F_{xyy} + y'^3F_{yyy} + 3y''F_{xy} + 3y'y''F_{yy} + y'''F_y.$$
14. For the DE $y' = 2y/x$, and the initial condition $y(1) = 1$, calculate the first four terms of the Taylor series of the solution.

9*. Radius of convergence. The DE $y' = 1 + y^2$ of Example 4 shows that the radius of convergence of power series solutions of a *nonlinear* DE $y' = F(x,y)$ can be much less than that of the function $F(x,y)$. For, the radius of convergence of the solution $\tan (x + c)$ of the DE $y' = 1 + y^2$ which satisfies $y(0) = \tan c = \gamma$ is only $\pi/2 - c$, the distance to the nearest singular point of the solution. This can be made arbitrarily small by making γ large enough, even though the radius of convergence of $F(x,y) = 1 + y^2$ is infinite.

The preceding situation is typical of nonlinear DE's, and shows that one cannot hope to establish an existence theorem for nonlinear DE's as strong as Theorem 3. The contrast with the situation for nonlinear DE's is further illustrated by the Riccati equation of Ch. II, § 3, (14).

EXAMPLE 5. The Riccati equation

$$dv/dx = -v^2 - p(x)v - q(x) \tag{33}$$

is satisfied by the ratio $v(x) = u'(x)/u(x)$, if $u(x)$ is any nontrivial solution of the second-order linear DE (4). Conversely, if $v(x)$ is any solution of the Riccati DE (33), then the function $u = \exp\, (\int v(x)dx)$ satisfies the linear DE (4).

Now let p, q be analytic and a, c given constants. Using Theorem 2 to find a solution u of (4) satisfying the initial conditions $u(a) = 1$ and

$u'(a) = c$, we obtain an analytic solution $v = u'/u$ of the Riccati equation (33) which satisfies $v(a) = c$. This gives a local existence theorem for the nonlinear Riccati DE (33).

However, this solution becomes infinite when $u = 0$; hence the radius of convergence of its power series can be made arbitrarily small by choosing c sufficiently large. Also, the location of the singular points of solutions of (33) is variable, depending on the zeros of u.

The Riccati equation also serves to illustrate Theorem 4. A simple computation gives, for $v = \sum_{1}^{\infty} a_k x^k$, the formula

$$v^2 = a_1^2 x^2 + 2a_1a_2x^3 + (a_2^2 + 2a_1a_3)x^4 + \cdots + \sum_{i=1}^{h-1} a_i a_{h-1} x^h + \cdots.$$

Substituting back into (33), we get the recursion relation

$$(h+1)a_{h+1} = -\sum_{i=1}^{h-1} a_i a_{h-1} - \sum_{i=1}^{h} a_i p_{h-1} - q_h.$$

This is, of course, just the special case of formula (31′) corresponding to $F(x,y) = -y^2 - \sum_{0}^{\infty} p_k x^k y - \sum_{0}^{\infty} q_k x^k$.

We shall now return to the general case. Let F be any function of x and y analytic in some neighborhood of (0,0). This means that F can be expanded into a double power series

$$F(x,y) = b_{00} + (b_{10}x + b_{01}y) + (b_{20}x^2 + b_{11}xy + b_{02}y^2) \cdots, \tag{34}$$

where b_{jk} are given real numbers, and the series is convergent for sufficiently small x and y. We will show that the series (30) referred to in Theorem 4, and defined by formula (31′), has a positive radius of convergence.

Analytic functions of two variables. To prove this, we shall need a few facts about analytic functions of two variables and the convergence of double power series like (34). The terms of any absolutely convergent series can be rearranged in any order without destroying the convergence of the series or changing the value of the sum. If one substitutes into a double power series like (34) convergent near (0,0), any power series $y = \sum_{k=0}^{\infty} a_k x^k$ having a positive radius of convergence, one will obtain an analytic function $F(x,f(x))$ which itself has a positive radius of convergence.

Finally, let the double power series (34) be convergent at (H,K), where $H > 0$ and $K > 0$. Then the terms of the series $\Sigma b_{jk} H^j K^k$ are bounded in magnitude by some finite constant $M = \max |b_{jk}| H^j K^k$. This gives the bound

$$|b_{jk}| \leqq M/H^j K^k, \qquad M < +\infty,$$

to the terms of the series (34). Comparing with the double geometric series mentioned in § 5,

$$G(x,y) = \frac{M}{\left(1 - \frac{x}{H}\right)\left(1 - \frac{y}{K}\right)} = \sum_{j=0}^{\infty}\sum_{k=0}^{\infty} (M/H^jK^k)x^jy^k, \tag{35}$$

and applying the Comparison Test, we see that the series (34) is absolutely convergent in the open rectangle $|x| < H$, $|y| < K$, and can be differentiated term-by-term there any number of times.

From the preceding remarks, we have the following immediate consequence:

Corollary. *If the power series* (30) *of Theorem* 4 *has a positive radius of convergence, then the function which it defines is a solution of the DE* (27) *for the initial condition* $y(0) = 0$.

10*. Method of Majorants. We will now complete the proof of an existence theorem for analytic first-order DE's by showing that the series (30) has a positive radius of convergence. This is again shown by the Method of Majorants, which we now extend to functions of two variables.

Consider the power series

$$\begin{aligned} y:&\quad a_1x + a_2x^2 + a_3x^3 + \cdots \\ F:&\quad b_{00} + b_{10}x + b_{01}y + b_{20}x^2 + b_{11}xy + \cdots, \end{aligned}$$

purely as infinite arrays of complex numbers, irrespective of any questions of convergence. Such power series can be added, subtracted, and multiplied algebraically as infinite polynomials, without ever being evaluated as functions of x and y. Such expressions are called *formal power series.* It is possible to substitute one formal power series into another: after rearranging terms, another formal power series is obtained. Two formal power series are considered identical when all their coefficients coincide.

Comparing F with the formal power series

$$G: \quad c_{00} + c_{10}x + c_{01}y + c_{20}x^2 + c_{11}xy + \cdots,$$

one says that the formal power series G *majorizes* the formal power series F when

$$|b_{jk}| \leqq c_{jk} \text{ for all } j, k = 0, 1, 2, \cdots.$$

In symbols,

$$F << G. \tag{36}$$

This implies that all coefficients c_{jk} are nonnegative.

The following lemma is immediate:

Lemma 1. *Let* F, G, H *be any three formal power series. Then* $F << G$ *and* $G << F$ *imply* $F = G$, *and* $F << G$ *and* $G << H$ *imply* $F << H$.

It is not true, however, that $F << F$ if F has any negative coefficient.

The relation (36) of majorization between formal power series is useful in estimating the radius of convergence of such series. From the Comparison Test for convergence, we obtain directly

LEMMA 2. *If F and G are formal power series, and if $F << G$, then F converges absolutely at any point (x,y) if G converges at $(|x|,|y|)$.*

The crucial result for the proof of convergence of the formal power series (30), obtained from Theorem 4, is the following

LEMMA 3. *Let $F << G$, and let f and g be the formal power series (without constant terms) obtained by solving $y' = F(x,y)$ and $y' = G(x,y)$ formally, as in Theorem 4, for the initial condition $y(0) = 0$. Then g majorizes f (that is, $f << g$).*

Proof. The polynomials p_h in Theorem 4 have nonnegative coefficients. Therefore

$$|a_{h+1}| = |p_h(b_{00},b_{10},b_{01},\cdots)| \leqq p_h(c_{00},c_{10},c_{01},\cdots)$$

for all h; hence the absolute value of each coefficient a_h is less than or equal to the corresponding coefficient of the formal power series g, q.e.d.

It is now a straightforward matter to prove our main result.

THEOREM 5. *Let $F(x,y)$ be analytic in the closed rectangle $|x| \leqq H$, $|y| \leqq K$, where H and K are positive. Then the formal power series solution (30) of the DE (27) has a positive radius of convergence.*

Proof. The power series for the function F is convergent at (H,K); as in § 9, it follows that for some finite $M = \max |b_{jk}H^jK^k|$,

$$|b_{jk}H^jK^k| \leqq M, \quad \text{whence} \quad |b_{jk}| \leqq \frac{M}{H^jK^k}.$$

That is, the formal power series F is majorized by the double geometric series (35):

$$G(x,y) = M \Big/ \left[\left(1 - \frac{x}{H}\right)\left(1 - \frac{y}{K}\right)\right] = M \sum_{j,k=0}^{\infty} \frac{x^jy^k}{H^jK^k}.$$

Furthermore, the DE $y' = G(x,y)$ can be solved in closed form by separation of variables. The solution satisfying $y(0) = 0$ is

$$y = K[1 - \sqrt{1 + (2MH/K)\ln(1 - (x/H))}], \tag{37}$$

where the principal values of the logarithmic and square root functions are taken, corresponding to the usual expansions of the functions $\sqrt{1+t}$ and $\ln(1+t)$ in power series with center at $t = 0$. The radius of convergence is given by the equation $(2MH/K)\ln[1-(x/H)]=-1$, or

$$R=H[1-e^{-K/2MH}] \tag{38}$$

since the binomial series for the radicand in (37) converges as long as $(2MH/K)\,|\ln[1-x/H]|<1$. This completes the proof.

By Theorem 5 of Chapter I, whose hypotheses are satisfied since F is continuously differentiable, the solution satisfying the initial condition $f(0)$ is unique. This proves the

COROLLARY. *Every solution of the analytic DE* (27) *is analytic. The solution satisfying the initial condition* $f(0)=0$ *is unique, and given by the power series* (30).

11*. Complex solutions. The preceding discussion applies with very minor changes to complex power series. Let

$$dw/dz = F(z,w) = \sum_{j,k} b_{jk}z^j w^k \tag{39}$$

be any analytic first-order DE, whose right side is a complex analytic function. (For F to be analytic, it is sufficient for the function F to be differentiable, since differentiability implies analyticity in any complex domain.†) Then all the formulas of § 9 remain valid; so do the lemmas about majorants in § 10.

For complex z, w, the domain D: $|z|\leqq H$, $|w|\leqq K$ of Theorem 5 is not a rectangle, but the four-dimensional product of two discs. Though this domain is harder to visualize than a rectangle, it has the advantage that Cauchy's integral formulas hold on it: the constant M in (38) is given explicitly by‡

$$M=\sup_{(z,w)\in D}|F(z,w)|.$$

These remarks cover the extension of Theorem 5 to complex DE's.

Dependence on initial value. We now consider the dependence of the solutions of real or complex analytic first-order DE's (27) or (39) on their initial values. This dependence is analytic; it follows that the solutions of any real normal DE form a *normal curve family.*

THEOREM 6. *Let* $f(x,c)$ *be the solution of the first-order analytic DE* $y'=F(x,y)$ *which satisfies the initial condition* $f(a,c)=c$. *Then* $f(x,c)$ *is a locally analytic function of the two variables* x *and* c, *near* $(a,0)$.

†Ahlfors, pp. 38, 39; Hille, pp. 72, 196.
‡See for example Picard, Vol. 2, p. 259.

Proof. As before, we can assume that $a = 0$; let $\eta = y - c$, so that $y = c + \eta$. For any fixed c, the function $\eta(x,c) = f(x,c) - c$ is the solution of

$$(40) \quad d\eta/dx = F_1(x,\eta) = F(x,c+\eta) = \sum b_{jk}x^j(c+\eta)^k = \sum \beta_{jk}x^j\eta^k,$$

satisfying the initial condition $\eta(0) = 0$. Here each $\beta_{jk} = \beta_{jk}(c)$ is an analytic function of c, the coefficients of whose power series expansion in c are *positive* multiples $\binom{k}{h}b_{jh}$ of some b_{jh}. By Theorems 4 and 5, the solution $\eta(x,c)$ of (40) is $\sum_{n=0}^{\infty} \alpha_n x^n$, where each coefficient $\alpha_n = \alpha_n(c)$ is a polynomial in the β_{jk} with *positive* rational coefficients. Hence the doubly infinite formal power series

$$\eta(x,c) = \sum \alpha_n(c)x^n = \sum \gamma_{mn}c^m x^n$$

obtained has coefficients γ_{mn} which are polynomials in the b_{jk} with *positive* coefficients. This series formally satisfies (40).

As in the proof of Theorem 5, this series is majorized by the power series solution without constant term of the DE

$$dz/dx = G(x,c+z) = M/[(1 - x/H)(1 - (c+z)/K)].$$

Integrating, we get

$$(41) \qquad \left(1 - \frac{c}{K}\right)z - \frac{z^2}{2K} = -MH \ln\left(1 - \frac{x}{H}\right).$$

Elementary algebraic manipulation now gives

$$[(z+c) - K]^2 = (c-K)^2 + 2MHK \ln\left(1 - \frac{x}{H}\right)$$

The branch of the function $z(x,c)$ which makes $z(0,0) = 0$ is given by the formula

$$z = K - c - \left\{(c-K)^2 + 2MHK \ln\left(1 - \frac{x}{H}\right)\right\}^{1/2}$$

The resulting function (as one sees by expanding the functions $\sqrt{1+u}$ and $\ln[1 - (x/H)]$ into power series) is analytic for x and c sufficiently small. That is, the power series solution of (41), $g(x,c) = \Sigma\delta_{mn}c^m x^n$ (in which all $\delta_{mn} \geqq 0$ as shown above) is also convergent. But this *majorizes* $f(x,c)$, whose power series expansion is therefore also convergent, completing the proof.

EXERCISES E

For the power series expansion of each function defined in Exs. 1–4, determine the domain of convergence:

1. $J_0(x+y)$.
2. $\sqrt{(1-x)(1-y)}$.
3. $1/[1 - (x^2+y^2)]$.
4. $1/[1 + (x^2+y^2)]$.

5. Show that the solution of $y' = G(x,y)$, where G is the geometric series (35), is the function (37).

6. Find the value of $\sum_{j=0}^{\infty} x^j y^k/(H^j K^k)$.

7. Find the value of $\sum_{j,k=0}^{\infty} jkx^j y^k/(H^j K^k)$.

Establish the following properties of the relation "$<<$." ($P = P(x,y)$, $Q = Q(x,y)$, $p = p(x)$, and $q = q(x)$ are formal power series.)

8. If $F << G$ and $P << Q$ then $F + P << G + Q$.

9. If $F << G$ and $P << Q$ then $FP << GQ$.

10. If $F << G$ and $p << q$, then $F(x,p(x)) << G(x,q(x))$.

11. If $F << G$, then $\partial F/\partial x << \partial G/\partial x$ (interpret the derivatives formally). Is the converse true?

CHAPTER IV

Linear Equations with Constant Coefficients

1. Characteristic polynomial. The n-th order linear DE with *constant coefficients* is

$$L[u] = u^{(n)} + a_1 u^{(n-1)} + a_2 u^{(n-2)} + \cdots + a_n u = r(x). \tag{1}$$

Here $u^{(k)}$ stands for the k-th derivative $d^k u/dx^k$ of the unknown function $u(x)$; $a_1, \cdots, a_n$ are arbitrary constants, real or complex,† and $r(x)$ is any continuous function.

As in Ch. II, § 5, the letter L stands for the *operator* defined by (1). This transforms functions of class $\mathcal{C}^n$ into functions of class $\mathcal{C}$. The operator L is *linear*. That is, $L[au + bv] = aL[u] + bL[v]$ for any functions u and v of class $\mathcal{C}^n$ and constants a and b.

We first consider the *homogeneous* case $r(x) = 0$:

$$L[u] = u^{(n)} + a_1 u^{(n-1)} + a_2 u^{(n-2)} + \cdots + a_n u = 0. \tag{2}$$

If one thinks of x as representing time, the DE (2) represents the most general *time-independent* linear DE. This gives DE's of the form (2) a special importance, which will be discussed at length in Chapter VI.

Solutions of (2) can be found by trying the *exponential substitution* $u = e^{\lambda x}$, where λ is a real or complex number to be determined later. Since $d^n(e^{\lambda x})/dx^n = \lambda^n e^{\lambda x}$, this substitution reduces (2) to the identity

$$L[e^{\lambda x}] = (\lambda^n + a_1\lambda^{n-1} + a_2\lambda^{n-2} + \cdots + a_n)e^{\lambda x} = 0.$$

This is satisfied if and only if λ is a root of the *characteristic polynomial* of the DE (1), defined as

$$p(\lambda) = p_L(\lambda) = \lambda^n + a_1\lambda^{n-1} + \cdots + a_{n-1}\lambda + a_n. \tag{3}$$

The Fundamental Theorem of Algebra‡ states that the characteristic polynomial p can be factored into (real or complex) linear factors

$$p(\lambda) = (\lambda - \lambda_1)^{k_1}(\lambda - \lambda_2)^{k_2} \cdots (\lambda - \lambda_m)^{k_m}, \tag{4}$$

where the λ_i are all distinct, $k_i > 0$, and $k_1 + \cdots + k_m = n$. The root λ_j is said to be of *multiplicity* k_j.

†Familiarity with complex polynomials and the complex exponential function will be assumed in this chapter.
‡Birkhoff and Mac Lane, p. 107.

If the characteristic polynomial has n distinct real or complex roots, the DE (2) has n solutions $e^{\lambda_j x}$, $j = 1, 2, \cdots, n$.

Operational calculus. The case of multiple roots can be treated similarly by using the operator notation more extensively. Denoting the operator d/dx by the letter D, we obtain the identity

$$L = p(D) = D^n + a_1 D^{n-1} + \cdots + a_n. \tag{5}$$

This formula means that $L[u] = p(D)[u]$ for any function $u \in \mathcal{C}^n$. Observe that since the coefficient-functions $a_1, \cdots, a_n$ are *constants*, the terms of L are all permutable with each other. That is,

$$D[a_k u] = a_k D[u], \qquad \text{for} \qquad k = 1, \cdots, n.$$

Generally, we have the identity

$$p(D)[q(D)[f]] = q(D)[p(D)[f]] = r(D)[f], \quad r(D) = p(D)q(D)$$

for any polynomials p and q with constant coefficients.

Using the operational calculus, it is easy to prove the following result.

THEOREM 1. *If λ is a root of multiplicity k of the characteristic polynomial* (3), *then the functions $x^r e^{\lambda x}$ $(r = 0, \cdots, k-1)$ are solutions of the linear DE* (2).

Proof. The result stated follows directly from the identity

$$(D - \lambda)[x^r e^{\lambda x}] = r x^{r-1} e^{\lambda x}.$$

Iterating this identity, an easy computation gives

$$(D - \lambda)^k [x^r e^{\lambda x}] = 0, \qquad \text{if} \qquad k > r. \tag{5'}$$

The operators $(D - \lambda_i)^{k_i}$ being permutable, we can write for any i,

$$L[u] = q_i(D)(D - \lambda_i)^{k_i}[u], \qquad q_i(D) = \prod_{j \neq i} (D - \lambda_j)^{k_j}$$

where $q_i(D)$ is the product of the $(D - \lambda_j)^{k_j}$ for $j \neq i$. But for $r < k_i$, $(D - \lambda_i)^{k_i}[x^r e^{\lambda_i x}] = 0$ as above. Substituting in the preceding identity, $L[x^r e^{\lambda_i x}] = q_i(D)[0] = 0$, completing the proof.

2. Real and complex solutions. The preceding theorem holds whether the coefficients a_k of the DE (2) are real or complex.

If all the coefficients a_j are real numbers, then more detailed information can be obtained about the solutions, as follows.

LEMMA. *Let the complex-valued function $w(x) = u(x) + iv(x)$ satisfy a homogeneous linear DE* (1) *with* real *coefficients. Then the functions $u(x)$ and $v(x)$ (the real and imaginary parts of $w(x)$) both satisfy the DE.*

Proof. The complex conjugate† $w^*(x) = u(x) - iv(x)$ of $w(x)$ satisfies the complex conjugate of the given DE (2), obtained by replacing every coefficient a_k by its complex conjugate a_k^*, because $L[w^*] = \{L[w]\}^* = 0$. If the a_k are real, then $a_k^* = a_k$, and so $w^*(x)$ also satisfies (2). Hence the linear combinations

$$u(x) = [w(x) + w^*(x)]/2 \quad \text{and} \quad v(x) = [w(x) - w^*(x)]/2i$$

also satisfy (2), as stated.

This result is also valid for DE's with variable coefficients $a_k(x)$.

Corollary 1. *If the DE* (2) *has* real *coefficients, and* $e^{\lambda x}$ *satisfies* (2), *then so does* $e^{\lambda^* x}$. *The complex roots of the characteristic polynomial* (3) *occur in conjugate pairs* $\lambda_j = \mu_j \pm i\nu_j$, *having the same multiplicity* k_j.

Now recall that if $\lambda = \mu + i\nu$, where μ and ν are real, then

$$e^{\lambda x} = e^{\mu x + i\nu x} = e^{\mu x}(\cos \nu x + i \sin \nu x).$$

Using this formula, we obtain

Corollary 2. *Each pair of complex conjugate roots* λ_j, λ_j^* *of* (3) *of multiplicity* k_j *gives real solutions of* (2) *of the form*

$$x^r e^{\mu_j x} \cos \nu_j x, \quad x^r e^{\mu_j x} \sin \nu_j x, \quad r = 0, \cdots, k_j - 1. \tag{6}$$

These solutions differ from the solutions $e^{\lambda x}$ with real λ in that they have infinitely many zeros in any infinite interval of the real axis; that is, they are *oscillatory* (see Ch. II, § 4). This proves

Theorem 2. *If the characteristic polynomial* (3) *with real coefficients has* $2r$ *complex roots, then the DE* (2) *has* $2r$ *linearly independent oscillatory real solutions of the form* (6).

Euler's DE. The homogeneous linear DE

$$x^n u^{(n)} + b_1 x^{n-1} u^{(n-1)} + b_2 x^{n-2} u^{(n-2)} + \cdots + b_n u = 0 \tag{7}$$

is called Euler's differential equation. Particular solutions of (7) can be found by substituting x^λ for u. One obtains an equation of the form $I(\lambda)x^{\lambda-n} = 0$, where $I(\lambda)$ is a polynomial of degree n, called the indicial equation. Any λ for which $I(\lambda) = 0$ gives a solution x^λ of (7).

The general solution of (7) can be found by making the change of independent variable

$$x = e^t, \qquad t = \ln x, \qquad xd/dx = d/dt. \tag{7'}$$

which reduces (7) to a DE of the form (2), whose solutions $t^r e^{\lambda t}$ give a basis of solutions for (7) of the form $(\ln x)^r x^\lambda$.

†The complex conjugate w^* of a complex number $w = u + iv$ is $u - iv$. Some authors use $\overline{w}$ instead of w^* to denote the complex conjugate of w.

We now consider the case $n = 2$ in greater detail; it is the DE

$$x^2u'' + pxu' + qu = 0, \quad p, q \text{ real constants.} \tag{8}$$

Trying $u = x^\lambda$, we get the *indicial equation* of (8):

$$\lambda(\lambda - 1) + p\lambda + q = 0. \tag{8'}$$

Alternatively, making the change of variable (7'), we get

$$\frac{d^2u}{dt^2} + (p - 1)\frac{du}{dt} + qu = 0, \qquad t = \ln x, \tag{8''}$$

since
$$\frac{d^2}{dt^2} = x\frac{d}{dx}\left(x\frac{d}{dx}\right) = x^2\frac{d^2}{dx^2} + x\frac{d}{dx}.$$

If $(p - 1)^2 > 4q$, the indicial equation has two distinct real roots $\lambda = \alpha$ and $\lambda = \beta$, and so the DE (8) has the two linearly independent *real* solutions x^α and x^β, defined for *positive* x. For positive or negative x, one has the solutions $|x|^\alpha$ and $|x|^\beta$, since the substitution of $-x$ for x does not affect (8).

When the discriminant $(p - 1)^2 - 4q$ is negative, the indicial equation has two conjugate complex roots $\lambda = \mu \pm i\nu$, where $\mu = (1 - p)/2$ and $\nu = [4q - (p - 1)^2]^{1/2}/2$. A basis of real solutions of (8'') is then $e^{\mu t} \cos \nu t$ and $e^{\mu t} \sin \nu t$; the corresponding solutions of the second-order Euler homogeneous DE (8) are $x^\mu \cos(\nu \ln x)$ and $x^\mu \sin(\nu \ln x)$. These are, for $x > 0$, the real and imaginary parts of the *complex power* function

$$x^\lambda = x^{\mu \pm i\nu} = e^{(\mu \pm i\nu)\ln x} = x^\mu[\cos(\nu \ln x) \pm i \sin(\nu \ln x)],$$

as follows from the above lemma. For $x < 0$, one can get real solutions by using $|x|$ in place of x. But for $x < 0$ the resulting real solutions of (8) are no longer the real and imaginary parts of x^λ, because $\ln(-x) = \ln x \pm i\pi$; cf. Ch. IX, § 1.

There remains the *exceptional case* $(p - 1)^2 = 4q$, where $\lambda = (1 - p)/2$ is a double root of the indicial equation (8'). In this case, the functions x^λ and $x^\lambda \ln x$ form a basis of solutions of (8) for $x > 0$, while $|x|^\lambda$ and $|x|^\lambda \ln |x|$ satisfy (8) for all real $x \neq 0$.

EXERCISES A

In Exs. 1–4, find a basis of real solutions of the DE specified:

1. $u'' + 5u' + 4u = 0$.
2. $u''' + 6u'' + 12u' + 8u = 0$.
3. $u^{\text{vi}} = u$.
4. $u^{\text{vi}} = -u$.

In Exs. 5–6, find a basis of complex solutions of the DE:

5. $u'' + 2iu' + 3u = 0$.
6. $u''' + 6u'' + 12u' + (8 + i)u = 0$.

7. Prove that the DE's of Exs. 5–6 have no nontrivial real solution.

In Exs. 8–9, find a basis of solutions for the Euler DE:

8. $x^2u'' + 5xu' + 4u = 0$.

9. $x^2u'' + 2ixu' + 3u = 0$.

10. Describe the behavior of the function z^i of the complex variable $z = x + iy$ as z traces the unit circle $r = e^{i\theta}$ around the origin.

11. Same question for the function z^ie^{iz}.

12. State an analog of Theorem 1 for Euler's DE, and give it a direct proof.

3. Linearly independent solutions. As in Ch. II, § 3, a set of n real or complex functions $f_1, f_2, \cdots, f_n$ defined on an interval (a,b) is said to be *linearly independent* when no linear combination with constant coefficients of the functions is identically zero; that is, when $\sum_{k=0}^{n} c_kf_k(x) \equiv 0$ implies $c_1 = c_2 = \cdots = c_n = 0$. A set which is not linearly independent is said to be *linearly dependent.*†

There are two notions of linear independence, according as we allow the coefficients c_k to assume only *real values*, or also *complex* values. In the first case, one says that the functions are linearly independent over the *real field*; in the second case, that they are linearly independent over the *complex field.*

LEMMA 1. *A set of real-valued functions on an interval (a,b) is linearly independent over the complex field if and only if it is linearly independent over the real field.*

Proof. Linear dependence over the real field implies linear dependence over the complex field, *a fortiori*. Conversely, the $f_j(x)$ being real, suppose that $\Sigma c_jf_j(x) \equiv 0$ for $a < x < b$. Then $[\Sigma c_jf_j(x)]^* \equiv 0$, hence $\Sigma c_j^*f_j(x) \equiv 0$. Subtracting, $\Sigma[(c_j - c_j^*)/i]f_j(x) \equiv 0$. If all c_j are real, there is nothing to prove. If some c_j is not real, some real number $(c_j - c_j^*)/i$ will not vanish, and we still have a vanishing linear combination with real coefficients.

A set of functions which is linearly dependent on a given domain may become linearly independent when the functions are extended to a larger domain. However, a linearly independent set of functions clearly remains linearly independent when the functions are extended to a larger domain.

LEMMA 2. *Any set of functions of the form*

$$f_{rj}(x) = x^re^{\lambda_jx}, \qquad j = 1, \cdots, n, \tag{9}$$

where the r are nonnegative integers and the λ_j complex numbers, is linearly independent over the complex field on any nonvoid open interval, unless two or more of the functions are identical.

†For the facts about linear independence and vectors assumed here, see Birkhoff and Mac Lane, Ch. VII, §§1–4.

Proof. Suppose $\Sigma c_{ri}f_{ri}(x) \equiv 0$. For any given λ_j, choose R to be the largest r such that $c_{rj} \neq 0$. Form the operator

$$q(D) = (D - \lambda_j)^R \prod_{i \neq j} (D - \lambda_i)^{k_i+1},$$

where k_i is the largest r associated with λ_i. Then $q(D)[f_{ri}] = 0$ unless $i = j$. Moreover, $q(D)[f_{rj}] = 0$ for $r < R$. Hence,

$$q(D)\left[\sum c_{ri}f_{ri}(x)\right] = c_{Rj}q(D)\left[x^R e^{\lambda_j x}\right].$$

On the other hand, as in § 1, (5′),

$$q(D)[x^R e^{\lambda_j x}] = (R!) \prod_{i \neq j} (\lambda_j - \lambda_i)^{k_i+1} e^{\lambda_j x} \neq 0.$$

Hence, substituting back, $c_{Rj} = 0$. Since we assumed $c_{Rj} \neq 0$, this gives a contradiction unless all $c_{rj} = 0$, proving linear independence.

From Theorem 1 we obtain

COROLLARY 1. *The DE* (2) *has at least n solutions of the form* $x^r e^{\lambda x}$ *which are linearly independent over the complex field.*

The analogous result for *real* solutions of a DE (2) with *real* coefficients can be proved as follows. For any two conjugate complex roots $\lambda = \mu + i\nu$ and $\lambda^* = \mu - i\nu$ of the characteristic equation of (2), the real solutions $x^r e^{\mu x} \cos \nu x$ and $x^r e^{\mu x} \sin \nu x$ are complex linear combinations of $x^r e^{\lambda x}$ and $x^r e^{\lambda^* x}$, and conversely. Hence they can be substituted for $x^r e^{\lambda x}$ and $x^r e^{\lambda^* x}$ in any set of solutions, without affecting their linear independence. Since linear independence over the complex field implies linear independence over the real field, this proves

COROLLARY 2. *A linear DE* (2) *with constant* real *coefficients* a_k *has a set of n solutions of the form* (6) *which is linearly independent over the* real *field in any nonvoid interval.*

4. Solution bases. We now show that *all* solutions of the real homogeneous linear DE (2) are linear combinations of the special solutions described in Theorem 2.† To this end, we consider more generally the homogeneous linear DE

$$L[u] = u^{(n)} + p_1(x)u^{(n-1)} + \cdots + p_n(x)u = 0, \tag{10}$$

with real continuous coefficient-functions $p_k(x)$.

As in Chapter II, a *basis* of solutions of the linear DE (10) is a set of n solutions $u_1(x), \cdots, u_n(x)$ such that the general solution of (10) can be

†The result is valid also for linear DE's with constant complex coefficients, by the uniqueness theorem of Chapter V.

uniquely expressed as a linear combination $c_1u_1(x) + \cdots + c_nu_n(x)$, the c_k being arbitrary constants. We now show that any n linearly independent solutions of (10) form a basis of solutions.

THEOREM 3. *Let $u_1, \cdots, u_n$ be n linearly independent real solutions of the n-th order linear homogeneous DE* (10) *with real coefficient-functions. Then, given arbitrary real numbers $a, u_0, u_0', \cdots, u_0^{(n-1)}$, there exist unique constants $c_1, \cdots, c_n$ such that $u(x) = \Sigma c_k u_k(x)$ is a solution of* (10) *satisfying*

$$u(a) = u_0, \quad u'(a) = u_0', \cdots, u^{(n-1)}(a) = u_0^{(n-1)}. \tag{11}$$

The functions $u_k(x)$ are a basis of solutions of (10).

The key to the proof of Theorem 3 is given by the following Lemma, which is also a special case of the much more general Uniqueness Theorem of Ch. V, § 3.

LEMMA. *Let $f(x)$ be a real or complex solution of the n-th order homogeneous linear DE* (10) *with continuous real coefficient-functions in the closed interval $[a,b]$. If $f(a) = f'(a) = \cdots = f^{(n-1)}(a) = 0$, then $f(x) \equiv 0$ on $[a,b]$.*

Proof. We first suppose $f(x)$ *real.* The function

$$\sigma(x) = f(x)^2 + f'(x)^2 + \cdots + f^{(n-1)}(x)^2 \geqq 0$$

satisfies the initial condition $\sigma(a) = 0$. Differentiating $\sigma(x)$, we find, since $\sigma(x)$ is real,

$$\sigma'(x) = 2[f(x)f'(x) + f'(x)f''(x) + \cdots + f^{(n-1)}(x)f^{(n)}(x)].$$

Using the inequality $|2\alpha\beta| \leqq \alpha^2 + \beta^2$ repeatedly $n-1$ times, we have

$$\sigma'(x) \leqq (f^2 + f'^2) + (f'^2 + f''^2) + \cdots + ([f^{(n-2)}]^2 + [f^{(n-1)}]^2) + 2f^{(n-1)}f^{(n)}.$$

Since $L[f] = 0$, $f^{(n)} = -\sum_{k=1}^{n} p_k f^{(n-k)}$. Hence the last term can be rewritten in the form

$$f^{(n-1)}f^{(n)} = -\sum_{k=1}^{n} p_k f^{(n-1)}f^{(n-k)}.$$

Applying the inequality $|2\alpha\beta| \leqq \alpha^2 + \beta^2$ again, we obtain

$$2\,|f^{(n-1)}f^{(n)}| \leqq \sum_{k=1}^{n} |p_k|([f^{(n-k)}]^2 + [f^{(n-1)}]^2).$$

Substituting and rearranging terms, we obtain

$$\sigma'(x) \leqq (1 + |p_n|)f^2 + (2 + |p_{n-1}|)f'^2 + (2 + |p_{n-2}|)f''^2 + \cdots$$
$$+ (2 + |p_2|)[f^{(n-2)}]^2 + (1 + |p_1| + \sum_{k=1}^{n} |p_k|)[f^{(n-1)}]^2.$$

Now let $K = 2 + \max |p_1(x)| + \max_{a \leqq x \leqq b} \sum_{k=1}^{n} |p_k(x)|$. Then it follows from the last inequality that $\sigma'(x) \leqq K\sigma(x)$. From this inequality and the initial condition $\sigma(a) = 0$, the identity $\sigma(x) \equiv 0$ follows by the lemma of Ch. I, § 10. Hence $f(x) \equiv 0$.

If $h(x) = f(x) + ig(x)$ (f,g real) is a *complex* solution of (10), then $f(x)$ and $g(x)$ satisfy (10) by the lemma of § 2. Moreover, $h(a) = h'(a) = \cdots = h^{(n-1)}(a) = 0$ implies the corresponding equalities on f and g. Hence, by the preceding paragraph, $h = f + ig \equiv 0 + 0 = 0$, completing the proof.

We are now ready to prove Theorem 3. Suppose that, for some a, u_0, u_0', $\cdots$, $u_0^{(n-1)}$, there were no linear combination $\Sigma c_k u_k(x)$ satisfying the given initial conditions (11). That is, suppose the n vectors

$$(u_k(a), u_k'(a), \cdots, u_k^{(n-1)}(a)), \quad k = 1, \cdots, n,$$

were *linearly dependent*. Then† there would exist constants $\gamma_1, \cdots, \gamma_n$, not all zero, such that

$$\sum_{k=1}^{n} \gamma_k u_k(a) = 0, \qquad \sum_{k=1}^{n} \gamma_k u_k'(a) = 0, \cdots, \qquad \sum_{k=1}^{n} \gamma_k u^{(n-1)}(a) = 0.$$

That is, the function $\phi(x) = \gamma_1 u_1(x) + \cdots + \gamma_n u_n(x)$ would satisfy

$$\phi(a) = \phi'(a) = \cdots = \phi^{(n-1)}(a) = 0.$$

From this it would follow, by the lemma, that $\phi(x) \equiv 0$.

Recapitulating, either one can find $c_1, \cdots, c_n$ not all zero such that

$$u(x) = c_1 u_1(x) + \cdots + c_n u_n(x)$$

satisfies (11), or one can find $\gamma_1, \cdots, \gamma_n$ not all zero such that

$$\phi(x) = \gamma_1 u_1(x) + \cdots + \gamma_n u_n(x) \equiv 0.$$

The second alternative contradicts the hypothesis of linear independence in Theorem 3, which proves the first conclusion there.

To prove the second conclusion, let $v(x)$ be *any* solution of (10). By the first conclusion, constants $c_1, \cdots, c_n$ can be found such that

$$u(x) = c_1 u_1(x) + \cdots + c_n u_n(x)$$

satisfies $u(a) = v(a)$, $u'(a) = v'(a)$, $\cdots$, $u^{(n-1)}(a) = v^{(n-1)}(a)$. Hence the difference $f(x) = u(x) - v(x)$ satisfies the hypotheses of the lemma above. Using the lemma, $u(x) \equiv v(x)$ and $v(x) = \sum c_k u_k(x)$, proving the second conclusion of Theorem 3.

COROLLARY 1. *Let* $\lambda_1, \cdots, \lambda_m$ *be the roots of the characteristic polynomial of the real‡ DE* (2), *with multiplicities* $k_1, \cdots, k_m$. *Then the functions* $x^r e^{\lambda_j x}$, $r = 0, \cdots, k_j - 1$, *are a basis of solutions of* (2).

†Birkhoff and Mac Lane, p. 169.

‡The preceding result can be proved more generally for linear DE's with constant complex coefficients, by similar methods. See Ch. V, § 10.

Referring to Theorem 2, we have also

COROLLARY 2. *If the coefficients of the DE (2) are real, then it has a basis of real solutions of the form $x^r e^{\lambda x}$, $x^r e^{\mu x} \cos \nu x$, and $x^r e^{\mu x} \sin \nu x$, where λ, μ, and ν are real constants.*

EXERCISES B

1. Solve the following initial value problems:
   (a) $u^{\mathrm{IV}} - u = 0$, $u(0) = u'(0) = u'''(0) = 0$, $u''(0) = 1$
   (b) $u^{\mathrm{IV}} + u'' = 0$, $u(0) = u''(0) = u'''(0) = 0$, $u'(0) = 1$
   (c) $u^{\mathrm{IV}} = 0$, $u'(0) = u''(0) = u'''(0) = 0$, $u(0) = 1$.
2. Knowing a basis of solutions of the DE (1) with constant coefficients, find a basis of solutions of the DE of order $2n$, $L[L[u]] = 0$.
3. Let $L_1[u] = 0$ and $L_2[u] = 0$ be two DE's of the form (1). Prove by induction that the DE's $L_1[L_2[u]] = 0$ and $L_2[L_1[u]] = 0$ coincide.
4. Knowing bases of solutions of $L_1[u] = 0$ and $L_2[u] = 0$ of the form given by Theorem 1, find a basis of solutions of $L_1[L_2[u]] = 0$.
5. Knowing a basis of solutions of (1), of the form given by Theorem 1, find a basis of solutions of $L^k[u] = 0$. ($L^k[u] = L[L^{k-1}[u]]$).
6. Extend Lemma 2 of § 3 to the case where the r_j are arbitrary complex numbers.

*7. State an analog of Corollary 2 of § 3 for Euler's DE, and prove this statement without assuming Corollary 2.

5. Stability. An important concept of physics is that of the stability of an equilibrium state of a physical system. An equilibrium state is said to be *stable* when small departures from equilibrium remain small with the lapse of time, and *unstable* when arbitrarily small initial deviations from equilibrium can ultimately become quite large.

General definitions of these concepts are given in Chapter VI; we treat here only the special homogeneous *linear* DE (1) with constant (that is, time-independent) coefficients. For systems governed by such a DE, the trivial solution $u \equiv 0$ represents an equilibrium state.

In considering the stability of this equilibrium, one thinks of the independent variable as representing time t; the DE (2) then can be rewritten as

$$\frac{d^n u}{dt^n} + a_1 \frac{d^{n-1} u}{dt^{n-1}} + a_2 \frac{d^{n-2} u}{dt^{n-2}} + \cdots + a_{n-1} \frac{du}{dt} + a_n u = 0. \tag{12}$$

DEFINITION. *The DE (12) is* stable *when every solution $u = f(t)$ of (12) remains bounded as $t \to +\infty$; it is* strictly stable *if it is stable, and in addition every solution tends to zero as $t \to +\infty$.*

Theorem 3, Corollary 2 gives algebraic tests for the stability and strict stability of (12). The condition for strict stability is that the real part μ_j of the exponent λ_j of every fundamental solution $t^r e^{\lambda_j t}$ be negative. Indeed, since there is a basis of solutions of the DE of the form $t^r e^{\mu t} \sin \nu t$, and $t^r e^{\mu t} \cos \nu t$, every solution of (12) remains bounded if and only if every solution belonging to this basis remains bounded.† Now, a function $t^r e^{\mu t}$ is bounded as $t \to \infty$ if and only if $\mu < 0$ or $r = \mu = 0$, and $t^r e^{\mu t} \sin \nu t$ (or $t^r e^{\mu t} \cos \nu t$) remains bounded if and only if either $\mu < 0$, or else $r = 0$ and $\mu = 0$; in the latter case one has the oscillatory solution $\sin \nu t$ (or $\cos \nu t$). We conclude that the DE (12) is stable if and only if every multiple root of the characteristic polynomial has a negative real part, and every simple root of the characteristic polynomial has a nonpositive real part.

Next, we derive the condition for (12) to be *strictly stable.* First, we remark that the DE is strictly stable if and only if all solutions belonging to a given basis tend to zero; for a linear combination of functions tending to zero will again be a function tending to zero. Now, a solution $t^r e^{\mu t} \sin \nu t$ or $t^r e^{\mu t}$ tends to zero if and only if $\mu < 0$. Summarizing, we have

THEOREM 4. *The real DE* (12) *is* stable *if and only if no root* λ_j *of its characteristic polynomial has a positive real part, and all multiple roots* (*with* $k_j > 1$ *in* (4)) *have negative real parts; it is* strictly stable *if and only if every root of its characteristic polynomial has a negative real part.*

Polynomials all of whose roots have negative real parts are said to be of *stable type.*‡ There are algebraic inequalities, called the *Routh-Hurwitz conditions,* on the coefficients of a polynomial, which are necessary and sufficient for it to be of stable type. Thus, consider a quadratic polynomial, the characteristic polynomial of the DE of the mass-spring system of Example 4, Ch. II, § 2. It is easily verified that the DE

$$\ddot{u} + a_1\dot{u} + a_2u = 0, \quad \ddot{u} = d^2u/dt^2, \quad \dot{u} = du/dt,$$

is strictly stable if and only if a_1 and a_2 are both positive (positive damping and positive restoring force). That is, when $n = 2$, the Routh-Hurwitz conditions are $a_1 > 0$ and $a_2 > 0$.

In the case of a third-order DE ($n = 3$), the test for strict stability is provided by the inequalities $a_j > 0$ ($j = 1, 2, 3$) and $a_1a_2 > a_3$. When $n = 4$, the conditions for strict stability are $a_j > 0$ ($j = 1, 2, 3, 4$), $a_1a_2 > a_3$, and $a_1a_2a_3 > a_1^2a_4 + a_3^2$.

Second-order linear DE's with constant coefficients, of the form $\ddot{u} + p\dot{u} + qu = 0$, have so many applications that it is convenient to summarize their properties in a diagram. We have just seen that they are stable if and only if $p > 0$ and $q > 0$. Again, their solutions are oscillatory if and only if $p^2 < 4q$, because this is the condition that $\lambda^2 + p\lambda + q$ should

†Because every finite linear combination of bounded functions is bounded. The proof of this fact is omitted.

‡See Birkhoff and Mac Lane, Ch. V, § 7. For polynomials of stable type of higher degree, see F. R. Gantmacher, *Applications of the Theory of Matrices,* Interscience, New York, 1959.

have complex roots. Figure IV-1 indicates these properties, and others to be derived in Chapter VI, by showing the loci in the (p,q)-plane corresponding to different types of roots of the characteristic equation. Thus, the first quadrant is the locus Re $\{\lambda_j\} > 0, j = 1, 2.$

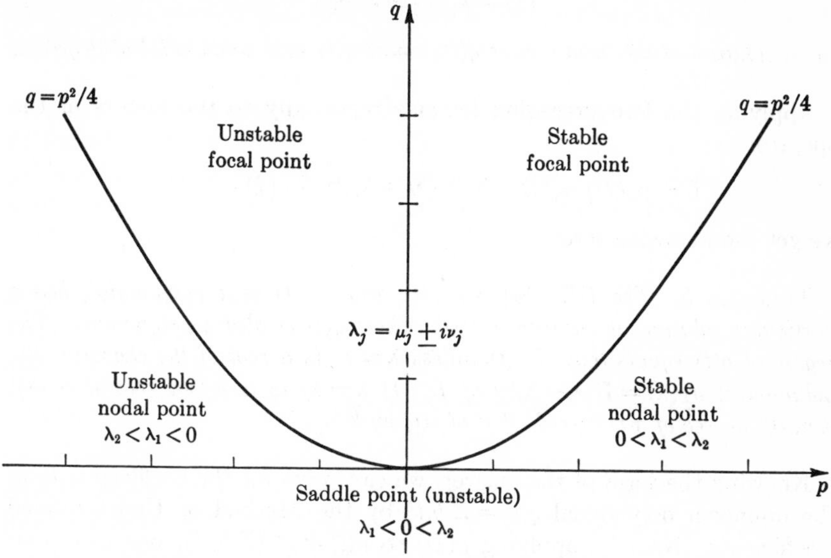

Figure IV-1. Stability Diagram for $\ddot{u} + p\dot{u} + qu = 0$

6. Inhomogeneous equations. We now return to the n-th order *inhomogeneous* linear DE with constant coefficients,

$$L[u] = \frac{d^n u}{dt^n} + a_1 \frac{d^{n-1}u}{dt^{n-1}} + \cdots + a_{n-1}\frac{du}{dt} + a_n u = r(t), \tag{13}$$

already introduced in § 1. We first describe a simple method for solving the DE (13) in closed form, in the special case that $r(t) = \Sigma\, p_k(t)e^{\lambda_k t}$ is a linear combination of polynomials and exponentials.

In the operational notation of § 1, one easily verifies the identity for all $f \in \mathfrak{C}^1$:

$$(D - \lambda)[e^{\lambda t}f(t)] = e^{\lambda t}f'(t).$$

As a corollary, since every polynomial of degree s is the derivative $r(t) = f'(t)$ of a suitable polynomial of degree $s + 1$, we obtain

LEMMA 1. *If $r(t)$ is a polynomial of degree s, then $(D - \lambda)[u] = e^{\lambda t}r(t)$ has a solution of the form $u = e^{\lambda t}q(t)$, where $q(t)$ is a polynomial of degree $s + 1$.*

More generally, one easily verifies the identity

$$(D - \lambda_1)[e^{\lambda t}f(t)] = e^{\lambda t}[(\lambda - \lambda_1)f(t) + f'(t)].$$

If $\lambda \neq \lambda_1$, and $f(t)$ is a polynomial of degree s, then the right side of the preceding identity is a polynomial of degree s times $e^{\lambda t}$. This proves

LEMMA 2. *If $r(t)$ is a polynomial of degree s and $\lambda \neq \lambda_1$, then*

$$(D - \lambda_1)[u] = e^{\lambda t}r(t)$$

has a solution of the form $u = e^{\lambda t}q(t)$, where $q(t)$ is a polynomial of degree s.

Applying the two preceding lemmas repeatedly to the factors of the operator

$$L = p_L(D) = (D - \lambda_1)^{k_1}(D - \lambda_2)^{k_2} \cdots (D - \lambda_m)^{k_m},$$

we get the following result.

THEOREM 5. *The DE $L[u] = e^{\lambda t}r(t)$, where $r(t)$ is a polynomial, has a particular solution of the form $e^{\lambda t}q(t)$, where $q(t)$ is also a polynomial. The degree of $q(t)$ equals that of $r(t)$ unless $\lambda = \lambda_j$ is a root of the characteristic polynomial $p_L(\lambda) = \Pi(\lambda - \lambda_j)^{k_j}$ of L. If $\lambda = \lambda_j$ is a k-fold root of $p_L(\lambda)$, then the degree of $q(t)$ exceeds that of $r(t)$ by k.*

Knowing the form of the answer, we can solve for the coefficients b_k of the unknown polynomial $q(t) = \Sigma\, b_k t^k$ by the Method of Undetermined Coefficients. Namely, applying $p(D)$ to $u(t) = e^{\lambda t}(\Sigma\, b_k t^k)$, one can compute the numbers P_{kl} in the formula

$$p(D)[u] = e^{\lambda t}\sum (P_{kl}b_l)t^k,$$

using formulas for differentiating elementary functions. One does not need to factor p_L. The simultaneous linear equations $\Sigma\, P_{kl}b_l = c_k$ can then be solved for the b_k, given $r(t) = \Sigma\, c_k t^k$, by elementary algebra. Theorem 5 simply states how many unknowns b_k must be used, to get a compatible system of linear equations.

7. Transfer function. Inhomogeneous linear DE's (13) are widely used to represent electrical and acoustical networks or *filters*. Such a filter may be thought of as a "black box," into which a current or a sound wave is fed as an *input* $r(t)$, and out of which comes a resulting *output* $u(t)$.

Mathematically, this amounts to considering an *operator* transforming the function r into a function u which is the solution of the inhomogeneous linear DE (13). Writing this operator as $u = F[r]$, one easily sees that $L[F[r]] = r$. Thus, such an input-output operator is a right-*inverse* of the operator L.

Since there are many solutions of the inhomogeneous DE (13) for a given input $r(t)$, the preceding definition of F is incomplete: the above equations do not define $F = L^{-1}$ unambiguously. This difficulty can often be resolved by insisting that $F[r]$ be in the class $B(-\infty, +\infty)$ of *bounded* functions; in

§§ 7–8, we will make this restriction. For, in this case, for any two solutions u_1 and u_2 of the inhomogeneous DE $L[u] = r$, the difference $v = u_1 - u_2$ would have to satisfy $L[v] = 0$. Unless the characteristic polynomial $p_L(\lambda) = 0$ has pure imaginary roots, this is impossible. Hence, in particular, the DE $L[u] = r$ has at most one bounded solution if the DE $L[u] = 0$ is *strictly stable*, an assumption which corresponds in electrical engineering to a passive electrical network with dissipation.

In §§ 9–10, we will define F by restricting its values to functions which satisfy $u(0) = u'(0) = \cdots u^{(n-1)}(0) = 0$; this also defines F unambiguously, by Theorem 3.

We now consider bounded solutions of (13) for some input functions, without necessarily assuming that the homogeneous DE is strictly stable.

Sinusoidal input functions are of the greatest importance; they represent alternating currents and simple musical notes of constant pitch. These are functions of the form

$$A \cos(kt + \alpha) = \mathrm{Re}\{ce^{ikt}\}, \quad A = |c|, \quad \alpha = \arg c;$$

A is called the *amplitude*, $k/2\pi$ the *frequency*, and α the *phase constant*. The frequency $k/2\pi$ is inversely proportional to the *period* $2\pi/k$.

One can find a particular solution of the DE (13) for the sinusoidal input $r(t) = ce^{ikt}$, by making the substitution $u = C(k)ce^{ikt}$, where $C(k)$ is to be determined. Substituting into the inhomogeneous DE (13), we see that $L[C(k)ce^{ikt}] = ce^{ikt}$ if and only if

$$C(k) = 1/p_L(ik), \qquad p_L(ik) \neq 0, \tag{14}$$

where $p_L(\lambda)$ is the characteristic polynomial defined by (3).

DEFINITION. *The complex-valued function $C(k)$ of the real variable k defined by* (14) *is called the* transfer function *associated with the linear, time-independent operator L. If $C(k) = \rho(k)e^{i\gamma(k)}$, then $\rho = |C(k)|$ is the* gain function, *and $\gamma(k) = \arg C(k)$ is the* phase lag *associated with k.*

The reason for this terminology lies in the relationship between the real part of $u(t)$ and that of the input $r(t)$. Clearly,

$$\mathrm{Re}\{u(t)\} = \mathrm{Re}\{C(k)ce^{ikt}\} = |C(k)| \cdot |c| \cos(kt + \alpha + \gamma).$$

This shows that the amplitude of the output is $\rho(k)$ times the amplitude of the input, and the phase of the output lags $\gamma = \arg C$ behind that of the input.

In the *strictly stable* case, the particular solution of the inhomogeneous linear DE $L[u] = ce^{ikt}$ found by the preceding method is the only bounded solution; hence $F[ce^{ikt}] = C(k)ce^{ikt}$ describes the effect of the input-output operator F on sinusoidal inputs. Furthermore, since every solution of the homogeneous DE (12) tends to zero as $t \to +\infty$, every solution of $L[u] = ce^{ikt}$ approaches $C(k)ce^{ikt}$ exponentially.

Resonance. The preceding method fails when the characteristic polynomial $p_L(\lambda)$ has one or more purely imaginary roots $\lambda = ik_j$ (in electrical engineering, this occurs in a "lossless passive network").

Thus, suppose that ik is a root of the equation $p_L(\lambda) = 0$, and that one wishes to solve the inhomogeneous DE $L[u] = e^{ikt}$. From the identity (cf. § 6)

$$L[te^{\lambda t}] = L\left[\frac{\partial}{\partial \lambda} e^{\lambda t}\right] = \frac{\partial}{\partial \lambda} L[e^{\lambda t}]$$

$$= \frac{\partial}{\partial \lambda} [p_L(\lambda)e^{\lambda t}] = p_L'(\lambda)e^{\lambda t} + p_L(\lambda)\lambda e^{\lambda t},$$

one obtains, setting $\lambda = ik$,

$$L[te^{ikt}] = p_L'(ik)e^{ikt}.$$

If ik is a simple root of the characteristic equation, $p_L'(ik) \neq 0$. Hence a solution of $L[u] = e^{ikt}$ is $u(t) = (1/p_L'(ik))te^{ikt}$. The amplitude of this solution is $(1/\,|\,p_L'(ik)\,|)t$, and it increases to infinity as $t \to \infty$. This is the phenomenon of *resonance,* which arises when a nondissipative physical system Σ is excited by a force whose period equals one of the periods of free vibration of Σ.

A similar computation can be made when ik is a root of multiplicity n of the characteristic polynomial, using the identity $L[t^n e^{ikt}] = p_L^{(n)}(ik)e^{ikt}$, which is proved in much the same way. In this case the amplitude of the solution again increases to infinity.

8*. Nyquist diagram. The transfer function $C(k) = 1/p_L(ik)$ of a linear differential equation with constant coefficients $L[u] = 0$ is of great help in the study of the inhomogeneous DE (13). To visualize the transfer function, one graphs the logarithmic gain $\ln \rho(k)$ and phase lag $\gamma(k)$ as functions of the frequency $k/2\pi$. If $\lambda_1, \cdots, \lambda_n$ are the roots of the characteristic polynomial, one has

$$\text{(15a)} \qquad \ln \rho(k) = -\sum_{j=1}^{n} \ln |\, ik - \lambda_j \,| = -\tfrac{1}{2}\sum \ln [(k - \nu_j)^2 + \mu_j^2]$$

$$\text{(15b)} \qquad \gamma(k) = -\sum_{j=1}^{n} \arg (ik - \lambda_j) = \sum \arctan [(k - \nu_j)/\mu_j],$$

from which these graphs are easily plotted. Figure IV-2(a) depicts the gain function and phase lag of the DE

$$u^{\text{iv}} + 0.8u''' + 5.22u'' + 1.424u' + 4.1309u = 0,$$

whose characteristic polynomial has the roots $\lambda_j = -0.1 \pm i, -0.3 \pm 2i$.

We now compute how the phase lag $\gamma(k)$ changes as the frequency $k/2\pi$ increases from $-\infty$ to $+\infty$. By (15b), it suffices to add the changes in the functions $\arg (ik - \lambda_j)$ for each λ_j. If Re $\{\lambda_j\}$ is negative, then the vertical straight line $ik + \lambda_j$ $(-\infty < k < \infty)$ lies in the left half of the

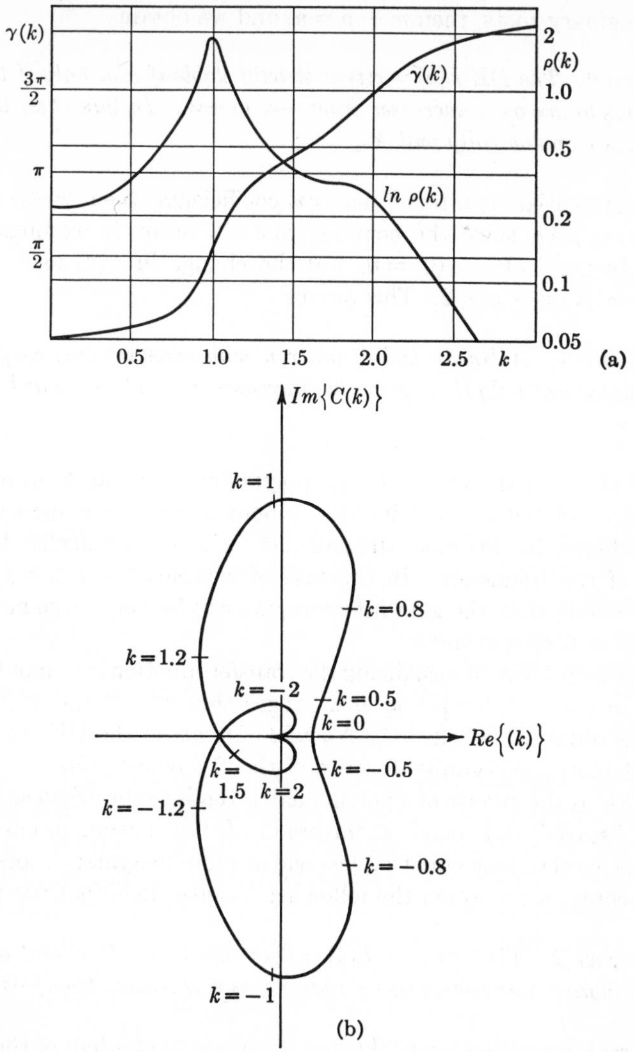

Figure IV-2. (a) Phase-Lag and Gain Functions, (b) Nyquist Diagram

complex plane; hence $-\arg(ik - \lambda_j)$ increases by π as k increases from $-\infty$ to $+\infty$. If $\mathrm{Re}\{\lambda_j\}$ is positive, then $-\arg(ik - \lambda_j)$ decreases by π for a similar reason. Hence, if there are no roots with zero real part, the change in $\gamma(k)$ is $(m - p)\pi$, where m is the number of λ_j with negative real part, and p is the number with positive real part.† If there are no

†For pure imaginary roots, the change of argument of λ is undefined (it could be π or $-\pi$). In this case, one makes the convention that the change in the argument is zero. The following theorem is true with the proviso that whenever the argument is undefined, the change is taken to be zero.

purely imaginary roots, then $m + p = n$, and we obtain

THEOREM 6. *The DE $L[u] = r(t)$ is strictly stable if and only if the phase lag increases by $n\pi$ as k increases from $-\infty$ to $+\infty$. In this case, the phase lag increases monotonically with k.*

If the differential operator L has *real* coefficients, then $\gamma(-k) = -\gamma(k)$ and $\rho(-k) = \rho(k)$, since the complex roots λ_j occur in conjugate pairs $\mu_j \pm i\nu_j$. In particular, $\gamma(0) = 0$, and the change in $\gamma(k)$ as k increases from 0 to ∞ is $(m - p)\pi/2$. This proves

COROLLARY 1. *A linear DE of order n with constant* real *coefficients is strictly stable if and only if the phase lag increases from 0 to $n\pi/2$ as k increases from 0 to ∞.*

If all roots λ_j of the characteristic polynomial are real, then one easily verifies that all $\ln | ik - \lambda_j |$ increase monotonically as k increases from 0 to ∞. Hence, in this case, the gain $\rho(k)$ is a monotonically decreasing function of the frequency. In the case of complex roots $\lambda_j = \mu_j \pm i\nu_j$, if μ_j is very small, then the gain function $\rho(k)$ will be very large near $k = \nu_j$; this is due to near *resonance*.

Another useful way of visualizing the transfer function is to plot the curve $z = C(k)$ in the *complex plane*, as k ranges through all real values. The curve thus obtained is called the *Nyquist diagram* of the DE (13). Figure IV-2(b) depicts the Nyquist diagram of the DE below (15b).

Since $C(k)$ is the inverse of a polynomial, it tends to the origin as $k \to \pm\infty$, that is, it "starts" and "ends" at the origin. It is a continuous curve except when the characteristic equation has one or more imaginary roots $\lambda_j = ik_j$. From Theorem 6 we obtain the following *Nyquist Stability Criterion*:

COROLLARY 2. *The equation $L[u] = 0$ is strictly stable if and only if the Nyquist diagram turns through $n\pi$ radians as k increases from $-\infty$ to $+\infty$.*

If L is real, then $C(-k) = C^*(k)$, and it suffices to plot half of the Nyquist diagram. The operator L is strictly stable if and only if the Nyquist diagram turns through $n\pi/2$ radians as k increases from 0 to ∞.

EXERCISES C

In Exs. 1–4, test the DE specified for stability and strict stability:

1. $u'' + 5u' + 4 = 0.$
2. $u''' + 6u'' + 12u' + 8u = 0.$
3. $u''' + 6u'' + 11u' + 6u = 0.$
4. $u^{\text{iv}} + 4u''' + 4u'' = 0.$
5. For which n is the DE $u^{(n)} + u = 0$ stable?

In Exs. 6–9, find a particular solution of the DE specified. In Exs. 6–8, find the solutions satisfying $u(0) = 0$; $u'(0) = 1$ and vice-versa.

6. $u'' = te^t$.
7. $u'' + u = te^t$.
8. $u'' - u = te^t$.
9. $u^{iv} = t^5e^t$.

In Exs. 10–13, plot the gain and transfer functions of the operator specified (I denotes the identity operator):

10. $D^2 + 4D + 4I$.
11. $D^3 + 6D^2 + 12D + 8I$.
12. $D^2 + 2D + 101I$.
13. $D^4 - I$.

14. For a strictly stable $L[u] = u'' + au' + bu = r(t)$ calculate the outputs (the *responses*) to the inputs $r(t) = 1$ and $r(t) = t$, for $a^2 > 4b$ and $a^2 < 4b$.

15. Same question for the step-function $h(t) = \begin{cases} 1 \text{ on } (0,1), \\ 0 \text{ elsewhere.} \end{cases}$

16. For $u'' + au' + bu = ce^{ikt}$ make graphs of the gain function versus the dimensionless frequency $k/\sqrt{b}$ for the values $\eta = 0$, $\eta = 1/2$, $\eta = 1/\sqrt{2}$, $\eta = 2$ of the parameter $\eta = a/2\sqrt{b}$ $(b > 0)$.

17. Show that, if $p_L(ik) = p_L'(ik) = \cdots = p_L^{(n-1)}(ik) = 0$, but $p_L^{(n)}(ik) \neq 0$, then a solution of $L[u] = e^{ikt}$ is $u(t) = (1/p_L^{(n)}(ik))t^ne^{ikt}$.

18. A DE (12) is stable at $t \to -\infty$ when all solutions of the DE remain bounded as $t \to -\infty$. Find necessary and sufficient conditions for stability at $-\infty$.

19. In Ex. 18, find necessary and sufficient conditions for strict stability at $-\infty$.

20. Show that no DE (12) can be strictly stable at both ∞ and $-\infty$.

21. Show that a DE (12) is stable at both ∞ and $-\infty$ if and only if every root of the characteristic equation is simple and a purely imaginary number.

9. Green's function. The concept of Green's function was introduced in Ch. II, § 7. For the inhomogeneous linear DE $L[u] = r(t)$, it is a function $G(t,\tau)$ such that

$$u = f(t) = \int_a^t G(t,\tau)r(\tau)d\tau \tag{16}$$

satisfies $L[u] = r(t)$, for any continuous function r. We now state a generalization of Theorem 8 of Ch. II, § 8, which describes the Green's function of a linear operator of arbitrary order.

THEOREM 7. *The* Green's function for the initial value problem *of the n-th order real linear differential operator with continuous coefficients*

$$L = \frac{d^n}{dt^n} + p_1(t)\frac{d^{n-1}}{dt^{n-1}} + \cdots + p_{n-1}(t)\frac{d}{dt} + p_n(t), \quad a \leqq t \leqq b, \tag{17}$$

is zero if $t < \tau$. For $t \geqq \tau$, it is that solution of the DE (for the independent variable t) $L[G] = 0$ which satisfies the initial conditions

$$G = \partial G/\partial t = \cdots = \partial^{n-2}G/\partial t^{n-2} = 0, \quad \partial^{n-1}G/\partial t^{n-1} = 1 \textit{ for } t = \tau.$$

In the case $p_i(t) = a_i$ of linear DE's with constant real coefficients, the existence of such a solution follows from the results of § 3. The Green's function is easily computed as a sum of polynomials times exponentials.

For variable coefficient-functions, existence will follow from the results of the next chapter.

We omit the proof of Theorem 7. It follows exactly the proof for second-order differential operators, given in Ch. II, § 8, and can be extended to the present case. One simply applies the rule for differentiation under the integral sign n times instead of twice.

The computation of Green's functions for linear DE's with constant coefficients is most easily performed, and its significance best understood, using the following result.

THEOREM 8. *The Green's function for the initial value problem of any linear differential operator with constant coefficients is a function* $G(t,\tau) = \Gamma(t-\tau)$ *depending only on the difference* $t-\tau$.

Proof. Let $\Gamma(t) = G(t,0)$; then $\Gamma(t) = 0$ if $t < 0$. If $t \geqq 0$, the function $\Gamma(t)$ is the solution of the DE $L[\Gamma] = 0$ which satisfies the initial conditions

$$\Gamma(0) = \Gamma'(0) = \cdots = \Gamma^{(n-2)}(0) = 0, \quad \Gamma^{(n-1)}(0) = 1.$$

We now remark that if $u(t)$ is a solution of the DE $L[u] = 0$, then for each fixed τ the function $u(t+\tau)$ of the variable t is also a solution of the DE. It follows that the function $F(t) = G(t+\tau,\tau)$ (for fixed τ) is a solution of the DE. This function satisfies the same initial conditions as the function Γ, because of the way in which the Green's function is defined. By the Uniqueness Theorem (Theorem 3) it follows that $\Gamma(t) = G(t+\tau,\tau)$. Hence, setting $s = t+\tau$, $\Gamma(s-\tau) = G(s,\tau)$, q.e.d.

Referring to Theorems 1 and 3, we obtain

COROLLARY 1. *In Theorem 8, the function* $\Gamma(t-\tau)$ *is of class* $\mathcal{C}^{n-2}$, *and* $\Gamma(s) = 0$ *for* $s < 0$, *while* $\Gamma(s)$ *is a linear combination of functions* $s^r e^{\lambda_j s}$ *for* $s > 0$.†

Changing variables in (16), we have

COROLLARY 2. *If* $r(t)$ *vanishes for* $t < a$ *and is bounded and continuous for* $a \leqq t$, *then the function*

$$f(t) = \int_{-\infty}^{\infty} \Gamma(t-\tau)r(\tau)d\tau = \int_{-\infty}^{\infty} \Gamma(s)r(t-s)ds \tag{17a}$$

is a solution of the inhomogeneous linear DE with constant coefficients (13) *which vanishes for* $t < a$ *and satisfies the initial conditions of Theorem* 7.

Indeed, since $r(\tau)$ vanishes for $\tau < a$ and $\Gamma(t-\tau)$ vanishes for $\tau > t$, the integral (17a) can be written as

$$f(t) = \int_a^t \Gamma(t-\tau)r(\tau)d\tau, \tag{17b}$$

and is equal to (16), by Theorem 8.

†The function $\Gamma(s)$ is of course *also* expressible for $s > 0$ as a *real* linear combination of functions of the form (6).

THEOREM 9. *If L is strictly stable as $t \to +\infty$, formulas (17a) remain valid for any bounded continuous function $r(t)$ defined for $-\infty < t < \infty$; for such a function, $f(t)$ is the only solution of the DE (13) which is bounded for $-\infty < t < \infty$.*

Proof. By Corollary 1 above, $\Gamma(s)$ is equal, for $s \geqq 0$, to a linear combination of the form

$$\Gamma(s) = \sum_{j=1}^{n} c_j s^{r_j} e^{\lambda_j s}, \qquad s \geqq 0.$$

If the equation $L[u] = 0$ is strictly stable, then the real parts of all λ_j are negative. Let $-m$ be the largest of these real parts. Then $-m < 0$, and

$$| e^{ms/2}\, \Gamma(s) | \leqq \sum_{j=1}^{n} | c_j s^{r_j} e^{(\lambda_j + (m/2))s} |.$$

Since $\operatorname{Re}\{\lambda_j\} + \dfrac{m}{2} < 0$ for $1 \leqq j \leqq m$, the right side remains bounded for $0 \leqq s \leqq \infty$. Let M be an upper bound for the right side. Then we obtain

$$| \Gamma(s) | \leqq M e^{-ms/2}, \qquad 0 \leqq s < \infty.$$

We next show that the integrals in (17a) are well-defined for any bounded continuous function r. The first integral can be rewritten in the form

$$\int_{-\infty}^{t} \Gamma(t - \tau) r(\tau) d\tau,$$

since $\Gamma(t - \tau) = 0$ for $t < \tau$. Using the above estimate for $\Gamma(s)$, and letting R be an upper bound for $| r(\tau) |$ on $-\infty < \tau < \infty$, we obtain,

$$\left| \int_{-\infty}^{t} \Gamma(t - \tau) r(\tau) d\tau \right| \leqq \int_{-\infty}^{t} \left| \Gamma(t - \tau) \right| \left| r(\tau) \right| d\tau$$
$$\leqq RM \int_{-\infty}^{t} e^{-m/2(t-\tau)} d\tau = \frac{2RM}{m} < +\infty$$

for all t. Hence the integral is well-defined and defines a bounded function $f(t)$. To show that f is a solution of the DE, we can use the method of Theorem 7, provided we can carry out the differentiation under the integral sign. This can indeed be justified;† instead, however, we shall give a direct argument.

Consider the sequence of functions $r_k(t)$ defined by the formulas

$$r_k(t) = \begin{cases} r(t) & \text{if } t \geqq -k \\ 0 & \text{if } t < -k, \end{cases} \quad k = 1, 2, \cdots.$$

Then the functions

$$f_k(t) = \int_{-k}^{t} \Gamma(t - \tau) r_k(\tau) d\tau = \int_{-\infty}^{\infty} \Gamma(t - \tau) r_k(\tau) d\tau$$

†Courant, Vol. 2, p. 312.

are solutions of the DE (13). We shall show that for t ranging over any interval $a \leqq t \leqq b$ the functions $f_k(t)$, as well as their derivatives of orders up to n, converge uniformly to the derivatives of the function $f(t)$. This will also prove that $f(t)$ is a solution of the DE (13).

From the expression of $\Gamma(s)$ as a linear combination of functions of the form $s^{r_j}e^{\lambda_j s}$, we see that all derivatives of $\Gamma(s)$ are also linear combinations of functions of the same form, for different r_j, but with the same sequence of exponents λ_j. That is, for the derivative of order ℓ we have

$$\Gamma^{(\ell)}(s) = \sum_{j=1}^{n} p_j(s)e^{\lambda_j s},$$

where the p_j are polynomials in the variable s, depending upon the order of differentiation ℓ.† It follows, as before, that

$$|\Gamma^{(\ell)}(s)| \leqq M_\ell e^{-ms/2}, \quad \ell = 1, 2, \cdots.$$

Now, from the expression

$$f_k^{(\ell)}(t) = \int_{-k}^{t} \Gamma^{(\ell)}(t-\tau)r_k(\tau)d\tau$$

we find, for sufficiently large k and j, where $k \geqq j$,

$$\begin{aligned} |f_k^{(\ell)}(t) - f_j^{(\ell)}(t)| &\leqq \int_{-k}^{t} \left|\Gamma^{(\ell)}(t-\tau)\right| \left|r_k(\tau) - r_j(\tau)\right| d\tau \\ &\leqq \int_{-k}^{-j} \left|\Gamma^{(\ell)}(t-\tau)\right| \left|r_k(\tau)\right| d\tau \\ &\leqq RM_\ell \int_{-k}^{-j} e^{-m(t-\tau)/2}d\tau, \end{aligned}$$

and the last integral clearly tends to zero as $j, k \to \infty$, uniformly for $a \leqq t \leqq b$. Therefore $|f_k^{(\ell)}(t) - f_j^{(\ell)}(t)| < \epsilon$ for sufficiently large k, j, uniformly for $a \leqq t \leqq b$. This completes the proof of the fact that f is a solution of the DE.

Lastly, one can easily see, by the following argument, that f thus defined is the only bounded solution. If f_1 were another bounded solution, then $f - f_1$ would be a bounded solution of the homogeneous DE. But, since the DE is *strictly* stable as $t \to \infty$, no nontrivial solution of the homogeneous DE can remain bounded as $t \to -\infty$ (cf. Theorem 4). Hence $f - f_1 \equiv 0$, and the proof is complete.

EXERCISES D

In Exs. 1–6, construct the Green's function for the initial value problem of the DE indicated:

1. $d^3u/dt^3 = r(t)$.
2. $d^nu/dt^n = r(t)$.
3. $u^{\text{iv}} - u = r(t)$.
4. $u''' + u = r(t)$.
5. $u^{\text{iv}} + u = r(t)$.

*6. $u^{\text{vi}} - u = r(t)$.

†This can be easily seen by applying Leibniz's rule, cf. Courant, Vol. 1, p. 212.

7. Find the Green's function of the DE $d^n u/dt^n = r(t)$.

8. Carry out in detail the proof of Theorem 7 for $n = 3$, performing all differentiations under the integral sign explicitly.

*9. Show that if (16) is defined for all t, and the Green's function $G(t,\tau) = \Gamma(t-\tau)$, then all coefficients $p_k(t)$ are constant.

*10. Show that if $u(t+\tau)$ is a solution of (16) with $r(t) = 0$ whenever $u(t)$ is, then the coefficients $p_k(t)$ are all constants.

10*. Laplace transforms. An effective technique for solving inhomogeneous linear DE's with constant coefficients is the Laplace transform. It is especially well suited to solving initial value problems.

DEFINITION. *The* Laplace transform $\phi = \mathcal{L}[f]$ *of an integrable function* $f(t)$, $0 \leqq t < \infty$, *is the function* ϕ *defined by the equation*

$$\phi(s) = \int_0^\infty e^{-st} f(t)dt. \tag{18}$$

It is well-defined for all real $s > M$ *provided* $|f(t)| \leqq Ke^{Mt}$ *for some finite* K; *the least real* s_c *such that (18) is defined for all* $s > s_c$ *is called the* abscissa of convergence.†

The variable s is allowed to take real or complex values. We shall consider it as a real variable in this section.

The Laplace transform is a linear operator:

$$\mathcal{L}[c_1 f_1 + c_2 f_2] = c_1\mathcal{L}[f_1] + c_2\mathcal{L}[f_2]$$

for any constants c_1, c_2 and functions f_1, f_2.

Some common Laplace transforms are the following:‡

$$\mathcal{L}[1] = 1/s. \tag{19–1}$$
$$\mathcal{L}[t^r] = \Gamma(r+1)/s^{r+1}. \tag{19–2}$$
$$\mathcal{L}[e^{at}] = 1/(s-a). \tag{19–3}$$
$$\mathcal{L}[t^r e^{at}] = \Gamma(r+1)/(s-a)^{r+1}. \tag{19–4}$$
$$\mathcal{L}[\cos bt] = s/(s^2+b^2). \tag{19–5}$$
$$\mathcal{L}[\log t] = \frac{\Gamma'(1)}{s} - \frac{\ln s}{s}. \tag{19–6}$$
$$\mathcal{L}[(\sin t)/t] = \arctan^{-1} s. \tag{19–7}$$
$$\mathcal{L}[J_0(t)] = 1/\sqrt{s^2+1}. \tag{19–8}$$

The abscissas of convergence are $s = 0$ or (for functions containing the factor e^{at}) $s = a$.

Not every function can be represented as a Laplace transform; Laplace

†Widder, Ch. XIII, where Lerch's Theorem is proved, p. 460, and the Laplace transforms (19) are given, p. 473.

‡Below Γ is the gamma function, and $\Gamma'(1)$ is the Euler constant $\gamma = 0.577257\cdots$.

transforms tend to zero as $s \to +\infty$. But functions whose Laplace transforms coincide (for sufficiently large s) are identical, by virtue of

LERCH'S THEOREM. *If $f(t)$ and $g(t)$ have the same Laplace transform $\mathcal{L}[f] = \mathcal{L}[g]$ for an infinite set of numbers $s = s_0 + nh$ $[h > 0,\ n = 1, 2, 3, \cdots]$ in an arithmetic progression, then $f(t) = g(t)$ for all positive t.*

The Laplace transform of the derivative of a function is easily computed. Integrating by parts, we obtain

$$\int_0^\infty e^{-st}f'(t)dt = \lim_{T\to\infty}\left\{[e^{-st}f(t)]_0^T + s\int_0^T e^{-st}f(t)dt\right\}$$
$$= -f(0) + s\int_0^\infty e^{-st}f(t)dt,$$

where the passage to the limit is easily justified if $f'(t)$ is bounded by Me^{Kt} for some $M > 0$ and $K < s$. By the definition of the Laplace transform, this asserts that

$$\mathcal{L}[f'] = s\,\mathcal{L}[f] - f(0). \tag{20}$$

From this rule, by induction on n, we can obtain the rule for taking the Laplace transform of the n-th derivative of a given function. This rule is

LEMMA. *If u is of class $\mathcal{C}^k$, and $|u^{(k)}(t)| \leqq Ke^{Mt}$ for some finite K and M, then*

$$\mathcal{L}[u^{(k)}] = s^k\mathcal{L}[u] - [s^{k-1}u(0) + s^{k-2}u'(0) + \cdots + u^{(k-1)}(0)]. \tag{21}$$

The Laplace transform can be applied to the inhomogeneous linear DE with constant coefficients,†

$$L[u] = u^{(n)} + a_1u^{(n-1)} + a_2u^{(n-2)} + \cdots + a_nu = r(t), \tag{22}$$

subject to the initial conditions of Theorem 7,

$$u = u' = u'' = \cdots = u^{(n-1)} = 0 \quad \text{when} \quad t = 0. \tag{23}$$

Taking the Laplace transform of both sides, we get

$$\int_0^\infty e^{-st}u^{(n)}dt + a_1\int_0^\infty e^{-st}u^{(n-1)}dt + \cdots + a_n\int_0^\infty e^{-st}u\,dt = \int_0^\infty e^{-st}r(t)dt.$$

We have

THEOREM 10. *Let u be the solution of $L[u] = r$ satisfying the initial conditions $u(0) = u'(0) = \cdots = u^{(n-1)}(0) = 0$. Then, for sufficiently large s,*

$$p_L(s)\mathcal{L}[u] = \mathcal{L}[r], \quad \textit{or} \quad \mathcal{L}[u] = \mathcal{L}[r]/p_L(s), \tag{24}$$

†Cf. Widder, Ch. XIV; R. V. Churchill, *Operational Mathematics*, 2d. ed., McGraw-Hill, 1958.

provided $|r(t)| \leqq Ke^{Mt}$ *for some finite* K *and* M. *Here* $p_L(s)$ *is the characteristic polynomial of the operator* L.

Proof. The solution u is given by the formula (17), for $f = u$ and $a = 0$. By Theorem 9, $|\Gamma(t)| \leqq ce^{mt}$ as $s \to \infty$, for some constants c and m. Hence

$$|u(t)| \leqq \int_0^t ce^{m(t-\tau)}Ke^{M\tau}d\tau \leqq Qe^{qt}$$

for some constants Q and q, for $t > 0$. Therefore $\mathfrak{L}[u]$ is defined for sufficiently large s.

Since the terms in square brackets in (21) vanish, formula (24) follows immediately.

Using Theorem 10, one can solve the initial value problem for $L[u] = r$ with the initial conditions (23), provided one can find the function whose Laplace transform is $\mathfrak{L}[r]/p_L(s)$. This can be done by consulting a table of Laplace transforms, after decomposing $p_L(s)$ into *partial fractions.*

When the roots $\lambda_1, \cdots, \lambda_n$ of a polynomial $p(s)$ are distinct, the reciprocal $1/p(s)$ has a particularly simple decomposition into partial fractions. One can determine the coefficients b_k in the expression

$$1/p(s) = b_1/(s - \lambda_1) + \cdots + b_n/(s - \lambda_n)$$

from the relation $b_k = \lim_{s \to \lambda_k} (s - \lambda_k)/p(s)$, which implies $b_k = 1/p'(\lambda_k)$. Hence

$$\frac{1}{p_L(s)} = \frac{b_1}{s - \lambda_1} + \frac{b_2}{s - \lambda_2} + \cdots + \frac{b_n}{s - \lambda_n}, \qquad b_k = 1/p'_L(\lambda_k).$$

As an application of the Laplace transform, we compute the formula for the Green's function $\Gamma(t)$ for the initial value problem. This is the solution of the DE $L[u] = 0$ for $t \geqq 0$ which satisfies the initial conditions $\Gamma(0) = \Gamma'(0) = \cdots = \Gamma^{(n-2)}(0) = 0$, $\Gamma^{(n-1)}(0) = 1$. Using the preceding theorem, we have

THEOREM 11. *The Laplace transform of the Green's function for the initial value problem of any linear differential operator* L *with constant coefficients is the function* $1/p_L(s)$.

Comparing with formula (14), we have

COROLLARY 1. *The Laplace transform* $\mathfrak{L}[\Gamma_L]$ *of the Green's function of* L *is* $C(-is)$, *where* $C(k)$ *is the transfer function of* L.

The function $b_k/(s - \lambda_k)$ is the Laplace transform of the function $b_k e^{\lambda_k t}$ (cf. formula 19)). Hence we have

COROLLARY 2. *If the characteristic equation* $p_L(s) = 0$ *has* n *distinct roots* $\lambda_1, \lambda_2, \cdots, \lambda_n$, *then the Green's function for the initial value problem for* $L[u]=r$ *is* $\Gamma(t-\tau)$ *where, for* $s>0$,

$$\Gamma(s)=b_1e^{\lambda_1 s}+\cdots+b_ne^{\lambda_n s},\quad b_k=1/p_L'(\lambda_k), \tag{25}$$

and $\Gamma(s)=0$ *for all* $s<0$.

11*. Generating functions; convolution. There is a close analogy between the Laplace transform of a function $f(t)$ defined for $t>0$, and the generating function of a sequence of numbers a_n, where $n\geqq 0$ is an integer. The generating function of $\{a_n\}$ is defined as the power series

$$g(x)=\sum_{n=0}^{\infty} a_nx^n. \tag{26}$$

When the series on the right converges in an interval this defines a function $g(s)$; otherwise the infinite series is a formal power series. In many cases useful information can be obtained about a sequence a_n by merely recognizing its generating function explicitly. Examples of generating functions can be found in exercises A10 and B8 of Chapter III; other examples can be found in exercises scattered throughout this book.

The Laplace transform is a continuous analog of a generating function. One replaces the discrete variable n by a continuous nonnegative real variable t; this replaces the sequence a_n, by a function $a(t)$. Replacing the sum by the analogous integral, one obtains the formula $g(x)=\int a(t)x^tdt$. Upon setting $x=e^{-s}$ we obtain the Laplace transform of the function $a(t)$, as in formula (18) above.

Convolution. An important property of the Laplace transform is related to the operation of convolution of two functions. Let $f(t)$ and $g(t)$ be functions defined for all real t. Their convolution is defined by the formula

$$h(x)=\int_{-\infty}^{\infty} f(x-t)g(t)dt$$

whenever the integral is finite. If the functions f and g are identically zero for $t<0$, then this formula simplifies to

$$h(x)=f*g(x)=\int_0^x f(t)g(x-t)dt.$$

In many ways this operation is analogous to the multiplication of two infinite series. It is commutative and associative, as can be easily seen. The relevant property of convolution is expressed by the formula $\mathcal{L}[f*g]=\mathcal{L}[f]\mathcal{L}[g]$; in other words, the Laplace transform of the convolution of two functions is the product of the single Laplace transforms. This property can be verified by a change in the order of integration, as follows:

$$\begin{aligned}\mathcal{L}[f*g] &= \int_0^\infty e^{-sx}\int_0^x f(t)g(x-t)dt\,dx = \int_0^\infty f(t)\int_t^\infty e^{-sx}g(x-t)dx\,dt \\ &= \int_0^\infty f(t)e^{-ts}dt\int_0^\infty g(v)e^{-vs}dv = \mathcal{L}[f]\mathcal{L}[g],\quad v=x-t\end{aligned}$$

For example, let 1 denote the function equal to one for $0 \leqq x < \infty$ and to zero for $x < 0$. Then $1 * 1 = x$, $1 * 1 * \cdots * 1 = \frac{1}{(n-1)!} x^{n-1}$. As an application, we obtain *Liouville's formula* for iterated integrals

$$1 * f = \int_0^x f(t)dt$$

$$\underbrace{1 * 1 * \cdots * 1 * f}_{n \text{ terms}} = \int_0^x \int_0^{t_n} \cdots \int_0^{t_2} f(t_1)dt_1 \cdots dt_n$$

$$= \frac{1}{\Gamma(n)} \int_0^x (x-t)^{n-1} f(t)dt.$$

The Laplace transform of $1 * f$ is $\frac{1}{s}\hat{f}(s)$, $\hat{f} = \mathfrak{L}[f]$. Therefore, the Laplace transform of the indefinite integral $\int_0^x f(t)dt$ is $\frac{1}{s}\hat{f}(s)$. More generally, the Laplace transform of $\frac{1}{\Gamma(n)} \int_0^x (x-t)^{n-1} f(t)dt$ is $s^{-n}\hat{f}(s)$.

As another application, we reinterpret Corollary 2 of Theorem 8. It states that the solution of the DE $L[u] = r(t)$ for the initial conditions $u(0) = u'(0) = \cdots = u^{(n-1)}(0) = 0$ is the convolution $r * \Gamma$ of r and the displaced Green's function Γ for the same initial conditions, provided $r \equiv 0$ for $t < 0$.

Theorem 9 can also be interpreted in terms of the convolution operation. It asserts that, for strictly stable L, the solution of the "input-output" problem $L[u] = r(t)$ is $r * \Gamma$ for any uniformly bounded "input" $r(t)$.

EXERCISES E

1–8. Derive formulas (19–1) through (19–8), respectively.

9. Show that if the Laplace transform of $f(t)$ is $\hat{f}(s)$, then that of: (a) $f(at)$ is $a^{-1}\hat{f}(sa^{-1})$; (b) $e^{-bt}f(t)$ is $\hat{f}(s+b)$; (c) $a^{-1}f(ta^{-1})$ is $\hat{f}(as)$.

In Exs. 10–11, find the solution of the DE specified which satisfies the initial condition $u(0) = u'(0) = 0$; (a) by using formula (21), (b) by the Method of Undetermined Coefficients:

10. $u'' - u = t$.

11. $u'' - 3u' + 2u = te^t$.

In Exs. 12–13, do the same for the initial conditions

$$u(0) = u'(0) = u''(0) = u'''(0) = 0:$$

12. $u^{\text{iv}} - u = t^2$.

13. $u^{\text{iv}} = t^2$.

*14. Let $f(t) \in \mathcal{C}^n$ satisfy $|f(t)| \leqq A + Bt^n$ for some finite A, B, on $0 \leqq t < +\infty$. Show that the Laplace transform of $f(t)$ has an abscissa of convergence $s_c \leqq 0$, and satisfies $\phi = 0(1/s^r)$ for large s, where $f^{(r)}$ is the first derivative of $f(t)$ which does *not* vanish at $t = 0$. (*Hint:* Use (20).)

15. Show that $\mathcal{L}[SI(kt)] = s^{-1} \arctan (k/s)$.

16. Prove that if $\phi(s)$ is a Laplace transform, then $e^{Ls}\phi(s) \to 0$ as $s \to 0$ for some $L > 0$.

17. Verify that convolution is a commutative and associative operation.

*18. Show that the Laplace transform of e^{-t} is $\sqrt{\pi}\, e^{s^2}$ erfc s.

ADDITIONAL EXERCISES

*1. Prove Theorem 2 directly, using the factorization of a real polynomial into linear and quadratic real polynomials.

2. Plot the function $x^\mu \cos (\nu \log x)$ for $x > 0$, for $\mu = 1$ and $\nu = 2$.

3. For the DE $x^2u'' + Axu' + Bu = 0$, A, B real, find necessary and sufficient conditions that every solution vanish infinitely often on $(-\infty, +\infty)$.

*4. Suppose that $p_L[\lambda] = (\lambda - \lambda_1)^k\phi(\lambda)$, where $\phi(\lambda_1) \neq 0$. Show that the DE $L[u] = e^{\lambda_1 t}q(t)$ has a solution of the form $e^{\lambda_1 t}Q_1(t)$, where the degree of the polynomial $Q_1(t)$ exceeds that of $q(t)$ by k.

5. Consider the system of linear DE's with constant coefficients $L[u] = v$, $M[v] = r(t)$. Show that the resulting DE $M[L[u]] = r(t)$ is stable if and only if both L and M are stable.

6. The system $L[u] = v$, $M[v] = u$ is said to have *feedback*. If L and M have constant coefficients, show that this system is strictly stable if and only if arg $\{p_L(ik)p_M(ik) - 1\}$ decreases by $n\pi$, where n is the sum of the orders of L and M.

7. Let L in (17) be defined for $-\infty < t < \infty$, and let, for fixed τ,

$$L_\tau[u] = \sum_{k=0}^{n} p_{n-k}(t + \tau)u^{(k)}, \quad p_0(t) \equiv 1.$$

Express the Green's function of L_τ in terms of the Green's function for L.

8. If $\Gamma(t)$ is the Green's function of a DE (13) with constant coefficients, show that

$$\Gamma^{(n)}(0) + a_1 = 0, \quad \Gamma^{(n+1)}(0) + a_1\Gamma^{(n)}(0) + a_2 = 0,$$
$$\Gamma^{(n+2)}(0) + a_1\Gamma^{(n+1)}(0) + a_2\Gamma^{(n)}(0) + a_3 = 0, \text{ etc.}$$

*9. (a) For $0 \leqq j \leqq n - 1$, let

$$U_j(t) = \Gamma^{(n-j-1)}(t) + a_1\Gamma^{(n-j-2)}(t) + \cdots + a_{n-j-1}\Gamma(t).$$

Show that $U_j^{(k)}(0) = 0$ for $0 \leqq k \leqq n - 1$, $k \neq j$ and $U_j^{(j)}(0) = 1$. (*Hint:* Use Ex. 8.)

(b) Show that every solution of $L[u] = 0$ is given by the formula

$$u(t) = \sum_{k=0}^{n-1} u^{(k)}(0)U_k(t).$$

*10. Show that the convolution of two bounded integrable functions on $0 \leqq t < \infty$ is a continuous function, even though the functions are discontinuous.

CHAPTER V

Existence and Uniqueness Theorems

1. First-order systems. One of the basic notions of analysis is that of a *system* of n first-order ordinary DE's in normal form:

$$
(1) \qquad \begin{aligned} dx_1/dt &= X_1(x_1,\cdots,x_n;t) \\ &\cdots\cdots\cdots \\ dx_n/dt &= X_n(x_1,\cdots,x_n;t). \end{aligned}
$$

The X_i are given functions of the n real variables $x_1,\cdots,x_n,t$. One wishes to find *solutions* of (1), that is, sets of n functions $x_1(t),\cdots,x_n(t)$, of class $\mathcal{C}^1$, which satisfy (1).

We shall assume the functions X_i to be continuous and real-valued in a given region R of the $(n+1)$-dimensional space† of the independent variables $x_1,x_2,\cdots,x_n,t$. A solution of a normal system (1) can be visualized as a curve in R defined by the functions $x_1(t),\cdots,x_n(t)$; when $n=1$, this specializes to the concept of a solution curve defined in Chapter I. For this reason, the curve in R defined by any solution of (1) is called a *solution curve* of (1).

A function $U(x_1,\cdots,x_n;t)$ defined in R and of class $\mathcal{C}^1$ is called an *integral* of (1) whenever $U(x_1(t),\cdots,x_n(t);t)$ is constant for any solution of (1). This implies that each solution curve lies on exactly one level surface $U(x_1,\cdots,x_n;t)=C$ of the function U. A case of particular importance arises when $U=u(x_1,\ldots,x_n)$ is independent of t. In this case, the level surfaces are cylinders parallel to the t-axis; the function $u\in\mathcal{C}^1$ is thus an integral if and only if every solution curve in R which touches the cylinder $u=C$ lies entirely on it.

EXAMPLE 1. Consider the system

$$dx/dt = tx/(x^2-y^2), \qquad dy/dt = ty/(y^2-x^2).$$

One easily verifies that when $x=x(t)$ and $y=y(t)$ are solutions, the two functions

$$V(x,y,t)=xy \quad \text{and} \quad W(x,y,t)=x^2+y^2-t^2$$

satisfy $dV/dt = x\,dy/dt + y\,dx/dt = 0$ and $dW/dt=0$. Therefore, V and W are integrals of the system. The intersection of two surfaces $V=c_1$ and $W=c_2$ is a solution curve of the system. Thus, every solution curve

†Except in §10, all functions and variables considered in this chapter are *real*.

lies on an intersection of a hyperbolic cylinder $xy = c_1$ and a hyperboloid (or cone) $x^2 + y^2 - t^2 = c_2$.

First-order systems of DE's (1) provide a standard form to which *all* ordinary DE's and systems of DE's can be reduced. Using (1), one can give a unified theory for the existence and uniqueness of solutions of DE's and systems of DE's of all orders, as we shall see in this chapter.

For example, one can reduce the solution of an n-th order DE to the solution of a system of n first-order DE's as follows. Let $u(t)$ be any solution of the given n-th order DE,

$$d^n u/dt^n = F(u, du/dt, d^2u/dt^2, \cdots, d^{n-1}u/dt^{n-1}; t).$$

Then the n functions $x_1(t) = u$, $x_2(t) = du/dt, \cdots, x_n(t) = d^{n-1}u/dt^{n-1}$ satisfy the normal first-order system

$$dx_k/dt = x_{k+1}, \quad k = 1, \cdots, n-1; \quad dx_n/dt = F(x_1, x_2, \cdots, x_n; t).$$

Conversely, given any solution of the preceding first-order system, the first component $x_1(t)$ will have the other components $x_2, \cdots, x_n$ as its derivatives of orders $1, \cdots, n-1$. Hence, substituting back, $x_1(t)$ will satisfy the given n-th order equation.

The simplicity of first-order normal systems becomes apparent when (1) is written in vector notation. A *vector* is an n-tuple $\mathbf{x} = (x_1, \cdots, x_n)$ of real (or complex) numbers. Thus the functions $X_i(x_1, \cdots, x_n; t) = X_i(\mathbf{x}, t)$, in (1) define $\mathbf{X} = (X_1, \cdots, X_n)$ as a *vector-valued* function of the vector variable $\mathbf{x}$ and the real variable t.

In vector notation, the system (1) assumes the very concise form

$$d\mathbf{x}/dt = \mathbf{X}(\mathbf{x}, t). \tag{2}$$

A *solution* of (2) is a vector-valued function $\mathbf{x}(t)$ of a real (scalar) variable t, such that $\mathbf{x}'(t) = \mathbf{X}(\mathbf{x}(t), t)$. The analogy between (2) and the normal first-order DE $y' = F(x,y)$ studied in Chapter I is apparent; the difference is that the dependent variable in (2) is a vector and not a number (or "scalar"). Hence one can call (2) a *normal first-order vector* DE.

2. Lipschitz condition. In order to make use of vector notation for systems of DE's, we recall a few facts about vectors in n-dimensional Euclidean space. Addition of two vectors and multiplication of vectors by scalars are defined component-wise, as in the plane and in space.† The *length* of a vector $\mathbf{x} = (x_1, x_2, \cdots, x_n)$ is defined as

$$|\mathbf{x}| = (x_1^2 + \cdots + x_n^2)^{1/2}.$$

†Birkhoff and Mac Lane, Ch. VII. The three-dimensional case is treated in Courant, Vol. 2, Ch. II; Widder, Ch. III; and in most other texts on the advanced calculus.

Length satisfies the triangle inequality

$$|\mathbf{x}+\mathbf{y}| \leqq |\mathbf{x}|+|\mathbf{y}|.$$

The dot product or *inner product* of two vectors is defined as

$$\mathbf{x}\cdot\mathbf{y} = x_1y_1 + \cdots + x_ny_n,$$

and satisfies the Schwarz inequality $|\mathbf{x}\cdot\mathbf{y}| \leqq |\mathbf{x}|\cdot|\mathbf{y}|$.

We shall integrate, differentiate, and take limits of vector functions $\mathbf{x}(t)$ of a scalar (real) variable t. All these operations can be carried out component by component as in vector addition.

For example, the derivative of a vector function

$$\mathbf{x}(t) = (x_1(t), x_2(t), \cdots, x_n(t))$$

is the vector function $\mathbf{x}'(t) = (x_1'(t), x_2'(t), \cdots, x_n'(t))$. The integral $\int_a^b \mathbf{x}(t)dt$ is the vector with components $\int_a^b x_1(t)dt, \int_a^b x_2(t)dt, \cdots, \int_a^b x_n(t)dt$. We shall often make use of the fundamental inequality†

$$\left|\int_a^b \mathbf{x}(t)dt\right| \leqq \int_a^b |\mathbf{x}(t)|\,dt. \tag{3}$$

A vector function $\mathbf{X}(\mathbf{x})$ of a vector variable is said to be *continuous* when each component X_i of $\mathbf{X}$ is a continuous function of the n variables $x_1, \cdots, x_n$, the components of the vector independent variable $\mathbf{x}$. This is equivalent to the following statement: The function $\mathbf{X}(\mathbf{x})$ is continuous at the point (vector) $\mathbf{c}$ whenever, given $\epsilon > 0$, there exists $\delta > 0$ such that, if $|\mathbf{x}-\mathbf{c}| < \delta$, then $|\mathbf{X}(\mathbf{x}) - \mathbf{X}(\mathbf{c})| < \epsilon$. We leave it as an exercise to verify that these definitions are equivalent.

Note that there is no such thing as "the" derivative of a function $\mathbf{X}(\mathbf{x})$ of a *vector* independent variable, but only *partial* derivatives relative to the different components $x_1, \cdots, x_n$.

The reader who is not accustomed to working with functions of vectors should make sure that he understands the differences between the following types of functions: vector-valued function of a scalar variable (such as $\mathbf{x}(t) = (x_1(t), x_2(t), \cdots, x_n(t))$); scalar-valued function of a vector variable (such as $|\mathbf{x}| = \sqrt{x_1^2 + \cdots + x_n^2}$); vector-valued function of a vector variable such as

$$\mathbf{X}(\mathbf{x}) = (X_1(x_1, x_2, \cdots, x_n),\ X_2(x_1, \cdots, x_n), \cdots,\ X_m(x_1, \cdots, x_n));$$

†This inequality is the continuous analog of the triangle inequality

$$|\mathbf{x}^{(1)} + \mathbf{x}^{(2)} + \cdots + \mathbf{x}^{(n)}| \leqq |\mathbf{x}^{(1)}| + |\mathbf{x}^{(2)}| + \cdots + |\mathbf{x}^{(n)}|.$$

It can be obtained from this inequality by recalling the definition of the integral $\int_a^b \mathbf{x}(t)dt$ as a limit of Riemann sums, using the triangle inequality for each of the Riemann sums, and passing to the limit on both sides.

vector-valued function of a vector variable and a parameter (such as $\mathbf{X}(\mathbf{x}, t)$).

A vector-valued function $\mathbf{X}(\mathbf{x})$ of a vector variable is said to be of class $\mathcal{C}^n$ in a given region, when each of the component functions $X_i(x_1,\cdots,x_n)$ is of class $\mathcal{C}^n$ there.

One can also easily extend the definition of a Lipschitz condition to vector-valued functions; as we shall see, this provides a simple sufficient condition for the uniqueness and existence of solutions for normal systems.

Definition. *A vector-valued function $\mathbf{X}(\mathbf{x}, t)$ satisfies a* Lipschitz condition *in a region $\mathcal{R}$ of $(\mathbf{x}, t)$-space if and only if, for some finite Lipschitz constant L,*

$$(4) \qquad | \mathbf{X}(\mathbf{x}, t) - \mathbf{X}(\mathbf{y}, t) | \leqq L \, | \mathbf{x} - \mathbf{y} |, \quad \text{if} \quad (\mathbf{x}, t) \in \mathcal{R}, \quad (\mathbf{y}, t) \in \mathcal{R}.$$

Note that both terms on the left side of (4) involve the same value of t.

Lemma. *If $\mathbf{X}(\mathbf{x}, t)$ is of class $\mathcal{C}^1$ in a bounded closed ("compact") convex*† *domain D, then it satisfies a Lipschitz condition there.*

Proof. Let M be the maximum of all partial derivatives $| \partial X_i/\partial x_j |$ in the closed domain D. For each component X_i we have, for fixed $\mathbf{x}, \mathbf{y}$, t and for variable s,

$$\frac{d}{ds}[X_i(\mathbf{x} + s\mathbf{y}, t)] = \sum_{k=1}^{n} \frac{\partial X_i}{\partial x_k} (\mathbf{x} + s\mathbf{y}, t) y_k.$$

Hence, by the Mean Value Theorem applied to the function $X_i(\mathbf{x} + s\mathbf{y}, t)$ of the variable s on the interval $0 \leqq s \leqq 1$,

$$X_i(\mathbf{x} + \mathbf{y}, t) - X_i(\mathbf{x}, t) = \sum_{k=1}^{n} \frac{\partial X_i}{\partial x_k} (\mathbf{x} + \sigma\mathbf{y}, t) y_k,$$

for some σ between 0 and 1. Squaring, and applying the Schwarz inequality to the right side, we get

$$| X_i(\mathbf{x} + \mathbf{y}, t) - X_i(\mathbf{x}, t) |^2 \leqq \left(\sum_{k=1}^{n} \left| \frac{\partial X_i}{\partial x_k} \right|^2 \right) \left(\sum_{k=1}^{n} | y_k |^2 \right) \leqq nM^2 \, | \mathbf{y} |^2.$$

Hence, summing over all components i, we obtain

$$| \mathbf{X}(\mathbf{x} + \mathbf{y}, t) - \mathbf{X}(\mathbf{x}, t) |^2 \leqq n^2 M^2 \, | \mathbf{y} |^2.$$

Taking square roots, the Lipschitz condition follows with Lipschitz constant $L = Mn$, q.e.d.

3. Well-set problems. For DE's to be useful in predicting the future behavior of a physical system from its present state, their solutions must exist, be unique, and depend continuously on their initial values. As

†A domain D in n-space is *convex* when the segment joining any two points of the domain D lies entirely within D.

stated in Ch. I, § 9, an initial value problem is said to be *well-set* when these conditions are satisfied. We now show that, if X satisfies a Lipschitz condition, then the vector DE (2) defines a well-set initial value problem.

We begin by proving uniqueness. As in the special case $n = 1$ of Ch. I, § 10, uniqueness does not follow from the continuity of $X(x, t)$ alone.

THEOREM 1 (Uniqueness Theorem). *If the function $X(x, t)$ satisfies a Lipschitz condition* (4) *in a domain* $\mathcal{R}$, *then there is at most one solution $x(t)$ of the vector DE* (2) *which satisfies a given initial condition $x(a) = c$ in* $\mathcal{R}$.

The proof of this theorem parallels that of Theorem 5 of Chapter I. We show that, if $x(t)$ and $y(t)$ are both solutions of (2), and if they are equal for one value of t, say $t = a$, then $x(t) \equiv y(t)$ in any domain in which a Lipschitz condition is satisfied.

Consider the square of the n-dimensional distance between the two vectors $x(t)$ and $y(t)$. By definition, this is

$$\sigma(t) = \sum [x_k(t) - y_k(t)]^2 = | x(t) - y(t) |^2 \geqq 0.$$

Differentiating $\sigma(t)$ we get, using the fact that x and y are solutions of the normal system (2),

$$\begin{aligned}\sigma'(t) &= 2\sum [x_k(t) - y_k(t)][X_k(x(t), t) - X_k(y(t), t)] \\ &= 2(x(t) - y(t)) \cdot [X(x(t), t) - X(y(t), t)].\end{aligned}$$

By the Schwarz inequality, therefore,

$$\begin{aligned}\sigma'(t) \leqq | \sigma'(t) | &= 2 | (x - y) \cdot (X(x, t) - X(y, t) | \\ &\leqq 2 | x - y | \cdot | X(x, t) - X(y, t) | \leqq 2L | x - y |^2 = 2L\sigma(t).\end{aligned}$$

By the Corollary of Lemma 2 of Ch. I, § 10, it follows that if $x(a) = y(a)$, that is, if $\sigma(0) = 0$, then $\sigma(t) \equiv 0$—that is, $| x(t) - y(t) |^2 \equiv 0$—for all $t \geqq a$.

A similar argument works for $t < a$: replacing t by $-t$, we get

$$d\sigma/d(-t) \leqq | \sigma'(t) | \leqq 2L\sigma(t),$$

using again the preceding inequality.

We shall prove next that the solutions of a normal first-order system (2) depend continuously on their initial values.

THEOREM 2 (Continuity Theorem). *Let $x(t)$ and $y(t)$ be any two solutions of the vector DE* (2), *where $X(x, t)$ is continuous and satisfies the Lipschitz condition* (4). *Then*

$$(5) \qquad | x(a + h) - y(a + h) | \leqq e^{L|h|} | x(a) - y(a) |.$$

Proof. Replacing $a + t$ by $a - t$, we can always reduce to the case $h \geqq 0$. Consider again $\sigma(t) = | x(t) - y(t) |^2$. As in the proof of Theorem 1,

$$\sigma'(t) = 2[x(t) - y(t)] \cdot [X(x(t) - X(y(t)] \leqq 2L | x - y |^2 = 2L\sigma(t).$$

Applying Lemma 2 of Ch. I, § 10 to $\sigma(t)$, we obtain $\sigma(a+h) \leqq \sigma(a)e^{2Lh}$. Taking the square root of both sides, we get the desired result.

From Theorem 2 we can easily infer the following important property of the solutions of the DE (2).

COROLLARY. *Let $\mathbf{x}(t,\mathbf{c})$ be the solution of the DE* (2) *satisfying the initial condition $\mathbf{x}(a,\mathbf{c}) = \mathbf{c}$. Let the hypotheses of Theorem* 2 *be satisfied, and let the functions $\mathbf{x}(t,\mathbf{c})$ be defined for $|\mathbf{c} - \mathbf{c}^0| \leqq K$ and $|t - a| \leqq T$. Then:*

(*a*) *$\mathbf{x}(t,\mathbf{c})$ is a continuous function of both variables;*
(*b*) *if $\mathbf{c} \to \mathbf{c}^0$, then $\mathbf{x}(t,\mathbf{c}) \to \mathbf{x}(t,\mathbf{c}^0)$* uniformly *for $|t - a| \leqq T$.*

Both properties follow immediately from the inequality (5).

In view of the preceding results, it remains only to prove an *existence* theorem, in order to show that the initial value problem is well-set for normal first-order systems (1). This will be done in Theorems 6–8 below.

EXERCISES A

1. Show that $u = x + y + z$ and $v = x^2 + y^2 + z^2$ are integrals of the linear system $dx/dt = y - z$, $dy/dt = z - x$, $dz/dt = x - y$. Interpret geometrically.

2. Reduce each of the following DE's to an equivalent first-order system, and determine in which domain or domains (e.g., entire plane, any bounded region, a half-plane, etc.) the resulting system satisfies a Lipschitz condition:

(a) $d^3x/dt^3 + x^2 = 1$, (b) $d^2x/dt^2 = x^{-1/2}$,
(c) $d^3x/dt^3 = (1 + (d^2x/dt^2)^2)^{1/2}$.

3. Reduce the following system to normal form, and determine in which domains a Lipschitz condition is satisfied:

$$du/dt + dv/dt = u^2 + v^2, \qquad 2du/dt + 3dv/dt = 2uv.$$

4. Show that the vector-valued function $(t + be^{at}, -e^{-at}/ab)$ satisfies the DE (2) with $\mathbf{X} = (1 - (1/x_2), 1/(x_1 - t))$, for any nonzero constants a, b.

5. State and prove a uniqueness theorem for the DE $y'' = F(x,y,y')$, with $F \in \mathcal{C}^1$. (*Hint:* Reduce to a first-order system, and use Theorem 1.)

6. (a) Show that any solution of the linear system $dx/dt = y$, $dy/dt = z$, $dz/dt = x$ satisfies the vector DE $d^3\mathbf{x}/dt^3 = \mathbf{x}$, where $\mathbf{x} = (x,y,z)$.

(b) Show that every solution of the preceding system can be written $\mathbf{x} = e^t\boldsymbol{a} + e^{-t/2}[\boldsymbol{b} \cos \sqrt{3}t/2 + \boldsymbol{c} \sin \sqrt{3}t/2]$, for suitable constant vectors $\boldsymbol{a}$, $\boldsymbol{b}$ and $\boldsymbol{c}$.

(c) Express $\boldsymbol{a}$, $\boldsymbol{b}$ and $\boldsymbol{c}$ in terms of $\mathbf{x}(0)$, $\mathbf{x}'(0)$ and $\mathbf{x}''(0)$.

7. Show that the general solution of the system $dx/dt = x^2/y$, $dy/dt = x/2$, is $x = 1/(at + b)^2$, $y = -1/[2a(at + b)]$.

8. Show that the curves defined parametrically as solutions $dx/dt = \partial F/\partial x$, $dy/dt = \partial F/\partial y$, $dz/dt = \partial F/\partial z$, are orthogonal to the surfaces $F(x,y,z) =$ constant. What differentiability condition on F must be assumed to make the above system satisfy a Lipschitz condition?

9. (a) Find a system of first-order DE's satisfied by all curves orthogonal to the spheres $x^2 + y^2 + z^2 = 2ax - a^2$.

(b) By integrating the preceding system, find the orthogonal trajectories in question. Describe the solution curves geometrically.

10. (a) In what sense is the following statement inexact? "The general solution of the DE $cy'' = (1 + y'^2)^{3/2}$ is the circle $(x - a)^2 + (y - b)^2 = c^2$, where a and b are arbitrary constants."

(b) Correct the preceding statement, distinguishing carefully between explicit, implicit, and multiple-valued functions.

11. (a) Given $\dot{x} = a(t)x + b(t)y$ and $\dot{y} = c(t)x + d(t)y$, prove that

$$\ddot{x} - [(a + d) + \dot{b}/b)]\dot{x} + [(ad - bc) - \dot{a} + (a\dot{b}/b)]x = 0.$$

(b) Given that $\ddot{x} + p(t)\dot{x} + q(t)x = r(t)$, prove that $v = \dot{x}$ satisfies

$$\ddot{v} + [p - (\dot{q}/q)]\dot{v} + [\dot{p} + q - (\dot{q}p/q)]v = \dot{r} - r\dot{q}/q.$$

12. For which values of α, β does the function $x^\alpha y^\beta$ satisfy a Lipschitz condition: (a) in the open square $0 < x,y < 1$, (b) in the quadrant $0 < x,y < +\infty$, (c) in the part of the domain (b) exterior to the square (a)?

13. For each of the following scalar-valued functions of a vector $\boldsymbol{x}$ and each of the following domains, state whether a Lipschitz condition is satisfied or not: (a) $x_1 + x_2 + \cdots + x_n$; (b) $x_1x_2 \cdots x_n$; (c) $y/(x^2 + y^2)$; (d) $|\boldsymbol{x}|$; in (i) $|\boldsymbol{x}| < 1$; (ii) $-\infty < x_k < \infty$; (iii) $-\infty < x_1 < \infty$, $|x_k| < 1$, $k \geqq 2$.

14. Let $\boldsymbol{X}(\boldsymbol{x}, t) = (X_1(\boldsymbol{x}, t), \cdots, X_n(\boldsymbol{x}, t))$ be a vector-valued function. Show that $\boldsymbol{X}$ satisfies a Lipschitz condition if and only if each scalar-valued component X_i satisfies a Lipschitz condition, and relate the Lipschitz constant of $\boldsymbol{X}$ to those of the X_i.

4. Continuity. We shall now prove a much stronger continuity property of the solutions of systems of DE's, namely that the solutions of (2) vary continuously when the function $\boldsymbol{X}$ varies continuously. Loosely speaking, the solution of a DE depends continuously upon the DE, for given initial values.

THEOREM 3. *Let $\boldsymbol{x}(t)$ and $\boldsymbol{y}(t)$ satisfy the DE's*

$$d\boldsymbol{x}/dt = \boldsymbol{X}(\boldsymbol{x}, t) \quad \text{and} \quad d\boldsymbol{y}/dt = \boldsymbol{Y}(\boldsymbol{y}, t),$$

respectively, on $a \leqq t \leqq b$. Further, let the functions $\boldsymbol{X}$ and $\boldsymbol{Y}$ be defined and continuous in a common domain D, and let

$$(6) \qquad |\boldsymbol{X}(\boldsymbol{z}, t) - \boldsymbol{Y}(\boldsymbol{z}, t)| \leqq \epsilon, \quad a \leqq t \leqq b, \quad \boldsymbol{z} \in D.$$

Finally, let $\boldsymbol{X}(\boldsymbol{x},t)$ satisfy the Lipschitz condition (4). *Then*

$$(7) \qquad |\boldsymbol{x}(t) - \boldsymbol{y}(t)| \leqq |\boldsymbol{x}(a) - \boldsymbol{y}(a)|\, e^{L|t-a|} + \frac{\epsilon}{L}\,[e^{L|t-a|} - 1].$$

The function $\boldsymbol{Y}$ is not required to satisfy a Lipschitz condition.

Proof. Consider the real-valued function $\sigma(t)$, defined for $a \leqq t \leqq b$ by

$$\sigma(t) = |\, \mathbf{x}(t) - \mathbf{y}(t) \,|^2 = \sum_{k=1}^{n} [x_k(t) - y_k(t)]^2.$$

From the last expression we see that σ is differentiable. Its derivative can be written in the form

$$\begin{aligned} \sigma'(t) &= 2[\mathbf{X}(\mathbf{x}(t), t) - \mathbf{Y}(\mathbf{y}(t), t)] \cdot [\mathbf{x}(t) - \mathbf{y}(t)] \\ &= 2\{[\mathbf{X}(\mathbf{x}(t), t) - \mathbf{X}(\mathbf{y}(t), t)] \cdot [\mathbf{x}(t) - \mathbf{y}(t)]\} \\ &\quad + 2\{[\mathbf{X}(\mathbf{y}(t), t) - \mathbf{Y}(\mathbf{y}(t), t)] \cdot [\mathbf{x}(t) - \mathbf{y}(t)]\}. \end{aligned}$$

We now apply the triangle inequality to the right side, and then the Schwarz inequality to each of the two terms of the last expression. This gives the inequality

$$\begin{aligned} |\, \sigma'(t) \,| &\leqq 2\, |\, \mathbf{X}(\mathbf{x}(t), t) - \mathbf{X}(\mathbf{y}(t), t) \,|\, |\, \mathbf{x}(t) - \mathbf{y}(t) \,| \\ &\quad + 2\, |\, \mathbf{X}(\mathbf{y}(t), t) - \mathbf{Y}(\mathbf{y}(t), t) \,|\, |\, \mathbf{x}(t) - \mathbf{y}(t) \,|. \end{aligned}$$

To the first term on the right side we now apply the Lipschitz condition which $\mathbf{X}$ satisfies; to the second term, we apply (6). This gives the following differential inequality for σ:

$$\sigma'(t) \leqq 2L\sigma(t) + 2\epsilon\sqrt{\sigma(t)}. \tag{8}$$

The theorem is now an immediate consequence of the following

LEMMA. *Let $\sigma(t) \geqq 0$, $a \leqq t \leqq b$ be a differentiable function satisfying the differential inequality* (8). *Then*

$$\sigma(t) \leqq [\sqrt{\sigma(a)}e^{L(t-a)} + \frac{\epsilon}{L}(e^{L(t-a)} - 1)]^2, \qquad a \leqq t \leqq b. \tag{9}$$

Proof. We shall apply Theorem 7 of Chapter I on differential inequalities to (8). The right side of (8), the function $F(\sigma,t) = 2L\sigma + 2\epsilon\sqrt{\sigma}$, satisfies a Lipschitz condition in any half-plane $\sigma \geqq \sigma_0$ which does not include the line $\sigma = 0$. Therefore, Theorem 7 of Chapter I applies when $\sigma(a) > 0$. For, if $\sigma(a) > 0$, then the solution of the DE

$$du/dt = 2\epsilon\sqrt{u} + 2Lu, \qquad u \geqq 0, \tag{9'}$$

which satisfies the initial condition $u(a) = \sigma(a)$, will have a nonnegative derivative, and therefore will remain, for $t > a$, within the half-plane $u \geqq \sigma(a)$.

The DE (9′) is a Bernoulli DE (Ch. I, Ex. B2). To find the solution satisfying $u(a) = \sigma(a)$, make the substitution $v(t) = \sqrt{u(t)}$. (The square root is well-defined because $u(t) \geqq \sigma(a) > 0$.) This gives the equivalent DE

$$2vv' = 2\epsilon v + 2Lv^2.$$

If $u(a) > 0$, then $u(t) > 0$ for all later t, since the derivative of u is positive.

This gives $v(t) > 0$, and we can therefore divide both sides of this DE by v. The resulting DE is $v' - Lv = \epsilon$, an inhomogeneous linear DE (Chapter I, § 5, Example 2), whose solution satisfying the initial condition $v(a) = \sqrt{u(a)}$ is the function

$$\sqrt{u(t)} = v(t) = \sqrt{u(a)}e^{L(t-a)} + (\epsilon/L)(e^{L(t-a)} - 1).$$

Upon applying Theorem 7 of Chapter I we obtain the inequality (9).

We must now consider the case $\sigma(a) = 0$, when Theorem 7 of Chapter I does not apply directly. In this case we consider the solution $u_n(t)$ of the differential equation (9′) which satisfies the initial condition $u_n(a) = 1/n$. Since the right side of (9′) is positive, $u_n(t)$ is an increasing function of t. We shall prove that $u_n(t) \geqq \sigma(t)$. Suppose that at some point $t_1 > a$ we had $u_n(t_1) < \sigma(t_1)$. Then among all numbers t such that $u_n(t) \geqq \sigma(t)$ there will be a largest, say t_0. Hence $u_n(t_0) = \sigma(t_0) > 0$ and $u_n(t) < \sigma(t)$ for $t_0 < t \leqq t_1$. But this is impossible, by what we have already proved, since in the interval $t_0 \leqq t \leqq t_1$ the functions $u(t)$ and $\sigma(t)$ stay away from 0, and therefore a Lipschitz condition is satisfied for (9′). We infer that

$$\sigma(t) \leqq [n^{-1/2}e^{L|t-a|} + (\epsilon/L)(e^{L|t-a|} - 1)]^2$$

for all $n \geqq 0$. Letting $n \to \infty$, we obtain the inequality (9) also in this case.

The following corollary follows immediately from Theorem 3:

COROLLARY. *Let $\mathbf{X}(\mathbf{x},t;\epsilon)$ be a set of continuous functions of $\mathbf{x}$ and t, defined for $|t - a| \leqq T$, $|\mathbf{x} - \mathbf{c}| \leqq K$ and depending on a parameter ϵ. Suppose that, as $\epsilon \to 0$, the functions converge uniformly in the domain to a function $\mathbf{X}(\mathbf{x}, t)$, and that the limit function $\mathbf{X}$ satisfies a Lipschitz condition. Let $\mathbf{x}(t;\epsilon)$ be a solution of $d\mathbf{x}/dt = \mathbf{X}(\mathbf{x}, t; \epsilon)$ satisfying the initial condition $\mathbf{x}(a;\epsilon) = \mathbf{c}$. Then $\mathbf{x}(t;\epsilon)$ converges to the solution of $d\mathbf{x}/dt = \mathbf{X}(\mathbf{x}, t)$ satisfying $\mathbf{x}(a) = \mathbf{c}$, uniformly in any closed subinterval $|t - a| \leqq T_1 \leqq T$ where all functions are defined.*†

EXERCISES B

1. Let $\mathbf{X}$ and $\mathbf{Y}$ be as in Theorem 3, and let $\mathbf{x}(a) = \mathbf{y}(a)$. Show that

$$|\mathbf{x}(t) - \mathbf{y}(t)| / |t - a|$$

remains bounded as $t \to a$.

2. Let $f(x)$ and $g(x)$ be respective solutions of $y' = \sin(xy)$ and $y' = xy$ such that $f(0) = g(0)$. Show that $|f(x) - g(x)| < 1/640$ for $|x| < 1/2$.

†It will follow from Theorem 8 that, if all functions $|\mathbf{X}(\mathbf{x}, t; \epsilon)| \leqq M$, then the $\mathbf{x}(t;\epsilon)$ converge in an interval at least as large as $|t - a| \leqq \min(T, K/M)$.

Obtain an expression for the difference between the solutions of the following pairs of DE's:

3. $y' = \sin xy$ and $y' = xy - \frac{x^3y^3}{3!} + \frac{x^5y^5}{5!} + \cdots + (-1)^n \frac{(xy)^{2n+1}}{(2n+1)!}$.

4. $y' = e^y$ and $y' = 1 + y + \cdots + \frac{y^n}{n!}$.

5. $d^2\theta/dt^2 = -\theta$ and $d^2\theta/dt^2 = -\sin\theta$.

6. To what explicit formulas does formula (7) specialize for the system $d\mathbf{x}/dt = \mathbf{X}(t)$? For the DE $dx/dt = ax + b$?

*7. Show that the conclusion of Theorem 3 holds if only a one-sided Lipschitz condition $(\mathbf{x} - \mathbf{y}) \cdot (\mathbf{X}(\mathbf{x},t) - \mathbf{X}(\mathbf{y},t)) \leqq L \mid \mathbf{x} - \mathbf{y} \mid$ is assumed for $\mathbf{X}$.

8. Let $\mathbf{X}(\mathbf{x},t,s)$ be continuous for $\mid \mathbf{x} - \mathbf{c} \mid \leqq K$, $\mid t - a \mid \leqq T$ and $\mid s - s_0 \mid \leqq S$, and let it satisfy $\mid \mathbf{X}(\mathbf{x},t,s) - \mathbf{X}(\mathbf{y},t,s)) \leqq L \mid \mathbf{x} - \mathbf{y} \mid$. Show that the solution $\mathbf{x}(t,s)$ of $\mathbf{x}' = \mathbf{X}(\mathbf{x},t,s)$ satisfying $\mathbf{x}(a,s) = \mathbf{c}$ is a continuous function of s.

5*. Normal systems. Many important mathematical problems have normal systems of DE's of order $m > 1$ as their natural formulation. We now give two examples, and show how to reduce every normal system of ordinary DE's to a first-order system.

DEFINITION. *A* normal system *of ordinary DE's for the unknown functions* $\xi_1(t), \xi_2(t), \cdots, \xi_m(t)$ *is any system of the form*

$$(10) \qquad \frac{d^{n(k)}\xi_k}{dt^{n(k)}} = F_k\left(\xi_1, \frac{d\xi_1}{dt}, \cdots; \xi_2, \frac{d\xi_2}{dt}, \cdots; \xi_m, \frac{d\xi_m}{dt}, \cdots; t\right),$$

$k = 1, \cdots, m$, *in which for each* k *only derivatives* $d^p\xi_j/dt^p$ *of any* ξ_j *of orders* $p < n(j)$ *occur on the right side.*

In other words, the requirement is that the derivative $d^{n(k)}\xi_k/dt^{n(k)}$ of highest order of each ξ_k constitutes the left side of one equation, and occurs nowhere else.

THEOREM 4. *Each normal system* (10) *of ordinary DE's is equivalent to a first-order normal system* (1) *(with* $n \geqq m$*).*

Proof. Each function F_k appearing on the right side of (10) is a function of several real variables. Denote these variables by $x_1, x_2, \cdots, x_n, t$, where $n = n_1 + \cdots + n_m$. We now construct a system for $x_1, \cdots, x_n$ by replacing each derivative $d^p\xi_j/dt^p$ of ξ_j of order $p < n(j)$ by a new variable, that is, by setting $x_1 = \xi_1$, $x_2 = d\xi_1/dt$, $x_3 = d^2\xi_1/dt^2, \cdots, x_{n_1} = d^{n_1-1}\xi_1/dt^{n_1-1}$, $x_{n_1+1} = \xi_2$, $x_{n_1+2} = d\xi_2/dt, \cdots, x_{n_1+n_2} = d^{n_2-1}\xi_2/dt^{n_2-1}$, etc. The equivalent system for the x_k is then the system

$$dx_1/dt = x_2, \; dx_2/dt = x_3, \; \cdots, \; dx_{n_1-1}/dt = x_n, \; dx_{n_1}/dt = F_1(x_1, \cdots, x_n)$$
$$dx_{n_1+1}/dt = x_{n_1+2}, \; \cdots, \; dx_{n_1+n_2}/dt = F_2(x_1, \cdots, x_n), \text{ etc.}$$

It is clear that this system satisfies the requirements of the theorem.

The *initial value problem* for the normal system (10) is the problem of finding a solution for which the variables

$$\xi_1,\ d\xi_1/dt, \cdots, d^{n_1-1}\xi_1/dt^{n_1-1}, \cdots, d^{n_m-1}\xi_m/dt^{n_m-1}$$

assume given values at $t = a$.

It is easily seen from the proof of Theorem 4 that, if the functions F_k, considered as functions of the vector variable $\mathbf{x} = (x_1, \cdots, x_n)$ and t, satisfy Lipschitz conditions, then so do the functions $X_k(\mathbf{x}, t)$ in the associated first-order systems (1). This gives the

COROLLARY. *If the functions F_k of the normal system* (10) *satisfy Lipschitz conditions in a domain D, then the system has at most one solution in D satisfying given initial conditions.*

EXAMPLE 2. (The n-body problem). Let n mass-points with masses m_j attract each other according to an inverse α-th power law of attraction. Then, in suitable units, their position coordinates satisfy a normal system of $3n$ second-order differential equations of the form

$$d^2x_i/dt^2 = \sum_{j\neq i} m_j(x_j - x_i)/r_{ij}^{\alpha+1},$$

and similarly for d^2y_i/dt^2 and d^2z_i/dt^2, where

$$r_{ij} = [(x_i - x_j)^2 + (y_i - y_j)^2 + (z_i - z_j)^2]^{1/2} = r_{ji}.$$

Then Theorem 1 asserts that the initial positions $(x_i(0), y_i(0), z_i(0))$ and velocities $(x_i'(0), y_i'(0), z_i'(0))$ of the mass-points *uniquely* determine their subsequent motion (if any such motion is possible). That is, the uniqueness theorem asserts the *determinacy of the n-body problem.* This theorem, taken with the continuity theorem, and Theorem 8 to follow, asserts that the n-body problem is well-set.

To see this, let $\boldsymbol{\xi} = (\xi_1, \cdots, \xi_{6n})$ be the vector with components defined as follows, for $k = 1, \cdots, n$.

$$\xi_k = x_k, \quad \xi_{n+k} = y_k, \quad \xi_{2n+k} = z_k,$$
$$\xi_{3n+k} = x_k', \quad \xi_{4n+k} = y_k', \quad \xi_{5n+k} = z_k'.$$

In this notation, the system (10) is equivalent to a first-order normal system of the form (1):

$$\frac{d\xi_h}{dt} = F_h(\boldsymbol{\xi}) = \begin{cases} \xi_{h+3n} & h = 1, \cdots, 3n \\ \sum_j m_j(\xi_{j-3n} - \xi_{h-3n})/r_{hk(j)}^{\alpha+1} & h = 3n+1, \cdots, 6n, \end{cases}$$

where $k(j)$ is the remainder of j when divided by n, and summation is extended to those $n - 1$ values of j such that $(h - 1)/n$ and $(j - 1)/n$ are distinct and have the same integral part. So long as no $r_{hj} = 0$, that is, so long as there are *no collisions*, a Lipschitz condition is evidently satisfied by the functions F_h. When one or more r_{hj} vanishes, however, some of the functions F_h become *singular* (they are undefined), and Theorem 1 is inapplicable.

EXAMPLE 3. The *Frenet-Serret formulas*† comprise the following normal system of first-order DE's:

$$\frac{d\boldsymbol{\alpha}}{ds} = \frac{\boldsymbol{\beta}}{R(s)}, \quad \frac{d\boldsymbol{\beta}}{ds} = -\frac{\boldsymbol{\alpha}}{R(s)} + \frac{\boldsymbol{\gamma}}{T(s)}, \quad \frac{d\boldsymbol{\gamma}}{ds} = -\frac{\boldsymbol{\beta}}{T(s)},$$

where $\boldsymbol{\alpha}, \boldsymbol{\beta}$ and $\boldsymbol{\gamma} = \boldsymbol{\alpha} \times \boldsymbol{\beta}$ are three-dimensional‡ vectors: the unit tangent, normal, and binormal vectors to a space curve. The curvature $\kappa(s) = 1/R(s)$ and torsion $\tau(s) = 1/T(s)$ are functions of the arc-length s; $\boldsymbol{\alpha} = d\boldsymbol{x}/ds$ is the derivative of vector position with respect to arc-length.

If we let $\boldsymbol{\eta}(s)$ be the nine-dimensional vector $(\alpha_1, \alpha_2, \alpha_3, \beta_1, \beta_2, \beta_3, \gamma_1, \gamma_2, \gamma_3)$, then the system can be written as the first-order vector DE

$$d\boldsymbol{\eta}/ds = \boldsymbol{Y}(\boldsymbol{\eta}; s).$$

Here $\boldsymbol{Y}(\boldsymbol{\eta}; s)$ is obtained by setting

$$Y_h(\boldsymbol{\eta}; s) = \begin{cases} \kappa(s)\eta_{h+3} & h = 1, 2, 3, \\ -\kappa(s)\eta_{h-3} - \tau(s)\eta_{h+3} & h = 4, 5, 6, \\ \tau(s)\eta_{h-3} & h = 7, 8, 9. \end{cases}$$

If $\kappa(s)$ and $\tau(s)$ are bounded, the function $\boldsymbol{Y}(\boldsymbol{\eta}; s)$ satisfies a Lipschitz condition (4), with $L = \sup\{|\kappa(s)| + |\tau(s)|\}$; hence for given initial tangent direction $\boldsymbol{\alpha}(0)$, normal direction $\boldsymbol{\beta}(0)$ perpendicular to $\boldsymbol{\alpha}(0)$, and binormal direction $\boldsymbol{\gamma}(0) = \boldsymbol{\alpha}(0) \times \boldsymbol{\beta}(0)$ there is only one set of directions satisfying the Frenet-Serret formulas. This proves that *a curve is determined up to a rigid motion by its curvature and torsion.*††

EXERCISES C

1. Find all solutions of the system

$$x\frac{d^2x}{dt^2} - y\frac{d^2y}{dt^2} = 0, \qquad \frac{d^2x}{dt^2} + \frac{d^2y}{dt^2} + x + y = 0.$$

2. Show that, if $a_{ihk} = -a_{khi}$, then $\Sigma\, x_i^2$ is an integral of the system

$$dx_i/dt = \Sigma\, a_{ihk}x_hx_k.$$

†Widder, p. 101.

‡$\boldsymbol{\alpha} \times \boldsymbol{\beta}$ denotes the cross product of the vectors $\boldsymbol{\alpha}$ and $\boldsymbol{\beta}$.

††This theorem of differential geometry can fail when $\kappa(s)$ is zero, because $\boldsymbol{\beta} = x''(x)/|x''(s)|$ is then geometrically undefined, so that the Frenet-Serret formulas do not necessarily hold.

3. The *one-body* problem is defined in space by the system

$$\ddot{x} = -xf(r), \quad \ddot{y} = -yf(r), \quad \ddot{z} = -zf(r), \quad r^2 = x^2 + y^2 + z^2.$$

(a) Show that the components $L = y\dot{z} - z\dot{y}$, $M = z\dot{x} - x\dot{z}$, and $N = x\dot{y} - y\dot{x}$, of the angular momentum vector (L,M,N) are integrals of this system.

(b) Show that any solution of the system lies in a plane $Ax + By + Cz = 0$.

(c) Construct an energy integral for the system.

4. Let $\alpha = 2$ in the n-body problem (Newton's Law of Gravitation), and define the potential energy as $V = -\sum_{i<j} m_i m_j / r_{ij}$.

(a) Show that the n-body problem is defined by the system

$$m_i d^2 x_i / dt^2 = -\partial V / \partial x_i.$$

(b) Show that the total energy $\Sigma\, m_i \dot{x}_i^2/2 + V(\mathbf{x})$ is an integral of the system.

(c) Show that the components $\Sigma\, m_i \dot{x}_i$, etc., of linear momentum are integrals.

(d) Same question for the components $\Sigma\, m_i(y_i \dot{z}_i - z_i \dot{y}_i)$, etc., of angular momentum.

5. Show that the general solution of the vector DE $d^3\mathbf{x}/dt^3 = d\mathbf{x}/dt$ is $\mathbf{a} + \mathbf{b}e^t + \mathbf{c}e^{-t}$, where $\mathbf{a}$, $\mathbf{b}$, $\mathbf{c}$ are arbitrary vectors.

Exercises 6–9 refer to the Frenet-Serret formulas.

6. Show that if $\boldsymbol{\alpha}(s)$, $\boldsymbol{\beta}(s)$, $\boldsymbol{\gamma}(s)$ are orthogonal vectors of length one when $s = 0$, this is true for all s provided they satisfy the Frenet-Serret formulas.

7. Show that if $1/T(s) \equiv 0$, and $d\mathbf{x}/ds = \boldsymbol{\alpha}$, then the curve $\mathbf{x}(s)$ lies in a plane. (*Hint:* Consider the dot product $\boldsymbol{\gamma} \cdot \mathbf{x}$.)

*8. Show that, if $T = kR$ (k constant), then the curve $\mathbf{x}(s)$ lies on a cylinder.

*9. Show that, if $R/T + (TR')' = 0$, then the curve $\mathbf{x}(s)$ lies on a sphere.

6. Equivalent integral equation. We now establish the *existence* of a solution of a normal first-order system of DE's for arbitrary initial values. To this end, it is convenient to reduce the problem to an equivalent one where integrals take the place of derivatives. One reason why this restatement of the problem makes it easier to treat is that one does not have to deal with differentiable functions directly, but only with continuous functions and their integrals. Every continuous function has an integral, while many continuous functions are not differentiable.

THEOREM 5. *Let $\mathbf{X}(\mathbf{x}; t)$ be a continuous vector function of the variables $\mathbf{x}$ and t. Then any solution $\mathbf{x}(t)$ of the vector integral equation*

$$\mathbf{x}(t) = \mathbf{c} + \int_a^t \mathbf{X}(\mathbf{x}(s), s)\,ds \tag{11}$$

is a solution of the vector DE (2) *which satisfies the initial condition $\mathbf{x}(a) = \mathbf{c}$, and conversely.*

The vector integral equation (11) is a system of integral equations for r unknown scalar functions $x_1(t), \cdots, x_r(t)$, the components of the vector function $\boldsymbol{x}(t)$. That is,

$$x_k(t) = c_k + \int_a^t X_k(x_1(s),x_2(s),\cdots,x_r(s), s)ds, \qquad 1 \leqq k \leqq r.$$

(In §§ 6–7, we will deal with r-dimensional vectors.)

Proof. If $\boldsymbol{x}(t)$ satisfies the integral equation (11), then $\boldsymbol{x}(a) = \boldsymbol{c}$ and, by the Fundamental Theorem of the Calculus, $x_k'(t) = X_k(\boldsymbol{x}(t); t)$ for $k = 1, \cdots, r$, so that $\boldsymbol{x}(t)$ also satisfies the system (2). Conversely, the Fundamental Theorem of the Calculus shows that $x_k(t) = x_k(a) + \int_a^t x'_k(s)ds$ for all continuously differentiable functions $\boldsymbol{x}(t)$. If $\boldsymbol{x}(t)$ satisfies the normal system of DE's (2), then $\boldsymbol{x}(t) = \boldsymbol{x}(a) + \int_a^t \boldsymbol{X}(\boldsymbol{x}(s); s)ds$; if in addition $\boldsymbol{x}(a) = \boldsymbol{c}$, the integral equation (11) is obtained, q.e.d.

Example 4. Consider the DE $dx/dt = e^x$, for the initial condition $x(0) = 0$. Separating variables, we see that this initial value problem has the (unique) solution $1 - e^{-x} = t$, $x = -\ln(1 - t)$. Theorem 5 shows that it is equivalent to the integral equation $x(t) = \int_0^t e^{x(s)}ds$, which therefore has the same (unique) solution. Since the solution is only defined in the interval $-\infty < t < 1$, we see again that only a *local* existence theorem can be proved.

Operator interpretation. The problem of finding a solution to the integral equation (11) can be rephrased in terms of operators on vector functions as follows. We define an operator $\boldsymbol{y} = U[\boldsymbol{x}] = U\boldsymbol{x}$ transforming vector functions $\boldsymbol{x}$ into vector functions $\boldsymbol{y}$ by the identity

$$\boldsymbol{y}(t) = U[\boldsymbol{x}(t)] = \boldsymbol{c} + \int_a^t \boldsymbol{X}(\boldsymbol{x}(s), s)ds. \tag{12}$$

If $\boldsymbol{X}(\boldsymbol{x}, t)$ is defined for all $\boldsymbol{x}$ in the slab $|t - a| \leqq T$ and is continuous, the domain of this operator can be taken to be the family of continuous vector functions defined in the interval $|t - a| \leqq T$; its range consists of all continuously differentiable vector functions defined in this interval, satisfying $\boldsymbol{y}(a) = \boldsymbol{c}$.

However, if $\boldsymbol{X}(\boldsymbol{x}, t)$ is not defined for all $\boldsymbol{x}$, then the domain of the operator U has to be determined with care. This is done in Theorem 8 below.

7. Successive approximation. Picard had the idea of iterating the integral operator U defined by (12), and proving that the successive integral transforms (Picard approximations)

$$\boldsymbol{x},\ U\boldsymbol{x},\ U^2[\boldsymbol{x}] = U[U\boldsymbol{x}],\ U^3[\boldsymbol{x}] = U[U^2[\boldsymbol{x}]],\ \cdots$$

converge to a solution. This idea works under various sets of hypotheses; one such set is the following.

Theorem 6. *Let the vector function* $\boldsymbol{X}(\boldsymbol{x}; t)$ *be continuous and satisfy the Lipschitz condition* (4) *on the interval* $|t - a| \leqq T$, *for all* $\boldsymbol{x}, \boldsymbol{y}$. *Then, for any constant vector* $\mathbf{c}$, *the vector DE* $\mathbf{x}'(t) = \mathbf{X}(\mathbf{x}; t)$ *has a solution defined on the interval* $|t-a| \leqq T$, *which satisfies the initial condition* $\mathbf{x}(a) = \mathbf{c}$.

Proof. As remarked at the end of the preceding section, the operator U is defined by (12) for all functions $\mathbf{x}(t)$ continuous for $|t-a| \leqq T$. In particular, since $U\mathbf{x}$ is again a continuous function on $|t-a| \leqq T$, the function $\mathbf{x}^2 = U^2[x] = U^2\mathbf{x}$ is well-defined. Similarly, the *iterates* $U^3\mathbf{x}$, $U^4\mathbf{x}$, etc., are well-defined. These iterates will always converge; a typical case is depicted in Figure V-1.

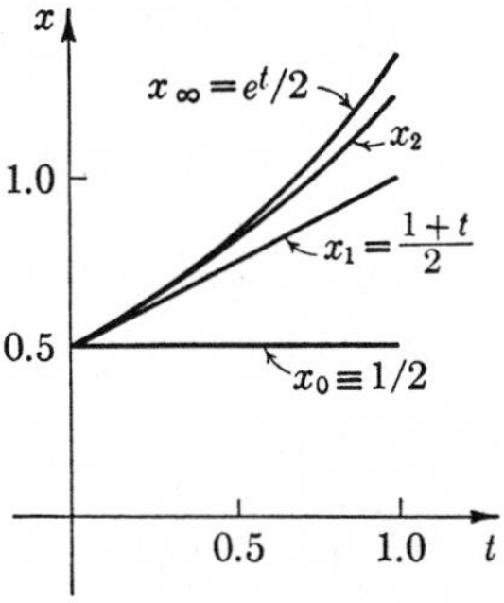

Figure V-1. Picard Approximation for $dx/dt = x$, $x(0) = 1/2$

LEMMA. *If* $\mathbf{x}^0(t) \equiv \mathbf{c}$, *then the sequence of functions defined recursively by* $\mathbf{x}^1 = U[\mathbf{x}^0]$, $\mathbf{x}^2 = U[\mathbf{x}^1] = U^2[\mathbf{x}^0], \cdots$, $\mathbf{x}^n = U[\mathbf{x}^{n-1}] = U^n[\mathbf{x}^0], \cdots$, *converges uniformly for* $|t-a| \leqq T$.

Proof. Let $M = \sup_{|t-a| \leqq T} |\mathbf{X}(\mathbf{c}; t)|$; the number M is finite because continuous functions are bounded on a closed interval. Without loss of generality we can assume that $a = 0$ and $t \geqq a$, that is, that the interval is $0 \leqq t \leqq T$; the proof for general a and for $t < a$ can be deduced from this case by the substitutions $t \to t + a$ and $t \to a - t$.

By the basic inequality (3) for vector-valued functions, the function $\mathbf{x}^1(t)$ satisfies the inequality

$$(13) \quad |\mathbf{x}^1(t) - \mathbf{x}^0(t)| = \left|\int_0^t \mathbf{X}(\mathbf{x}^0(s), s)ds\right| \leqq \int_0^t |\mathbf{X}(\mathbf{x}^0, s)|\, ds$$

$$\leqq M \int_0^t ds = Mt.$$

By (3), again, the function $\mathbf{x}^2 = U[\mathbf{x}^1]$ satisfies the inequality

$$|\mathbf{x}^2(t) - \mathbf{x}^1(t)| = \left|\int_0^t [\mathbf{X}(\mathbf{x}^1(s), s) - \mathbf{X}(\mathbf{x}^0(s), s)]ds\right|$$

$$\leqq \int_0^t |\mathbf{X}(\mathbf{x}^1(s), s) - \mathbf{X}(\mathbf{x}^0(s), s)|\, ds.$$

We now use the assumption that the function X satisfies a Lipschitz condition with Lipschitz constant L. This gives, by (13), the inequality

$$\begin{aligned} | x^2(t) - x^1(t) | &\leqq \int_0^t | X(x^1(s), s) - X(x^0(s), s) | \, ds \\ &\leqq \int_0^t L \, | x^1(s) - x^0(s) | \, ds \leqq L \int_0^t Ms \, ds = LMt^2/2. \end{aligned}$$

Similarly, for any $n = 1, 2, 3, \cdots$,

$$\begin{aligned} | x^{n+1}(t) - x^n(t) | &\leqq \int_0^t | X(x^n(s), s) - X(x^{n-1}(s), s) | \, ds \\ &\leqq L \int_0^t | x^n(s) - x^{n-1}(s) | \, ds. \end{aligned}$$

We now proceed by induction. Assuming that

$$| x^n(t) - x^{n-1}(t) | \leqq (M/L)(Lt)^n/n!$$

we infer that

$$(14) \quad | x^{n+1}(t) - x^n(t) | \leqq L\left(\frac{M}{L}\right) \int_0^t \frac{(Ls)^n}{n!} \, ds = \frac{M}{L}(Lt)^{n+1}/(n+1)!$$

Next, we show that the sequence of functions $x^n(t)$ $(n = 0, 1, 2, \cdots)$ is uniformly convergent for $0 \leqq t \leqq T$. Indeed, the infinite series

$$(M/L)\sum_{n=0}^{\infty}(Lt)^{n+1}/(n+1)!$$

of positive terms is convergent to $(M/L)(e^{LT} - 1)$, and uniformly convergent for $0 \leqq t \leqq T$. Hence, by the Comparison Test,† the series $\sum_{k=0}^{\infty} [x^{k+1}(t) - x^k(t)]$ is uniformly convergent for $0 \leqq t \leqq T$. The n-th partial sum of this series is the function $x^n(t)$. It follows that the sequence of functions $x^n(t)$ is uniformly convergent. This completes the proof of the lemma.

To complete the proof of Theorem 6, let $x^\infty(t)$ denote the limit function of the sequence $x^n(t)$; it suffices by Theorem 5 to show that $x^\infty(t)$ is a solution of the integral equation (11). To this end, we consider the limit of the equations $x^{n+1} = U[x^n]$, namely the equations

$$x^{n+1}(t) = c + \int_0^t X(x^n(s), s) ds.$$

The left side converges uniformly, by the preceding lemma. By the Lipschitz condition, $| X(x^m(s), s) - X(x^n(s), s) | \leqq L \, | x^m(s) - x^n(s) |$, and so the integrand on the right side also converges uniformly. Since the inte-

†Courant, Vol. 1, p. 392; see also Widder, p. 285.

grands on the right side form a uniformly convergent sequence, their indefinite integrals are also uniformly convergent;† hence, passing to the limit, we have

$$x^\infty(t) = c + \int_0^t X(x^\infty(s), s)ds.$$

This demonstrates (11) and completes the proof of Theorem 6.

EXERCISES D

Solve the following integral equations:

1. $u(t) = 1 + \int_0^t su(s)ds.$
2. $u(t) = 1 + \int_0^t su^2(s)ds.$
3. $u(t) + e^t = \int_0^t su(s)ds.$
4. $u(t) = 1 - \int_0^t u(s) \tan s\, ds.$
5. $u(t) = \int_0^t [u(s) + v(s)]ds, \quad v(t) = 1 - \int_0^t u(s)ds.$

6. Show that the n-th iterate for the solution of $y' = yx$ such that $y(0) = 1$ is the sum of the first $n + 1$ terms of the power series expansion of $e^{x^2/2}$.

For the following initial value problems, obtain an expression for the n-th function of the sequence of Picard approximations $x^n = U^n[x^0]$ to the exact solutions:

7. $dx/dt = x, \quad x(0) = 1.$
8. $dx/dt = y, \quad dy/dt = -4x.$ $\quad x(0) = 0, \quad y(0) = 1.$
9. $dx/dt = tx, \quad x(0) = 1.$
10. $dx/dt = ty, \quad dy/dt = -tx.$ $\quad x(0) = 0, \quad y(0) = 1.$

For the following initial value problems, compute the functions x^1, x^2, x^3 of the sequence of Picard approximations:

11. $dx/dt = x^2 + t^2, \quad x(0) = 0.$
12. $dx/dt = y^2 + t^2, \quad dy/dt = x^2 + t^2, \quad x(0) = y(0) = 0.$
13. $dx/dt = x(1 - 2t), \quad x(0) = 1.$

*14. Show that, in Ex. 13, the sequence of Picard approximations converges for all t, but that this is not so in Ex. 11. In Ex. 13, is the convergence uniform?

15. Let $X(x,t) = Ax$, where A is a constant matrix. Show that each component of the n-th Picard approximation to any solution is a polynomial function of degree at most n.

16. Establish the following inequalities for the sequence of Picard approximations:

$$| x^n(t) - x^{n-1}(t) | \leqq \frac{M}{L}\left(\frac{(L\,|\,t-a\,|)^n}{n!}\right)$$

$$| x^n(t) - x^\infty(t) | \leqq \frac{M}{L} \sum_{k=n+1}^{\infty} \frac{(L\,|\,t-a\,|)^k}{k!}.$$

8. Linear systems. A first-order system of DE's (1) is said to be *linear* when it is of the form

$$(15) \qquad dx_i/dt = \sum_{j=1}^{n} a_{ij}(t)x_j(t) + b_i(t), \qquad 1 \leqq i \leqq n.$$

†Courant, Vol. 1, p. 395; Widder, p. 304.

In this case, $X_i(\mathbf{x}, t) = \sum_{j=1}^{n} a_{ij}(t)x_j + b_i(t)$. In vector notation, the linear system (15) is written in the form

$$(16) \qquad d\mathbf{x}/dt = A(t)\mathbf{x} + \mathbf{b}(t),$$

where $A(t)\mathbf{x}$ stands† for the matrix $\| a_{ij}(t) \|$ applied to the vector $\mathbf{x}$, and $\mathbf{b}$ stands for the vector $(b_1, \cdots, b_n)$.

When $\mathbf{b}(t) \equiv 0$, the system (16) is said to be *homogeneous.* Otherwise, it is called *inhomogeneous.* The homogeneous system obtained from a given inhomogeneous system (15) by setting the b_j equal to zero is called the *reduced* system associated with (15).

A basic property of a linear system of DE's (16) is that the difference $\mathbf{x} - \mathbf{y}$ of any two solutions of (16) is a solution of the reduced system. It can be immediately verified that any linear combination‡ of solutions of a homogeneous linear system is again a solution.

We shall now establish the existence of solutions of linear systems, and describe the set of all solutions.

LEMMA. *Any linear system* (15) *with continuous coefficient-functions on a closed interval I satisfies a Lipschitz condition* (4), *with*

$$L = \sum_{i,j} \sup_{t \in I} | a_{ij}(t) |.$$

Proof. Since $\mathbf{X}(\mathbf{x},t) - \mathbf{X}(\mathbf{y},t)$ is the vector sum of n^2 vectors $\mathbf{z}_{ij}$, with i-th component $a_{ij}(x_j - y_j)$ and other components zero, repeated use of the triangle inequality gives

$$\begin{aligned} | \mathbf{X}(\mathbf{x}, t) - \mathbf{X}(\mathbf{y}, t) | &\leqq \sum_{i,j} | \mathbf{z}_{ij} | \leqq \sum_{i,j} | a_{ij}(t) | \cdot | x_j - y_j | \\ &\leqq \sum_{i,j} \sup_{t \in I} | a_{ij}(t) | \cdot | \mathbf{x} - \mathbf{y} |. \end{aligned}$$

The functions $a_{ij}(t)$, being continuous on a closed interval, are bounded.†† Hence the Lipschitz constant L can be taken to be the one defined above. This completes the proof of the lemma.

We can now state the existence theorem for homogeneous linear systems.

THEOREM 7. *A linear homogeneous system* (15), *with the* $a_{ij}(t)$ *and* $b_i(t)$ *defined and continuous for* $| t - a | \leqq T$ *has a unique solution on* $| t - a | \leqq T$ *satisfying any given initial condition* $\mathbf{x}(a) = \mathbf{c}$.

†For the definition and elementary properties of matrices, see Birkhoff and Mac Lane, pp. 170 ff. In this chapter no matrix algebra beyond the definition of a matrix is used.

‡If $\mathbf{x}(t) = (x_1(t), \cdots, x_n(t))$ and $\mathbf{y}(t) = (y_1(t), \cdots, y_n(t))$ are vector-valued functions, a *linear combination* with real coefficients a and b is the function $a\mathbf{x}(t) + b\mathbf{y}(t) = (ax_1(t) + by_1(t), \cdots, ax_n(t) + by_n(t))$. Cf. Birkhoff and Mac Lane, pp. 164 ff. For more than two functions the definition is similar.

††Courant, Vol. 1, p. 63.

Proof. The preceding lemma shows that such a system satisfies the hypotheses of Theorem 6. This gives the existence of the solution. The uniqueness follows from Theorem 1, again by the preceding lemma.

For homogeneous systems we can construct a basis of solutions, as follows.

COROLLARY 1. *Let* $\mathbf{x}^i(t)$ *be the solution of a homogeneous linear system* $d\mathbf{x}/dt = A(t)\mathbf{x}$ *which satisfies the initial condition* $x_k{}^i(a) = 0, i \neq k, x_i{}^i(a) = 1$. *Then the solution* $\mathbf{x}(t)$ *satisfying the initial condition* $\mathbf{x}(a) = \mathbf{c} = (c_1, c_2, \cdots, c_n)$ *is equal to the linear combination* $\mathbf{x}(t) = c_1\mathbf{x}^1(t) + c_2\mathbf{x}^2(t) + \cdots + c_n\mathbf{x}^n(t)$.

Proof. The vector-valued function $\mathbf{y}(t) = \mathbf{x}(t) - \sum_{j=1}^{n} c_j\mathbf{x}^j(t)$ is a solution of the linear system, since it is a linear combination of solutions. This function satisfies the initial condition $\mathbf{y}(a) = (0,0,\cdots,0)$, because of the way in which the initial conditions for the solutions $\mathbf{x}^i$ have been chosen. Since the identically zero function is also a solution of the linear system, it follows from the uniqueness in Theorem 7 that $\mathbf{y}(t) \equiv 0$, q.e.d.†

The reduction of an n-th order normal DE to a first-order system sketched in § 1, when applied to a linear n-th order DE in normal form

$$d^n u/dt^n = p_1(t)d^{n-1}u/dt^{n-1} + p_2(t)d^{n-2}u/dt^{n-2} + \cdots + p_{n-1}(t)du/dt + p_n(t)u, \tag{17}$$

transforms this DE into a homogeneous linear system $d\mathbf{x}/dt = A(t)\mathbf{x}$, where the matrix $\| a_{ij}(t) \| = A(t)$ is defined as follows: $a_{ij}(t) = 0$ if $1 \leqq i \leqq n-1$ and $j \neq i+1$; $a_{i,i+1}(t) = 1$ if $1 \leqq i \leqq n-1$; $a_{nj}(t) = p_{n-j}(t)$.

We therefore obtain

COROLLARY 2. *An* n*-th order DE* (17) *in normal form, with coefficients* $p_j(t)$ *continuous for* $|t-a| \leqq T$, *has a basis of solutions* $u_j(t)$ $(1 \leqq j \leqq n)$ *satisfying the initial‡ conditions* $u_j{}^{(i)}(0) = \delta_j{}^{i+1}$, $0 \leqq i \leqq n-1$.

9. Local existence theorem. In Theorem 6, it was assumed that $\mathbf{X}(\mathbf{x}, t)$ was defined for all $\mathbf{x}$ and that a Lipschitz condition held for all $\mathbf{x}, \mathbf{y}$. But this is often not the case. For instance, this assumption does not hold for the DE $dx/dt = e^x$ of Example 4. The ratio

$$| X(x,t) - X(0,t) | / | x - 0 | = (e^x - 1)/x$$

is unbounded if the domain of e^x is unrestricted††.

†In algebraic terms, Corollary 1 states that the solutions of a homogeneous linear system of dimension n form an n-dimensional vector space. Therefore, any $n+1$ solutions of such a system are always linearly dependent.

‡$\delta_j{}^i$ is the Kronecker delta function: $\delta_j{}^i = 0$ if $i \neq j$ and $\delta_i{}^i = 1$. For the concept of a basis of solutions of (17), see Ch. IV, § 4.

††The same complications arise with the DE $y' = 1 + y^2$, as has already been shown in Ch. III, § 9.

Correspondingly, the conclusion of Theorem 6 fails for this DE: the solution which takes the value c at $t = 0$ is the function $x(t) = -\ln(e^{-c} - t)$, and this function is only defined in the interval $-\infty < t < e^{-c}$. Hence there is *no* $\epsilon > 0$ such that the DE $dx/dt = e^x$ has a solution defined on all of $|t| < \epsilon$, for every initial value: the interval of definition of a solution changes with the initial value.

To take care of this situation, and also of cases when the function $\mathbf{X}$ is defined only in a small region of $(x_1, \cdots, x_n)$-space, we now prove a *local* existence theorem, whose assumptions and conclusions refer only to neighborhoods of a given point.

THEOREM 8. *Suppose that the function* $\mathbf{X}(\mathbf{x}, t)$ *in* (2) *is defined and continuous in the closed domain* $|\mathbf{x} - \mathbf{c}| \leqq K$, $|t - a| \leqq T$, *and satisfies a Lipschitz condition* (4) *there. Let* $M = \sup |\mathbf{X}(\mathbf{x}, t)|$ *in this domain. Then the DE* (2) *has a unique solution satisfying* $\mathbf{x}(a) = \mathbf{c}$, *and defined on the smaller interval* $|t - a| \leqq \min(T, K/M)$.

Proof. All steps in the proof of Theorem 6 can be carried out, provided one knows that the functions $\mathbf{x}^n(t)$ referred to there take their values within the domain in which $\mathbf{X}(\mathbf{x}, t)$ is defined. The proof is therefore a corollary of the following

LEMMA. *Under the hypotheses of Theorem* 8, *the operator* U *defined by* (12) *carries functions* $\mathbf{x}(t)$ *satisfying the conditions* (*i*) $\mathbf{x}(t)$ *is defined and continuous on* $|t - a| \leqq \min(T, K/M)$, (*ii*) $\mathbf{x}(a) = \mathbf{c}$, (*iii*) $|\mathbf{x}(t) - \mathbf{c}| \leqq K$ *on the interval* $|t - a| \leqq \min(T, K/M)$, *into functions satisfying the same conditions.*

Proof. In (12), suppose that $\mathbf{x}(s)$ satisfies conditions (i), (ii), (iii). We must show that $\mathbf{y}(t)$ satisfies the same conditions. Clearly (i) and (ii) are satisfied by $\mathbf{y}(t)$. By the inequality (3) we have (taking again $t \geqq a$ for simplicity)

$$|\mathbf{y}(t) - \mathbf{c}| = \left| \int_a^t \mathbf{X}(\mathbf{x}(s), s)\,ds \right| \leqq \int_a^t |\mathbf{X}(\mathbf{x}(s), s)|\,ds.$$

If M is the maximum of $\mathbf{X}$, and if $|t - a| \leqq K/M$, this gives

$$|\mathbf{y}(t) - \mathbf{c}| \leqq MK/M = K.$$

Therefore, (iii) is satisfied and $\mathbf{y}(t)$ is defined for $|t - a| \leqq \min(T, K/M)$, completing the proof.

Using the reduction of § 1, taking an n-th order normal DE

$$u^{(n)} = F(u, u', u'', \cdots, u^{(n-1)}, t) \tag{18}$$

into an equivalent first-order normal system (1), we obtain the

COROLLARY. *Let the function $F(x_1,x_2,\cdots,x_n, t)$, be continuous in the cylinder $|t-a| \leqq T$, $|\mathbf{x}-\mathbf{c}| \leqq K$. Let $(x_2^2+x_3^2+\cdots+x_n^2+F^2)^{1/2} \leqq M$, and let F satisfy a Lipschitz condition there. Then, on the interval $|t-a| \leqq \min(T, K/M)$ the DE (18) has one and only one solution which satisfies the initial conditions $u^{(i)}(a) = c_{i+1}$, $0 \leqq i \leqq n-1$.*

10*. Analytic equations. We shall now consider the vector DE (2) under the additional assumption that $\mathbf{X}(\mathbf{x}, t)$ is an analytic function of all variables $x_1,\cdots,x_n, t$. The essential principle to be established is that *all solutions of analytic DE's are analytic functions.*†

The result is true whether the variables are real or complex; we shall first consider the complex case. To emphasize that we are dealing with complex variables, we rewrite the vector DE (2) as

$$(19) \qquad d\mathbf{z}/dt = \mathbf{z}'(t) = \mathbf{Z}(\mathbf{z}, t), \quad t=r+is,$$

where $z_j = x_j + iy_j$ and $Z_j = X_j + iY_j$ are complex-valued functions.

We assume that the $Z_j(z_1,\cdots,z_n, t)$ are analytic functions of the variables $z_1,z_2,\cdots,z_n$ and t in the closed domain C: $|t-a| \leqq T$, $|\mathbf{z}-\mathbf{c}| \leqq K$, with maximum M there. By the lemma of § 2, this implies that a Lipschitz condition holds in C, for some constant L.

Vector notation can be adapted to complex vectors with the following changes. The length (or norm) of a vector $\mathbf{z} = (z_1,z_2,\cdots,z_n)$ with complex components z_k is defined as

$$|\mathbf{z}| = (z_1z_1^* + z_2z_2^* + \cdots + z_nz_n^*)^{1/2}.$$

The Hermitian *inner product* of two complex vectors $\mathbf{z}$ and

$$\mathbf{w} = (w_1,w_2,\cdots,w_n)$$

is defined as

$$\mathbf{z} \cdot \mathbf{w} = (z_1w_1^* + z_2w_2^* + \cdots + z_nw_n^*).$$

note that $\mathbf{z} \cdot \mathbf{w} = (\mathbf{w} \cdot \mathbf{z})^*$.

Now let γ be any path in the complex t-plane, defined parametrically by the equation $t = t(\sigma) = r(\sigma) + is(\sigma)$, where $r,s \in \mathcal{C}^1$ and σ is a *real* parameter. On the path γ, (19) is equivalent to the system of *real* DE's

$$(19') \qquad \begin{aligned} \mathbf{x}'(\sigma) &= \mathbf{X}(\mathbf{x},\mathbf{y}, \sigma)r'(\sigma) - \mathbf{Y}(\mathbf{x},\mathbf{y}, \sigma)s'(\sigma) \\ \mathbf{y}'(\sigma) &= \mathbf{X}(\mathbf{x},\mathbf{y}, \sigma)s'(\sigma) + \mathbf{Y}(\mathbf{x},\mathbf{y}, \sigma)r'(\sigma). \end{aligned}$$

Theorems 1–8 apply to this system, which satisfies a Lipschitz condition.

Using the complex vector notation described above, one can also prove analogs of these theorems directly, for the DE $\mathbf{z}'(\sigma) = \mathbf{Z}(\mathbf{z}, t(\sigma))t'(\sigma)$ equivalent to (19′), and hence to (19), on the path γ.

†This section requires a knowledge of elementary complex function theory such as is found in the books by Hille (Vol. 1) and Ahlfors.

The analog of the operator U of formula (12) is the operator W, defined by the line integral

$$w(t) = W[z(t)] = c + \int_a^t Z(z(\zeta), \zeta)d\zeta. \tag{20}$$

Since each component function Z_j is analytic, the line integral defining the operator W is independent of the path from 0 to t in the complex t-plane, provided this path stays within the domain C where the function Z is defined.† By Morera's theorem the function w is therefore also analytic. Thus, the operator W transforms analytic functions into analytic functions. Moreover, the lemma of § 9 still holds, because the integrals in (20) can be taken along straight line segments in the complex ζ-plane. This gives the

LEMMA. *For $|t-a| \leqq \min(T, K/M)$, the operator W defined by* (20) *takes analytic complex-valued vector functions $z(t)$ with $|z(t) - c| \leqq K$ into analytic vector functions $w(t)$ with $|w(t) - c| \leqq K$.*

By repeated applications of this lemma, it follows that the functions $W^n[w^0] = w^n(t)$ defined by the Picard process of iterated quadrature, in the domain $|t-a| \leqq \min(T, K/M)$ of the complex t-plane, are all analytic.

We now apply the following result‡ from function theory.

Weierstrass Convergence Theorem. If a sequence $\{f_n(t)\}$ of complex analytic functions converges uniformly to $f(t)$ in a domain D, then $f(t)$ is analytic in D.

By this theorem, the sequence of functions $w^n(t)$ converges uniformly for $|t-a| \leqq \min(T, K/M)$ to an *analytic* solution $w^\infty(t)$ of the integral equation

$$z(t) = c + \int_a^t Z(z(\zeta), \zeta)d\zeta = W[z(t)], \tag{21}$$

and hence of the complex DE (19). The proof in § 8 for the real case can be repeated, and leads to

THEOREM 9. *In Theorem* 8, *replace the real variables t, x_j, X_j by complex variables t, z_j, Z_j. Under the same hypotheses, if the $Z_j(z, t)$ are complex analytic functions, the vector DE* (19) *has a unique complex analytic solution $z(t)$ for given initial conditions.*

From this result and the uniqueness theorem, we obtain

†This is true because the disc $|t-a| \leqq T$ where Z is defined is *simply connected.*

‡Ahlfors p. 138. The result contrasts sharply with the case of functions of a real variable. By the Weierstrass Approximation Theorem, every continuous function on a real interval $a \leqq x \leqq b$ is a uniform limit of polynomial (hence analytic) functions.

COROLLARY 1. *Let* $\mathbf{Z}(\mathbf{z}, t)$ *be analytic in any simply-connected domain of the complex t-plane, and let* $\mathbf{z}(t)$ *be any solution of the DE* (19). *Then* $\mathbf{z}(t)$ *is analytic.*†

Real analytic DE's. A *real* function $X(\mathbf{x}, t)$ of real variables $x_1, \cdots, x_n$ and t is said to be analytic at $(\mathbf{c}, a)$ when it can be expanded into a power series with real coefficients in the variables $(x_k - c_k)$ and $(t - a)$, convergent in the cylinder $|\mathbf{x} - \mathbf{c}| < \eta$, $|t - a| < \epsilon$, for sufficiently small positive η and ϵ. When $X(\mathbf{x}, t)$ is analytic, its power series is convergent also in the *complex* cylinder $|\mathbf{z} - \mathbf{c}| < \eta$, $|t - a| < \epsilon$ (t complex), and defines a complex-valued analytic function there.

Now let a normal system of real DE's (1) be given, the $X_j(\mathbf{x}, t)$ being analytic. From Theorem 9, it follows that the resulting complex DE $d\mathbf{x}/dt = \mathbf{X}(\mathbf{x}, t)$ has a unique complex analytic solution for given real initial values. On the other hand, it also has a unique (local) real solution by Theorems 1 and 8. Hence the two solutions must coincide, proving

COROLLARY 2. *If* $\mathbf{X}(\mathbf{x}, t)$ *is an analytic real function of the real variables* $x_1, \cdots, x_n$ *and t, then every solution of* (1) *is analytic.*

EXERCISES E

1. (a) Obtain an equivalent first-order system for $d^2x/dt^2 = t^2x$. Find the n-th term of the Picard sequence of iterates for the initial values $x(0) = 1$, $x'(0) = 0$.

(b) Prove that this initial value problem has a unique solution on $(-\infty, \infty)$.

2. (a) Obtain an equivalent system for the DE $d^2x/dt^2 = x^2 + t^2$ and find the Lipschitz constant for the resulting system in the domain $|t| \leqq A$, $|x| \leqq B$, $|x'| \leqq c$.

(b) State and prove a local existence theorem for solutions of this DE, for the initial conditions $x(a) = b$, $u(a) = c$. Estimate the largest T, U such that a solution is defined on $a - U \leqq t \leqq a + T$.

3. Show that if $F(y)$ is continuous for $|y| \leqq K$, and $|F(y)| \leqq M$, every solution of $y' = F(y)$ can be uniformly approximated arbitrarily closely for $|x| \leqq K/M$ by a solution of a DE $y' = P(y)$, where P is a polynomial.

4. Compute the n-th Picard approximation to the solution of the complex system $dw/dt = iz$, $dz/dt = w$, which satisfies the initial conditions $w(0) = 1$, $z(0) = i$.

5. In the complex t-plane, determine a domain in which the system $dw/dt = tz^2$, $dz/dt = tw^2$ has an analytic solution satisfying given initial conditions $w(0) = w_0$ $z(0) = z_0$.

6. Show that the solution of the complex analytic DE $w'(z) = M\left[\frac{1}{2}\left(1 + \frac{w}{K}\right)\right]^{1/n}$, ($|z| < K$) satisfying the initial condition $w(0) = 0$, is the function

$$w(z) = K\left[\left(1 + \frac{z}{c}\right)^{n/(n-1)} - 1\right], \qquad c = 2^{1/n}Kn/(n-1)M.$$

†An alternative proof can be based directly on (19). If the $z_k(t)$ satisfy (19), they are continuously differentiable. Hence they are analytic (Ahlfors, pp. 38, 101; Hille, Vol. 1, pp. 72, 88).

*7. Using the result of Ex. 6, show that the bound given by Theorem 8 for the domain of existence of a solution is "best possible" for analytic functions of a complex variable.

11. Continuation of solutions.† Even when the function $X(x, t)$ is of class $\mathcal{C}^1$ and is defined for all x and t, Theorem 8 establishes the existence of solutions only in the neighborhood of a given initial value. In other words, it establishes only the *local* existence of solutions. We shall now study how such local solutions can be joined together to give a *global* solution which is defined up to the boundary of the domain of definition of the function X.

THEOREM 10. *Let $X(x, t)$ be defined and of class $\mathcal{C}^1$ in an open region $\mathcal{R}$ of (x, t) space. For any point (c,a) in the region $\mathcal{R}$, the DE (2) has a unique solution $x(t)$ satisfying the initial condition $x(a) = c$ and defined for an interval $a \leqq t < b$ $(b \leqq \infty)$ such that, if $b < \infty$, either $x(t)$ approaches the boundary of the region or $x(t)$ is unbounded as $t \to b$.*

Proof. Consider the set S of all local solutions of the system (2) which satisfy the given initial condition $x(a) = c$. These are defined on intervals of varying lengths of the form $[a,T)$. Given two solutions x and y in this set, defined on intervals I and I' respectively, the function z, defined to be equal to x or to y wherever either is defined, and hence also where both are defined, is also a solution defined on their union $I \cup I'$.

We now construct a single solution x, called the *maximal* solution, defined on the union of *all* the intervals in which some local solution is defined, by letting $x(t)$ be equal to the value of any of the solutions of S defined at the point t. This maximal solution $x(t)$ is a well-defined function of class $\mathcal{C}^1$, by the Uniqueness Theorem. Furthermore, the interval of definition of this solution is the union of all the intervals of definition, and therefore is itself an interval of the form $a \leqq t < b$.

Consider the limiting behavior of $x(t)$, as $t \uparrow b$. By the Bolzano-Weierstrass Theorem,‡ any infinite bounded set of points $(x(t_n),t_n)$ in (x,t)-space must contain a limit point. Hence either $b = +\infty$, or $\lim_{t \uparrow b} | x(t) | = +\infty$, or there exists a limit point (d,b) of a sequence of points $(x(t_n),t_n)$ on the above solution, with $t_n \uparrow b$. In the second case, the maximal solution may be said to "recede to infinity." In the third case, we shall prove that the point (d,b) is on the boundary of the region $\mathcal{R}$, and that $\lim_{t \to b} x(t) = d$.

Suppose that the point (d,b) were in the interior of the region $\mathcal{R}$. We shall see that this is impossible for the maximal solution x. Consider a neighborhood $| x - d | \leqq \epsilon$, $| t - b | \leqq \epsilon$ which is entirely contained within $\mathcal{R}$, and

†In this section we consider only *real* vectors and functions. The results can however be extended to complex-valued and analytic functions, in much the same way as in § 10.

‡Cf. Courant, Vol. 2, pp. 95 ff, where the Bolzano-Weierstrass Theorem in several dimensions is proved.

let M be the maximum of $|X|$ in this neighborhood. Then, for t and s in this neighborhood, the Mean Value Theorem gives $|x(t) - x(s)| \leqq M|t - s|$. Therefore $\lim_{t \to b} x(t) = d$. If (d,b) is interior to the region $\mathcal{R}$, then there exists a solution $y(t)$ of the DE (2) satisfying the initial condition $y(b) = d$, defined in some interval $b - \delta \leqq t \leqq b + \delta$ containing the point b. By the Uniqueness Theorem, y coincides with x for $b - \delta \leqq t \leqq b$ and therefore $x(t)$ could be prolonged beyond b, contradicting the assumption that $x(t)$ is a maximal solution.†

The maximum length $b - a$ of definition of the solution x is called the *escape time* of the solution for $t > a$. There is a similar notion of the escape time for $t < a$.

A solution with a *finite* escape time is one for which $|x(t)|$ becomes unbounded as $t \to b < \infty$; on the other hand, a solution with an infinite escape time is one which remains within the domain of definition of X as $t \to \infty$. For example, every solution of the DE $dx/dt = x$ has infinite escape time, whereas every nonzero solution of the DE $dx/dt = x^2$, namely every function $x = 1/(c - t)$, has finite escape time.

12*. Perturbation equation. Theorem 2 shows that the solutions of a first-order system in normal form depend continuously on their initial values. We shall now strengthen this result as follows.

THEOREM 11. *Let the vector function X be of class $\mathcal{C}^1$, and let $x(t,c)$ be the solution of the normal system (2), taking the initial value c at $t = a$. Then $x(t,c)$ is a differentiable function of the components c_j of c.*

Proof. Change one component c_j of c by the amount Δc_j, and let $\Delta x(t,c)$ be the resulting change in the function $x(t,c)$. Thus,

$$\Delta x(t,c) = x(t,c_1,c_2,\cdots,c_{j-1},c_j + \Delta c_j,c_{j+1},\cdots,c_n) - x(t,c_1,c_2,\cdots,c_n).$$

Since each component of X is continuously differentiable, we have, by Taylor's theorem for functions of several variables‡,

$$(22)\quad X_i(x + \Delta x,t) - X_i(x, t) = \sum_{k=1}^{n} \frac{\partial X_i}{\partial x_k}(x, t)\Delta x_k + \epsilon_i\,|\Delta x|,\ 1 \leqq i \leqq n,$$

where ϵ_i is a function of Δx and t which tends to zero as Δx tends to zero. By Theorem 2, Corollary, Δx tends to zero with Δc_j uniformly for t in any bounded interval. Hence the same is true of the ϵ_i.

Since

$$\partial \Delta x_i(t,c)/\partial t = \Delta \partial x_i(t,c)/\partial t = X_i(x + \Delta x, t) - X_i(x, t),$$

we have, dividing by Δc_j, that the functions $\Delta x_i(t,c)/\Delta c_j$ $(1 \leqq i \leqq n)$ of the

†If (2) is analytic, then the continuation of solutions is equivalent by Theorem 9 to *analytic continuation*, in the sense of complex function theory.
‡Courant, Vol. 2, p. 80.

variable t, for fixed $\mathbf{c}$ and Δc_j, are solutions of the following system of DE's for the unknown functions h_i

$$(23) \quad \frac{dh_i}{dt} = \sum_{k=1}^{n} \frac{\partial X_i}{\partial x_k}(\mathbf{x}(t,\mathbf{c}),t)h_k + \epsilon_i \mid \mathbf{h} \mid, \quad 1 \leqq i \leqq n, \quad \mathbf{h} = (h_1,\ldots,h_n).$$

As $\Delta c_j \to 0$, $\epsilon_i \to 0$, and the right side of each equation of this system tends uniformly for $|\mathbf{h}|$ bounded, $|t-a| \leqq \min(T, K/M)$ to the right side of the system

$$(24) \quad \frac{dh_i}{dt} = \sum_{k=1}^{n} \frac{\partial X_i}{\partial x_k}(\mathbf{x}(t,\mathbf{c}),t)h_k, \qquad 1 \leqq i \leqq n.$$

This system is linear, and therefore satisfies a Lipschitz condition (cf. § 7, Lemma).

We now apply the Corollary to Theorem 3 and infer that any solution of the system (23) satisfying the initial conditions $h_i(a) = \delta_i^j$ tends, as $\epsilon_i \to 0$, to the solution of the system (24) satisfying the same initial conditions. But such solutions of (23) are precisely the functions $\Delta x_i(a,\mathbf{c})/\Delta c_j$. We have therefore proved that the limit of the difference quotient $\Delta x_i(a,\mathbf{c})/\Delta c_j$ exists, q.e.d.

The linear DE (24) is called the *perturbation equation* or *variational equation* of the normal system (2), because it describes approximately the perturbation of the solution caused by a small perturbation of the initial conditions.

In the course of the preceding argument we have also proved the

COROLLARY. *If $\mathbf{x}(t,\mathbf{c})$ is a solution of the normal system* (2), *satisfying the initial condition $\mathbf{x}(a) = \mathbf{c}$ for each $\mathbf{c}$, and if each component of the function $\mathbf{X}$ is of class $\mathcal{C}^1$, then for each j the partial derivative $\partial\mathbf{x}(t,\mathbf{c})/\partial c_j$ is a solution of the perturbation equation* (24) *of the system.*

In the case of *linear* systems $d\mathbf{x}/dt = A(t)\mathbf{x} + \mathbf{b}(t)$, the perturbation equation is the reduced equation $d\mathbf{h}/dt = A(t)\mathbf{h}$ of the given system, and is the same for all solutions. But in *nonlinear* systems, the perturbation equation (24) depends on the particular solution $\mathbf{x}(t,\mathbf{c})$ whose initial value is being varied.

13*. Peano existence theorem. The existence theorems for normal systems (1) proved so far have assumed that the functions X_i satisfy Lipschitz conditions. We shall now derive an existence theorem assuming only continuity. As shown in Chapter I, solutions of such systems need not be uniquely determined by their initial values.

THEOREM 12 (Peano existence theorem). *If the function $\mathbf{X}(\mathbf{x}, t)$ is continuous for $|\mathbf{x} - \mathbf{c}| \leqq K$, $|t - a| \leqq T$, and if $|\mathbf{X}(\mathbf{x}, t)| \leqq M$ there, then the* *vector DE* (2) *has at least one solution* $\mathbf{x}(t)$, *defined for*

$$|t-a| \leqq \min(T, K/M),$$

satisfying the initial condition $\mathbf{x}(a) = \mathbf{c}$.

Proof. Using an elegant method due to Tonelli, we shall consider the equivalent integral equation (11) of Theorem 5,

$$(24') \qquad \mathbf{x}(t) = \mathbf{c} + \int_a^t \mathbf{X}(\mathbf{x}(s), s)ds,$$

and prove that this has a solution. Let $T_1 = \min(T, K/M)$. We may assume that $a = 0$ and that the interval is $0 \leqq t \leqq T_1$. In this interval we construct a sequence of functions $\mathbf{x}^n(t)$ as follows. For $0 \leqq t \leqq T_1/n$ set $\mathbf{x}^n(t) \equiv \mathbf{c}$. For $T_1/n < t \leqq T_1$ define $\mathbf{x}^n(t)$ by the formula

$$(25) \qquad \mathbf{x}^n(t) = \mathbf{c} + \int_0^{t-T_1/n} \mathbf{X}(\mathbf{x}^n(s), s)ds.$$

This formula defines the value of $\mathbf{x}^n(t)$ in terms of the previous values of $\mathbf{x}^n(s)$ for $0 \leqq s \leqq t - T_1/n$.

It follows as in the lemma of § 9 that the functions $\mathbf{x}^n(t)$ are defined for $0 \leqq t \leqq T_1$. Also, we have

$$|\mathbf{x}^n(t)| \leqq |\mathbf{c}| + \int_0^t M\,ds \leqq |\mathbf{c}| + T_1 M.$$

Hence the sequence of functions $|\mathbf{x}^n(t)|$ $(n = 1, 2, \cdots)$ is uniformly bounded.

Next, we prove that the sequence $\mathbf{x}^n$ is *equicontinuous* in the following sense.

Definition. *A family* $\mathfrak{F}$ *of vector-valued functions* $\mathbf{x}(t)$, *defined on an interval* I: $|t-a| \leqq T$, *is said to be* equicontinuous *when, given* $\epsilon > 0$, *a number* $\delta > 0$ *exists such that*

$$|t-s| < \delta \quad \text{implies} \quad |\mathbf{x}(t) - \mathbf{x}(s)| < \epsilon$$

for all *functions* $\mathbf{x} \in \mathfrak{F}$, *provided* $s, t \in I$.

Indeed, using the inequality (3), we have

$$|\mathbf{x}^n(t_1) - \mathbf{x}^n(t_2)| \leqq \int_{t_1-T_1/n}^{t_2-T_1/n} |\mathbf{X}(\mathbf{x}^n(s), s)|\,ds \leqq M|t_2 - t_1|,$$

from which it is evident that the $\mathbf{x}^n(t)$ are equicontinuous.

We now apply to the sequence $\mathbf{x}^n$ the Theorem of Arzelà-Ascoli, which is stated below without proof.†

†Rudin, pp. 129 ff. The proof given here is for real-valued functions, but the same proof applies to vector-valued functions.

ARZELÀ-ASCOLI THEOREM. *Let* $\mathbf{x}^n(t)$ $(n = 1, 2, 3, \cdots)$ *be a bounded equicontinuous sequence of scalar or vector functions, defined for* $a \leqq t \leqq b$. *Then there exists a subsequence* $\mathbf{x}^{n_i}(t)$ $(i = 1, 2, \cdots)$ *which is uniformly convergent in the interval.*

Applying this result to the sequence $\mathbf{x}^n(t)$, we see that it must contain a uniformly convergent subsequence $\mathbf{x}^{n_i}(t)$, converging to a continuous function $\mathbf{x}^\infty(t)$ as $n_i \to \infty$.

It is now easy to verify that this limit function $\mathbf{x}^\infty(t)$ satisfies the integral equation (24′). Indeed, (25) can be written in the form

$$\mathbf{x}^{n_i}(t) = \mathbf{c} + \int_0^t \mathbf{X}(\mathbf{x}^{n_i}(s), s)ds - \int_{t-T_1/n_i}^t \mathbf{X}(\mathbf{x}^{n_i}(s), s)ds. \tag{26}$$

As $n_i \to \infty$, $\int_0^t \mathbf{X}(\mathbf{x}^{n_i}(s), s)ds \to \int_0^t \mathbf{X}(\mathbf{x}^\infty(s), s)ds$ because $\mathbf{X}(\mathbf{x},t)$ is uniformly continuous; and the last term of (26) tends to zero, because, by the inequality (3),

$$\left| \int_{t-T_1/n_i}^t \mathbf{X}\, ds \right| \leqq \int_{t-T_1/n_i}^t M\, ds = M \frac{T_1}{n_i} \to 0.$$

Therefore, taking limits on both sides of (26) as $n_i \to \infty$, we find that $\mathbf{x}^\infty$ satisfies the integral equation (24′), q.e.d.

EXERCISES F

1. Let $F(x,y)$ be continuous for $|x - a| \leqq T$, $|y - c| \leqq K$. Show that the set of all solutions of $y' = F(x,y)$, satisfying the same initial condition $f(a) = c$, is equicontinuous.

2. Show that, if $\mathbf{X}(\mathbf{x}, t)$ is continuous and satisfies a Lipschitz condition for $a \leqq t \leqq b$, then every solution of the DE (2) satisfying $\mathbf{x}(a) = \mathbf{c}$ is bounded for $a \leqq t \leqq b$. Show that the corresponding result is not true for open intervals $a < t < b$.

3. Let $xX(x,y) + y^3Y(x,y) = 0$, where X and Y are of class $\mathcal{C}^1$. Show that the system $x' = X(x,y)$, $y' = Y(x,y)$ has infinite escape time. (*Hint:* Show that $2x^2 + y^4$ is an integral of the system.)

4. Let the function $\mathbf{X}(\mathbf{x}, t)$ be defined for $0 \leqq t < \infty$ and for all $\mathbf{x}$, and let $|\mathbf{X}(\mathbf{x}, t) - \mathbf{X}(\mathbf{y}, t)| \leqq L(t)\,|\mathbf{x} - \mathbf{y}|$, where $\int_0^\infty L(t)dt < \infty$. Show that the DE $d\mathbf{x}/dt = \mathbf{X}(\mathbf{x}, t)$ has a solution on $0 \leqq t < +\infty$ for every initial condition $\mathbf{x}(a) = \mathbf{c}$. Show that if one solution is bounded, then all are.

5. Let $\mathbf{X}(\mathbf{x}, t,s)$ be of class $\mathcal{C}^1$ for $|\mathbf{x} - \mathbf{c}| \leqq K$, $|t - a| \leqq T$, $|s - s_0| \leqq S$. Let $\mathbf{x}(t,s)$ be the solution of $\mathbf{x}' = \mathbf{X}(\mathbf{x}, t,s)$ satisfying $\mathbf{x}(a) = \mathbf{c}$. Show that $\mathbf{x}$ is a differentiable function of s.

*6. Under the assumptions of Ex. 5, suppose that $\mathbf{X}(\mathbf{x}, t,s)$ is of class $\mathcal{C}^n$. Show that $\mathbf{x}(t,s)$ has n continuous partial derivatives relative to s.

*7. Show that if there are two distinct solutions f and g of $y' = F(x,y)$ satisfying the same initial condition $c = f(a) = g(a)$ (F continuous in $|x - a| \leqq T$, $|y - c| \leqq K$), then there are infinitely many of them.

*8. Show that there is a *maximal* and a *minimal solution* $f_M(x)$ and $f_m(x)$ of the DE in Ex. 7, such that $f_m(x) \leqq f(x) \leqq f_M(x)$ for any other solution f such that $f(a) = f_M(a) = f_m(a)$. (*Hint:* See Ch. I, Ex. E4.)

*9. Let $F(x,y)$ and $G(x,y)$ be continuous for $a \leqq x \leqq T$, $|y - c| \leqq K$, and $F(x,y) \leqq G(x,y)$. Let f be a solution of $y' = F(x,y)$, and let g be the maximal solution of $y' = G(x,y)$. Show that if $f(a) \leqq g(a)$, then $f(x) \leqq g(x)$ for $x > a$.

ADDITIONAL EXERCISES

*1. Let $dx/dt = X(x,y,t)$ and $dy/dt = Y(x,y,t)$, where

$$(x - x')[X(x,y,t) - X(x',y',t)] + (y - y')[Y(x,y,t) - Y(x',y',t)]$$

is everywhere negative or zero. Show that, for $t > 0$, the above system has at most one solution satisfying a given initial condition $x(0) = c$.

In Exercises 2–4, f_+' means the right-derivative; prove the implication specified. You may assume the existence of f_+' and g_+' freely.

2. If $f_+'(x) \leqq g_+'(x)$, then $f(x) - f(y) \leqq g(x) - g(y)$ for $x \geqq y$.
3. If $|f_+'(x)| \leqq K|f(x)|$ then $|f(x)| \leqq |f(a)| e^{K|x-a|}$ for $x \geqq a$.
4. If $|f_+'(x)| \leqq K|f(x)| + \epsilon$, then $|f(x)| \leqq |f(a)| e^{K|x-a|} + (\epsilon/K)(e^{K|x-a|} - 1)$.
5. Let $dz_i/dt = Q_i(z_1,\cdots,z_n)$, where the Q_i are quadratic polynomials. Show that, for any initial condition, the n-th Picard approximation to the solution is a polynomial in t of degree at most $2^n - 1$.
6. (a) Prove that if there is a normal k-th order ordinary DE satisfied by two functions u and v, and if $n > k$, then there is a normal n-th order DE satisfied by both functions. State your differentiability assumptions.

   (b) Prove that if the given k-th order DE is linear, then the n-th order DE can also be chosen to be linear.

   (c) Prove that there is no fourth-order normal DE $u^{\text{iv}} = F(u,u',u'',u''',t)$ satisfied by both $u = t^4$ and $v = t^6$, for all real t.

   (d) Prove that $u = t^6$ satisfies no normal linear homogeneous DE of degree six or less, with continuous coefficients.
7. Show that, if $X_1,\cdots,X_n$ satisfy Lipschitz conditions on a compact domain, then so does any polynomial function of the X_i.
8. Show that if $X(t) = \| x_{ij}(t) \|$ is a matrix whose columns are solutions of the homogeneous linear system $X' = A(t)X$, then $\det X(t) = (\det X(a)) \exp \int_a^t \sum a_{kk}(s)ds$.
9. A matrix $X(t)$ is a *fundamental matrix* for $a \leqq t \leqq a + T$ of a homogeneous linear system $X' = A(t)X$ if its columns are solutions of the system and $\det(X(t)) \neq 0$. Show that if the columns of X are solutions of the system, and if $\det X(a) \neq 0$, then X is a fundamental matrix.

*10. Show that if $X(t)$ is a fundamental matrix of the reduced linear system, the function $\mathbf{x}(t) = X(t) \int_a^t X^{-1}(s)\mathbf{b}(s)ds$ is the solution of the inhomogeneous system such that $\mathbf{x}(a) = 0$. (X^{-1} is the matrix inverse of X.)

*11. (Nagumo) Let X be continuous for $|t-a| \leqq T$, $|x-c| \leqq K$, and $|t-a| \, |X(x, t) - X(y, t)| \leqq |x-y|$. Show that the solution of (2) satisfying $x(a) = c$ is unique. (*Hint:* Use the equivalent integral equation, and consider the maximum of $|x(t) - y(t)|/(t-a)$ for $t \geqq a$.)

12. Let X be continuous for $|x-c| \leqq K$, $|t| \leqq T$, and let

$$2(x-c) \cdot X(x, t) \leqq \psi(|x-c|^2, t),$$

where $\psi(u,t)$ is positive and increasing in u for fixed t, for $u \geqq 0$. Let $\phi \in \mathcal{C}^1$ satisfy $\phi'(t) > \psi(\phi(t),t)$, and $\phi(0) = 0$. Show that if x is a solution of (2) such that $x(0) = c$, then $|x(t) - c| \leqq \sqrt{\phi(t)}$. (*Hint:* Show that $\sigma'(t) \leqq \psi(\sigma(t),t)$, where $\sigma(t) = |x(t) - c|^2$.)

*13. Assume that X is continuous for $|t-a| \leqq T$, $|x-c| \leqq K$, and that

$$|X(x, t)| \leqq \psi(|x-c|, |t-a|),$$

where $\psi(u,t)$ is nonnegative, continuous, increasing in u for fixed t, defined for $|t-a| \leqq T$ and $u \geqq 0$. Let $\phi(t)$ be of class $\mathcal{C}^1$ and $\phi'(t) > \psi(\phi(t),t)$ for $|t-a| \leqq T$, and $\phi(0) = 0$. Let $x(t)$ be a solution of (2) such that $x(a) = \mathbf{c}$. Show that

$$|x(t) - c| \leqq \phi(|t-a|).$$

*14. Let X be continuous for $|t-a| \leqq T$, let $\phi(u)$ be continuous and increasing for $u \geqq 0$, and let $\lim_{N\to\infty} \int_1^N du/\phi(u) = \infty$. Show that if $|X(x, t)| \leqq \phi(|x|)$, then all solutions of (2) are bounded on $|t-a| \leqq T$. (*Hint:* Use Ex. 13.)

CHAPTER VI

Plane Autonomous Systems

1. Autonomous systems. A system of first-order DE's of the form

$$(1) \qquad dx_i/dt = X_i(x_1,\cdots,x_n), \qquad i = 1,\cdots,n,$$

is said to be *autonomous*. The characteristic property of autonomous systems is the fact that the functions X_i do not depend on the independent variable t. When this variable is thought of as representing time, autonomous systems are thus *time-independent* or *stationary*.

In the vector notation of Ch. V, §1, the autonomous system (1) reduces to

$$(1') \qquad d\mathbf{x}/dt = \mathbf{X}(\mathbf{x}).$$

Each first-order autonomous system is characterized by its *vector field*†: To every system (1) there corresponds a unique vector field $\mathbf{X}(\mathbf{x})$ in Euclidean n-space, and conversely. Throughout this chapter, we will consider only vector fields which are of class $\mathcal{C}^1$, and so satisfy a Lipschitz condition in every compact domain. As shown in Chapter V, this implies that one and only one *solution* $\mathbf{x}(t,\mathbf{c})$ of the autonomous system (1) satisfies the initial condition $\mathbf{x}(0) = \mathbf{c}$, and that this solution depends continuously on $\mathbf{c}$.

When $n = 3$, the autonomous system (1) can be imagined as representing the steady flow of a fluid in space: To each point $\mathbf{x}$ in a region of space there is associated a vector $\mathbf{X}(\mathbf{x})$ which describes the velocity of the fluid at that point in magnitude and direction. The flow is called *steady* because its velocity depends only on position and does not vary with time. The solution $\mathbf{x}(t,\mathbf{c})$ of the autonomous system (1) then has a simple physical interpretation: it is the *streamline* (*path*, *orbit*, or *trajectory*) of a moving fluid particle, whose position is given as a function of the time t.

When the preceding path $\mathbf{x}(t,\mathbf{c})$ is considered as a set of points (that is, as a geometrical curve), without reference to its parametric representation, it is also called an *integral curve*‡ of the autonomous system (1), or of the associated vector field $\mathbf{X}(\mathbf{x})$. If $\mathbf{x}(t,\mathbf{c})$ is a solution of the autonomous system (1), then so is $\mathbf{x}(t + a, \mathbf{c})$ for any constant a; this can be interpreted

†For the concept of a vector field, see Courant, Vol. 2, p. 82.
‡Integral curves are thus solution curves (Ch. V, § 1), but considered in $\mathbf{x}$-space rather than $(\mathbf{x}, t)$-space because of the invariance under time translation mentioned below.

as the path of a particle which passes through the point $\mathbf{c}$ at time $t = -a$. Thus there is always a one-parameter family of *solutions* of (1) describing the same integral curve in Euclidean n-space.

EXAMPLE 1. The solutions of the autonomous system

$$dx/dt = mx, \qquad dy/dt = ny, \tag{2}$$

are $x = c_1 e^{mt}$, $y = c_2 e^{nt}$; they may be found by inspection. The corresponding integral curves are the loci $y^m = kx^n$. Figure VI-1 depicts sample curves for the case $m = 2$, $n = 3$.

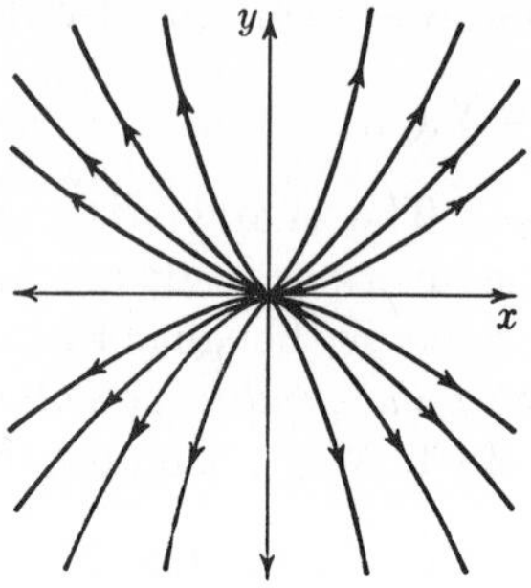

Figure VI-1. Integral Curves of $\dot{x} = 2x$, $\dot{y} = 2y$

In Figure VI-1, the origin (0,0) is evidently a very special point: integral curves emanate from it both horizontally and vertically. This is only possible because the vector field (mx, ny) defined there reduces to the null vector $\mathbf{0} = (0,0)$, whose direction is indeterminate. Such points are of particular importance for the study of autonomous systems; they are called critical points.

DEFINITION. *A point $\mathbf{x} = (x_1, \cdots, x_n)$ where all the functions X_i are equal to zero is called a* critical point *of the autonomous system* (1), *and of the associated vector field $\boldsymbol{X}(\mathbf{x})$.*

If $\mathbf{x} = \mathbf{c}$ is a critical point of (1), then the functions $x_i(t) \equiv c_i$ define a trivial solution $\mathbf{x}(t) = \mathbf{c}$ of (1), which does not describe a curve, but just a point. In the terminology of hydrodynamics, $\mathbf{c}$ is called a *stagnation point* of the velocity field $\boldsymbol{X}(\mathbf{x})$.

Every normal system of $(n - 1)$ first-order DE's

$$dx_i/dt = X_i(x_1, \cdots, x_{n-1}; t), \qquad i = 1, \cdots, n-1, \tag{3}$$

is equivalent to an autonomous system in n variables. To see this, introduce an additional variable $x_n = t$, and rewrite (3) as

$$dx_i/dt = X_i(x_1, \cdots, x_n), \quad i = 1, \cdots, n-1, \quad dx_n/dt = 1. \tag{3'}$$

Evidently, the system (3′) so constructed has no critical points.

2. Plane autonomous systems. When $n = 2$ in (1), it is convenient to write (1) in the form

$$\frac{dx}{dt} = X(x,y), \qquad \frac{dy}{dt} = Y(x,y); \tag{4}$$

one then speaks of a *plane* autonomous system. The plane autonomous system (4) evidently has the solutions of the first-order DE

$$\frac{dy}{dx} = \frac{Y(x,y)}{X(x,y)}, \tag{4'}$$

for integral curves; hence (4) can be thought of as a generalization of the first-order normal DE $y' = F(x,y)$. The main advantage of this generalization is that points $X(x,y) = 0$ of vertical tangency of the solutions of the DE (4′) are no longer singular points of the corresponding plane autonomous system (4).

This advantage is apparent in the following example, already treated in Ch. I, § 2.

EXAMPLE 2. Consider the autonomous system

$$\frac{dx}{dt} = -y, \qquad \frac{dy}{dt} = x, \tag{5}$$

whose solutions are the function-pairs $x = r \cos(t + c)$, $y = r \sin(t + c)$, where r and c are arbitrary constants. The graphs of these solutions are concentric circles, with center at the origin. The solutions of the corresponding first-order DE

$$\frac{dy}{dx} = -\frac{x}{y} \tag{5'}$$

are the functions $y = \pm\sqrt{r^2 - x^2}$, which are defined only for $|x| < |r|$. Whereas the function $-x/y$ is undefined where $y = 0$, the functions $X(x,y) = -y$ and $Y(x,y) = x$ in the system (5) are defined throughout the plane. This gives an obvious advantage to the system (5) over the DE (5′).

Referring to the definition of Ch. I, § 3, we see that the circles $x^2 + y^2 = r^2$ form a regular† curve family in the "punctured" (x,y)-plane, the critical point of (5) at the origin (0,0) being deleted. This result can be generalized.

THEOREM 1. *If the functions X and Y satisfy local Lipschitz conditions, then the integral curves of the plane autonomous system* (4) *form a regular curve family, in any domain which contains no critical points.*

Proof. By the uniqueness theorem of Ch. V, § 3, there is a unique integral curve of (4) passing through each point **c** not a critical point. As

†Note that this regular curve family is not normal, whereas the graphs of the functions $y = \sqrt{r^2 - x^2}$ form a normal curve family in the domain $y > 0$.

shown in Ch. V, § 11, each such integral curve goes all the way to the boundary. Finally, since Lipschitz conditions imply continuity, the directions of the vectors $(X(x,y),Y(x,y))$ vary continuously with position, except near a critical point, completing the proof.

Plane autonomous systems have an interesting relation to contour lines (cf. Ch. I, § 4). Namely, we have

THEOREM 2. *For any continuously differentiable function $V(x,y)$, the integral curves of the plane autonomous system*

$$\frac{dx}{dt} = \frac{\partial V}{\partial y}(x,y), \qquad \frac{dy}{dt} = -\frac{\partial V}{\partial x}(x,y), \tag{6}$$

lie on contour lines $V(x,y) = constant$.

The proof is immediate: along any integral curve,

$$\frac{dV}{dt} = \frac{\partial V}{\partial x}\cdot\frac{dx}{dt} + \frac{\partial V}{\partial y}\cdot\frac{dy}{dt} = \frac{\partial V}{\partial x}\cdot\frac{\partial V}{\partial y} - \frac{\partial V}{\partial y}\cdot\frac{\partial V}{\partial x} = 0,$$

and so $V(x(t),y(t)) = \text{constant}$. Observe that the associated steady flow is divergence-free or *area conserving*:

$$\text{div}\,(\partial V/\partial y, -\partial V/\partial x) = \partial^2 V/\partial x\,\partial y - \partial^2 V/\partial y\,\partial x = 0.$$

In fluid mechanics, such a steady flow (6) is called *incompressible*, and V is called its stream function.

The advantage of the representation (6) over the DE

$$dy/dx = -(\partial V/\partial x)/(\partial V/\partial y) \tag{6'}$$

considered in Ch. I, § 4, is the following. Whereas the solution curves of (6′) terminate wherever $\partial V/\partial y$ vanishes, those of (6) only terminate where the function V has a *critical point* (maximum, minimum, or saddle-point), in the sense that grad $V = 0$. This happens exactly where the autonomous system (6) has critical points.

If we set $V = -(x^2 + y^2)/2$ in Theorem 2, we get the system (5) of Example 2, having circular streamlines. If $\mu(x,y)$ is nonvanishing, then the system $dx/dt = -y\mu$, $dy/dt = x\mu$ also has circles for integral curves, and one can construct a wide variety of autonomous systems having the same integral curves in this way.

Another illustration of Theorem 2 is obtained by setting

$$V(x,y) = (x^3 + y^3)/xy = r(\cos^3\theta + \sin^3\theta)/\cos\theta\sin\theta,$$

and letting $\mu(x,y) = x^2y^2$. We get

EXAMPLE 3. The plane autonomous system

$$dx/dt = x(2y^3 - x^3), \qquad dy/dt = -y(2x^3 - y^3) \tag{7}$$

has as integral curves the curves $x^3 + y^3 - 3cxy = 0$, where c is an arbitrary constant. Each such integral curve is a folium of Descartes, as in Figure VI-2. The coordinate axes are also integral curves. The origin is the only critical point of (7); correspondingly, the folia of Descartes in Figure VI-2 form with the axes a curve family which is regular except at the origin.

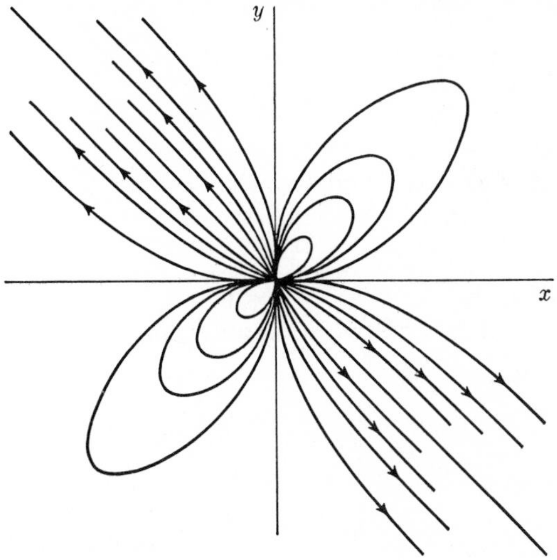

Figure VI-2. Folia of Descartes

Note that the trajectories of any autonomous system are endowed with a natural sense or *orientation*, namely, the direction of increasing t. This orientation is indicated in drawings of integral curves by arrows pointing in this direction. Note also that the curves of Figure VI-2 form a family of *similar curves*, all similar to $x^3 + y^3 = 3xy$ under a transformation $\dot{x} \to cx$, $y \to cy$, $t \to t/c^3$, where c is a constant. This is because the DE

$$dy/dx = -y(2x^3 - y^3)/x(2y^3 - x^3)$$

is homogeneous of degree zero (see the end of Ch. I, §7).

3. Poincaré phase-plane. An important class of plane autonomous systems (4) is obtained from *dynamical systems* with one degree of freedom. Let a particle be constrained to move on a straight line (or other curve) and let its acceleration $\ddot{x}$ be determined by Newton's Second Law of Motion as a function of its instantaneous position x and velocity $\dot{x}$. Then

$$\ddot{x} = F(x, \dot{x}), \tag{8}$$

where we have adopted Newton's notation, representing time-derivatives by dots placed over the variable differentiated.

It is usual to denote $\dot{x} = dx/dt$ by the letter v, and call the (x,v)-plane the *Poincaré phase-plane.* Since the variables x and mv are conjugate position and momentum variables, the Poincaré phase-plane is a special instance of the concept of phase-space in classical dynamics.

Since (8) is time-independent, it is called an *autonomous* second-order DE. In the (x,v)-plane, the second-order autonomous DE (8) is equivalent to the first-order plane autonomous system

$$(8') \qquad dx/dt = v, \qquad dv/dt = v\,dv/dx = F(x,v).$$

The integral curves of this autonomous system in the Poincaré phase-plane depict graphically the types of motions determined by the DE (8).

EXAMPLE 4. Consider the *damped linear oscillator* defined by the second-order linear DE with constant coefficients

$$(9) \qquad \ddot{x} + p\dot{x} + qx = 0, \qquad p,\, q \text{ constant},$$

discussed in Ch. II, § 2. The associated autonomous system in the Poincaré phase-plane is

$$(9') \qquad dx/dt = v, \qquad dv/dt = -pv - qx.$$

The direction field of this system is easily plotted for any p, q.

For example, let $p = q = -1$. This describes the motion of a negatively damped particle in a repulsive force field; it is the opposite of the case $p > 0$, $q > 0$ most frequent in mechanics, that is, oscillations about an attractive center damped by friction. Sample solution-curves are sketched in Figure VI-3.

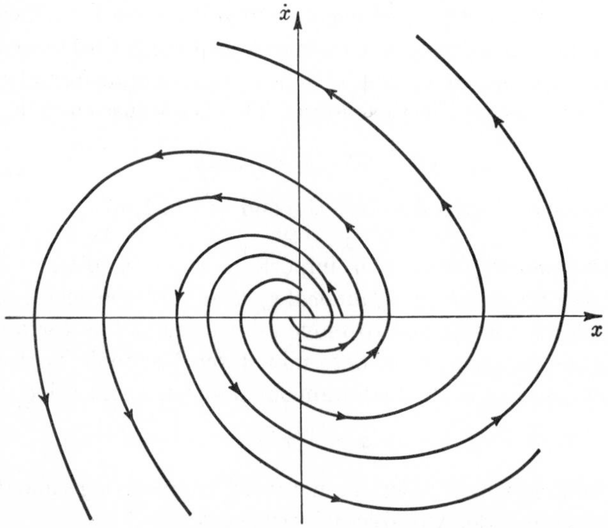

Figure VI-3. Solution Curves of $\ddot{x} = \dot{x} + x$ in Poincaré Phase-Plane

EXAMPLE 5. The DE of a simple pendulum of length ℓ is

$$\frac{d^2\theta}{dt^2} = -k^2 \sin\theta, \qquad k^2 = g/\ell, \tag{10}$$

where θ is the angle of deflection. The corresponding autonomous system in the Poincaré phase-plane is

$$\dot{\theta} = v, \qquad \dot{v} = -k^2 \sin\theta. \tag{10'}$$

Since the function $\sin\theta$ is periodic, the integral curves form a periodic pattern, in the sense that if $(\theta(t), v(t))$ is a solution, so is $(\theta(t) + 2\pi, v(t))$. They are sketched in Figure VI-4. There are infinitely many critical points, at $v = 0$ and $\theta = \pm n\pi$, $n = 0, 1, 2, \cdots$. The integral curves of (10′) are given by $v = \pm(2k^2 \cos\theta + c)^{1/2}$, $-2k^2 \leqq c < +\infty$. The closed ovals inside the "separatrices" $v = \pm 2k \cos(\theta/2)$ passing through the unstable critical points $((2n+1)\pi, 0)$ correspond to periodic oscillations; the wavy lines outside these separatrix curves correspond to whirling motions of the pendulum, which are also periodic.

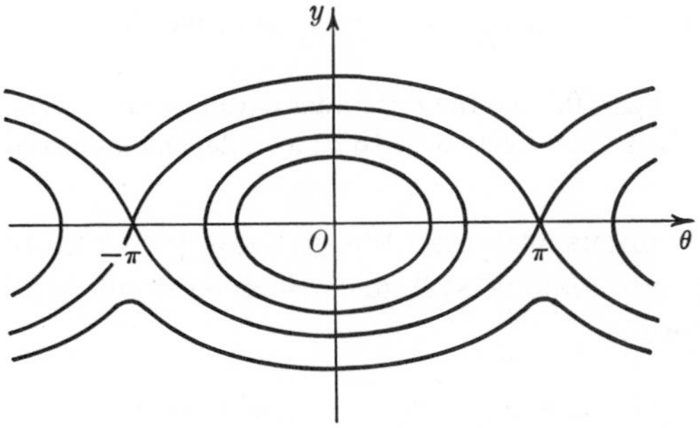

Figure VI-4. Simple Pendulum in Poincaré Phase-Plane

EXERCISES A

1. Find and describe geometrically the integral curves of the following vector fields: (a) (x,y,z), (b) (ax,by,cz), (c) $(y,-x,1)$, (d) (y,z,x).

2. Show that the integral curves of the autonomous system

$$dx/dt = e^x - 1, \qquad dy/dt = ye^x,$$

are the curves $y = c(e^x - 1)$.

3. Show that the functions xyz and $x^2 + y^2$ are integrals of the system

$$dx/dt = xy^2, \qquad dy/dt = -x^2y, \qquad dz/dt = z(x^2 - y^2).$$

Describe the loci xyz = constant, and sketch typical integral curves.

The *gradient field* of a scalar function $V(\mathbf{x})$ is defined as the vector field

$$\text{grad } V = (\partial V/\partial x_1, \cdots, \partial V/\partial x_n).$$

In Exs. 4–6, find the integral curves of the gradient fields of the following functions:

4. $V = xy$.
5. $V = x^2 + y^2 - 2z^2$.
6. $V = \ln [(x - a)^2 + y^2/[(x + a)^2 + y^2]]$.

7. Is the following statement true or false? If $f \in \mathcal{C}^1$, then the integral curves of the gradient field of the function $f(V)$ coincide with those of V. Prove the statement, or construct a counterexample.

8. Show that a function $\phi(x_1,\cdots,x_n)$ of class $\mathcal{C}^1$ is an integral of the system (1) if and only if it satisfies the partial DE $X_1\, \partial\phi/\partial x_1 + \cdots + X_n\, \partial\phi/\partial x_n = 0$.

9. Show that if $\partial X/\partial x = \partial Y/\partial y$ and $\partial X/\partial y = -\,\partial Y/\partial x$, then the plane autonomous system (4) is equivalent to a single first-order *complex* analytic DE, and conversely.

*10. Let $e_1, \cdots, e_n$ and $a_1, \cdots, a_n$ be real constants, and let

$$r_j = [(x - a_j)^2 + y^2 + z^2]^{1/2}.$$

Show that, if $V = \Sigma\, e_j/r_j$, then the functions

$$\psi = \Sigma\, e_j \arccos \alpha_j, \qquad \alpha_j = (x - a_j)/r_j \quad \text{and} \quad \theta = \arctan (z/y)$$

are integrals of $\dot{x} = \partial V/\partial x$, $\dot{y} = \partial V/\partial y$, $\dot{z} = \partial V/\partial z$. Express the integral curves as intersections of the surfaces defined by the preceding equations.

11. Determine the integral curves of $\ddot{x} = -x^3$ in the Poincaré phase-plane, and sketch typical curves.

*12. Prove that if $X_n \neq 0$, then the n-th order autonomous system (1) is equivalent to a normal $(n - 1)$-st order system, with x_n as independent variable.

4. Linear autonomous systems. We shall now give a thorough discussion of *linear* plane autonomous systems. Such systems are, by definition, systems of the form

$$dx/dt = ax + by, \qquad dy/dt = cx + dy, \tag{11}$$

where a, b, c, d are constants. The matrix $A = \begin{pmatrix} a & b \\ c & d \end{pmatrix}$ of constants is nonsingular unless its determinant $ad - bc = 0$. The origin (0,0) is always a critical point of the system (11). Since the simultaneous linear equations $ax + by = cx + dy = 0$ have no solution except $x = y = 0$ unless A is singular, we see that the origin is the only critical point of the system (11), unless $ad = bc$ (the *degenerate* case $|\, A \,| = 0$).

Applying the construction of § 2 to (11), we get the linear fractional DE

$$dy/dx = (cx + dy)/(ax + by), \tag{12}$$

studied in Ch. I, § 6. Theorem 1 shows that the integral curves of (12) form a regular curve family if $ad \neq bc$, except near the origin; the types of such curve families will be described below in § 8.

For any p, q, the Poincaré phase-plane representation (9′) of the damped linear oscillator (9) defines a plane linear autonomous system, with coefficient-matrix $A = \begin{pmatrix} 0 & 1 \\ -q & -p \end{pmatrix}$. Conversely, it can be shown (Theorem 5) that almost every linear plane autonomous system is equivalent to one obtained in this way. To show this, one needs to introduce a new concept.

DEFINITION. *The* secular equation *of* (11) *is*

$$\ddot{u} - (a + d)\dot{u} + (ad - bc)u = 0. \tag{13}$$

THEOREM 3. *If* $(x(t), y(t))$ *is any solution of the plane autonomous system* (11), *then* $x(t)$ *and* $y(t)$ *are solutions of the secular equation* (13) *of* (11).

Proof. We shall prove that $x(t)$ is a solution of (13); the proof for $y(t)$ is the same, replacing a by d and b by c. The first equation of (11) implies $by = \dot{x} - ax$, whence $\ddot{x} - a\dot{x} = b\dot{y}$. From the second equation, it follows that

$$\ddot{x} - a\dot{x} = bc\dot{x} + bd\dot{y} = bc\dot{x} + d(\dot{x} - ax).$$

Transposing, we see that $x(t)$ satisfies (13).

The secular equation (13) of (11) has many interesting properties. Thus, referring to Ch. IV, § 1, we see that the *characteristic polynomial* of (13) is

$$\lambda^2 - (a + d)\lambda + (ad - bc) = \begin{vmatrix} a - \lambda & b \\ c & d - \lambda \end{vmatrix} = | A - \lambda I |; \tag{13'}$$

it is (apart from the sign of λ) the characteristic polynomial† of the coefficient-matrix of (11). But its most important property is the *equivalence* of most autonomous systems having the same secular equation, in a sense which will be made precise in the next section.

Systems in n variables. In general, the autonomous system (1) is called *linear* when the functions X_i are linear homogeneous functions, so that

$$dx_i/dt = a_{i1}x_1 + \cdots + a_{in}x_n, \qquad i = 1, \cdots, n. \tag{14}$$

Hence a linear autonomous system is just a (homogeneous) linear system of DE's with constant coefficients. Such a system is determined by the square *matrix* $A = \| a_{ij} \|$ of its coefficients, and its vector field satisfies $\mathbf{X}(\mathbf{x}) = A\mathbf{x}$.

Clearly, the origin $\mathbf{0} = (0, \cdots, 0)$ is always a critical point for the system (14); unless the matrix A is singular, so that $A\mathbf{x} = \mathbf{0}$ for some $\mathbf{x} \neq \mathbf{0}$, the system has no other critical point. Conversely, in the neighborhood of any critical point $\mathbf{c}$ of any analytic autonomous system (1), Taylor's

†For the characteristic polynomial of a matrix and its properties, see Birkhoff and Mac Lane, Ch. X.

Theorem implies

(15) $d\xi_i/dt = \sum a_{ij}\xi_j + R_i(\xi), \quad i, j = 1, \cdots, n, \quad \xi_i = x_i - c_i,$

where the R_i are infinitesimals of the second order in the ξ_i (that is, $| R_i(\xi) | \leqq M | \xi |^2$).

The preceding observation suggests that the behavior of the solutions of any analytic autonomous system such as (15) near any critical point is approximately like that of the solutions of the associated *linearized* autonomous system (14). Much of the importance of the study of linear autonomous systems is due to the fact that this is often (though not always) true.

5. Equivalent systems. One can often simplify the form of a DE or system of DE's by an appropriate transformation of coordinates. For instance, consider the system

$$(16) \qquad \begin{aligned} dx/dt &= (3x^4 - 12x^2y^2 + y^4)/(x^2 + y^2)^{3/2}, \\ dy/dt &= (6x^3y - 10xy^3)/(x^2 + y^2)^{3/2}. \end{aligned}$$

In polar coordinates $r = (x^2 + y^2)^{1/2}$, $\theta = \arctan(y/x)$ with inverse functions $x = r \cos \theta$, $y = r \sin \theta$, this system reduces to

$$(16') \qquad dr/dt = 3r \cos 3\theta, \qquad d\theta/dt = \sin 3\theta.$$

In this form, one sees at a glance that the rays $\theta = n\pi/3$ are integral curves, for $n = 0, \cdots, 5$. Other integral curves are sketched in Figure VI-5.

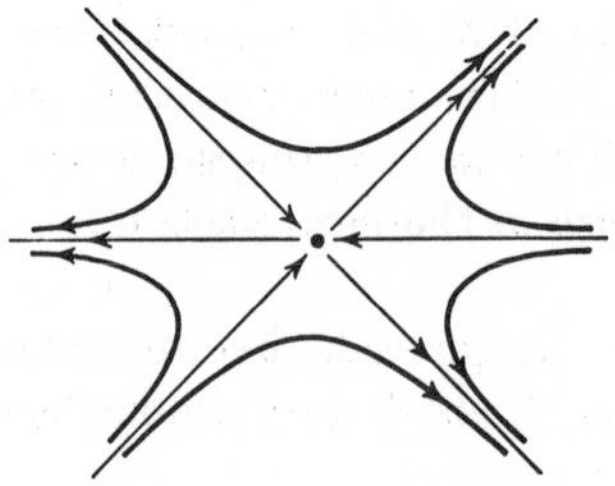

Figure VI-5. $\dot{r} = 3r \cos 3\theta$, $\dot{\theta} = \sin 3\theta$

We shall study below how far one can simplify *linear* autonomous systems by such coordinate transformations. Our study will be based on a general concept of *equivalence by transformation*, which we now define precisely. Let

$$(17) \qquad u_i = f_i(x_1, \cdots, x_n), \qquad i = 1, \cdots, n,$$

be continuously differentiable functions with inverse functions

$$(17') \qquad x_j = g_j(u_1, \cdots, u_n), \qquad j = 1, \cdots, n,$$

so that $\boldsymbol{f}(\boldsymbol{g}(\boldsymbol{u})) = \boldsymbol{u}$ and $\boldsymbol{g}(\boldsymbol{f}(\boldsymbol{x})) = \boldsymbol{x}$. For such inverse functions to exist locally and be continuously differentiable, it is necessary and sufficient (by the Implicit Function Theorem†) that the Jacobian of (17) be nonvanishing: that $|\partial f_i/\partial x_j| \neq 0$.

If $\boldsymbol{x}(t)$ is any solution of the autonomous system

$$(18) \qquad dx_j/dt = X_j(x_1, \cdots, x_n), \qquad j = 1, \cdots, n,$$

then the functions

$$(19) \qquad u_i(t) = f_i(x_1(t), \cdots, x_n(t)), \qquad i = 1, \cdots, n,$$

satisfy the autonomous system

$$(18') \quad du_i/dt = U_i(\boldsymbol{u}), \qquad U_i = \sum_{j=1}^{n} \frac{\partial f_i}{\partial x_j}\frac{dx_j}{dt} = \sum_{j=1}^{n} \frac{\partial f_i}{\partial x_j}(\boldsymbol{g}(\boldsymbol{u}))\, X_j(\boldsymbol{g}(\boldsymbol{u})),$$

and conversely. In this sense, the autonomous systems (18) and (18′) are *equivalent.* We formalize the preceding discussion in a definition.

DEFINITION. *Let* $d\boldsymbol{x}/dt = \boldsymbol{X}(\boldsymbol{x})$ *and* $d\boldsymbol{u}/dt = \boldsymbol{U}(\boldsymbol{u})$ *be autonomous systems, defined in regions* R *and* R' *of n-dimensional space, respectively. The two systems are* equivalent *if and only if there exists a one-one transformation* $\boldsymbol{u} = \boldsymbol{f}(\boldsymbol{x})$ *of coordinates, of class* $\mathcal{C}^1$ *and with nonvanishing Jacobian, which maps* R *onto* R' *and carries* $d\boldsymbol{x}/dt = \boldsymbol{X}(\boldsymbol{x})$ *into* $d\boldsymbol{u}/dt = \boldsymbol{U}(\boldsymbol{u})$.

Under these circumstances, the inverse transformation is also of class $\mathcal{C}^1$ with nonvanishing Jacobian: the relation of equivalence is symmetric, reflexive, and transitive; it is an equivalence relation.‡ It follows from the preceding discussion that equivalent autonomous systems have integral curves obtainable from each other by a coordinate transformation. If the systems (18) and (18′) are equivalent under the change of coordinates (19), and if $V(\boldsymbol{u})$ is an integral of (18′), then $V(\boldsymbol{f}(\boldsymbol{x}))$ is an integral of (18).

However, two autonomous systems may have the same integral curves, without being equivalent. Thus the integral curves of

$$(20) \qquad \dot{x} = (x^2 + y^2)y, \qquad \dot{y} = -(x^2 + y^2)x$$

are concentric circles, as in Example 2 ($\dot{x} = -y$, $\dot{y} = x$). Yet the two systems are not equivalent: all solutions of $\dot{x} = -y$, $\dot{y} = x$ are periodic with period 2π, whereas those of (20) have variable periods.

We now establish a fundamental result about the trajectories of autonomous systems. This states that, near any noncritical point, the trajectories of an autonomous system look like a family of parallel straight lines. We give the proof for the case $n = 2$.

†See Ch. I, § 2. The Jacobian of (17) is the determinant of the square matrix $\| \partial f_i/\partial x_j \|$ of first partial derivatives. See Widder, p. 28 ff.
‡Birkhoff and Mac Lane, p. 31.

THEOREM 4. *Any plane autonomous system* (4) *where* X *and* Y *are of class* $\mathcal{C}^1$ *is equivalent, in some neighborhood of any point which is not a critical point, to the system* $du/dt = 1$, $dv/dt = 0$.

Proof. Let the point be (a,b); without loss of generality, we may assume that $X(a,b) \neq 0$. Let the solution of the system for the initial values $x(0) = a$, $y(0) = c$ be $x = \xi(t,c)$, $y = \eta(t,c)$ so that $\partial\xi/\partial t = X$, $\partial\eta/\partial t = Y$. Then by Ch. V, Theorem 11, the transformation $(t,c) \to (\xi(t,c), \eta(t,c))$ is of class $\mathcal{C}^1$, and the Jacobian

$$\frac{\partial(\xi,\eta)}{\partial(t,c)} = \frac{\partial\xi}{\partial t}\cdot\frac{\partial\eta}{\partial c} - \frac{\partial\xi}{\partial c}\cdot\frac{\partial\eta}{\partial t} = X(a,b)\cdot 1 - 0\cdot Y(a,b) \neq 0$$

at (a,b), since $x(0)$ does not vary with c. Hence, by the Implicit Function Theorem, the inverse transformation $u = t(x,y)$, $v = c(x,y)$ is of class $\mathcal{C}^1$. In the (u,v)-coordinates, the solutions reduce to $u = t$, $v = c =$ constant; hence the DE assumes the form stated, q.e.d.

COROLLARY. *Any two plane autonomous systems are locally equivalent, except near critical points.*

The system $\dot{u} = 1$, $\dot{v} = 0$ is therefore locally a *canonical form* for plane autonomous systems near noncritical points; in hydrodynamics, the corresponding velocity field is called a uniform flow.

6. Linear equivalence. In dealing with linear autonomous systems, it is natural to consider equivalence under *linear* transformations of coordinates

$$(20') \qquad u_i = k_{i1}x_1 + \cdots + k_{in}x_n, \qquad i = 1, \cdots, n.$$

Two systems which are equivalent under a homogeneous linear transformation of the form (20) are called *linearly equivalent.* Writing $\mathbf{u} = K\mathbf{x}$ in vector notation, the inverse transformation is then just $\mathbf{x} = K^{-1}\mathbf{u}$, where K^{-1} is the inverse of the square matrix K. Note that $K = \| \partial u_i/\partial x_j \|$, so that the Jacobian of the transformation is just the determinant $|K|$ of K.

Also, if $\mathbf{x}(t)$ is a solution of the linear autonomous system $d\mathbf{x}/dt = A\mathbf{x}$, and $\mathbf{u} = K\mathbf{x}$ is given by (20), then

$$(21) \qquad d\mathbf{u}/dt = K d\mathbf{x}/dt = KA\mathbf{x} = (KAK^{-1})\mathbf{u}.$$

In algebraic language, linearly equivalent linear autonomous systems are associated with *similar*† matrices A and KAK^{-1}. Therefore, the reduction of linear autonomous systems to a standard simplified (or "canonical") form amounts to reducing matrices to canonical form. The simplified

†Birkhoff and Mac Lane, p. 248. For reduction to diagonal form and Jordan canonical form, see *ibid.*, pp. 277, 334. For the companion matrix form $\begin{pmatrix} 0 & 1 \\ -p & -q \end{pmatrix}$, see *ibid.*, p. 318.

forms usually preferred are diagonal, companion matrix, or (for complex matrices) Jordan canonical form. This problem will be treated here only for 2×2 matrices — i.e., for linear plane autonomous systems:

$$dx/dt = ax + by, \qquad dy/dt = cx + dy. \tag{22}$$

Its solution enables one to classify critical points of plane autonomous systems. We first prove a useful

LEMMA. *Linearly equivalent linear plane autonomous systems have the same secular equation.*

Proof. This result follows immediately from (13′) and (21), and general identities of linear algebra. If $B = KAK^{-1}$, then

$$\begin{aligned} |B - \lambda I| &= |KAK^{-1} - \lambda I| = |K(A - \lambda I)K^{-1}| \\ &= |K| \cdot |A - \lambda I| \cdot |K^{-1}| = |A - \lambda I|. \end{aligned}$$

(The lemma is also a corollary of Theorem 3, unless there are two linearly independent equations $\ddot{u} + p\dot{u} + qu = 0$ satisfied by both components of all solutions of $d\mathbf{x}/dt = A\mathbf{x}$.)

THEOREM 5. *Unless $a = d$ and $b = c = 0$, the linear plane autonomous system* (22) *is linearly equivalent to the Poincaré phase-plane representation*

$$du/dt = v,\ dv/dt = -qu - pv,\ p = -(a + d),\ q = (ad - bc), \tag{23}$$

of its secular equation (13).

Proof. If $b \neq 0$, let $u = x$, $v = ax + by$; that is, let $K = \begin{pmatrix} 1 & 0 \\ a & b \end{pmatrix}$. Then (22) reduces to

$$\dot{u} = v, \quad \dot{v} = a\dot{x} + b\dot{y} = (a^2 + bc)x + (ab + bd)y. \tag{23′}$$

The last expression in (23′) is equal to

$$(a^2 + ad)x + (ab + bd)y - (ad - bc)x = (a + d)v - (ad - bc)u,$$

by definition of u,v; hence (22) is equivalent to

$$\dot{u} = v, \quad \dot{v} = (a + d)v - (ad - bc)u = -pv - qu,$$

that is, to (23). This shows in particular that $KAK^{-1} = \begin{pmatrix} 0 & 1 \\ -q & -p \end{pmatrix}$ is the *companion matrix* of the secular equation of (22).

This proves Theorem 5 for the case $b \neq 0$. The case $c \neq 0$ can be treated in just the same way, letting $u = y$ and $v = cx + dy$.

When $b = c = 0$, let $u = x + y$, $v = ax + dy$; if $a \neq d$, we can set $x = (du - v)/(d - a)$, $y = (au - v)/(a - d)$. By (22), with $b = c = 0$, $\dot{u} = \dot{x} + \dot{y} = ax + dy = v$. Likewise,

$$\dot{v} = a\dot{x} + d\dot{y} = a^2x + d^2y.$$

Comparing with the expression

$$(a+d)v-(ad)u=[(a^2+ad)x+(ad+d^2)y-adx-ady],$$

we verify (23) also in this case.

Exceptional case. The case $a=d$, $b=c=0$ of

$$\dot{x}=ax, \qquad \dot{y}=ay \tag{24}$$

is genuinely exceptional. The secular equation of (24) is $\ddot{x}-2a\dot{x}+a^2x=0$, just as it is for the system

$$\dot{x}=ax, \qquad \dot{y}=x+ay, \tag{24'}$$

but (24) and (24′) are not linearly equivalent. Every component of every solution of (24) satisfies $\dot{u}=au$, but this is not true of the solution (e^{at}, te^{at}) of (24′).

The exceptional case arises when the characteristic polynomial of the secular equation (13) has equal roots, that is, when its *discriminant* $\Delta=p^2-4q=(a-d)^2+4bc$ vanishes. This gives the

COROLLARY. *Unless the discriminant $(a-d)^2+4bc$ vanishes, two linear plane autonomous systems are linearly equivalent if and only if they have the same secular equation.*

EXERCISES B

1. (a) Show that the characteristic equation of the system

$$\dot{x}=\mu x-\nu y, \qquad \dot{y}=\nu x+\mu y, \tag{*}$$

has the complex roots $\lambda=\mu\pm i\nu$.

(b) Infer that any linear plane autonomous system (11) with discriminant $\Delta<0$ is linearly equivalent to (*), for some μ, ν.

(c) Show that, in polar coordinates, the system (*) defines the flow $r\to e^{\mu t}r$, $\theta\to\theta+\nu t$.

(d) Show that (*) is the real form of the first-order complex linear DE $\dot{z}=\lambda z$, $z=x+iy$.

2. Consider the system $dx/dt=\alpha x$, $dy/dt=\beta y$ for $\alpha\neq 0$.

(a) Show that its integral curves are $y=C\,|\,x\,|^p$, $p=\beta/\alpha$.

(b) Prove that any linear plane autonomous system (11) with positive discriminant is linearly equivalent to a DE of the above form, under a suitable change of basis.

(*c) Show that, in the punctured plane $x^2+y^2>0$, the systems $dx/dt=\alpha x$, $dy/dt=\beta y$ and $dx/dt=k\alpha x$, $dy/dt=k\beta y$ are equivalent if $k\neq 0$, but that they are not equivalent in any domain which contains the origin unless $k=\pm 1$.

3. Show that any linear plane autonomous system (11) with zero determinant is equivalent to $dx/dt=y$, $dy/dt=0$, or to $dx/dt=dy/dt=0$. Describe the associated flows geometrically.

4. (a) Show that, if $ad \neq bc$, the linear fractional DE

$$dy/dx = (cx + dy + f)/(ax + by + e)$$

is equivalent by an (affine) transformation to one of the canonical forms of Exs. 1–3.

(b) Derive a set of canonical forms for the exceptional case $ad = bc$.

5. The *elliptic functions* $u = \text{sn}\, t$, $v = \text{cn}\, t$, $w = \text{dn}\, t$, may be defined (cf. Ch. III, § 1) as the solutions of the system

$$(*) \qquad du/dt = vw, \qquad dv/dt = -wu, \qquad dw/dt = -k^2uv$$

having the initial values $u(0) = 0$, $v(0) = w(0) = 1$.

(a) Establish the identities $(\text{sn}\, t)^2 + (\text{cn}\, t)^2 = 1$, $k^2(\text{sn}\, t)^2 + (\text{dn}\, t)^2 = 1$.

(b) Using (a), show that the three functions specified are defined and analytic for all real t.

(c) Expand the solutions in power series through terms in t^5.

6. (a) Show that, in Ex. 5, if $k^2 < 1$, the function $\text{cn}\, t$ vanishes at

$$t = K = \int_0^1 dx/\sqrt{(1 - x^2)(1 - k^2x^2)}.$$

(b) Prove the addition formulas, valid with $k' = \sqrt{1 - k^2}$.

$$\text{sn}\,(t + K) = \text{cn}\, t/\text{dn}\, t, \qquad \text{cn}\,(t + K) = -k'\, \text{sn}\, t/\text{dn}\, t$$
$$\text{dn}\,(t + K) = k'/\text{dn}\, t,$$

(*Hint:* Show that the vector-valued function $(v/w, -k'u/w, k'/w)$ satisfies (*), and that this vector reduces at $t = K$ to $(1,0,k')$.)

(c) Prove that $\text{sn}\,(-t) = -\text{sn}\, t$, $\text{cn}\,(-t = \text{cn}\, t$, $\text{sn}\,(t + 2K) = -\text{sn}\, t$,

$$\text{cn}\,(t + 2K) = -\text{cn}\, t, \qquad \text{dn}\,(t + 2K) = \text{dn}\, t.$$

(d) Show that $\text{sn}\, t$ and $\text{cn}\, t$ have infinitely many zeros, and that the zeros of $\text{sn}\, t$ separate those of $\text{cn}\, t$.

7. Show that the system $dx/dt = -x + y$, $dy/dt = -x - y$ goes into

$$dx/dt = (y - x)/2 \qquad dy/dt = (-x - y)/2$$

under the transformation $r \to r^2$, $\theta \to 2\theta$ of polar coordinates. In what domain are the two systems "equivalent"?

8. Prove that, in the exceptional case (24) of $a = d$ and $b = c = 0$,

$$|\, \mathbf{x}(t)\, | = e^{at}\, |\, \mathbf{x}(0)\, |.$$

7. Stability. The concepts of stability and strict stability, already defined for linear DE's with constant coefficients in Ch. IV, § 5, apply to the critical points of any autonomous system. Loosely speaking, a critical point P is stable when the solution curves originating near P stay uniformly near it at all later times; P is strictly stable if, in addition, each such individual solution curve gets and stays arbitrarily near P, as t increases without limit. In vector notation, the precise definition is as follows.

DEFINITION. *The critical point* $\mathbf{a}$ *of the autonomous system* (1′) *is* stable *if and only if, given* $\epsilon > 0$, *there exists a* $\delta > 0$ *so small that, if* $|\, \mathbf{x}(0) - \mathbf{a}\, | < \delta$, *then* $|\mathbf{x}(t) - \mathbf{a}| < \epsilon$ *for all* $t > 0$. *A stable critical point which is* asymptotically stable *in the sense that, for some sufficiently small* $\delta > 0$,

$$(25) \qquad |\mathbf{x}(0) - \mathbf{a}| < \delta \textit{ implies } \lim_{t\to\infty} |\mathbf{x}(t) - \mathbf{a}| = 0,$$

is called strictly stable. *A critical point which is not stable is called* unstable; *a stable critical point which is not strictly stable is called* neutrally stable.

Evidently, any strictly stable critical point is stable, so that there are exactly three possibilities: strictly stable, neutrally stable, and unstable critical points.

THEOREM 6. *For a linear plane autonomous system, the critical point* **0** *is strictly stable if and only if its secular equation is strictly stable.*

It follows from Ch. IV, § 5 that the conditions for strict stability are $p = -(a + d) > 0$, $q = ad - bc > 0$, or $a + d < 0$, $ad > bc$.

Proof. The general solution is a linear combination

$$(26) \qquad x(t) = c_{11}f_1(t) + c_{12}f_2(t), \quad y(t) = c_{21}f_1(t) + c_{22}f_2(t),$$

where $f_1(t) = e^{\lambda t}$ and $f_2(t) = e^{\mu t}$ or (in the exceptional case $\mu = \lambda$ of a double root) perhaps $f_2(t) = te^{\mu t}$. In either case, the system (11) is strictly stable, i.e., the general solution $(x(t),y(t))$ tends to **0** as $t \to +\infty$, if and only if λ and μ both have negative real part. But this is the condition for the secular equation to be strictly stable, completing the proof.

A similar argument shows that a linear autonomous system (14) of *any* order is strictly stable if and only if all roots of the characteristic polynomial $|A - \lambda I|$ have negative real parts.

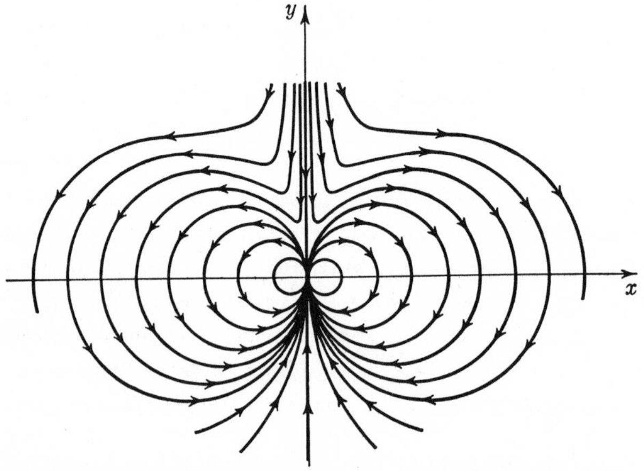

Figure VI-6. Unstable Critical Point

Caution. The asymptotic stability condition (25) implies strict stability for *linear* autonomous systems. However, one can construct unstable nonlinear systems which are asymptotically stable, as follows†. Figure VI-6 depicts sample solution curves.

EXAMPLE 6. Let D_1 be the lower half-plane $y \leqq 0$; let D_2 be the locus $x^2 + y^2 \leqq 2 \mid x \mid$, consisting of the discs $(x \pm 1)^2 + y^2 \leqq 1$; let D_3 be the half-strip $\mid x \mid \leqq 2$, $y > 0$, exterior to D_2; let D_4 be the locus $\mid x \mid > 2$, $y > 0$, all as in Figure VI-6. The system

$$\dot{x} = \begin{cases} 2xy \text{ on } D_1 \cup D_2 \cup D_3 \\ \\ 2xy/[3 - (4/\mid x \mid)] \text{ on } D_4 \end{cases}$$

$$\dot{y} = \begin{cases} y^2 - x^2 \text{ on } D_1 \cup D_2 \\ 4 \mid x \mid - y^2 - 3x^2 \text{ on } D_3 \\ (4 \mid x \mid - y^2 - 3x^2)/[3 - 4|x|] \text{ on } D_4 \end{cases}$$

is unstable, yet $\lim_{t\to\infty} \mid \mathbf{x}(t) \mid = 0$ for all orbits $\mathbf{x}(t)$.

Dynamical systems. If the DE's for an autonomous dynamical system are written in normal form, as

$$d^2q_i/dt^2 = F_i(\mathbf{q}, d\mathbf{q}/dt) = F_i(\mathbf{q},\dot{\mathbf{q}}), \qquad i = 1, \cdots, m, \tag{27}$$

and conjugate velocity variables $p_i = dq_i/dt$ are introduced, then (27) defines an autonomous system of first-order DE's

$$dq_i/dt = p_i, \qquad dp_i/dt = F_i(\mathbf{q},\mathbf{p}), \tag{27'}$$

in an associated $2m$-dimensional *phase-space.* A given point $(\mathbf{q},\mathbf{p})$ of phase-space is a *critical* point for the system (27′) if and only if $\mathbf{p} = \mathbf{0}$, and $\mathbf{F}(\mathbf{q},0) = \mathbf{0}$, so that $\mathbf{q}$ is an *equilibrium* point of the dynamical system (27).

The dynamical system (27) is called *conservative* when $F_i(\mathbf{q},\dot{\mathbf{q}}) = -\partial V/\partial q_i$ for a suitable *potential energy* function $V(\mathbf{q})$. For any conservative system, the total energy function $E(\mathbf{q},\mathbf{p}) = (\Sigma m_i p_i^2/2) + V(\mathbf{q})$ is an integral of the system (27). Moreover the point $(\mathbf{a},0)$ is a critical point of (27′) if and only if the gradient $\nabla V(\mathbf{a}) = \mathbf{0}$, so that the potential energy function has a stationary value.‡ The point is neutrally stable if the potential energy has a (strict) local minimum at $\mathbf{q} = \mathbf{a}$; it is never strictly stable.

Thus, consider the simple pendulum of Example 5, § 3, with $k = 1$. For $c = -2$, the "integral curve" reduces to a set of isolated critical points $v = 0$, $\theta = \pm 2n\pi$. If $\mid c \mid < 2$, then $\mid \theta - 2n\pi \mid < \theta_0$, where $\theta_0 < \pi$ is the smallest positive angle such that $\cos \theta_0 = -c/2$. Therefore the integral

†The authors are indebted to Mr. Thomas Brown for constructing Example 6.

‡Courant, Vol. 2, p. 186. Points where the value of a function is stationary are also often called "critical points."

curves for $-2 < c < 2$ are closed curves (loops) surrounding the origin or any one of the critical points for $\theta = \pm 2n\pi$. As $c \to -2$, these loops tend to the origin. Therefore, the origin and its translates $\theta = \pm 2n\pi$, $v = 0$, are neutrally *stable*. For $c = 2$, we have the separatrix curve defined by $v = \pm 2 \cos(\theta/2)$. From the first of equations (10′) it is seen that the direction of the motion is from $-\pi$ to π for $v > 0$, and from π to $-\pi$ for $v < 0$. Therefore the critical points $v = 0$, $\theta = \pm(2n+1)\pi$ are *unstable*. These unstable critical points occur when the pendulum is balanced vertically above the point of support.

8. Focal, nodal, and saddle-points. The results of §§ 6–7 lead to a complete classification of linear plane autonomous systems (22). This classification is based on a study of the possible root-pairs λ_1, λ_2 of the characteristic equation (cf. (13′))

$$\lambda^2 - (a+d)\lambda + (ad - bc) = \lambda^2 + p\lambda + q = 0 \tag{28}$$

of (22). By Theorem 5, it suffices to display one autonomous system for each such root-pair: any two will be equivalent! We now enumerate the different possibilities, which depend largely on the sign of the *discriminant*

$$\Delta = p^2 - 4q = (a-d)^2 + 4bc \tag{29}$$

of the characteristic equation (28). We begin with the case $\Delta \neq 0$, $q \neq 0$ of distinct nonzero roots $\lambda_1 \neq \lambda_2$.

A. *Focal points.* Suppose $\Delta < 0$, so that the characteristic equation (28) has distinct *complex* roots $\lambda_j = \mu \pm i\nu$ $(\nu \neq 0)$. This is the case $q = (\mu^2 + \nu^2)^{1/2} > 0$ and $0 \leqq p^2 = 4\mu^2 < 4q$ of a harmonic oscillator. We choose the canonical form (see the Corollary of Theorem 5 and Exs. B1–B3)

$$dx/dt = \mu x - \nu y, \qquad dy/dt = \nu x + \mu y \tag{30a}$$

for (22), whose solutions are the equiangular *spirals* $r = \rho e^{\mu t}$, $\theta = \nu t + \tau$ in polar coordinates, where $\rho \geqq 0$ and τ are arbitrary constants. When $p > 0$, the spirals approach the origin (*stable* focal point); when $p < 0$, they diverge from it (*unstable* focal point); when $p = 0$, they are closed curves representing periodic oscillations (neutrally stable *vortex* points). See Figures VI-7a and VI-7b.

B. *Nodal points.* Suppose that $\Delta > 0$ and $q > 0$, so that the roots $\lambda = \mu_1$, μ_2 of the characteristic equation (28) are real, distinct, and of the same sign. We choose as the linearly equivalent canonical form,

$$dx/dt = \mu_1 x, \quad dy/dt = \mu_2 y, \quad 0 < |\mu_1| < |\mu_2|, \tag{30b}$$

whose general solution is $(ae^{\mu_1 t}, be^{\mu_2 t})$. The system is stable when μ_1 and μ_2 are negative, and unstable when they are positive (the two subcases are related by the transformation $t \to -t$ of time reversal). Geometrically, the

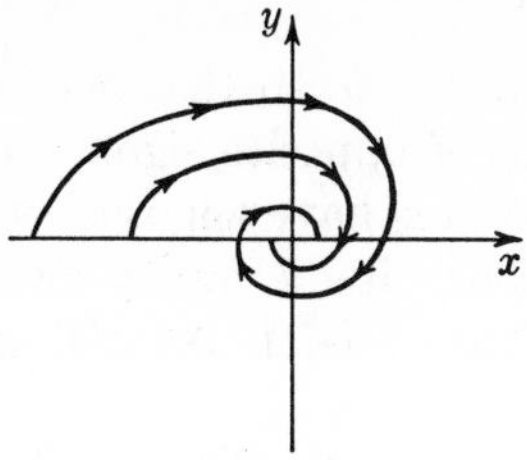

(**a**) Focal Point

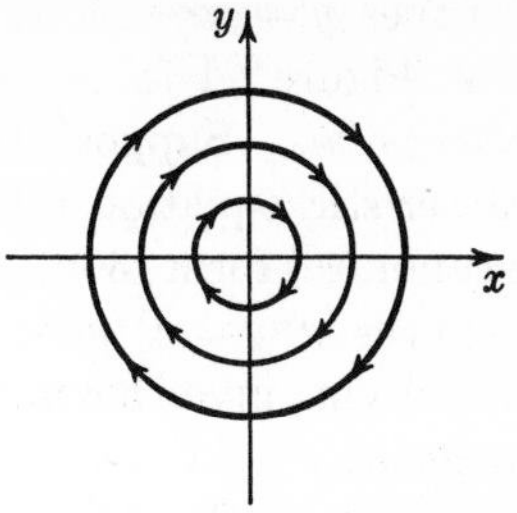

(**b**) Vortex Point

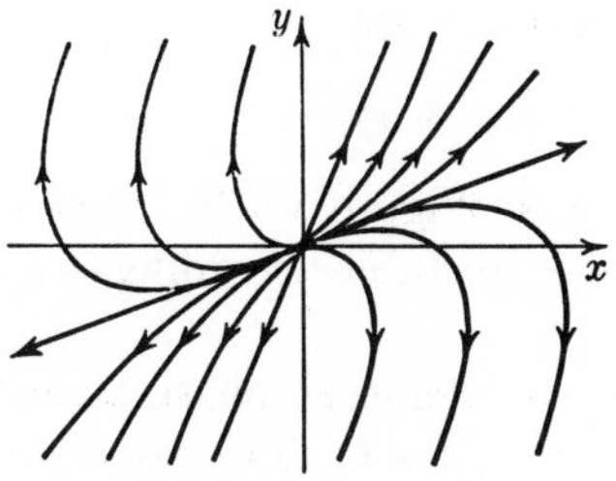

(**c**) Nodal Point

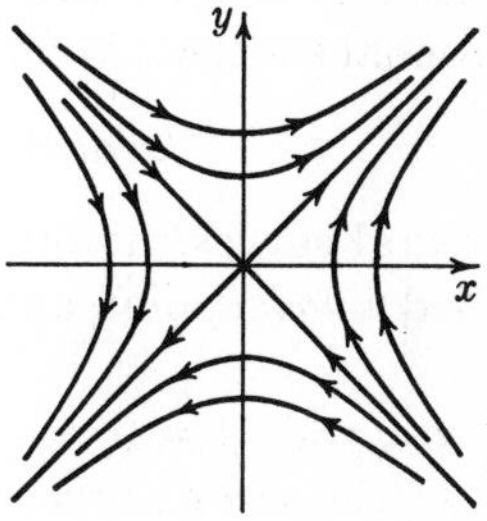

(**d**) Saddle Point

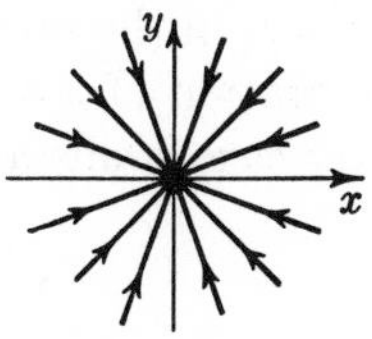

(**e**) Star Point

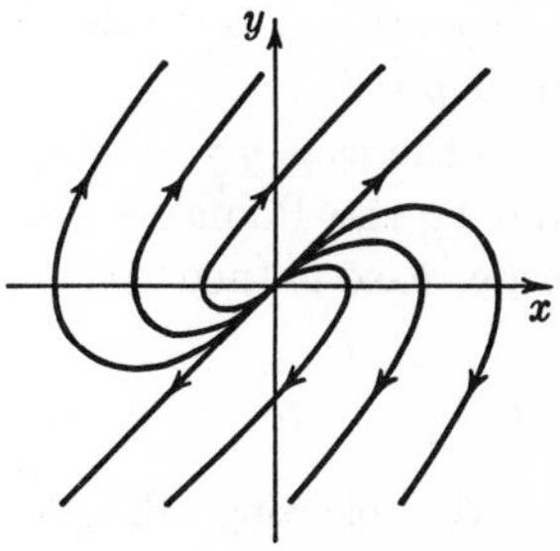

(**f**) Nodal Point

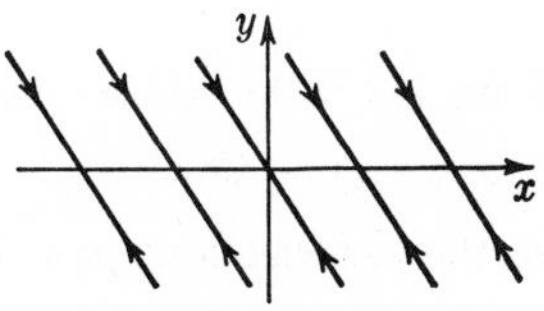

(**g**) Degenerate Case

Figure VI-7.

integral curves $y = cx^{\mu_2/\mu_1}$ look like a sheaf of parabolas, tangent at the origin, as in Figure VI-7c.

C. *Saddle-points.* Suppose that $\Delta > 0$ but $q < 0$, so that the roots of the characteristic equation (28) are real and of opposite sign. We again have the canonical form (30b). But since μ_1 and μ_2 have opposite signs, the integral curves $x^m y = c$, $m = -\mu_2/\mu_1 > 0$, look like a family of similar hyperbolas having given asymptotes, as in Figure VI-7d. A saddle-point is always *unstable.*

We now come to the degenerate case $\Delta = 0$, $q \neq 0$. The simplest such case is the exceptional case (24). In this subcase, $q = a^2 > 0$, and the integral curves consist of the straight lines through the origin, and the configuration formed by them is called a *star*, as in Figure VI-7e. In the nonexceptional subcase, we have the canonical form

$$dx/dt = ax, \qquad dy/dt = x + ay, \tag{30c}$$

whose integral curves have the appearance of Figure VI-7f. Such a point is also called a *nodal* point, and it is stable or unstable according as $a < 0$ or $a > 0$.

The case $q = 0$, $\Delta \neq 0$ corresponds to the Poincaré phase-plane representation of the second-order DE $\ddot{x} + p\dot{x} = 0$, $p \neq 0$. This corresponds to a rowboat "coasting" on a lake, with no wind and the oars shipped. The boat comes to rest in a finite distance, in infinite time. The integral curves form a family of parallel straight lines $\dot{x} + px =$ constant, as in Figure VI-7g. The origin is a stable (but not strictly stable) critical point if $p > 0$, unstable if $p < 0$.

Finally, the case $q = \Delta = 0$ reduces to $\dot{x} = \dot{y} = 0$ in the exceptional case (24), and to the Poincaré phase-plane representation of $\ddot{x} = 0$ otherwise. The former case is (neutrally) stable: the latter case is unstable.

EXERCISES C

1. For the following DE's, determine the stability and type of the solution-curves in the Poincaré phase-plane, sketching typical curves in each case:

(a) $\ddot{u} + u = 0$, (d) $\ddot{u} + \dot{u} - u = 0$,
(b) $\ddot{u} + \dot{u} + u = 0$, (e) $\ddot{u} + 2\dot{u} + u = 0$,
(c) $\ddot{u} - \dot{u} + u = 0$, (f) $\ddot{u} + 4\dot{u} + u = 0$.

2. For which of the following is $x = 0$ a stable critical point:

$$\dot{x} = x^2, \qquad \dot{x} = -x^2, \qquad \dot{x} = x^3, \qquad \dot{x} = -x^3?$$

3. Determine conditions on the coefficients a, b, c, d of (11) necessary and sufficient for neutral stability.

4. Show that $\dot{x} = X(x)$ has a strictly stable critical point at $x = 0$ if $X(0) = 0$ and $X'(0) < 0$.

5. Show that the plane autonomous system $\dot{x} = x - y$, $\dot{y} = 4x^2 + 2y^2 - 6$ has critical points at (1,1) and (−1,−1), both of them unstable.

6. Show that the system $dx/dt = \ln(1 + x + 2y)$, $dy/dt = (x/2) - y + (x^2/2)$ has an unstable critical point at the origin.

*7. Is the system (*) of Ex. B5 strictly stable, neutrally stable, or unstable at (0,0,0)?

8. Show that the autonomous system

$$dx/dt = (1/2)e^{2x} \sin 3y + 2 \sin x \cos x + e^z - 1,$$
$$dy/dt = \sin(2x + 3y), \qquad dz/dt = \tan(2x + z),$$

has an unstable critical point at $x = y = z = 0$.

9. Show that the DE $\ddot{x} + x \sin(1/x) = 0$ is neutrally stable at $x = 0$.

*10. Let $S = S(\mathbf{x})$ be a function of class $\mathcal{C}^1$ in some neighborhood of the origin, such that $S(\mathbf{0}) = 0$, while $S(\mathbf{x}) > 0$ if $0 < |\mathbf{x}| < \epsilon$, for some $\epsilon > 0$.

(a) Prove that the system $d\mathbf{x}/dt = \mathbf{X}(\mathbf{x})$ is *unstable* at the origin if $\Sigma X_i \, \partial S/\partial x_i > 0$ there, and is strictly stable if $\Sigma X_i \, \partial S/\partial x_i < 0$ there.

(b) Derive from (a) a stability criterion for the autonomous n-th order DE

$$d^n x/dt^n = \Phi(x, dx/dt, \cdots, d^{n-1}x/dt^{n-1}).$$

11. Show that the integral curves in Example 6 are the semicircles

$$x^2 + y^2 = \pm 2ax \text{ in } D_1 \cup D_2,$$

and of the form $x(x^2 - 2|x| + y^2) = \text{constant}$ in $D_3 \cup D_4$.

9. Method of Liapounov. Formula (15) of § 4 shows that a first approximation to autonomous systems generally, near critical points, is provided by homogeneous linear systems. But it does not show how closely the *solutions* of an autonomous system, near a critical point, resemble those of the associated linear system obtained by omitting higher-order terms. We now show that, so far as the *strict stability* of critical points is concerned, the linear terms are decisive.

THEOREM 7. *If the critical point* (0,0) *of the linear plane autonomous system* (11) *is strictly stable, then so is that of the perturbed system*

$$\dot{x} = ax + by + \xi(x,y), \qquad \dot{y} = cx + dy + \eta(x,y), \tag{31}$$

provided† $|\xi(x,y)| + |\eta(x,y)| = 0(x^2 + y^2)$.

Idea of proof. The proof is based on a simple geometrical idea due to Liapounov. Let $E(x,y)$ be any function having a strict local minimum at the origin. For small positive C, the level curves $E(x,y) = E(0,0) + C$ constitute a family of small concentric loops, roughly elliptical in shape, enclosing the origin. Now examine the direction of the vector field defined by (31) on these small loops. Intuition suggests that the critical point will be strictly stable whenever, for all small enough loops, the vector field points inwards. For this implies that any trajectory which once crosses a loop is forever trapped inside it. For to leave it, the trajectory would have

†The symbol $0(x^2 + y^2)$ stands for a function bounded by $M(x^2 + y^2)$ for some constant M and all sufficiently small x, y.

to cross the loop from inside out, and so the vector at the crossing-point could not point inward. Such a function $E(x,y)$ is called a *Liapounov function*; one can think of it as a generalized *energy function*, and the geometrical picture just described as stating that energy is constantly being lost near the critical point under consideration. The problem is to construct the appropriate Liapounov function having a negative time-derivative along trajectories.

We now construct such a Liapounov function, for each of the three canonical forms (30a)–(30c) derived in § 8. Since the definition of stability is invariant under linear transformations of coordinates, it suffices to consider these three cases.

As regards the linear terms in (31), the necessary calculations are simple. The Liapounov function can be taken as a positive definite quadratic function $E = \alpha x^2 + 2\beta xy + \gamma y^2$, $\alpha > 0$, $\alpha\gamma > \beta^2$, whose level curves are a family of concentric coaxial ellipses. We will show, by considering cases separately, that $\dot{E} \leqq -kE$ for some positive constant k.

In (30a), the Liapounov function $E = x^2 + y^2$ satisfies

$$\dot{E} = 2(x\dot{x} + y\dot{y}) = 2\mu E.$$

In the strictly stable case, $\mu < 0$. In (30b), the same Liapounov function satisfies $\dot{E} = 2(x\dot{x} + y\dot{y}) = 2\mu_1 x^2 + 2\mu_2 y^2 \leqq 2\mu_1 E$, in the strictly stable case $0 > \mu_1 \geqq \mu_2$. (By allowing equality, we take care also of the exceptional case of a star-point.) In (30c), the Liapounov function $E = x^2 + a^2y^2$ satisfies, in the strictly stable case $a < 0$

$$\dot{E} = 2(x\dot{x} + a^2y\dot{y}) = 2(ax^2 + a^2xy + a^3y^2) = aE + a(x + ay)^2 \leqq aE.$$

Hence, in the three possible cases of strict linear stability, $\dot{E} = 2\mu E$, $\dot{E} \leqq 2\mu_1 E$, or $\dot{E} \leqq aE$, where the coefficient on the right side is negative. Thus, $\dot{E} \leqq -kE$ for some $k > 0$, in every case. Since the quadratic function $E(x,y)$ is positive definite, $E(x,y) \geqq K(x^2 + y^2)$ for some constant $K > 0$.

We now consider the nonlinear system (31). Since E_x and E_y are linear functions of x and y,

$$| E_x\xi + E_y\eta | = 0(| x | + | y |)(x^2 + y^2).$$

Hence, for some $\epsilon > 0$, $E(x,y) \leqq \epsilon$ implies $| E_x\xi + E_y\eta | \leqq kE(x,y)/2$.

Now let $(x(t),y(t))$ be a trajectory of (31) such that $E(x(t_0),y(t_0)) \leqq \epsilon$. Along this trajectory, for $t \geqq t_0$, $E(t) = E(x(t),y(t))$ will satisfy

$$\dot{E}(t) \leqq -kE + | E_x\xi + E_y\eta | \leqq -kE(t)/2.$$

By Theorem 7 of Chapter I, it follows that $E(t) \leqq E(t_0)e^{-k(t-t_0)/2}$. Hence $E(t)$ approaches zero exponentially. Since $E(x,y) \geqq K(x^2 + y^2)$, it follows at once that the trajectory tends to the origin.

10. Undamped nonlinear oscillations. The classification made in § 8 covers linear oscillators near equilibrium points, which correspond to critical points in the Poincaré phase-plane. We will now study the nonlinear oscillations of a particle with one degree of freedom, about a position of stable equilibrium. The case of undamped (i.e., frictionless) oscillations will be treated first. This case is described by the second-order DE

$$\ddot{x} + q(x) = 0. \tag{32}$$

In the Poincaré phase-plane, this corresponds to the plane autonomous system

$$dx/dt = v, \qquad dv/dt = -q(x). \tag{33}$$

By a translation of coordinates, we can move any position of equilibrium to $x = 0$; hence we can let $q(0) = 0$. If equilibrium is stable, then the "restoring force" $q(x)$ must act in a direction opposite to the displacement x, at least for small displacements. Hence we assume $xq(x) > 0$ for $x \neq 0$ sufficiently small. This will make the system (33) have an isolated critical point at $x = v = 0$, as in the case of the simple pendulum (Example 5, § 3).

The key to the analysis of systems (32) is the *potential energy* integral

$$V(x) = \int_0^x q(\xi)d\xi. \tag{34}$$

Since $xq(x) > 0$, the function $V(x)$ is increasing when x is positive and decreasing when x is negative; it has a local minimum $V(0) = 0$ at $x = 0$. Differentiating the *total energy*

$$E(x,v) = v^2/2 + V(x), \tag{35}$$

with respect to t, we get $\dot{E} = \dot{x}[\ddot{x} + q(x)] = 0$, hence $E(x,v)$ is a constant along any trajectory in the Poincaré phase-plane. We also note that $E(x,v)$ has a strict local minimum at (0,0).

THEOREM 8. *If $q \in \mathcal{C}^1$, and if $xq(x) > 0$ for small nonzero x, then the critical point (0,0) of the system (33) is a vortex point*†.

Proof. For any given positive constant E, the locus $v^2/2 + V(x) = E$ is an integral curve, where $V(0) = 0$ and $V(x)$ increases with $|x|$, on both sides of $x = 0$. These curves are symmetric under reflection $(x,v) \to (x, -v)$ in the x-axis; they slope down with slope $-q(x)/v$ in the first and third quadrants, and up in the second and fourth quadrants. For any given small value of E, the function $E - V(x)$ has a maximum at $x = 0$, and decreases monotonically on both sides, crossing zero at points $x = -B$ and $x = A$, where B and A are small and positive. Hence each locus $v^2 = 2[E - V(x)]$ is a simple closed curve, symmetric about the x-axis.

†As in the linear case, a critical point of a plane autonomous system is called a *vortex point* when nearby solution curves are concentric simple closed curves.

As the energy parameter E decreases, so does $|v| = \sqrt{2[E - V(x)]}$; hence the simple closed curves defined by the trajectories of (34) shrink monotonically towards the origin as $E \downarrow 0$. In fact, consider the new coordinates (u,v), defined by $u = \pm\sqrt{2V(x)}$, according as x is positive or negative. The transformation $(x,v) \to (u,v)$ is of class $\mathcal{C}^1$ with a nonvanishing Jacobian, near (0,0), if $q'(0)$ exists and is positive. Hence the integral curves of (33) resemble a distorted family of circles $u^2 + v^2 = 2E$.

11. Soft and hard springs. The most familiar special case of (32) is the undamped linear oscillator

$$\ddot{x} + qx = 0, \qquad q = k^2 > 0, \tag{36}$$

for which $q(x) = k^2x$. The general solution of (36) is the function $x = A\cos[k(t - t_0)]$, representing an *oscillation* of *amplitude* A, *frequency* $k/2\pi$ (period $2\pi/k$), and *phase* t_0.

In other cases, the DE (32) can be imagined as determining the motion of a unit mass, attached to an *elastic spring* which resists a displacement x by a force $q(x)$, independent of the velocity $\dot{x}$. The ratio $h(x) = q(x)/x$ is called the *stiffness* of the spring; it is bounded for bounded x if $q \in \mathcal{C}^1$ and $q(0) = 0$. The case (36) of a linear spring is the case of constant stiffness (Hooke's Law). For linear springs, the formulas of the last paragraph show that the frequency $f = k/2\pi$ increases as the square root of the stiffness k^2, and is independent of the amplitude. We will now show that, for *nonlinear* springs, the frequency f still increases with the stiffness, but is amplitude-dependent in general.

Indeed, the force-law (32) implies $\dot{x} = v = \sqrt{2[E - V(x)]}$. Hence if the limits of oscillation (i.e., the smallest negative and positive roots of the equation $V(x) = E$) are $x = -B$ and $x = A$, then the period T of the complete oscillation is

$$T = 2\int_{-B}^{A} \frac{dx}{\sqrt{2[E - V(x)]}}. \tag{37}$$

The integral (37) is improper, but it converges provided $q(x)$ does not vanish at $-B$ or A; hence it converges for all sufficiently small amplitudes if $q \in \mathcal{C}^1$ in the stable case $h(0) > 0$.

We now compare the periods T and T_1 of the oscillation of two springs, having stiffness $h(x)$ and $h_1(x) \geqq h(x)$, and the same limits of oscillation $-B$ and A. By (35), $E = \int_0^A q(u)du = V(A)$; hence $E - V(x) = \int_x^A q(u)du$. By the stiffness inequality assumed above, therefore,

$$E - V(x) = \int_x^A q(u)du \leqq \int^A q_1(u)du = E - V_1(x), \qquad 0 \leqq x \leqq A.$$

Reversing the sign of x, we can prove the same inequality for $-B \leqq x \leqq 0$.

Substituting into (37), we get $T \geqq T_1$. We thus get the following Comparison Theorem.

THEOREM 9. *For any two oscillations having the same span* $[-B, A]$, *the period becomes shorter and the frequency greater as the stiffness* $q(x)/x$ *increases in* (32).

Springs for which $h(x) = h(-x)$ are called symmetric; this makes $q(-x) = -q(x)$ and $V(-x) = V(x)$, so that $B = A$ in the preceding formulas: symmetric springs oscillate symmetrically about their equilibrium position. Hence, for symmetric springs, the phrase "span $[-B, A]$" in Theorem 9 can be replaced by "amplitude A."

For any symmetric spring, $h'(0) = 0$; if $h''(0)$ is positive, so that $h(x)$ increases with $|x|$, the spring is said to be "hard"; if $h''(0)$ is negative, so that $h(x)$ decreases as $|x|$ increases, it is said to be "soft." Thus the simple pendulum of Example 5, § 3, acts as a "soft" spring. We now show that the period of oscillation is amplitude-dependent, at least for symmetric hard and soft springs.

THEOREM 10. *The period of a hard symmetric spring decreases as the span of oscillation increases; the period of a soft symmetric spring increases with the span.*

Proof. The period is given by (37); it suffices to compare the periods of quarter-oscillations, say from 0 to A and from 0 to A_1, with $A_1 > A$. We write $A_1 = cA$, with $c > 1$. To study the period p_1 of the quarter-oscillation from 0 to $cA = A_1$, we let $x = cy$ in (32). The equivalent DE for y is

$$d^2y/dt^2 + yh(cy) = 0, \tag{38}$$

where $h(x) = q(x)/x$. The oscillation of amplitude cA for (32) corresponds to the oscillation of amplitude A for (38); and, since the independent variable t is unchanged, the periods of oscillation are the same for both. Therefore it suffices to compare the quarter-periods p and p_1 for amplitude A for the two springs (32) and (38), respectively. Using Theorem 9, we find that for $y > 0$, if $yh(cy) \geqq q(y) = yh(y)$, that is, if $h(cy) \geqq h(y)$ for $c > 1$ (hard spring), then $p_1 \leqq p$, that is, the period decreases as the amplitude increases. Soft springs can be treated similarly.

EXERCISES D

1. (a) Show that the integral curves of $\ddot{x} - x + x^3 = 0$ in the Poincaré phase-plane are the curves $v^2 - x^2 + x^4/2 = C$.

(b) Sketch the curves.

(c) Show that the autonomous system defining these curves has a saddle-point at (0,0) and vortex points at $(0, \pm 1)$.

2. Duffing's equation without forcing term is $\ddot{x} + qx + rx^3 = 0$. Show that, for oscillations of small but finite half-amplitude L, the period T is

$$T = 4\sqrt{2}\int_0^{\pi/2} \frac{d\theta}{\sqrt{2q + rL^2(1 + \sin^2\theta)}}.$$

Verify Theorem 10 in this special case as a corollary.

3. (a) From the assumptions of Ex. B5, show that the function $u = \operatorname{sn} t$ satisfies the second-order DE

$$(**) \qquad \ddot{u} + (1 + k^2)u - 2k^2u^3 = 0.$$

(b) Infer from (**), that $\dot{u}^2 + (1 + k^2)u^2 - k^2u^4 = \text{constant}$.

(c) Sketch the integral curves of the DE (**) in the Poincaré phase-plane, marking the special curve ($\operatorname{sn} t$, $\operatorname{cn} t \operatorname{dn} t$), and any other critical points.

(d) Determine the nature of the other critical points, if any.

*4. (a) Show that a one-parameter family of solutions of $\ddot{\theta} + k^2 \sin\theta = 0$ is given by $\sin(\theta/2) = \sin(\alpha/2)\operatorname{sn}[k(t - t_0)]$, where α is the amplitude of oscillation.

(b) Show that $\ddot{\theta} = 2k \sin(\alpha/2)\operatorname{cn}[k(t - t_0)]$.

5. The Weierstrass p-function satisfies the DE $d^2p/dx^2 = 6p^2 - g_2/2$, g_2 a constant. What are its critical points in the (p,p')-plane, that is, the Poincaré phase-plane, and what are their types?

6. The equation of a falling stone in air satisfies approximately the DE

$$\ddot{x} = g - \dot{x}^2/v^2,$$

where v is the "terminal velocity." Sketch the integral curves of this DE in the Poincaré phase-plane, and interpret them physically.

*7. A stone thrown through the air satisfies approximately the system of DE's

$$dv/dt = -g[(v/V)^2 + \sin\theta], \qquad d\theta/dt = (g\cos\theta)/v,$$

where θ is the angle with the horizontal and V is the terminal velocity. Sketch the integral curves in the (v,θ)-*cylinder*. (N.B. The variable θ is periodic modulo 2π.)

8. Show that the origin is a stable critical point of the system

$$\dot{x} = ax + by + \epsilon_1(x,y), \qquad \dot{y} = cx + dy + \epsilon_2(x,y),$$

if $a + d < 0$, $ad > bc$, and $|\epsilon_1(x,y)| + |\epsilon_2(x,y)| = 0(x^2 + y^2)$.

9. Discuss the dependence on the sign of the constant μ, of the critical point at the origin of the system

$$\dot{u} = -v + \mu u^3, \qquad \dot{v} = u + \mu v^3.$$

10. (a) Show that the trajectories of $\ddot{x} + q(x) = 0$ in the Poincaré phase-plane are convex closed curves if $q(x)$ is an increasing function with $q(0) = 0$.

(b) Is the converse true?

11. Show that if $\dot{x} = ax + by$, $\dot{y} = cx + dy$ is unstable at the origin, if $ad \neq bc$, and

$$X(x,y) = ax + by + 0(x^2 + y^2), \qquad Y(x,y) = cx + dy + 0(x^2 + y^2),$$

and $\Delta \neq 0$, then the system $\dot{x} = X(x,y)$, $\dot{y} = Y(x,y)$ is unstable there.

*12. Show that the plane autonomous system $\dot{x} = y - x^3$, $\dot{y} = -x^3$ is stable, though its linearization is unstable. (*Hint:* Show that $x^{10} + 5y^2$ is a Liapounov function.)

*13. Show that for the analytic plane autonomous system

$$\dot{x} = 2x^3y, \qquad \dot{y} = x^2y^2 - x^4 - y^{11}$$

the origin is an unstable critical point which is asymptotically stable. (*Hint:* Study Example 6. To prove instability, show that the ellipse $4y^2 = x - x^2$ cannot be crossed from the left in the first quadrant.)

12. Damped nonlinear oscillations. The equation of motion for a particle of mass m having an equilibrium point at $x = 0$, in the presence of a restoring force $mq(x)$ and a friction force $f(x,v) = mvp(x,v)$, is

$$(39) \qquad \ddot{x} + p(x,\dot{x})\dot{x} + q(x) = 0, \qquad q(x) = xh(x), \qquad p \in \mathcal{C}^2, h \in \mathcal{C}^1.$$

When $h(0)$ is positive, the equilibrium point is called *statically stable.* This is because the restoring force tends to restore equilibrium under static conditions (when $v = 0$). The conservative system (32) obtained from any statically stable system (39), by omitting the friction term $\dot{x}\, p(x,\dot{x})$, is neutrally stable by Theorem 8.

The DE (39) has a very simple interpretation in the Poincaré phase-plane, as

$$(40) \qquad dx/dt = v, \qquad dv/dt = -vp(x,v) - q(x).$$

The critical points of the system (40) are all on the x-axis, where $\dot{x} = v = 0$; they are the equilibrium points $(x,0)$ where $q(x) = 0$ in (39). Since $q(0) = 0h(0) = 0$ in (39), the origin is always a critical point of (40); unless $h(0)$ changes sign, there is no other.

We will consider below only the case $h(x) > 0$ of static stability in the large, which is the case of greatest interest for applications. For simplicity, we will also assume that $p(0,0) \neq 0$.

Under these assumptions, the origin is the only critical point of (40). Moreover the direction field, whose slope is

$$dv/dx = \tau(x,v) = -p(x,v) - q(x)/v,$$

points to the right in the upper half-plane, where $\dot{x} = v > 0$, and to the left in the lower half-plane. On the x-axis, the solution curves have finite curvature $q(x)$; they cut it vertically downward on the positive x-axis and vertically upward on the negative x-axis; thus the solution curves have a general clockwise orientation.

Conversely, any continuous oriented direction field with the properties specified represents a DE of the form (39) in the Poincaré phase-plane. From this it is clear that the behavior of the solutions of the DE's of the form (39) can be extremely varied. We discuss below only a few simple possibilities.

By Theorem 7, the critical point at the origin is strictly stable when the *damping* factor $p(0,0)$ is *positive.* The equilibrium point $x = 0$ of (39) is then said to be *dynamically stable*: the solution curves tend towards the origin, in the vicinity of the origin.

When $p(0,0)$ is negative, the system is said to be *negatively damped*, and the equilibrium point to be *dynamically unstable*. Since (39) can be rewritten as

$$\frac{d^2x}{d(-t)^2} - p\left(x, \frac{dx}{d(-t)}\right)\frac{dx}{d(-t)} + xh(x) = 0, \tag{40'}$$

we see that the substitutions $t \to -t$, $x \to x$, $v \to -v$, of time-reversal reverse the sign of $p(x,\dot{x})$, but do not affect (39) otherwise. Hence, if $p(0,0) < 0$, all solution curves of (40) tend outwards near the origin.

13.* Limit cycles. We now come to a major difference between nonlinear oscillations and linear oscillations. When a linear oscillator is negatively damped, the amplitude of oscillation always increases exponentially without limit. Whereas the amplitude of oscillation of a negatively damped, statically stable, nonlinear oscillator commonly tends to a finite limit. The limiting periodic oscillation of finite amplitude so approached is called a *limit cycle*.

The simplest DE which gives rise to a limit cycle is the *Rayleigh equation*

$$\ddot{x} - \mu(1 - \dot{x}^2)\dot{x} + x = 0, \qquad \mu > 0. \tag{41}$$

The characteristic feature of this DE is the fact that the damping is negative for small $\dot{x}$ and positive for large $\dot{x}$. Hence it tends to increase the amplitude of small oscillations, and to decrease the amplitude of large oscillations. In between these two types of motions there is an oscillation of constant amplitude, a limit cycle.

If one differentiates the Rayleigh equation (41), and sets $y = \dot{x}/\sqrt{3}$, one gets the *van der Pol equation*

$$\ddot{y} - \mu(1 - y^2)\dot{y} + y = 0, \qquad \mu > 0. \tag{42}$$

This DE arises in the study of vacuum tubes. The sign of the damping term depends on the magnitude of the displacement y. The remarks about the Rayleigh equation made above apply also to the van der Pol equation.

As stated in § 12, negatively damped nonlinear oscillators can give rise to a great variety of qualitatively different solution curve configurations in the Poincaré phase-plane. For any particular DE (39), such as the Rayleigh or van der Pol equation with given μ, one can determine the behavior of solutions by integrating the DE

$$[v + p(x,v)]dv + q(x)dx = dE + p(x,v)dv$$

graphically (Ch. I, § 7). Figure VI-8 depicts sample integral curves for the van der Pol equation with $\mu = 0.1$, $\mu = 1$, and $\mu = 10$ so obtained. More accurate results can be had using numerical integration. With modern computing machines, using the techniques to be described in Chapter VIII, it is a routine operation to obtain such families of integral curves.

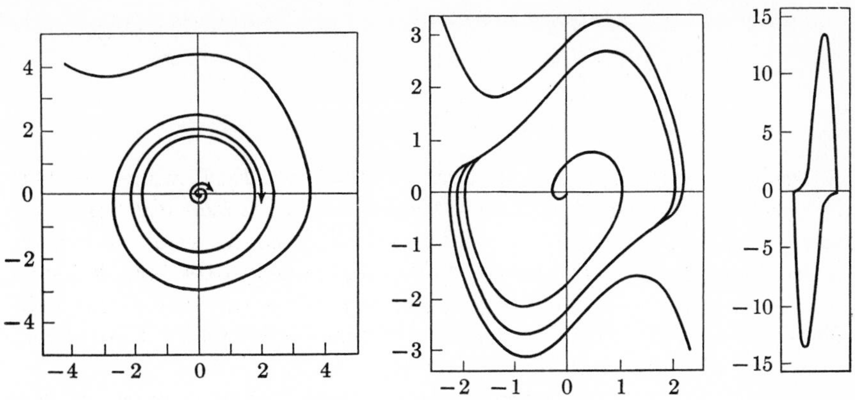

Figure VI-8. Van der Pol Equation

Liénard equation. General criteria are also available which determine the qualitative behavior of the oscillations directly from that of the coefficient-functions. Such criteria are especially useful for DE's depending on parameters, because graphical integration then becomes very tedious. They are available for DE's of the form

$$\ddot{x} + f(x)\dot{x} + q(x) = 0 \qquad \text{(Liénard equation).} \tag{43}$$

The van der Pol equation is a Liénard equation; moreover it is *symmetric* in the sense that $-x(t)$ is a solution if $x(t)$ is a solution. This holds whenever $q(-x) = -q(x)$ is odd and $f(-x) = f(x)$ is even.

One can prove the *existence* of limit cycles for a wide class of Liénard equations, and even that *every* nontrivial solution is either a limit cycle, or a spiral which tends towards a limit cycle as $t \to +\infty$. This is true if: (i) $xq(x) > 0$ for $x \neq 0$, (ii) $f(x)$ in (43) is negative in an interval $a < x < b$ containing the origin, and positive outside this interval, and

$$\int_0^\infty f(x)dx = \int_{-\infty}^0 f(x)dx = +\infty. \tag{44}$$

We sketch the proof†.

In the (x,v)-plane, solution curves satisfy

$$dv/dx + f(x) + q(x)/v = 0 \qquad \text{if} \qquad v \neq 0. \tag{45}$$

It follows, since $xq(x) > 0$, that they can only cross the x-axis downwards if $x > 0$, and upwards if $x < 0$. Also, between successive crossings of the x-axis, $v(x)$ is a bounded single-valued function, decreasing in magnitude if $x > b$ in the upper half-plane, and if $x < a$ in the lower half-plane, all by (45).

†For a complete proof, see Lefschetz, p. 247, or Niemytskii and Stepanov.

Now consider the *Liénard function*

$$E(x,v) = \tfrac{1}{2}[v + F(x)]^2 + U(x), \quad F(x) = \int_0^x f(x)dx, \tag{46}$$
$$U(x) = \int_0^x q(x)dx \geqq 0.$$

A straightforward calculation gives $dE/dt = -q(x)F(x)$, where by (44) $F(x)$ becomes positively infinite as $|x| \to \infty$. For sufficiently large $|x|$, since $xq(x) > 0$, dE/dt is identically negative. Since the set of all (x,v) for which $E(x,v) \leqq E_0$, any finite constant, is contained in the bounded strip $x + F(x) \leqq 2E_0$, it also follows that solution curves can stay in one half-plane ($v > 0$ or $v < 0$) for only a finite distance (and time): if nontrivial, they must cut the x-axis infinitely often.

Let $x_0, x_1, x_2, \cdots$ be successive zero-crossings; we can assume $x_{2n} > 0$ and $x_{2n+1} < 0$ without loss of generality. If $x_2 = x_0$, then (by uniqueness) $x_{2n} = x_0$ and $x_{2n+1} = x_1$ for all $n > 0$; the solution curve is a limit cycle. Likewise, if $x_2 > x_0$, then $x_{2n} > x_{2n-2}$ and $x_{2n+1} < x_{2n-1}$ for all $n > 0$, and the solution curve spirals outwards as t increases. Similarly, if $x_2 < x_0$, then the solution curve must spiral inward.

Finally, since $f(0) < 0$, Theorem 7 applies if $f, g \in \mathcal{C}^1$: solution curves near the origin must spiral outwards. Also,

$$E(x_{2n},0) - E(x_{2n-1},0) = -\int_{x_{2n-1}}^{x_{2n}} q(x)F(x)dx,$$

and the definite integral is negative for sufficiently large oscillations since $xq(x) > 0$ and $F(\pm\infty) = +\infty$, by (44). Hence every solution curve sufficiently far from the origin must spiral inwards. Therefore, every oscillation of sufficiently large initial amplitude must spiral inwards towards a limit cycle of maximum amplitude. Likewise, every oscillation of sufficiently small initial amplitude must spiral outwards to a smallest limit cycle.

For the Rayleigh and van der Pol equations, these limit cycles are the same. Hence every nontrivial solution tends to a unique limit cycle, which is stable. The preceding result holds under much more general conditions. We quote one set of such conditions without proof.

LEVINSON–SMITH THEOREM. *In* (43), *let* $q(x) = xh(x)$, *where* $h(x) > 0$, *and let* $f(x)$ *be negative in an interval* (a,b) *containing the origin, and positive outside this interval. Let* $q(-x) = -q(x)$, $f(-x) = f(x)$, *and let* (44) *hold. Then* (43) *has a unique stable limit cycle in the Poincaré phase-plane, towards which every nontrivial integral curve tends.*

EXERCISES E

1. Show that any DE

$$\ddot{x} + (px^2 - q)\dot{x} + rx = 0,$$

where q and r are positive constants, can be reduced to the van der Pol DE by a change of dependent and independent variables.

2. (a) Show that the autonomous plane system

$$\dot{u} = u - v - u^3 - uv^2, \qquad \dot{v} = u + v - v^3 - u^2v$$

has a unique critical point, which is unstable, and a unique limit cycle.

(b) Discuss the stability of the related system

$$\dot{u} = -u - v + u^3 + uv^2, \qquad \dot{v} = u - v + v^3 + u^2v,$$

with special reference to oscillations of very small and very large amplitude.

3. In the DE $\ddot{x} + q(x) = 0$, let $V(x) = \int_0^x q(u)du$, and let q be a continuous function satisfying a Lipschitz condition. Show that if $V(x_1) = V(x_2)$ and $V(x) > V(x_1)$ for $x_1 < x < x_2$, then the equivalent autonomous system (40) has a periodic solution passing through the points $(x_1,0)$ and $(x_2,0)$.

4. Show that the plane autonomous system

$$\dot{r} = (r^3 - r)/100, \qquad \dot{\theta} = 1, \qquad \text{(polar coordinates)}$$

has just one limit cycle.

5. Discuss the limit cycles of the system

$$\dot{r} = (r/100)\sin(1/r), \qquad \dot{\theta} = 1.$$

6. Prove in detail that, for $\mu = 1$ and the initial condition $x(0) = 10$, $\dot{x}(0) = 0$, the amplitude of successive oscillations decreases in the Rayleigh DE (41).

7. Same question for the van der Pol DE, if $y(0) = 10$, $\dot{y}(0) = 0$.

8. Sketch the integral curves of the van der Pol DE in the Poincaré phase-plane for $\mu = 100$. (*Hint.* Most of the time, the integral curves are "relaxation oscillations," near $\dot{y} = 0$ or $y = 1$.)

9. Same question for the Rayleigh DE.

ADDITIONAL EXERCISES

1. Locate the critical points of the DE $\dot{x} = x(1 - x)(a - x)$, and discuss how their stability or instability varies with a.

2. Same question for $\dot{x} = x(1 - x)(x - a)$.

3. Show that, in the complex domain, every system $\dot{x} = ax + by$, $\dot{y} = cx + dy$ is linearly equivalent to either $\dot{x} = \lambda x$, $\dot{y} = \mu y$ or to $\dot{x} = \lambda x$, $\dot{y} = \lambda y + x$, for suitable λ, μ.

4. Show that, in the *punctured* plane $x^2 + y^2 > 0$, two linear systems (11) are equivalent provided their discriminants Δ, Δ' are not zero, and they both have either (a) stable focal points, (b) unstable focal points, (c) vortex points, (d) stable nodal points, (e) unstable nodal points, or (f) saddle-points.

5. Consider the linear autonomous system

$$\dot{x} = a_1x + a_2y + a_3z, \qquad \dot{y} = b_1x + b_2y + b_3z, \qquad \dot{z} = c_1x + c_2y + c_3z.$$

(a) Show that the x-component of any solution satisfies

$$(\sigma) \qquad \frac{d^3x}{dt^3} = p_1\ddot{x} - p_2\dot{x} + p_3x, \qquad \text{where} \qquad p_1 = a_1 + b_2 + c_3,$$

$$p_2 = a_1b_2 - a_2b_1 + b_2c_3 - b_3c_2 + c_3a_1 - c_1a_3, \qquad p_3 = \begin{vmatrix} a_1 & a_2 & a_3 \\ b_1 & b_2 & b_3 \\ c_1 & c_2 & c_3 \end{vmatrix}.$$

(b) Show that the *secular equation* (σ) is invariant under any nonsingular linear transformation of the variables x,y,z.

(c) Conversely, show that if the polynomial $\lambda^3 = p_1\lambda^2 + p_2\lambda + p_3$ has distinct real roots $\lambda_1, \lambda_2, \lambda_3$, then the given DE is linearly equivalent to $\dot{\xi}_j = \lambda_j\xi_j (j = 1, 2, 3)$.

(*d) Work out a set of real canonical forms for the given DE, with respect to linear equivalence, in the general case.

6. Let $\nabla U = \mathbf{X}$, $U = U(x, \sqrt{y^2 + z^2})$, be any axially symmetric gradient field of class $\mathcal{C}^1$. Show that the DE $\dot{\mathbf{x}} = \nabla U$ admits as an integral the "stream function" $V = \int r[(\partial U/\partial x)dr + (\partial U/\partial r)dx]$, the integral being independent of the path.

7. Sketch the integral curves in the Poincaré phase-plane for:

(a) $\ddot{x} + x + \dfrac{A}{x - a} = 0$,

(b) $\ddot{x} + \dot{x}/|\dot{x}| = 0$ (Coulomb friction),

(c) $\ddot{x} + \dot{x}|\dot{x}| + k \sin x = 0$.

8. Let $q(x)$ be an increasing function, with $q(0) = 0$ and $q(-L) = -q(L)$; let $Q(x) = [q(x) - q(-x)]/2$. Show that the period of oscillation of half-amplitude L for $\ddot{x} + Q(x) = 0$ is less than that for $\ddot{x} + q(x) = 0$, unless $q(-x) = -q(x)$ for all $x \in [0,L]$.

9. Show that the DE's $\dot{x} = 2x + \sin x$ and $\dot{x} = 2x$ are equivalent on $(-\infty,+\infty)$, but that $\dot{x} = x + x^3$ is not equivalent to $\dot{x} = x$. (*Hint:* Consider the escape time.)

10. Show that if $a_1 < a_2 < \cdots < a_n$ and $b_1 < b_2 < \cdots < b_n$, then the DE's $\dot{x} = \Pi(x - a_i)$ and $\dot{x} = \Pi(x - b_i)$ are equivalent.

CHAPTER VII

Approximate Solutions

1. Introduction. In many problems, one needs to know not the exact solution of a DE for given initial conditions, but only a good approximation to the solution over a limited range, together with an estimate of the error. Such approximate solutions are usually constructed as functions which *nearly* satisfy the given DE, deviating from it by very little.

DEFINITION. *A vector function* $\mathbf{y}(t)$ *is an* approximate solution *with* deviation *at most* ϵ *in the interval* $a \leqq t \leqq a + T$ *of the vector DE*

$$(1) \qquad d\mathbf{x}/dt = \mathbf{X}(\mathbf{x}, t), \qquad a \leqq t \leqq a + T,$$

when $\mathbf{y}(t)$ *is continuous, and satisfies the differential inequality*

$$(2) \qquad | \mathbf{y}'(t) - \mathbf{X}(\mathbf{y}(t), t) | \leqq \epsilon$$

for all except a finite number of points t of the interval $[a, a + t]$.

Note that the definition requires that the function $\mathbf{y}$ be differentiable except at a finite — possibly empty — set of points. Such a function is said† to be of class $\mathfrak{D}^1$.

EXAMPLE 1. The function $y(t) \equiv 1$ is an approximate solution of the DE $dx/dt = x/100$ on the interval $[0, \infty)$, with deviation 0.01.

EXAMPLE 2. The function $y(t) \equiv 0$ is an approximate solution of the DE $dx/dt = x^{2/3} + 10^{-4}$ on the interval $[0,\infty)$ with deviation 0.0001.

The preceding example shows that the deviation of an approximate solution of a DE is not necessarily a good measure of the difference between it and the exact solution satisfying the same initial conditions, that is, of the *error*.

In this chapter and the next, we shall study methods for computing approximate solutions of ordinary DE's, and for estimating their errors. These methods will differ radically from those considered so far. Thus Picard's method of successive approximation (Ch. V, § 7) is ineffective for the purpose at hand, because it involves repeated quadratures which can rarely be performed explicitly. Power series methods (Ch. III), though more effective, are limited in practice to analytic DE's over short intervals.

†Widder, p. 400.

Approximate function tables. The most effective methods for computing approximate solutions of DE's proceed directly to the construction of an approximate *function table*, giving approximate values of the solution at a sequence of points $t_0 < t_1 < t_2 < t_3 < \cdots$. These tabulated values are computed recursively; between them, the approximate solution is defined by a suitable *interpolation formula.*

Actually, the most effective methods for computing approximate solutions (Runge-Kutta, Milne) are too complicated to serve as a good introduction to the underlying theory. Therefore, in this chapter, we will only discuss a few of the simpler methods for computing approximate function tables, deferring the subject of efficient numerical integration of ordinary DE's to the next chapter.

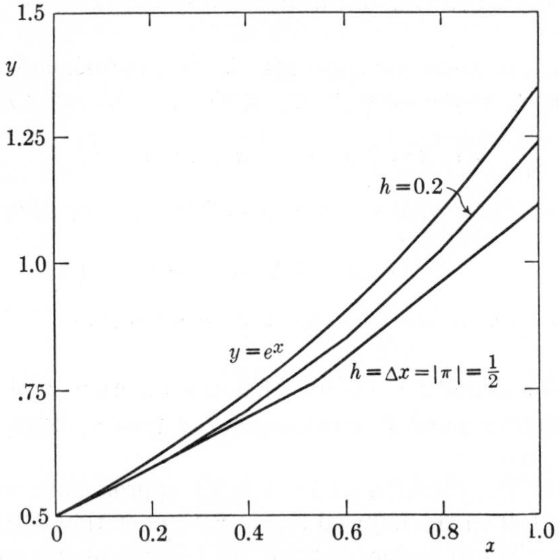

Figure VII-1. Cauchy Polygons for $dx/dt = x$, $x(0) = 1/2$

2. Cauchy polygons. The simplest way to construct an approximate function table for the solution of the DE (1) satisfying a given initial condition, is to generalize the *Riemann sum* formula† used in establishing the Fundamental Theorem of the Calculus. This formula is

$$(3) \quad \int_a^{t_m} f(t)\,dt \simeq \sum_1^m f(t_{k-1})\Delta t_k, \quad \Delta t_k = t_k - t_{k-1}, \quad t_0 = a, \quad t_k < t_{k+1},$$

where the symbol $\simeq$ is to be read "is approximately equal to." The generalization referred to may be described as follows.

†Courant, Vol. 1, Ch. II.

Divide the interval $[a,b]$ into m parts by a partition

(4) $$\pi: \ a = t_0 < t_1 < t_2 < \cdots < t_m = b.$$

For any given initial value $x(a) = c$, the entry $x_k = x_\pi(t_k)$ in the approximate function table is defined by

(5) $$x_0 = c, \quad x_k = x_{k-1} + X(x_{k-1}, t_{k-1})(t_k - t_{k-1}), \quad k = 1, \cdots, m.$$

This formula is *recursive*; each value x_k can be computed knowing x_{k-1} alone. For this reason, formula (5) is also called a *one-level* formula (see § 12*).

From the approximate function table just defined, one can also construct an *approximate solution* by linear interpolation. This approximate solution is defined by the formula

(5′) $$x_\pi(t) = x_{k-1} + X(x_{k-1}, t_{k-1})(t - t_{k-1}) \quad \text{on} \quad [t_{k-1}, t_k].$$

Evidently, the graph of the approximate solution (5′) consists of m segments of straight lines; it is a *polygon* in the $(n+1)$-dimensional (t,x)-space. The function defined by (5) and (5′) for each partition π and initial value c is called the *Cauchy polygon* approximation to the solution.†

The Cauchy polygon approximation is continuous throughout the interval $[a,b]$, and differentiable at all points except $t_0, t_1, \cdots, t_m$, where it has a left-hand and a right-hand derivative. It is intuitively plausible that if the partition π is made sufficiently fine, the Cauchy polygon $x_\pi(t)$ will be a good approximation to an actual solution. To make this idea precise, we now introduce a numerical measure for the fineness of a partition.

DEFINITION. *The* norm *of the partition* (4) *of the interval* $[a,b]$ *is*

(6) $$|\pi| = \max\{\Delta t_1, \cdots, \Delta t_m\} = \max_{k=1,\cdots,m}\{t_k - t_{k-1}\}.$$

For continuous functions X not satisfying a Lipschitz condition, such as the function $x^{2/3} + 10^{-4}$ of Example 2, the intuitive idea stated above is not always correct. However, one can always make the *deviation* arbitrarily small by making the norm sufficiently small, as we now show.

THEOREM 1. *Let the vector function $X(x, t)$ be continuous on the cylinder R: $|x - c| \leqq K$, $a \leqq t \leqq a + T$, and let $|X(x, t)|$ be bounded by M there. Let T_1 be the lesser of the two numbers T, K/M, and let $\epsilon > 0$ be given. Then one can find $\delta > 0$ such that every Cauchy polygon $x_\pi(t)$ with $|\pi| < \delta$, satisfying the initial condition $x_\pi(a) = c$, is an* approximate solution *of* (1) *with deviation at most ϵ in the interval $[a, a + T_1]$.*

Proof. First, we show that the Cauchy polygons are well-defined by (5) and (5′). This requires only that, for $t_k \in [a, a + T_1]$, every vertex

†It was Cauchy who first proved their convergence to exact solutions, though Euler had used "Cauchy polygons" a century earlier.

$(\mathbf{x}_k, t_k)$ shall lie in the cylinder R where $\mathbf{X}(\mathbf{x}, t)$ is given. But, by formula (5),

$$\mathbf{x}_k = \mathbf{c} + \mathbf{X}(\mathbf{x}_0, t_0)(t_1 - t_0) + \cdots + \mathbf{X}(\mathbf{x}_{k-1}, t_{k-1})(t_k - t_{k-1}),$$

whence, by the triangle inequality,

$$|\mathbf{x}_k - \mathbf{c}| \leqq \sum_{i=1}^{k} |\mathbf{X}(\mathbf{x}_i, t_i)| \cdot |t_i - t_{i-1}| \leqq M \sum_{i=1}^{k} (t_i - t_{i-1}) \leqq MT_1 \leqq K.$$

We shall work exclusively in the interval $[a, a + T_1]$, as has already been done with the local existence theorem of Ch. V, § 9. Given $\epsilon > 0$, choose $\delta > 0$ so that

$$|\mathbf{X}(\mathbf{x}, t) - \mathbf{X}(\mathbf{y}, s)| < \epsilon \tag{7}$$

whenever $|\mathbf{x} - \mathbf{y}| < \delta$ and $|t - s| < \delta$. This is possible since any function continuous on a compact (i.e., closed, bounded) region is uniformly continuous.† The idea of the proof is to make the sides of the Cauchy polygon so short that, by (7), the variation in $\mathbf{X}$ along any one side is at most ϵ.

This is accomplished by taking any partition whose norm satisfies

$$|\pi| \leqq \delta/(M + 1).$$

We show that this choice of the norm gives deviation at most ϵ. For t in the open interval (t_{k-1}, t_k), using formula (5′),

$$|\mathbf{x}_\pi'(t) - \mathbf{X}(\mathbf{x}_\pi(t), t)| = |\mathbf{X}(\mathbf{x}_{k-1}, t_{k-1}) - \mathbf{X}(\mathbf{x}_\pi(t), t)|. \tag{8}$$

But $|t_{k-1} - t_k| < \delta/(M + 1)$ and, again by (5′),

$$|\mathbf{x}_\pi(t) - \mathbf{x}_{k-1}| = |t - t_{k-1}| \cdot |\mathbf{X}(\mathbf{x}_{k-1}, t_{k-1})| \leqq \frac{\delta}{M+1} M < \delta.$$

It follows from (7) that the right side of (8) is less than ϵ. Hence so is the left side, except at the points t_k of the partition, which are finite in number. Thus $\mathbf{x}_\pi$ is an approximate solution with deviation at most ϵ, q.e.d.

3. Error bound. We now show that if the vector function $\mathbf{X}(\mathbf{x}, t)$ satisfies a Lipschitz condition

$$|\mathbf{X}(\mathbf{x}, t) - \mathbf{X}(\mathbf{y}, t)| \leqq L |\mathbf{x} - \mathbf{y}|, \tag{9}$$

then it is possible to make the error $|\mathbf{x}_\pi(t) - \mathbf{x}(t)|$ as well as the deviation arbitrarily small by making $|\pi|$ sufficiently small. To establish this, we now prove a general result, bounding the error in terms of the deviation.

THEOREM 2. *Let $\mathbf{x}(t)$, $\mathbf{y}(t)$ be approximate solutions of the DE (1) for the same initial value, with deviations ϵ, η. If $\mathbf{X}(\mathbf{x}, t)$ satisfies a Lipschitz con-*

†Graves, p. 66; Rudin, p. 68.

dition (9), *then*

$$(10) \qquad | \mathbf{x}(t) - \mathbf{y}(t) | \leqq \frac{\epsilon + \eta}{L} \{e^{L(t-a)} - 1\} \quad if\ t \geqq a.$$

Proof. Let $\mathbf{x}(t)$ and $\mathbf{y}(t)$ be any two approximate solutions to the DE (1) for the same initial value $\mathbf{x}(a) = \mathbf{y}(a) = \mathbf{c}$, with deviations at most ϵ and η, respectively. Consider the square

$$\sigma(t) = | \mathbf{r}(t) |^2 = [\mathbf{x}(t) - \mathbf{y}(t)] \cdot [\mathbf{x}(t) - \mathbf{y}(t)]$$

of the magnitude of the vector difference $\mathbf{r}(t) = \mathbf{x}(t) - \mathbf{y}(t)$. By (2), we will have (except on a finite set)

$$\begin{aligned} \sigma'(t) &= 2[\mathbf{x}(t) - \mathbf{y}(t)] \cdot [\mathbf{x}'(t) - \mathbf{y}'(t)] \\ &= 2[\mathbf{x}(t) - \mathbf{y}(t)] \cdot [\mathbf{X}(\mathbf{x}(t), t) - \mathbf{X}(\mathbf{y}(t), t) + \boldsymbol{\epsilon} + \boldsymbol{\eta}] \\ &\leqq 2L\sigma(t) + 2(\epsilon + \eta)\sqrt{\sigma(t)}, \end{aligned}$$

where $\boldsymbol{\epsilon} = \mathbf{x}'(t) - \mathbf{X}(\mathbf{x}(t), t)$ and $\boldsymbol{\eta} = \mathbf{y}'(t) - \mathbf{X}(\mathbf{y}(t), t)$ are vector deviations of magnitude at most ϵ and η, respectively, and $\sqrt{\sigma(t)} = | \mathbf{x}(t) - \mathbf{y}(t) |$. Theorem 2 now follows from the lemma of Ch. V, § 4, which applies to functions of class $\mathfrak{D}_1$ (Ch. V, Additional Exercise 4).

Corollary. *Let* $\mathbf{y}(t)$ *be an approximate solution of* (1) *with deviation at most* ϵ, *and let* $\mathbf{x}(t)$ *be the exact solution assuming the same initial values* $\mathbf{x}(a) = \mathbf{y}(a) = \mathbf{c}$. *Then*

$$(11) \qquad | \mathbf{y}(t) - \mathbf{x}(t) | \leqq \frac{\epsilon}{L} \{e^{L|t-a|} - 1\}.$$

Note that, in (11), the inequality $t \geqq a$ is no longer assumed, and that (11) applies if $\mathbf{y}(t) = \mathbf{x}_\pi(t)$ is a Cauchy polygon.

EXERCISES A

1. (a) What is the deviation of the approximate solution $x = t^2/2 - t^4/24$ of the initial value problem defined by $dx/dt = \sin t$, $x(0) = 0$ on the interval $0 \leqq t \leqq 1$?

(b) Compare the difference $1 - (\cos 1) - 11/24$ with the bound given by formula (11), for the deviation computed in (a).

(c) For the initial value $x(0) = 1$, bound the difference between the solutions of $dx/dt = \sin t$ and $dx/dt = t - (t^3/6)$.

In Exs. 2–5, for the initial value problem specified: (a) use the Cauchy polygon method to compute an approximate function table for $t_k = 0.1, 0.2, \cdots, 1.0$, (b) find the deviation of the approximate solution obtained from this table by linear interpolation, (c) find the exact solution, (d) find the error.

2. $\dot{x} = x$, $x(0) = 1$.
3. $\dot{x} = 1 - 2x$, $x(0) = 0$.
4. $\dot{x} = y$, $\dot{y} = -x$, $x(0) = 0$, $y(0) = 1$.
5. $\dot{x} = y$, $\dot{y} = x$, $x(0) = 1$, $y(0) = 0$.
6. For the DE $y' = 3y^{2/3}$, find the deviation and the error of the approximate solution $y = 10^{-6}$, on [0,1].

7. On the interval [0,1], for any $\epsilon > 0$, construct an approximate solution with deviation ϵ to a suitable first-order DE, for which the exact solution with the same initial value is unbounded.

8. For the DE $y' = x + \sin y$, y in radians, what is the maximum deviation of approximate solutions obtained by the Cauchy polygon method with $\Delta x_k = 0.01$? Use this result to bound the maximum error in this approximate solution, for the initial value $y(1) = 0$, on $1 \leqq x \leqq 2$.

4. Order of accuracy. The cumulative error of the Cauchy polygon approximation to solutions of DE's may be roughly estimated as follows. Define the *directional derivative* $\partial \mathbf{X}/\partial \boldsymbol{\xi}$ of the vector function $\mathbf{X}(\mathbf{x},t)$ in the direction $\boldsymbol{\xi} = (\xi_0,\xi_1,\cdots,\xi_n)$ in $(t,\mathbf{x})$-space, for any vector $\boldsymbol{\xi}$ of unit length, as the sum $\xi_0 \partial \mathbf{X}/\partial t + \sum_{k=1}^{n} \xi_k \, \partial \mathbf{X}/\partial x_k$. It follows as in the proof of the lemma of Ch. V, § 2, that

$$| \mathbf{X}(t, \mathbf{x}) - \mathbf{X}(u, \mathbf{y}) | \leqq | \partial \mathbf{X}/\partial \xi | \cdot | (t, \mathbf{x}) - (u, \mathbf{y}) |,$$

where $\boldsymbol{\xi}$ is the unit vector in $(t,\mathbf{x})$-space pointing in the direction $(t - u, \mathbf{x} - \mathbf{y})$. This inequality gives a bound on the change in $\mathbf{X}(\mathbf{x}, t)$ along any side of a Cauchy polygon, which we use to prove the following result.

THEOREM 3. *In the cylinder* R: $| t - a | \leqq T_1$, $| \mathbf{x} - \mathbf{c} | \leqq K$ *of Theorem* 1, *let* $\mathbf{X}(\mathbf{x}, t) \in \mathcal{C}^1$. *Let*

$$\sup_R | \mathbf{X}(\mathbf{x}, t) | = M \quad \textit{and} \quad \sup_{R, |\xi|=1} | \partial \mathbf{X}/\partial \xi | = L_1. \tag{12}$$

Then, $\mathbf{x}$ *and* $\mathbf{x}_\pi$ *being as in Theorem* 1,

$$| \mathbf{x}_\pi(t) - \mathbf{x}(t) | \leqq \{e^{L_1 |t-a|} - 1\}(1 + M) \, | \pi |. \tag{13}$$

Proof. The k-th side of the Cauchy polygon defined by $\mathbf{x}_\pi(t)$ is the hypotenuse of a right triangle with base at most $| \pi |$ and altitude at most $M| \pi |$; hence its length is at most $(1 + M)| \pi |$. Hence by the inequality displayed above and (12), the change in $\mathbf{X}(\mathbf{x}_\pi(t),t)$ along the side is at most $L_1(1 + M)| \pi |$. But the *deviation* of $\mathbf{x}_\pi(t)$ from the DE (1) is equal to the maximum of this change. Hence the deviation of $\mathbf{x}_\pi(t)$ is at most $L_1(1 + M)| \pi |$. By (11), this implies the desired result.

COROLLARY. *Under the hypotheses of Theorem* 3, *let the interval* $[a, a + T_1]$ *of Theorem* 2 *be divided into* n *equal parts of length* $h = T_1/n$. *Then the error of the Cauchy polygon approximation is bounded by* Nh, *where* N *is a constant independent of* h.

Proof. Set $N = [\exp(L_1 T_1) - 1](1 + M)$, and use the inequality (13).
This result can be rephrased as follows. A method of numerical inte-

gration based on a subdivision of the interval of integration into "steps" or subintervals of length h is said to have the *order of accuracy* $0(h^n)$ when the cumulative error is bounded by Nh^n for all sufficiently smooth functions, where the constant N depends on the function X but is independent of h. Theorem 3 asserts that the Cauchy polygon approximation has order of accuracy $0(h)$. By contrast, the order of accuracy of the other methods of numerical integration to be studied in this chapter is $0(h^2)$, while the emphasis in Chapter VIII will be on more complicated methods whose order of accuracy is $0(h^4)$.

EXAMPLE 3. Consider the linear DE $dx/dt = x$, with a constant mesh-length h. The Cauchy polygon method gives $x_k = (1 + h)x_{k-1}$, and so $x_n = (1 + h)^n x_0$.

Hence if one tabulates values of the solution of the DE for the initial value $x_0 = 1$, calculated by the Cauchy polygon method applied to the interval [0, 1] with the constant mesh-length $h = 1/n$, one gets $[1 + (1/n)]^n$ instead of e. By the binomial theorem, the cumulative error over the interval is thus the difference between

$$e = 1 + 1 + 1/2! + 1/3! + 1/4! + \cdots, \qquad \text{and}$$
$$[1 + (1/n)]^n = 1 + 1 + n(n-1)/2n^2 + n(n-1)(n-2)/6n^3 + \cdots.$$

This difference exceeds $1/2n$, so that it would take 5000 steps to achieve four-place accuracy!

Note that, in Example 3, the error made in each individual step is only $0(h^2)$. Since the number of steps is proportional to $1/h$, the cumulative error is still $0(h)$. More generally, the order of magnitude of the cumulative error is an infinitesimal of order one less than that of the error per step. It is the same as that of the *relative error* per step, defined as the error divided by the length of the step.

5. Midpoint quadrature. In studying formulas for numerical integration having higher orders of accuracy than the Cauchy polygon formula, it is helpful to begin with *quadrature* formulas for integrating numerically DE's of the form $y' = F(x)$. For such DE's, the Cauchy polygon formula reduces to

$$\int_a^b F(x)dx \simeq \sum_{i=1}^n F(x_{i-1})\Delta x_i, \quad \Delta x_i = x_i - x_{i-1}, \tag{14}$$

where the symbol $\simeq$ again means "is approximately equal to."

The simplest formula for numerical quadrature having a higher order of accuracy than the Cauchy polygon formula (14) is the *midpoint quadrature* formula

$$\int_a^b F(x)dx \simeq M_\pi[F] = \sum_{i=1}^n F(m_i)\Delta x_i, \quad m_i = (x_{i-1} + x_i)/2. \tag{15}$$

Given the partition π of the interval of integration $[a,b]$ by points of subdivision $a = x_0 < x_1 < \cdots < x_n = b$, the midpoint approximation $M_\pi[F]$ is easily computed; it takes its name from the fact that m_i is the midpoint of the i-th interval of subdivision. We now derive an *error bound* for the midpoint quadrature formula (15).

THEOREM 4. *If $F \in \mathcal{C}^2$, then*

$$(16)\quad \left| \int_a^b F(x)dx - \sum_{i=1}^n F(m_i)\Delta x_i \right| \leqq | F'' |_{\max} | \pi |^2 (b-a)/24.$$

Proof. On each interval $[x_{i-1},x_i] = [m_i - \Delta x_i/2, m_i + \Delta x_i/2]$, Taylor's formula implies that

$$F(m_i + t) - F(m_i) - tF'(m_i) = t^2 F''(m_i + \tau)/2,$$

where τ is between 0 and t. But $F''(m_i + \tau)$ is bounded below by the minimum $F''_{\min}$ of $F''(x)$ on $[a,b]$, and above by its maximum value $F''_{\max}$. Hence

$$F''_{\min} t^2/2 \leqq F(m_i + t) - F(m_i) - tF'(m_i) \leqq F''_{\max} t^2/2.$$

Integration of this inequality over $-\Delta x_i/2 \leqq t \leqq \Delta x_i/2$ gives

$$F''_{\min} \Delta x_i^3/24 \leqq \int_{x_{i-1}}^{x_i} F(x)dx - F(m_i)\Delta x_i \leqq F''_{\max} \Delta x_i^3/24.$$

Summing over i, and noting that $0 \leqq \Delta x_i^2 \leqq |\pi|^2$, we get (16).

Theorem 4 shows that the midpoint quadrature formula (15) has order of accuracy $O(h^2)$, one order higher than the Cauchy polygon method.

Error estimate. By considering the higher-order terms in Taylor's formula, one can derive a much more accurate estimate of the error of the midpoint quadrature formula, at least for subdivisions into intervals of constant length.

THEOREM 5. *For $F \in \mathcal{C}^6$, let all intervals of subdivision have the same length $\Delta x_i = 2k = h$. Then*

$$(17)\quad M_\pi[F] = \int_a^b F(x)dx - \frac{h^2}{24}[F'(b) - F'(a)] + \frac{7h^4}{5760}[F'''(b) - F'''(a)] + O(h^6).$$

Proof. By Taylor's formula with remainder, since $F \in \mathcal{C}^6$,

$$F(m_i + t) = \sum_{r=0}^{5} F^{(r)}(m_i)t^r/(r!) + F^{(6)}(\xi)t^6/720,$$

where ξ is some number between m_i and $m_i + t$. On each i-th interval

(x_{i-1},x_i), the final term ("remainder") is bounded in magnitude by $Mk^6/720$, where $M = \max | F^{(6)}(\xi) |$, the maximum being taken on the entire interval $a \leqq \xi \leqq b$. Integrating over $-k \leqq t \leqq k$, we get

$$\int_{x_{i-1}}^{x_i} F(x)dx = 2kF(m_i) + k^3F''(m_i)/3 + k^5F^{\text{iv}}(m_i)/60 + 0(k^6)\Delta x_i,$$

where the factor $0(k^6)$ is bounded in magnitude by $Mk^6/720$. Summing over i, there results the estimate

$$\text{(18)} \qquad \sum_{i=1}^{n} F(m_i)\Delta x_i = \int_a^b F(x)dx - (k^2/6)\sum_{i=1}^{n} F''(m_i)\Delta x_i - (k^4/120)\sum_{i=1}^{n} F^{\text{iv}}(m_i)\Delta x_i + 0(k^6).$$

An application of (18) to the function $F''(x) \in \mathfrak{C}^4$ gives similarly (one term being dropped to compensate for the loss in differentiability)

$$\text{(18')} \qquad \sum_{i=1}^{n} F''(m_i)\Delta x_i = \int_a^b F''(x)dx - (k^2/6)\sum_{i=1}^{n} F^{\text{iv}}(m_i)\Delta x_i + 0(k^4);$$

applied to $F^{\text{iv}}(x) \in \mathfrak{C}^2$, it gives

$$\text{(18'')} \qquad \sum_{i=1}^{n} F^{\text{iv}}(m_i)\Delta x_i = \int_a^b F^{\text{iv}}(x)dx + 0(k^2).$$

Substituting from (18′) and (18″) back into (18), and combining terms, we get

$$\sum_{i=1}^{n} F(m_i)\Delta x_i = \int_a^b F(x)dx - \frac{k^2}{6}\int_a^b F''(x)dx + \frac{7k^4}{360}\int_a^b F^{\text{iv}}(x)dx + 0(k^6).$$

Setting $k = h/2$, formula (17) follows immediately.

Note that the error estimate (17) implies the very accurate *corrected* midpoint formula

$$\text{(19)} \qquad \int_a^b F(x)dx = \sum_{i=1}^{n} F(m_i)\Delta x_i + h^2[F'(b) - F'(a)]/24 - 7h^4[F'''(b) - F'''(a)]/5760 + 0(h^6).$$

EXERCISES B

In each of Exs. 1–4, a numerical quadrature formula is specified for approximately evaluating $\int_{-h}^{h} f(x)dx$. In each case: (a) compute the truncation error for $f(x) = x^n$, $n = 0, 1, 2, 3, \cdots$, and (b) find the order of accuracy of the formula, using Taylor's formula with remainder, assuming $f(x)$ to be analytic.

1. Simpson's Rule: $S[f] = \frac{h}{3}[f(-h) + 4f(0) + f(h)]$.

2. Cotes' Rule: $C[f] = \frac{h}{4}[f(-h) + 3f(-h/3) + 3f(h/3) + f(h)]$.

3. Weddle's Rule:

$$W[f] = \frac{h}{10}\left[f(-h) + 5f\left(-\frac{2h}{3}\right) + f\left(-\frac{h}{3}\right) + 6f(0) + f\left(\frac{h}{3}\right) + 5f\left(\frac{2h}{3}\right) + f(h)\right].$$

4. Hermite Rule: $H[f] = h[f(h) + f(-h)] + \frac{h^2}{3}[f'(h) - f'(-h)]$.

5. (a) By expanding in Taylor's series about each point, show that if $h = (b-a)/n$ and $x_i = a + ih$, then

$$\int_a^b f(x)dx = h\sum_{i=0}^{n-1}\left[f(x_i) + \frac{h}{2}f'(x_i) + \frac{h^2}{6}f''(x_i)\right] + 0(h^3).$$

(b) By using the preceding formula on $f'(x)$, show that

$$\int_a^b f(x)dx = h\sum_{i=0}^{n-1}f(x_i) + \frac{h}{2}[f(x_n) - f(x_0)] - \frac{h^2}{12}\sum_{i=0}^{n}f''(x_i) + 0(h^3).$$

(c) Applying the result of (a) to $f''(x)$, show that

$$\int_a^b f(x)dx = \frac{h}{2}\sum_{i=1}^{n}[f(x_i) + f(x_{i-1})] - \frac{h^2}{12}[f'(b) - f'(a)] + 0(h^3).$$

*6. In Ex. 3, find weighting coefficients w_k such that the approximation

$$w_0f(-h) + w_1f\left(-\frac{2h}{3}\right) + w_2f\left(-\frac{h}{3}\right) + w_3f(0) + w_4f\left(\frac{h}{3}\right) + w_5f\left(\frac{2h}{3}\right) + w_6f(h)$$

to $\int_{-h}^{h} f(x)dx$ has a maximum order of accuracy. Compare with Weddle's Rule.

7. Use (17) to estimate the difference

$$\ln 2 - \left[\sum_{k=1}^{10}\frac{2}{19+2k} - \frac{1}{800}\right].$$

Use (17), with $h = 0.2$, to evaluate the following numbers approximately:

8. $\ln 2 = \int_1^2 dx/x$.

9. $\arctan 1 = \int_0^1 dx/(1+x^2)$.

10. $\int_0^1 \sqrt{1+x^4}\, dx$

11. $\int_0^1 \sin(x^2)dx$.

12. Show that if $|F''(x)| \leqq \epsilon$ on $[x_{i-1},x_i]$, then the error in the midpoint quadrature formula is bounded by $\epsilon(b-a)\,|\Delta x_i|^2/24$.

6. Trapezoidal quadrature. The formula for *trapezoidal quadrature* is

(20) $$\int_a^b F(x)dx \simeq T_\pi[F] = \sum_{i=1}^{n}[F(x_{i-1}) + F(x_i)]\Delta x_i/2.$$

Though more familiar than the midpoint quadrature formula, it is less accurate and harder to analyze theoretically.

To find an *error bound* for trapezoidal quadrature, when $F \in \mathcal{C}^2$, consider first the case $n = 1$ of a single interval $a = x_0 < x_1 = b$. Consider the linear function

$$(21) \qquad L(x) = F(a) + (x - a)[F(b) - F(a)]/h, \quad h = b - a,$$

defined by linear interpolation between the values $F(a)$ and $F(b)$, and let $R(x) = F(x) - L(x)$. Then $R''(x) \equiv F''(x)$, and $R(a) = R(b) = 0$. We now prove

LEMMA 1. *For any s in the interval* (a,b),

$$(22) \qquad R(s) = (s - a)(s - b)F''(\sigma)/2 \text{ for some } \sigma \in (a,b).$$

Proof. By inspection, the quadratic polynomial

$$Q(x) = L(x) + R(s)(x - a)(b - x)/(s - a)(b - s)$$

satisfies $Q(a) = L(a) = F(a)$, $Q(b) = F(b)$, and $Q(s) = L(s) + R(s) = F(s)$: it is the quadratic polynomial approximation to $F(x)$ defined by *parabolic interpolation* (Ch. VIII, § 3) through the values $F(a)$, $F(s)$, $F(b)$. Hence $r(x) = F(x) - Q(x)$ vanishes at $x = a$, $x = s$, and $x = b$. Therefore, by Rolle's Theorem, $r'(x)$ vanishes in each of the subintervals (a,s) and (s,b). Applying Rolle's Theorem again to $r'(x)$, we see that $r''(x)$ must vanish at some point $\sigma \in (a,b)$:

$$0 = r''(\sigma) = F''(\sigma) - Q''(\sigma) = F''(\sigma) - 2R(s)/(s - a)(s - b).$$

This is equivalent to formula (22), q.e.d.

Now write $R(x) = F(x) - L(x)$ as before; from (22),

$$L(x) - F(x) = (x - a)(b - x)F''(\sigma)/2,$$

where $(x - a)(b - x)$ is positive on (a,b). This gives the inequality

$$(x - a)(b - x)F''_{\min}/2 \leqq L(x) - F(x) \leqq (x - a)(b - x)F''_{\max}/2.$$

Since $\int_a^b (x - a)(b - x)dx = (b - a)^3/6$ and trapezoidal quadrature is exact for linear functions $L(x)$, integration gives

$$F''_{\min}(b - a)^3/12 \leqq T_\pi[F] - \int_a^b F(x)dx \leqq F''_{\max}(b - a)^3/12.$$

Now setting $a = x_{i-1}$ and $b = x_i$, we see that if $F \in \mathcal{C}^2$, then

$$\frac{1}{12}F''_{\min}\Delta x_i^3 \leqq \frac{1}{2}[F(x_{i-1}) + F(x_i)]\Delta x_i - \int_{x_{i-1}}^{x_i} F(x)dx \leqq \frac{1}{12}F''_{\max}\Delta x_i^3.$$

Since $F'' \in \mathcal{C}$ and a continuous function assumes every value between its minimum and its maximum, this proves

LEMMA 2. *If $F \in \mathcal{C}^2$, then for some ξ_i in (x_{i-1}, x_i),*

$$\frac{1}{2}[F(x_{i-1}) + F(x_i)]\Delta x_i - \int_{x_{i-1}}^{x_i} F(x)dx = \frac{1}{12}F''(\xi_i)\Delta x_i^3. \tag{23}$$

Since $\Delta x_i^3 \leqq |\pi|^2 \Delta x_i$, summation over i now gives our final result.

THEOREM 6. *The error bound for trapezoidal quadrature is given by the inequality*

$$\left| T_\pi[F] - \int_a^b F(x)dx \right| \leqq |F''|_{\max}(b-a)|\pi|^2/12. \tag{24}$$

7*. Accurate error estimates. Error estimates having higher-order accuracy can also be derived for trapezoidal quadrature with intervals of subdivision of constant length $\Delta x_i = 2k = h$. For any $F \in \mathcal{C}^6$, Taylor's formula with remainder gives, much as in the proof of Theorem 5,

$$F(m_i + k) + F(m_i - k) = 2F(m_i) + k^2 F''(m_i) + k^4 F^{\text{iv}}(m_i)/12 + 0(k^6).$$

Multiplication by $\Delta x_i/2$, followed by summation over i, now gives the further estimate

$$T_\pi[F] = M_\pi[F] + \frac{k^2}{2}M_\pi[F''] + \frac{k^4}{24}M_\pi[F^{\text{iv}}] + 0(k^6). \tag{25}$$

The right side of (25) can be evaluated by repeated use of the midpoint quadrature formula error estimate (17). The conclusion is the truncated Euler-Maclaurin formula.

THEOREM 7. *For $F \in \mathcal{C}^6$, let all intervals of subdivision have the same length $\Delta x_i = 2k = h$. Then*

$$T_\pi[F] = \int_a^b F(x)dx + h^2[F'(b) - F'(a)]/12 \tag{26}$$
$$- h^4[F'''(b) - F'''(a)]/720 + 0(h^6).$$

Proof. Replacing h by $2k$ in (17) and then substituting from (17) into (25), we obtain as the contribution from the first term on the right of (25)

$$\int_a^b F(x)dx - k^2[F'(b) - F'(a)]/6 + 7k^4[F'''(b) - F'''(a)]/360 + 0(k^6).$$

That from the second term is

$$(k^2/2)\left\{\int_a^b F''(x)dx - (k^2/6)[F'''(b) - F'''(a)] + 0(k^4)\right\},$$

while the third term gives $(k^4/24)[F'''(b) - F'''(a)] + 0(k^6)$. Adding these three contributions together, simplifying, and writing $k = h/2$, we get (26).

Simpson's Rule. Comparing the error estimates (17) and (26) for midpoint and trapezoidal quadrature, we are led to an error estimate for Simpson's Rule. For a given partition π, this is defined as

$$S_\pi[F] = \frac{2}{3} M_\pi[F] + \frac{1}{3} T_\pi[F] \tag{27}$$

$$= \sum_{i=1}^{n} [F(x_{i-1}) + 4F(m_i) + F(x_i)]\Delta x_i/6.$$

Forming the linear combination indicated for subdivisions into double steps of constant length $2k = h$, we get

$$S_\pi[F] = \int_a^b F(x)dx + \frac{k^4}{180}[F'''(b) - F'''(a)] + 0(k^6). \tag{28}$$

Simpson's Rule will be studied further in Ch. VIII, § 9.

Exact error. Using the Green's function for the two-endpoint problem $u'' = r(x)$, $u(-k) = u(k) = 0$, one can also obtain an exact formula for the error in trapezoidal quadrature over a single interval. As in Ch. II, § 10, we have

$$R(x) = \int_{-k}^{k} G(x,\xi)R''(\xi)d\xi = \int_{-k}^{k} G(x,\xi)F''(\xi)d\xi,$$

where $R(x)$, defined as in § 6 to be the difference between the function $F(x)$ and its trapezoidal approximation $L(x)$, vanishes at the endpoints and satisfies $R'' = F''$. The Green's function $G(x,\xi)$ is given by

$$G(x,\xi) = \begin{cases} (\xi x/k + \xi - x - k)/2, & \xi < x, \\ (\xi x/k - \xi + x - k)/2, & \xi > x. \end{cases} \tag{29}$$

The error in trapezoidal quadrature over $(-k,k)$ is

$$T_\pi[F] - \int_{-k}^{k} F(x)dx = \int_{-k}^{k} [L(x) - F(x)]dx = \int_{-k}^{k} R(x)dx.$$

Substituting for $R(x)$ the integral expression displayed above, and interchanging the order of integration in the resulting double integral, we get

$$T_\pi[F] - \int_{-k}^{k} F(x)dx = \int_{-k}^{k}\left\{\int_{-k}^{k} G(x,\xi)dx\right\}F''(\xi)d\xi.$$

But by direct calculation, $\int_{-k}^{k} G(x,\xi)dx = (k^2 - \xi^2)/2$. Hence

THEOREM 8. *The error in trapezoidal quadrature over a single interval* $(-k,k)$ *is* $\int_{-k}^{k} (k^2 - \xi^2)F''(\xi)d\xi/2$.

EXERCISES C

1. Use (26) to estimate the difference

$$\ln 2 - \left[\frac{1}{20} + \frac{1}{40} + \sum_{k=1}^{9} \frac{1}{10+k} + \frac{1}{400}\right].$$

In Exs. 2–5, use (26) with $h = 0.2$ to evaluate the following numbers approximately:

2. $\ln 2 = \int_1^2 dx/x.$

3. $\arctan 1 = \int_0^1 dx/(1+x^2).$

4. $\int_0^1 \sqrt{1+x^4}\, dx.$

5. $\int_0^1 \sin (x^2)\, dx.$

In Exs. 6–9, use Simpson's Rule (27) with double step $2k = h = 0.2$ to evaluate approximately the numbers defined in Exs. 2–5, respectively,

10. For a subdivision into $2n$ intervals of length $k = (b-a)/2n$, Simpson's approximation to $\int_a^b f(x)dx$ is $\sum_{i=1}^{n} \frac{k}{3}[f(x_{2i-2}) + 4f(x_{2i-1}) + f(x_{2i})]$.

Show that the truncation error is $(h^5/90)\sum_{i=1}^{n} f^{iv}(x_{2i-1}) + 0(h^6)$.

11. Derive (23) from Theorem 8, noting that $\int_{-k}^{k} (k^2 - \xi^2)d\xi = 4k^3/3$.

*12. Show that $\int_{-h}^{h} F(x)dx = 2hF(0) + \frac{1}{6}\left[\int_{-h}^{h} (|h| - |x|)^3 F''(x)dx\right].$

(*Hint:* Construct the Green's function for the initial value problem defined by $u'' = F''(x)$ and $F(0) = F'(0) = 0$, and study the proof of Theorem 8.)

8. Trapezoidal integration. The trapezoidal quadrature formula has an immediate extension to arbitrary systems of first-order DE's — and hence to DE's of arbitrary order†. Namely, for the system $d\mathbf{x}/dt = \mathbf{X}(\mathbf{x}, t)$, *trapezoidal integration* is defined *implicitly*‡ by the recursion formula

$$\mathbf{y}_k = \mathbf{y}_{k-1} + [\mathbf{X}(\mathbf{y}_{k-1}, t_{k-1}) + \mathbf{X}(\mathbf{y}_k, t_k)]\Delta t_k/2, \tag{30}$$

where $\Delta t_k = t_k - t_{k-1}$. From a given initial value $\mathbf{y}_0 = \mathbf{c}$ and partition π, formula (30) defines a sequence of values $\mathbf{y}_k = \mathbf{y}_\pi(t_k)$, that is, a *function table* describing approximately the solution of the DE $\dot{\mathbf{x}} = \mathbf{X}(\mathbf{x}, t)$ satisfying the initial value $\mathbf{x}(a) = \mathbf{c}$.

EXAMPLE 4. Consider the solution of the *linear* DE

$$dx/dt + 2tx = 1, \tag{31}$$

taking the initial value $x(0) = 0$. By the formula of Ch. I, § 5, the solution

†As in Ch. V, § 4. This does not mean that reduction to a first-order system is recommended in numerical integration.

‡For large Δt_k, the equation (30) may have more than one solution. This difficulty will be taken up in § 10.

is the function $x = e^{-t^2}\int_0^t e^{s^2}\,ds$. Looking up values of the definite integral in a table,† we get the first row of entries in the following display:

t	0.1	0.2	0.3	0.4	0.5	0.6	0.7	0.8	0.9
x	0.0993	0.1948	0.2826	0.3599	0.4244	0.4748	0.5105	0.5321	0.5407
y	0.0990	0.1941	0.2818	0.3590	0.4235	0.4739	0.5097	0.5315	0.5404
z	0.100	0.195	0.283	0.360	0.424	0.474	0.509	0.531	0.539

These entries may be compared with values y_k of the approximate function table constructed using the trapezoidal integration formula (30), with constant mesh-length $h = 0.1$, $a = c = 0$ and $b = 0.9$. With this value of h, the formula in Example 4 reduces to

$$y_k = [1 + (10 - t_{k-1})y_{k-1}]/[10 + t_k].$$

The entries in the second row of the above table were calculated from the preceding formula, rounding off all numbers to six decimal digits, and then rounding off the final values to four decimals.

Example 4 illustrates an important point. Tables of the definite integral $\int_0^t e^{s^2}\,ds$ are *not* computed in practice by numerical quadrature formulas for large t, because the integrand grows so rapidly. Instead, one calculates the solution $x(t)$ of the DE (31)satisfying $x(0) = 0$, by one of the efficient processes of numerical integration to be described in Chapter VIII, and then computes the integral in question as the product $\int_0^t e^{s^2}\,ds = e^{t^2}x(t)$.

Elaborate manipulations with special tricks of integration and special functions are not usually helpful in obtaining numerical values for solutions of DE's; they are more useful for describing the singularities of such solutions, and for indicating the dependence of the solutions on parameters which may be involved in the DE's defining them.

9. Order of accuracy. The cumulative error in the function table constructed by the trapezoidal integration formula (30) can be bounded in terms of properties of the vector-valued function $\boldsymbol{X}$ alone. This will be shown below, for simplicity, only in the case $dx/dt = X(x,t)$ of a single first-order DE. In this section, we will actually bound only the error made in a single step; the cumulative effect of such errors will be derived later, in § 12.

Let the *discrepancy* of an exact solution $x(t)$ of the DE $dx/dt = X(x,t)$

†E. Jahnke and F. Emde, *Tables of Functions*, Dover, 1943, p. 32; W. L. Miller and A. R. Gordon, *J. Phys. Chem.* 35 (1931), p. 2878.

from the recursion formula (30) at the k-th step be defined as the difference

$$\delta_k = x_k - x_{k-1} - [X(x_{k-1},t_{k-1}) + X(x_k,t_k)]\Delta t_k/2,$$

where $\Delta t_k = t_k - t_{k-1}$ and $x_k = x(t_k)$ as usual. Lemma 2 of § 6 shows that the discrepancy is $(\Delta t_k^3/12)\ddot{X}(x(t),t)$, where t is some number in the interval (t_{k-1},t_k), and

$$(32) \qquad \ddot{X} = \frac{d^3x}{dt^3} = \frac{\partial^2 X}{\partial t^2} + 2X\frac{\partial^2 X}{\partial x \partial t} + X^2\frac{\partial^2 X}{\partial x^2} + \frac{\partial X}{\partial x}\frac{\partial X}{\partial t} + X\left(\frac{\partial X}{\partial x}\right)^2.$$

In Example 4, this gives $\ddot{X} = -4 + 12xt + 4t^2 - 8xt^3$. If one substitutes calculated values of (x_k,t_k) into (32), one gets an estimate of the discrepancy δ_k at the k-th step. By considering the range of these values, one can also *bound* this discrepancy.

Having estimated the discrepancy δ_k of the exact solution $x(t)$ of $dx/dt = X(x,t)$ at the k-th step from (32), it is easy to bound the error introduced by the approximate integration formula (30). The first step is typical; for given $x_0 = y_0 = c$, the error introduced at the first step is $\gamma_1 = y_1 - x_1$. If the function X satisfies a Lipschitz condition with Lipschitz constant L, then (30) implies

$$y_1 - x_1 = [X(y_1,t) - X(x_1,t)]\Delta t_k/2 + \delta_1.$$

Since $| X(y_1,t) - X(x_1,t) | \leqq L | y_1 - x_1 |$, it follows that

$$| \gamma_1 | \leqq | \delta_1 | + L | \gamma_1 | \Delta t_1/2, \quad \text{or}$$

$$(33) \qquad | \gamma_1 | = | y_1 - x_1 | \leqq | \delta_1 |/(1 - L\Delta t_1/2).$$

Hence, if $\Delta t_1 \leqq 1/L$, then $| \gamma_1 | \leqq 2 | \delta_1 |$.

Since $| \delta_k | \leqq (| \pi |^2 | \ddot{X} |_{max}/12)\Delta t_k$, by Lemma 2 of § 6, it follows that the *absolute* error $\gamma_k = \epsilon_k \Delta t_k$ introduced at the k-th step† is at most twice this amount, and so the *relative* error $\epsilon_k = \gamma_k/\Delta t_k$ is bounded by $| \pi |^2 | \ddot{X} |_{max}/6$, provided $| \pi | \leqq 1/L$. As will be shown in § 12, the cumulative error has the same order of magnitude as the relative error. Hence we conclude that the order of accuracy of trapezoidal integration is $0(h^2)$.

EXERCISES D

In Exs. 1–4, compute the trapezoidal approximations to the solutions of the initial value problems specified, over the range $0 \leqq t \leqq 1$, with $h = 0.1$.

1. $\dot{x} = -tx, \quad x(0) = 1.$
2. $\dot{x} = 1 + x^2, \quad x(0) = 0.$
3. $\dot{x} = y, \quad \dot{y} = 0$; $x(0) = 0, \ y(0) = 1.$
4. $\dot{x} = y, \quad \dot{y} = x + y$; $x(0) = 0, \ y(0) = 1.$

†This is defined (for one-step processes) as the difference $y_k - \tilde{x}_k$ between the computed value y_k and the exact solution $\tilde{x}_{k-1}(t_k)$ of the given DE for the initial condition $\tilde{x}(t_{k-1}) = y_{k-1}$.

5. For the DE $y' = F(x,y)$, show that the truncation error of the Cauchy polygon method, in one step $0 \leqq x \leqq h$, is

$$\frac{h^2}{2}\left[\frac{\partial F}{\partial x}(0,y_0) + F(0,y_0)\frac{\partial F}{\partial y}(0,y_0)\right] + 0(h^3), \quad y_0 = y(0).$$

In Exs. 6–9, compute the truncation error for trapezoidal integration over one interval of length h, in terms of the Taylor series expansions of the functions involved:

6. $\dot{x} = p(t)x$, p analytic.
7. $\dot{x} = 1 + x^2$.
8. $\dot{x} = y$, $\dot{y} = 0$.
9. $\dot{x} = y$, $\dot{y} = x + y$.

10. For the DE $y'' = F(x,y)$ what is the order of accuracy of the formula

$$y_{n+1} = y_{n-1} + 2hF(x_n,y_n),$$

if all $\Delta x_k = h$?

10. Improved Euler method. The trapezoidal method is very convenient for getting approximate solutions to *linear* DE's like (31), when moderate (two or three decimal-place) accuracy is desired. But it is awkward when it comes to *nonlinear* DE's, because of the difficulty of solving (30) for $\boldsymbol{y}_k$. In general, formula (30) does not define the vectors $\boldsymbol{y}_k$ recursively, but only implicitly. To determine each $\boldsymbol{y}_k$, one has to solve an equation† (30) where $\boldsymbol{y}_k$ is the unknown, $\boldsymbol{y}_{k-1}$ having been previously determined.

For small Δt_k, one can do this by *iteration*: one starts with a trial value of $\boldsymbol{y}_k$ (say $\boldsymbol{y}_{k-1} + \boldsymbol{X}(\boldsymbol{y}_{k-1}, t_{k-1})\Delta t_k$), substitutes this trial value $\boldsymbol{y}_k^0$ into the right side of (30) to get a better approximation $\boldsymbol{y}_k^1$, and then repeats the process:

$$\boldsymbol{y}_k^{r+1} = \boldsymbol{y}_{k-1} + [\boldsymbol{X}(\boldsymbol{y}_{k-1}, t_{k-1}) + \boldsymbol{X}(\boldsymbol{y}_k^r, t_k)]\Delta t_k/2,$$

until (30) is satisfied up to the error tolerated.

Rather than solving the implicit equation (30) accurately by many iterations, one usually gets greater accuracy for the same amount of work by using a finer mesh and stopping after one or two iterations. If one stops after a single iteration, one gets the *improved Euler method*, which is useful for many nonlinear engineering problems requiring moderate accuracy (two significant decimal digits, say).

In the improved Euler method, therefore, one constructs an *approximate function table* for the solution of $dx/dt = X(x,t)$ for a given initial value $x(a) = c$ and partition defined by points of subdivision $a = t_0 < t_1 < t_2 < \cdots$, as follows. (More generally, for any vector DE $d\boldsymbol{x}/dt = \boldsymbol{X}(\boldsymbol{x}, t)$ and vector initial value $\boldsymbol{x}(a) = \boldsymbol{c}$, one computes an approximate function table for each *component* $x_i(t)$ of $\boldsymbol{x}(t)$.)

†The vector equation (30) is, of course, equivalent to a system of n simultaneous equations in the components. For linear systems, these equations can be solved by Gauss elimination instead of iteration.

Starting with $z_0 = c$, one computes an approximate function table of values $z_1, z_2, z_3, \cdots$, using *two* formulas at each step.

A *first* approximation to the true value is, by the Cauchy polygon construction applied to z_{k-1},

$$p_k = z_{k-1} + X(z_{k-1},t_{k-1})\,\Delta t_k. \tag{34}$$

The number p_k thus computed is a first approximation to the number z_k desired. It is called the *predictor*. Next, we compute the number z_k using the predictor by applying formula (30),

$$z_k = z_{k-1} + [X(z_{k-1},t_{k-1}) + X(p_k,t_k)]\,\Delta t_k/2. \tag{34'}$$

This formula is called the *corrector formula*. The slope used in computing z_k by the corrector formula is the average of the slope at the point (z_{k-1},t_{k-1}) and the slope at the point (p_k,t_k) computed by means of the predictor. In this way, the sequence z_k is calculated *explicitly* without solving any implicit equations such as (30), employing two steps to determine each of the z_k.

The improved Euler method consists in determining the sequence of z_k by performing these two substitutions in alternation. In the case $X(x,t) = F(t)$ of quadrature, it is equivalent to the trapezoidal method.

Applied to the initial value problem of Example 4, the improved Euler method gives the approximate solution tabulated in the last row of the table of § 8; in this example, the work was carried to three decimal places to reduce the cumulative error to 0.01.

To apply the improved Euler method to first-order systems, one simply substitutes vectors for scalars in formulas (34)–(34′). We illustrate the procedure by an example.

EXAMPLE 5. Consider the initial value problem defined by the non-linear system

$$dx/dt = x^2 + y^2, \quad dy/dt = 1 + x^2 - y^2, \quad x(0) = y(0) = 0. \tag{35}$$

There is little hope that formal methods of integration will help in the computation, but a straightforward application of the improved Euler method enables one to calculate an approximate solution.

The calculations to be performed give, for this example, the double sequence of numbers x_k, y_k defined by $x_0 = y_0 = 0$, and by the formulas

$$\begin{aligned} p_k &= x_{k-1} + (x_{k-1}^2 + y_{k-1}^2)\,\Delta t_k \\ q_k &= y_{k-1} + (1 + x_{k-1}^2 - y_{k-1}^2)\,\Delta t_k \end{aligned} \tag{36}$$

and

$$\begin{aligned} x_k &= x_{k-1} + (x_{k-1}^2 + y_{k-1}^2 + p_k^2 + q_k^2)\,\Delta t_k/2, \\ y_k &= y_{k-1} + (2 + x_{k-1}^2 - y_{k-1}^2 + p_k^2 - q_k^2)\,\Delta t_k/2. \end{aligned} \tag{36'}$$

Each step requires squaring four numbers and performing fourteen additions and subtractions and four multiplications. These can all be accomplished by hand in a total of ten minutes per time step or less, especially if $h = \Delta t_k = 0.1$, say, and a table of squares is available.

For a subdivision into intervals of constant length h, the relative error committed in using the improved Euler method is $0(h^2)$, provided the function $X(x,t)$ is of class $\mathfrak{C}^2$. For, expanding the exact solution $x(t)$ of $dx/dt = X(x,t)$ into power series, we have

$$(37)\qquad x_k = x(t_k) = x_{k-1} + hX_{k-1} + \frac{h^2}{2}\left[X\frac{\partial X}{\partial x} + \frac{\partial X}{\partial t}\right]_{k-1} + 0(h^3),$$

where X_{k-1} denotes $X(x_{k-1},t_{k-1}) = X(x(t_{k-1}),t_{k-1})$, and similarly for derivatives. The improved Euler method (34)–(34′) gives

$$(38)\qquad y_k = y_{k-1} + hY_{k-1} + \frac{h^2}{2}\left[Y\frac{\partial Y}{\partial x} + \frac{\partial Y}{\partial t}\right]_{k-1} + 0(h^3),$$

where Y_{k-1} denotes $X(y_{k-1},t_{k-1})$, etc. The *relative* error committed in substituting (38) for (37) is thus $0(h^2)$.

A more explicit error bound is deduced in § 12.

11. Modified Euler method. The improved Euler method has the advantage over the trapezoidal method of being explicit. Various other explicit methods can also be constructed, which are about as accurate as the improved Euler and trapezoidal methods. For instance, one can use the following adaptation of the midpoint quadrature formula:

$$(39)\qquad w_k = w_{k-1} + hX(w_{k-1} + hX_{k-1}/2,\ t_{k-1} + h/2),\quad h = \Delta t_k.$$

This *midpoint* or *modified Euler* method is about twice as accurate as the trapezoidal and improved Euler methods, in the special case $dx/dt = F(t)$ of quadrature, as a comparison of formulas (17) and (26) shows. (In this case, the improved Euler method *is* the trapezoidal method.)

But for first-order DE's generally, no such simple error comparison holds. To see this, let $X = \Sigma b_{jk}t^jx^k$ be expanded into a double power series, and let $x(t)$ satisfy $\dot{x} = X(x,t)$. Then, just as in Ch. III, § 8, $\ddot{x} = X_t + XX_x$, and

$$d^3x/dt^3 = X_{tt} + 2XX_{tx} + X^2X_{xx} + X_tX_x + XX_x^2.$$

We now introduce the abbreviations

$$C = b_{10} + b_{00}b_{01},\qquad B = b_{20} + b_{11}b_{00} + b_{02}b_{00}^2,\qquad B^* = b_{10}b_{01} + b_{00}b_{01}^2.$$

Expanding out to infinitesimals of the fourth order, we find that the *exact* solution of the DE $dx/dt = X(x,t)$ for the initial condition $x(0) = 0$ has the expansion

$$(40)\qquad x(h) = hb_{00} + h^2C/2 + h^3(2B + B^*)/6 + 0(h^4).$$

With the trapezoidal approximation (30), one gets

(41) $$y(h) = hb_{00} + h^2C/2 + h^3(2B + B^*)/4 + 0(h^4),$$

giving a truncation error $h^3(B/6 + B^*/12) + 0(h^4)$. With the improved Euler approximation (34)–(34′), one gets

(42) $$z(h) = hb_{00} + h^2C/2 + h^3B/2 + 0(h^4),$$

with error $h^3(B - B^*)/6 + 0(h^4)$. With the midpoint approximation (39), one gets finally

(43) $$w(h) = hb_{00} + h^2C/2 + h^3B/4 + 0(h^4),$$

so that the error is $-h^3(B/12 + B^*/6) + 0(h^4)$.

Corrected trapezoidal method. Theorem 7, when combined with Theorem 5 of Chapter V, shows that the exact solution $x(t)$ of the first-order DE $dx/dt = X(x,t)$ satisfies

(44) $$x_k = x_{k-1} + [X_{k-1} + X_k]\Delta t_k/2 + [\dot{X}_{k-1} - \dot{X}_k]\Delta t_k^2/12 + 0(\Delta t_k^4),$$

where X_k denotes $X(x_k,t_k)$ and $\dot{X}$ denotes $\partial X/\partial t + X\partial X/\partial x$. Dropping the last term, one gets a *corrected* trapezoidal integration formula, which may be expected to have a cumulative error of only $0(|\pi|^3)$.

For instance, when applied to the linear DE $\dot{x} = 1 - 2tx$ of Example 4, in which $\dot{X} = -2x - 2t + 4xt^2$, this formula gives the approximate recursion formula

$$x_k[1 + t_k\Delta t_k + (-1 + 2t_k^2)\Delta t_k^2/6]$$
$$= x_{k-1}[1 - t_{k-1}\Delta t_k + (-1 + 2t_{k-1}^2)\Delta t_k^2/6] + \Delta t_k + \Delta t_k^3/6,$$

with absolute error $0(\Delta t_k^4)$ and relative error $0(\Delta t_k^3)$.

EXERCISES E

In Exs. 1–4, compute approximate function tables on [0,1], with $\Delta t_k = 0.1$, by the improved Euler method for the following initial value problems:

1. $\dot{x} = -tx$, $x(0) = 1$.
2. $\dot{x} = (1 + x^2)$, $x(0) = 0$.
3. $\dot{x} = y$, $\dot{y} = 0$, $x(0) = 0$, $y(0) = 1$.
4. $\dot{x} = y$, $\dot{y} = x + y$, $x(0) = 0$, $y(0) = 1$.

In Exs. 5–8, compute approximate function tables for the data of Exs. 1–4 using the *midpoint* (or modified Euler) method instead of the improved Euler method.

9. Obtain an expression through terms in h^5 for the error committed in applying (a) the improved Euler method, and (b) the midpoint method, to the DE $\dot{x} = p(t)x$, $p(t)$ analytic.

10. For the analytic DE $y' = F(x,y)$, and one interval $0 \leq x \leq h$, let the exact solution be given by $y(h) = a_0 + a_1h + a_2h^2 + a_3h^3 + 0(h^4)$ and let

$$y = c_0 + c_1h + c_2h^2 + c_3h^3 + 0(h^4)$$

be the approximate value given by trapezoidal formula. Show that $c_0 = a_0$, $c_1 = a_1$, $c_2 = a_2$, and $c_3 = 3a_3/2$.

11. Show that, through the terms computed in Ex. 10, the improved Euler method gives the same result for c_0, c_1, c_2 as trapezoidal integration.

12*. Cumulative error. All the methods for constructing approximate function tables which have been described in this chapter have had one feature in common. Namely, the k-th entry in the table has been constructed from the immediately preceding entry alone, the $(k-1)$-st entry, without reference to the earlier entries. Such methods are called *one-level* or *one-step* methods.

Given a one-level method for approximately integrating the DE $dx/dt = X(x,t)$, that is, for constructing an approximate function table with entries $y_k = y(t_k)$, one can express the preceding property by writing

$$y_k = \phi(y_{k-1}, t_{k-1}, t_k;\ X). \tag{45}$$

Here ϕ is the function expressing y_k in terms of y_{k-1} and the data of the problem. Bounds for the errors associated with one-level methods can be obtained using the following general theorem, which applies equally to the Cauchy polygon method, the trapezoidal method, and the improved Euler and midpoint methods.

THEOREM 9. *In any one-level method for numerical integration of the DE* $dx/dt = X(x,t)$, *where X satisfies the Lipschitz condition*

$$| X(x,t) - X(y,t) | \leqq L \, | x - y |,$$

let the relative error at each step be at most ϵ. *Then, over an interval of length T, the cumulative error is at most* $(\epsilon/L)(e^{LT} - 1)$.

Proof. For any partition π, let ϵ_k denote the error introduced at the k-th step. That is, if $\tilde{x}_k(t)$ is that exact solution of the given DE satisfying the initial condition $\tilde{x}_k(t_k) = y_k$, where y_k is the value of the computed approximate solution at t_k, let

$$\epsilon_k = | y_k - \tilde{x}_{k-1}(t_k) | = | \tilde{x}_k(t_k) - \tilde{x}_{k-1}(t_k) |.$$

By the definition of "relative error," $\epsilon_k \leqq \epsilon \Delta t_k$. The magnitude of the cumulative error is, by definition,

$$| y_m - x(t_m) | = | \tilde{x}_m(t_m) - x_0(t_m) | = \Big| \sum_{k=1}^{m} [\tilde{x}_k(t_m) - \tilde{x}_{k-1}(t_m)] \Big|$$

$$\leqq \sum_{k=1}^{m} | \tilde{x}_k(t_m) - \tilde{x}_{k-1}(t_m) |.$$

But $| \tilde{x}_k(t_m) - \tilde{x}_{k-1}(t_m) |$ is the magnitude of the difference, at $t = t_m$, of two solutions of the given DE which differ by ϵ_k at $t = t_k$. By Theorem 2 of Chapter V, this is at most

$$\epsilon_k e^{L(t_m - t_k)} \leqq \epsilon e^{L(t_m - t_k)} \Delta t_k,$$

since $\epsilon_k \leqq \epsilon \Delta t_k$. Here ϵ is any upper bound to the relative error. Summing over k, we get the following upper bound to the cumulative error:

$$| y_\pi(t_m) - x(t_m) | \leqq \epsilon \sum_{k=1}^{m} [e^{L(t_m - t_k)} \Delta t_k] \leqq \epsilon e^{Lt_m} \sum_{k=1}^{m} [e^{-Lt_k} \Delta t_k].$$

But the final sum is the Riemann lower sum approximation to the definite integral $\int_{t_0}^{t_m} \exp(-Lt)\,dt = [\exp(-Lt_0) - \exp(-Lt_m)]/L$. Hence

$$|y_\pi(t_m) - x(t_m)| \leqq \epsilon\,[e^{LT} - 1]/L,$$

and Theorem 9 follows.

Trapezoidal integration. For trapezoidal integration, the discussion of § 9 shows that the truncation error ϵ_k at the k-th step is bounded by

$$(|\pi|^2|\ddot{X}|_{\max})\,\Delta t_k/[1 - (L\Delta t_k/2)].$$

Hence, in this case, an error bound is given by the

COROLLARY. *The error in the approximate function table constructed by the trapezoidal formula* (30) *is at most*

$$(46)\qquad |\pi|^2|\ddot{X}|_{\max}(e^{Lt} - 1)/L[1 - (L|\pi|/2)], \quad \text{if } |\pi| \leqq 1/L.$$

Similar error bounds can be found for the midpoint and improved Euler approximate integration methods.

Approximate solutions. The error bound (46) refers to the approximate function table constructed by the trapezoidal integration formula (30). Using linear interpolation between successive values, one can obtain from this function table a continuous approximate solution to the DE $dx/dt = X(x,t)$. Since the error in linear interpolation is bounded by $|\ddot{x}|_{\max}|\pi|^2/2$, where $\ddot{x} = \dot{X} = \partial X/\partial t + X\partial X/\partial x$, we see that the order of accuracy of this approximate solution is also $0(|\pi|^2)$.

EXERCISES F

1. Let $x(t)$ and $y(t)$ be approximate solutions of the system (1) with deviations ϵ_1 and ϵ_2, defined for $a \leqq t \leqq b$. Show that (9) implies:

$$|x(t) - y(t)| \leqq |x(a) - y(a)|\,e^{L|t-a|} + (\epsilon_1 + \epsilon_2)\frac{e^{L|t-a|} - 1}{L}.$$

2. Let $F(x,y)$ and $G(x,y)$ be everywhere continuous, let F satisfy a Lipschitz condition with Lipschitz constant L, and let $|F(x,y) - G(x,y)| \leqq K$. Show that if $f(x)$ and $g(x)$ are approximate solutions of the DE's $y' = F(x,y)$ and $z' = G(x,z)$ with deviations ϵ and η, then

$$|f(x) - g(x)| \leqq |f(a) - g(a)|\,e^{L|x-a|} + (K + \epsilon + \eta)[e^{L|x-a|} - 1]/L.$$

*3. Assume that, for equally spaced subdivisions of mesh-length h, the truncation error of a given approximate method $I_h[f]$ is $Mh^n + 0(h^{n+1})$, where M is independent of h. Prove that the *extrapolated* estimate

$$I_h^*(f) = (2^n I_{h/2}[f] - I_h[f])/(2^n - 1)$$

has a truncation error $0(h^{n+1})$.

*4. (a) Show that the extrapolation of Ex. 3 gives the trapezoidal approximation from the Cauchy polygon approximation, and Simpson's Rule from the trapezoidal approximation.

(b) Show that Simpson's Rule satisfies the hypotheses of Ex. 3, with $n = 4$. Derive an extrapolation estimate for Simpson's Rule.

*5. For the DE $dx/dt + tx = 0$, and the mesh-length $h_n = 1/(10 \mid t_n \mid + 1)$, show that the truncation error of the trapezoidal method tends to zero as $t \to \infty$, regardless of the initial value $x(0)$. What is the limiting truncation error as $t \to -\infty$?

*6. Let $f(t)$ be an analytic function, and $f(t+1) = f(t)$. Show that trapezoidal integration of $\int_0^1 f(t)$ for $h = 1/n$ has an infinite order of accuracy as $n \to \infty$.

7. Show that the error is $O(h^7)$ in the extended Simpson's Rule

$$\int_{x-h}^{x+h} F(x)dx \simeq \frac{h}{90}\{114F(x) + 34[F(x+h) + F(x-h)] - [F(x+2h) + F(x-2h)]\}.$$

8. (a) Let $z_k = z_0 + i^{k-1}h$, $i = \sqrt{-1}$. Show that, if $F(z)$ is any complex polynomial of degree five or less, then

$$(*) \qquad \int_{z_3}^{z_1} F(z)dz = \frac{h}{15}[24F_0 + 4(F_1 + F_3) - (F_2 + F_4)].$$

(b) Infer that, if $F(z)$ is a complex analytic function, then (*) holds with an error which is $O(h^7)$.

*9. Let $F(x,y)$ be bounded and continuous on the strip $0 \leqq x \leqq 1$, $-\infty < y < +\infty$; let $\{\pi_n\}$ be any sequence of partitions of [0,1] with $\mid \pi_n \mid \to 0$; and let $f_n(x)$ be the Cauchy polygon approximate solution, defined by π_n for the initial value $y(0) = 0$.

(a) Show that, if the $f_n(x)$ converge to a limit function $f(x)$, then $f(x)$ is a solution of $y' = F(x,y)$.

(b) Show that, in any case, a uniformly convergent subsequence $\{f_{n(i)}(x)\}$ can be found, $n(i) < n(i+1)$. (*Hint:* See Ch. V, § 13.)

*10. In Ex. 9, show that if the DE $y' = F(x,y)$ admits only one solution for the initial value $y(0) = 0$, then any sequence of Cauchy polygon approximations defined for $y(0) = 0$ by partitions whose norms tend to zero, must converge to the exact solution.

CHAPTER VIII

Efficient Numerical Integration

1. Introduction. The concepts of approximate solution of a DE and approximate function table were introduced in the preceding chapter, with some simple but useful examples. These referred exclusively to normal first-order systems

$$(1) \qquad dx/dt = X(x,t).$$

The simplicity of the methods treated made possible a rigorous theoretical analysis of their errors.

However, the methods studied in Chapter VII are rarely used when more than two decimal places of accuracy are wanted, because they converge so slowly (require so many steps). To obtain more accurate results with a moderate expenditure of effort, one uses more refined methods having higher orders of accuracy. Such methods are available provided X is really smooth, say $X \in \mathcal{C}^4$, an assumption which makes the (exact) solutions of (1) be of class $\mathcal{C}^5$.

Like the schemes already analyzed in Chapter VII, the schemes for numerical integration to be studied below will refer to an assumed partition π of the interval $[a,b]$ of integration by a finite number of points (the *mesh*),

$$(2) \qquad \pi:\ a = t_0 < t_1 < t_2 < \cdots < t_n = b = a + T.$$

Typically, the partition is into *steps* $\Delta t_k = t_k - t_{k-1}$ of constant length h, so that $t_r = a + rh$; one then speaks of a *uniform mesh.*

On the mesh (2), the DE (1) is approximated by a suitable *difference equation.* This difference equation is then solved step-by-step, using ordinary arithmetic supplemented by readings from available function tables.

One can obtain difference approximations to DE's by simply replacing derivatives by difference quotients, as in the Cauchy polygon method. With ordinary DE's, it is more usual to replace the system (1) by the equivalent vector integral equation (Ch. V, (11)):

$$(3) \qquad x(t) = x(a) + \int_a^t X(x,s)ds,$$

using a numerical quadrature formula (e.g., trapezoidal quadrature or Simpson's Rule) to replace (3) by a discrete approximation.

In either case, the step-by-step solution of the resulting difference equations yields an *approximate function table,* where the interval of tabulation is constant if the mesh is uniform. This function table, when combined with a suitable *interpolation* formula, then defines an *approximate solution,* whose value $\mathbf{y}(t)$ for any t can be computed to the degree of accuracy desired.

From these introductory remarks, it is clear that one must make a preliminary study of difference equations and interpolation formulas, before one can understand the art of efficient numerical integration. This preliminary study will be the subject of §§ 2–6 below.

2. Difference operators. In the study of difference equations (or ΔE's, as we will write for short), one is concerned with the *forward* difference operator Δ, the *backward* difference operator ∇, and the *central* difference operator δ, defined by the formulas

$$\Delta f(x) = f(x+h) - f(x), \tag{4a}$$
$$\nabla f(x) = f(x) - f(x-h), \tag{4b}$$
$$\delta f(x) = f(x+\tfrac{1}{2}h) - f(x-\tfrac{1}{2}h). \tag{4c}$$

In the preceding formulas, the symbols Δ, ∇, δ stand for *linear operators* transforming functions into functions. Unlike the linear differential operators of Ch. II, § 5, they apply to *all* functions.

These operations are useful in obtaining approximate solutions because they yield approximations to the derivative $f'(x)$. If $f \in \mathfrak{C}^1$, the derivative $f'(x)$ is the limit of the *divided differences*

$$f'(x) = \lim_{h\to 0} (\Delta f)/h = \lim_{h\to 0} (\nabla f)/h = \lim_{h\to 0} \delta f/h.$$

These are called, respectively, the *forward, backward* and *central* divided differences of f at x.

The difference operators (4a)–(4c) can be applied to any *function table* defined on a uniform mesh with step h, consisting of the equally spaced points

$$x_r = x_0 + rh, \quad r = 0, \pm 1, \pm 2, \cdots; \quad h > 0. \tag{5}$$

Using the standard abbreviations $y_r = f_r = f(a + rh)$, one obtains the identity

$$f_1 - f_0 = f(x+h) - f(x) = \Delta f_0 = \nabla f_1 = \delta f_{\frac{1}{2}}.$$

This shows that the usual difference notation is highly redundant.†

†It is also inconsistent with the usual notation $\Delta t_i = t_i - t_{i-1}$ employed in writing Riemann sums, which was used in Ch. VII.

This redundancy is apparent also when one *iterates* the difference operators (4a)–(4c), to define the *second differences*

(6a) $\Delta^2 f(x) = \Delta(\Delta f(x)) = \Delta(f(x+h) - f(x)) = f(x+2h) - 2f(x+h) + f(x)$,

(6b) $\nabla^2 f(x) = \nabla(\nabla f(x)) = \nabla(f(x) - f(x-h)) = f(x) - 2f(x-h) + f(x-2h)$,

(6c) $\delta^2 f(x) = f(x+h) - 2f(x) + f(x-h)$.

One easily verifies the identities $\delta^2 f(x) = \Delta(\nabla f(x)) = \nabla(\Delta f(x))$.

EXERCISES A

1. Show that, if the function $f(x) = \Sigma a_k x^k$ is a polynomial of degree m, then $\Delta^m f = \nabla^m f = \delta^m f = h^m f^{(m)}$, where $f^{(m)}$ denotes the m-th derivative of f.
2. Show that, if $y \in \mathfrak{C}^r$, then $\delta^r y = O(h^r)$ and $\Delta^r y = O(h^r)$.
3. Show that $\delta^r y_j = \sum_{k=0}^{r} (-1)^k \dfrac{r!}{k!(r-k)!} y_{j-k+r/2}$.

3. Polynomial interpolation. The difference notation of § 2 permits one to write down simple expressions for the polynomials of least degree interpolated through given values on any uniform mesh. Simplest is the *linear* interpolation formula (for fixed h and variable k)

$$p(x_0 + k) = y_0 + \frac{k}{h}(y_1 - y_0), \quad 0 < k < h. \tag{7}$$

The next easiest case is that of *parabolic* interpolation. Using the second central difference notation of formula (6c),

$$\delta^2 y_i = y_{i+1} - 2y_i + y_{i-1},$$

one has the quadratic interpolation formula

$$q(x_1 + k) = y_1 + \frac{k}{2h}\left(y_2 - y_0 + \frac{k}{h}\delta^2 y_1\right). \tag{8}$$

If second differences are tabulated, as they are in many tables, this formula requires only two multiplications and three additions†.

In a similar way one can derive the *quartic* (fourth order) *interpolation formula*

$$f(x_2 + k) = y_2 + \frac{k}{2h}\left(y_3 - y_1 + \frac{k}{h}\delta^2 y_2\right) + k(k^2 - h^2)[(\delta^2 y_3 - \delta^2 y_1)/12h^3 + k\delta^4 y_2/24h^4]. \tag{9}$$

Here $\delta^4 y_2 = \delta^2(\delta^2 y_2) = y_4 - 4y_3 + 6y_2 - 4y_1 + y_0$.

†We do not count the division required to calculate k/h, since this only requires a decimal point shift in most tabulations.

The preceding formulas are based on central differences. For polynomial interpolation between $n+1$ successive values on a uniform mesh, one often uses the *Gregory-Newton interpolation formula*

$$(10)\qquad p(x) = f(x_0) + \sum_{k=1}^{n} \Delta^k f(x_0)\left[\prod_{j=0}^{k-1} (x - x_0 - jh)\right] \Big/ h^k(k!),$$

where $n = (x_n - x_0)/h$, and where Δ^k is the iterated forward difference operator. This formula gives an approximation to $f(x)$ in terms of the differences of n equally spaced values of f. This formula is a difference analog of Taylor's formula, without a remainder term.

Lagrange interpolation formula. The Gregory-Newton formula, in turn, can be regarded as a special case of a very general interpolation formula due to Lagrange. Given the numbers $x_0 < x_1 < \cdots < x_n$ and $y_0, y_1, \cdots, y_n$, it can be shown† that there exists a unique polynomial $p(x)$ of degree n or less which satisfies $p(x_k) = y_k$ for $k = 0, 1, \cdots, n$—i.e., which assumes the $n+1$ given values at the points specified. Let

$$Q(x) = (x - x_0)(x - x_1)\cdots(x - x_n),$$
$$p_k(x) = Q(x)/(x - x_k) = \prod_{j \neq k} (x - x_j).$$

Then the polynomial

$$(11)\qquad p(x) = \sum_{k=0}^{n} \frac{p_k(x)}{p_k(x_k)} y_k = Q(x) \sum_{k=0}^{n} \frac{y_k}{Q'(x_k)(x - x_k)}$$

takes exactly the values $p(x_k) = y_k$, $0 \leq k \leq n$. Indeed $p_k(x_j) = 0$ for $j \neq k$, so that substituting $x = x_j$ in (11) we have

$$p(x_j) = \sum_{k=0}^{n} \frac{p_k(x_j)}{p_k(x_k)} y_k = \frac{p_j(x_j)}{p_j(x_j)} y_j = y_j.$$

Formula (11) is the Lagrange interpolation formula. Since the polynomial $p(x)$ in (11) is unique, (11) is equivalent to (10) if $x_j = a + jh, j = 0, 1, \cdots, n$. Hence, regarded as approximations to a function tabulated at equal intervals, (10) and (11) have the same error.

4. Interpolation error. Let a function $f(x)$ be tabulated at $n+1$ points $x_0 < x_1 < \cdots < x_n$, and let $p(x)$ be the polynomial of degree n or less which satisfies $p(x_k) = f(x_k)$, $k = 0, 1, \cdots, n$. What is the *error* of $p(x)$, considered as an approximation to $f(x)$? An answer to this question, when $f(x)$ is sufficiently smooth, is provided by the following

THEOREM 1. *Let $p(x) = a_0 + a_1x + \cdots + a_nx^n$ be the polynomial satisfying $p(x_i) = f(x_i)$, for $x_0 < x_1 < \cdots < x_n$. If $f \in \mathcal{C}^{n+1}$ in any interval I*

†Birkhoff and Mac Lane, p. 64.

containing $[x_0,x_n]$, *then for every* x *in* I *there exists* ξ *in* I *such that*

$$f(x) - p(x) = \frac{(x - x_0) \cdots (x - x_n)}{(n+1)!} f^{(n+1)}(\xi). \tag{12}$$

Proof. Let $e(x) = f(x) - p(x)$ denote the error function. Since $p(x)$ is a polynomial of degree n, $p^{(n+1)}(x) \equiv 0$, hence

$$e^{(n+1)}(x) = f^{(n+1)}(x)$$

for all x, and $e(x_0) = e(x_1) = \cdots = e(x_n) = 0$. Consider now the function

$$\phi(t) = Q(x)e(t) - Q(t)e(x), \tag{13}$$

where Q is the polynomial $Q(x) = (x - x_0)(x - x_1) \cdots (x - x_n)$. We consider ϕ as a function of t on I, for x fixed. Clearly $\phi \in \mathcal{C}^{n+1}$; moreover $\phi(x_k) = 0$, $k = 0, 1, \cdots, n$, and in addition $\phi(x) = 0$. By Rolle's Theorem, between any two points where ϕ vanishes there is at least one point where ϕ' vanishes. Since the function ϕ vanishes at $n+1$ points, the function ϕ' vanishes for at least n points. Repeating the same argument for higher derivatives, we eventually conclude that $\phi^{(n+1)}(t)$ vanishes for at least one point ξ in the interval I. Differentiating (13) relative to t, $n+1$ times, we obtain

$$0 = \phi^{(n+1)}(\xi) = Q(x)\, e^{(n+1)}(\xi) - (n+1)!\, e(x).$$

Since $e^{(n+1)}(\xi) = f^{(n+1)}(\xi)$ and $e(x) = f(x) - p(x)$, this gives

$$f(x) - p(x) = e(x) = \frac{1}{(n+1)!} f^{(n+1)}(\xi) Q(x), \quad \text{q.e.d.}$$

COROLLARY. *If* p *is the Lagrange interpolation polynomial of a function* $f(x)$ *of class* $\mathcal{C}^{n+1}$ *in the interval* $[x_0, x_n]$, *at* $x_0 < x_1 < \cdots < x_n$, *then the error at any point* $x \in [x_0,x_n]$ *is at most*

$$| f(x) - p(x) | \leqq \frac{1}{(n+1)!} N_n M_n$$

where $M_n = \max_{x_0 \leqq \xi \leqq x_n} | f^{(n+1)}(\xi) |$ *and* $N_n = \max_{x_0 \leqq x \leqq x_n} | Q_n(x) |$.

When the mesh points are equally spaced, we can compute N_n explicitly. Thus $N_2 = h^2/4$; if $x_1 < x < x_2$, $N_4 = 9h^2/16$, etc.

Applications. For example, if $x = x_j + k$, $0 < k < h$, the magnitude of the error in linear interpolation is $| k(h - k)f''(\xi) |/2 \leqq h^2 | f''(\xi) |/8$, for some $\xi \in [x_j, x_j + h]$. Likewise, parabolic interpolation through $f(x_j - h)$, $f(x_j)$, and $f(x_j + h)$ gives an approximate value differing from $f(x_j + k)$ by $| k(h^2 - k^2)f'''(\xi) |/6$. For $| k | \leqq h/2$, the error is therefore bounded by $h^3 | f''' |_{\max}/16$. Since one would naturally choose j to minimize $| x - x_j |$, this bounds the error in parabolic interpolation. The maximum error in the interval $(x_j - h, x_j + h)$ is slightly larger; see Ex. 8.

Ordinarily, parabolic interpolation is sufficiently accurate. For example, with $\sin x$, $|f'''|_{\max} = 1$; hence the error is bounded by $h^3/16$ in radian units. Therefore parabolic interpolation gives one four-place accuracy in a table at 6° intervals! More generally, unless $|f'''|_{\max} > 10$, six-place tables can be extended by parabolic interpolation to all x if $h = 0.01$, without an appreciable loss of accuracy. The same is true of nine-place tables if $h = 0.001$ (and of three-place tables, if $h = 0.1$).

For these reasons, higher-order interpolation is unnecessary for most tables in common use.

Caution. The *approximations* to a given function $f(x)$ on a fixed interval, defined by polynomial *interpolation* over that interval are not necessarily *good* approximations to $f(x)$, even if $f(x)$ is analytic. Thus, the approximations to the analytic function $f(x) = 1/(1 + x^2)$ obtained by the Gregory-Newton interpolation formula (10) *do not converge*† to $f(x)$ on the interval $-5 \leqq x \leqq 5$, but oscillate more and more wildly as the step length h tends to zero.

This shows that Newtonian interpolation cannot be used to define the approximating polynomials referred to in the Weierstrass Approximation Theorem. To get the best such *uniform* polynomial approximations, one must use a very different method due to Chebyshev (see Ch. XI, § 7).

EXERCISES B

In Exs. 1–4, verify the formulas indicated for $f \in \mathcal{C}^4$, a uniform mesh with step h, $0 < \theta < 1$, and $\bar{\theta} = (1 - \theta)$:

1. $f(x_0 + \theta h) = y_0 + \theta \Delta y_0 - (\theta\bar{\theta}/2)\Delta^2 y_0 + 0(h^3)$. (Newton)
2. $f(x_0 + \theta h) = y_0 + \theta \delta y_{1/2} - (\theta\bar{\theta}/4)(\delta^2 y_0 + \delta^2 y_1) + 0(h^3)$. (Bessel)
3. $f(x_0 + \theta h) = (\bar{\theta} y_0 + \theta y_1) + [(\bar{\theta}^3 - \bar{\theta})\delta^2 y_0 + (\theta^3 - \theta)\delta^2 y_1]/6 + 0(h^4)$. (Everett)

*4. $f(x_0 + \theta h) = \frac{1}{2}(y_0 + y_1) + (\theta - \frac{1}{2})\delta y_{1/2} - (\theta\bar{\theta}/4)(\delta^2 y_0 + \delta^2 y_0)$
$- [\theta\bar{\theta}(2\theta - 1)/12]\delta^3 y_{1/2} + 0(h^4)$. (Bessel)

5. Find the truncation errors of the formulas of Ex. 1–3, for quartic polynomials $q(x) = a + bx + cx^2 + dx^3 + ex^4$.

6. (a) Find the cubic polynomial $c(x)$ which satisfies $c(0) = y_0$, $c'(0) = y_0'$, $c(h) = y_1$, $c'(h) = y_1'$.

(b) Derive your formula as a limiting case of the four-point Lagrange interpolation formula.

7. Estimate the largest h such that parabolic interpolation in a six-place table of $\log_{10} x$ on $2 \leqq x \leqq 3$ with mesh-length h will yield five-place accuracy.

8. Show that, with parabolic interpolation between $y(-h)$, $y(0)$, and $y(h)$, the maximum error is normally near $x = \pm h/\sqrt{3}$, and is about $h^3|f'''(x)|/9\sqrt{3}$ there.

5. Roundoff error. In the preceding discussion, as in the error estimates and error bounds derived in Chapter VII, it has been tacitly assumed that all arithmetic operations and readings from function tables were *exact*, to an unlimited number of decimal places. In reality, however, only a finite

†See J. F. Steffensen, *Interpolation*, Williams and Wilkins, Baltimore, 1927, pp. 35–38 and the references given there.

number of significant figures are used. This leads to a source of error called the *roundoff error*, which has been ignored previously in this book. The errors discussed previously are referred to technically as *truncation errors*, or *discretization errors*.

In polynomial interpolation of low order, the roundoff error is not a serious problem. For $|k| < h$, formulas (7)–(9) show that the roundoff error affects only the last decimal place tabulated. For instance, writing $k/h = r$, parabolic interpolation gives $f(x_1 + rh) = w_0y_0 + w_1y_1 + w_2y_2$, where $w_0 = (r^2 - r)/2$, $w_1 = 1 - r^2$, $w_2 = (r + r^2)/2$, and $|r| < \frac{1}{2}$ if the three nearest tabulated values are used. Since

$$|w_0| + |w_1| + |w_2| \leqq 1 + r + 2r^2 \leqq 2,$$

and tabulated values are correct to $\frac{1}{2}$ in the last decimal place, the roundoff error is at most one in the last decimal place.

In numerical quadrature formulas, which also have the form $\Sigma w_k y_k$ per step with Σw_k equal to the mesh-length, the *maximum* roundoff error is similarly bounded by the length of the interval multiplied by the maximum tabulation error (ordinarily $\frac{1}{2}$ in the last decimal place).

Moreover the roundoff errors are nearly independent, and randomly distributed in the first untabulated decimal place with mean nearly zero. Hence† the cumulative roundoff error has a roughly normal distribution on a Gaussian curve, and the *probable* cumulative roundoff error with n equal subdivisions is only $0(1/\sqrt{n})$ times the maximum roundoff error.

Similar results hold for the numerical integration formulas to be considered below. The roundoff errors may be thought of as "noise", superimposed on the systematic truncation error. Both are amplified in the course of the calculation by a factor at most $e^{L(a-b)}$, where $L = \sup \partial F/\partial x$ is the one-sided Lipschitz constant and $(b - a)$ is the interval of integration.‡ This is because for L as defined above,

$$[y(x) - z(x)]' = F(x,y) - F(x,z) \leqq L(y - z) \quad \text{if} \quad y > z;$$

see also Ch. I, Ex. E12.

6. Numerical differentiation. The idea that divided differences (or difference quotients) can be used to approximate derivatives of tabulated functions has already been suggested in § 2. Using Taylor's formula, one can obtain estimates of the truncation errors incurred in such formulas for *numerical differentiation*.

For example, if $f \in \mathcal{C}^5$, the first two approximations to $f'(x)$ mentioned

†By the Central Limit Theorem of probability theory.
‡For a careful analysis of the cumulative roundoff error, see Henrici.

in § 2 give rise to the truncation error estimates

(14a) $$\Delta f/h - f'(x) = f''(x)h/2 + f'''(x)h^2/6 + f^{iv}(\xi)h^3/24,$$

(14b) $$\delta f/h - f'(x) = f'''(x)h^2/24 + f^{v}(\xi)h^4/1920,$$

where ξ is in the interval over which the difference is being taken. This illustrates the general principle that *central* difference quotients give more accurate approximations to derivatives than forward or backward difference quotients of the same order. One can obtain *truncation error bounds* similarly:

(14c) $$|[f(x+h) - f(x-h)]/2h - f'(x)| \leqq |f'''|_{max} h^2/6.$$

Note that the interval in (14c) is twice as long as in (14b); hence the truncation error is multiplied by about four.

It is interesting to compare the preceding truncation error bound with the corresponding *roundoff error* bound, which is $10^{-m}/2h$ if an m-place table is used. When $h < (3/10^m|f'''|_{max})^{1/3}$, therefore, the roundoff error exceeds the truncation error. To minimize the sum $(|f'''|_{max}h^2/6) + (10^{-m}/2h)$, which is the maximum total error if both terms have the same sign, set $2h^3 = 3/10^m|f'''|_{max}$. This shows that the maximum total error cannot be reduced below

$$\frac{1}{4}\sqrt[3]{18\,|f'''|_{max}/10^{2m}},$$

and that it is not advantageous, if $|f'''_{max}| < 2$, to choose h smaller than 0.04 if a four-place table is used to approximate $f'(x)$ by a central difference quotient.

Similar approximations can be made to $f''(x)$, using second difference quotients. For $f \in \mathcal{C}^2$, we have

$$\begin{aligned}\delta^2 f(x) &= f(x+h) - 2f(x) + f(x-h)\\ &= [f(x) + hf'(x) + h^2 f''(\xi_1)/2] - 2f(x) + [f(x) - hf'(x) + h^2 f''(\xi_2)/2]\\ &= h^2[f''(\xi_1) + f''(\xi_2)]/2,\end{aligned}$$

for some numbers ξ_1 and ξ_2 in the intervals $[x, x+h]$ and $[x-h, x]$, respectively. Hence $\delta^2 f/h^2$ lies between the minimum and maximum values of $f''(\xi)$ for ξ ranging over the interval $x - h \leqq \xi \leqq x + h$. Since a continuous function assumes all values between its minimum and its maximum, and since $f''(x)$ is continuous in the interval, we conclude that $\delta^2 f = h^2 f''(\xi)$, for some ξ in $[x-h, x+h]$. This shows that the difference quotient $\delta^2 f/h^2$ is a good approximation to the derivative f'' for small h. Since $\delta^2 f/h^2$ can be computed by consulting a numerical table of $f(x)$, the preceding formula may again be regarded as one for *approximate numerical differentiation.* This is written in the form $f''(x) \simeq \delta^2 f(x)/h^2$, where the symbol $\simeq$ means "is approximately equal to", as in Ch. VII, § 2.

For $f \in \mathcal{C}^4$, the preceding analysis can be refined so as to give an estimate of the truncation error. Taylor's formula with remainder gives

$$f(x \pm h) = f(x) \pm hf'(x) + h^2 f''(x)/2 \pm h^3 f'''(x)/6 + h^4 f^{\text{iv}}(\xi)/24,$$

where $x - h \leqq \xi \leqq x + h$. Since $f^{\text{iv}}(\xi)$ assumes all values between its minimum and maximum values on the above interval, we can write

$$\delta^2 f - h^2 f''(x) = h^4 f^{\text{iv}}(\xi)/12, \quad x - h \leqq \xi \leqq x + h. \tag{15}$$

This formula gives the truncation error estimate

$$f''(x) - \delta^2 f/h^2 = h^2 f^{\text{iv}}(\xi)/12,$$

in the formula $f''(x) \simeq \delta^2 f(x)/h^2$ for numerical differentiation. This formula shows that the truncation error is of the order of h^2, and tends to zero fairly rapidly when the step h is taken smaller and smaller.

However, for small h, the roundoff error is again dominant. Using m-place tables, the maximum roundoff error in the formula $f'' - \delta^2 f/h^2$ is found to be $2 \times 10^{-m}/h^2$, a quantity which increases without limit as h tends to zero.

For example, for the function $f(x) = \sin x$, where $f^{(\text{iv})}(x) = \sin x$, since $f^{\text{iv}}(x)$ ranges between -1 and 1, the maximum truncation error is approximately $h^2/12$, and the maximum roundoff error is $2 \times 10^{-5}/h^2$ using five-place tables. To minimize the greater of the truncation error (which tends to zero with h) and the maximum roundoff error, one must make $h^2/24 \simeq 10^{-5}/h^2$. Hence we minimize the maximum total error near $h^4 = 2.4 \times 10^{-4}$, or $h \simeq 0.13$ radian, $\simeq 8°$, roughly, a surprisingly large interval!

Roundoff errors are not considered further in this chapter. This is partly because, with high-speed computing machines, truncation errors are usually bigger unless h is very small (most modern machines carry at least ten decimal digits), and partly because the analysis of roundoff errors involves difficult statistical considerations.

Higher-order derivatives. The preceding truncation error estimates and bounds are special cases of a general result. This is

THEOREM 2. *If $f \in \mathcal{C}^{(n+2)}$ on $[x - nh/2, x + nh/2]$, then*

$$f^{(n)}(x) = \delta^n f/h^n - nh^2 f^{(n+2)}(\xi)/24, \quad \xi \in I. \tag{16}$$

Proof. The cases $n = 1, 2$ have been treated above. Proceeding by induction, we get

$$\delta f(x) = \int_{-h/2}^{h/2} f'(x+t)dt, \quad \delta^2 f(x) = \int_{-h/2}^{h/2} dt \int_{-h/2}^{h/2} f''(x+t+u)du, \cdots,$$

$$\delta^n f(x) = \int_{-h/2}^{h/2} dt_1 \int_{-h/2}^{h/2} dt_2 \cdots \int_{-h/2}^{h/2} f^{(n)}(x + t_1 + \cdots + t_n)dt_n.$$

This is a multiple integral over an n-dimensional domain D with center $t = 0$ and volume h^n, symmetric under the reflection $t_j \to -t_j$ ($j = 1, \cdots, n$). The arithmetic mean of the integrands at symmetrically placed points $x - T$ and $x + T$ is by Taylor's formula,

$$\tfrac{1}{2}[f^{(n)}(x+T) + f^{(n)}(x-T)] = f^{(n)}(x) + (T^2/2)f^{(n+2)}(x+\theta T),$$

for some θ, $0 \leqq \theta \leqq 1$. Hence, setting $T = t_1 + \cdots + t_n$ and integrating over D,

$$(m/2)\int T^2 dt_1 \cdots dt_n \leqq \delta^n f/h^n - f^{(n)}(x) \leqq (M/2)\int T^2 dt_1 \cdots dt_n,$$

where m and M are the least and greatest values of $f^{(n+2)}(\xi)$ for ξ in the given interval. Since

$$\int_{-h/2}^{h/2} t_k^2 dt_k = h^3/12 \quad \text{and} \quad \int_{-h/2}^{h/2} t_\ell t_k dt_\ell = 0,\ k \neq \ell,$$

and since $f^{(n+2)}(\xi)$, being continuous, assumes all values between its extreme values m and M, formula (16) follows.

COROLLARY. *Under the hypothesis of Theorem* 2, *we have the truncation error bound*

(17) $$|f^{(n)}(x) - \delta^n f/h^n| \leqq nMh^2/24,$$

where M is the maximum of $f^{(n+2)}(\xi)$ when ξ ranges over the given interval.

EXERCISES C

1. Show that the effect of roundoff errors on tenth differences is bounded by about 500×10^{-n} in n-place tables.
2. Show that $hf'(x_0 + h/2) = \delta y_{1/2} - (1/24)\delta^3 y_{1/2} + 0(h^5)$.
3. Show that $hf'(x_0 + h/2) = \delta y_{1/2} - \delta^3 y_{1/2}/24 + 3\delta^5 y_{1/2}/640 + 0(h^7)$.
4. Given a six-place table of $\sin x$ (x in radians), show that the approximate formula $f_0'' \simeq \delta^2 f_0/h^2$ has a combined truncation and roundoff error bounded by $2/10^6 h^2 + h^2/12$, and that this expression has a minimum of about 0.0008, assumed for h about 0.07.
5. (a) Show that $h^2 f'' = \delta^2 f - \delta^4 f/12 + 0(h^6)$.
   (*b) Show that $h^2 f'' = \delta^2 f - \delta^4 f/12 + \delta^6 f/90 + 0(h^8)$.
6. Show that, for $y \in \mathfrak{C}^8$, $\delta^2 y_0 = h^2[y_0'' + \delta^2 y_0''/12 - \delta^4 y_0''/240] + 0(h^8)$.

7. Difference equations. The truncation error estimate (14a) is related to that obtained in Chapter VII for the Cauchy polygon formula

(18) $$y_{k+1} - y_k = F(x_k, y_k)(x_{k+1} - x_k).$$

Formula (18) is obtained from the DE $y' = F(x,y)$ if one approximates y' by the forward† difference quotient $\Delta y_k/\Delta x_k = (y_{k+1} - y_k)/(x_{k+1} - x_k)$.

†N.B. The forward difference notation $\Delta x_k = x_{k+1} - x_k$ of (4a) is used here, and *not* the notation $\Delta x_k = x_k - x_{k-1}$ of the calculus, used in Ch. VII.

In the case $\Delta x_k = h$ of a uniform mesh, the central difference quotient $(y_{k+1} - y_{k-1})/2h$ approximates y_k' much better, by (14b).

This comparison suggests that a more accurate function table for the solution of $y' = F(x,y)$ satisfying $y(x_0) = y_0$ will result if (18) is replaced by the *two-level midpoint formula*

$$y_{k+1} - y_{k-1} = F(x_k,y_k)(x_{k+1} - x_{k-1}) = 2h\, F(x_k,y_k). \tag{19}$$

This is an explicit *two-step* difference equation, in the following sense.

DEFINITION. *A difference equation of order m, or an* m-step ΔE, *is an expression of the form*

$$\Delta^m y_n = F(n,y_n,\Delta y_n, \cdots, \Delta^{m-1} y_n), \tag{20}$$

where F is a given function. A solution *of* (20) *is a sequence* $y_0, y_1, y_2, \cdots, y_n, \cdots$ *which satisfies* (20) *for* $n \geqq m$.

Since $\Delta^k y_n$ is a linear combination of $y_n, y_{n+1}, \cdots, y_{n+k}$, one can rewrite the ΔE (20) in the equivalent form

$$y_{n+m} = \phi(n,y_n,y_{n+1}, \cdots, y_{n+m-1}), \tag{21}$$

where ϕ is a function determined by F. Thus, the solutions of (20) are the sequences y_n satisfying (21).

The ΔE (20) is the difference analog of the m-th order DE

$$y^{(m)} = F(x,y, \cdots, y^{(m-1)}).$$

In contrast to the case of DE's, however, the problem of proving the existence and uniqueness of solutions of the ΔE (20) for given initial values $y_0, y_1, \cdots, y_{m-1}$ is trivial. Clearly, (21) determines y_m from $y_0, y_1, \cdots, y_{m-1}$. By induction on n, the same is true for y_{m+n} for any positive integer n.

The preceding remark brings out a disadvantage in using two-step ΔE's like (19) for integrating first-order DE's. To apply such two-step methods, one must first calculate y_1 from y_0 by a separate process. A similar extra calculation, by a separate process, must be made every time the mesh-length is changed. For *analytic* DE's, power series (Chapter III) are often used for this purpose.

EXAMPLE 1. For the DE $y' = y$, the central difference approximation (19), with mesh-length h, gives

$$y_{k+1} = y_{k-1} + 2hy_k, \qquad h > 0. \tag{22}$$

For $h = 0.1$ and $y_0 = y(0) = 1$, the exponential series truncated after five terms gives $y_1 = 1.1052$, rounded off to four decimal places. Substituting into (22), we can compute the approximate function table for

$y_r = \exp(r/10)$:

$x = 0.1$	0.2	0.3	0.4	0.5	0.6	0.7
$y = 1.1052$,	1.2210,	1.3494,	1.4809,	1.6476,	1.8204,	2.0117,

etc. After ten steps, this gives the approximate value $e = 2.7159$, whose error is about -0.0023.

8. Characteristic equation: Stability. The ΔE (22) belongs to the important class of *linear ΔE's with constant coefficients*:

$$y_{n+m} = a_0 y_n + a_1 y_{n+1} + \cdots + a_{m-1} y_{n+m-1}, \tag{23}$$

where a_k are given constants. The solutions of such a ΔE can be obtained by a substitution similar to the exponential substitution of Ch. IV, § 1. One tries the sequence $y_r = \rho^r$, where ρ is a number to be determined. This gives from (23) the *characteristic equation*

$$\rho^m - a_0 - a_1\rho - \cdots - a_{m-1}\rho^{m-1} = 0. \tag{24}$$

For each root ρ_k of this characteristic equation, the sequence $y_r = \rho_k^{\,r}$ is the solution of the linear ΔE (23) satisfying the initial conditions $y_0 = 1$, $y_1 = \rho_k, \cdots, y_{m-1} = \rho_k^{\,m-1}$.

Thus, in Example 1, the characteristic equation is $\rho^2 = 1 + 2h\rho$, with distinct roots

$$\rho_i = h \pm \sqrt{1 + h^2} = \pm 1 + h \pm h^2/2 \mp h^4/8 \pm \cdots.$$

For $h = 0.1$, this gives $\rho_1 = 1.10499$, $\rho_2 = -0.90499$ when rounded off to five decimal places. The first root gives a fair approximation to the exact solution $e^{r/10}$, for which $\rho = 1.10517$. The discrepancy of 0.00018 is enough to explain the error in the approximate function table computed in § 7. It indicates that little can be gained by reducing the roundoff error to less than 0.00005 per step — i.e., by carrying out computations to more than four decimal places.

When the characteristic equation (24) has m distinct roots, the sequences $\rho_k^{\,r}$ form a *basis* of solutions of the ΔE (23). This means that every solution of (23) can be expressed as a linear combination

$$y_r = A_1\rho_1^{\,r} + A_2\rho_2^{\,r} + \cdots + A_m\rho_m^{\,r}$$

of the particular solutions $\rho_k^{\,r}$. The preceding result holds since the vectors $(1, \rho_k, \rho_k^2, \cdots, \rho_k^{m-1})$ are linearly independent,† so that any initial value vector $(y_0, y_1, \cdots, y_{m-1})$ is a suitable linear combination of them.

Even if the characteristic equation has multiple roots, a basis of solutions of the form $r^j\rho_k^{\,r}$ can still be constructed, much as in Chapter IV, Theorem 1.

†Their determinant is the Vandermonde determinant, and so is not zero (Birkhoff and Mac Lane, p. 303, Ex. 6c).

Stability. In analogy with Ch. IV, § 5, one says that the homogeneous linear n-th order ΔE with constant coefficients (23) is *stable* when all solutions y_r are *bounded* sequences, and *strictly stable* when all solutions are sequences tending to zero as $r \to \infty$.

Since one can obtain a basis of solutions of (23) of the form $r^j \rho_k{}^r$, the ΔE (23) is strictly stable if and only if all roots of the characteristic equation (24) are less than one in absolute value. This condition is obviously necessary; it is sufficient because $\lim_{r\to\infty} r^j \rho^r = 0$ whenever $|\rho| < 1$.

The concept of stability brings out a significant aspect of the effectiveness of the central difference approximation (22) for integrating numerically the DE $y' = y$. The general solution of (22) is $A\rho_1{}^r + B\rho_2{}^r$, where $\rho_i = h \pm (1 + h^2)^{1/2}$ as above and A, B are arbitrary constants. The positive root ρ_1, which is approximately equal to $e^{0.1}$, is *dominant* in the sense that $|\rho_1| > |\rho_2|$. Therefore the term $B\rho_2{}^r$ can be neglected in comparison to $A\rho_1{}^r$ for large r, provided $A \neq 0$.

When one uses (22) to compute an approximate function table for negative $x = -rh$, the reverse is true: we have the curious phenomenon of an *unstable* difference approximation to a *stable* DE. Unless $B = 0$, $A\rho_1{}^{-r} << B\rho_2{}^{-r}$ if r is sufficiently large. Setting $t = -x$, this shows that the central difference approximation to $dy/dt + y = 0$ can only be used to compute good approximate function tables for solutions of the initial value problem over very limited ranges.

One can avoid instabilities of the preceding type by using higher-order *backward* difference approximations to y', with small h. The simplest such approximation is

$$y_r' \simeq (3y_r - 4y_{r-1} + y_{r-2})/2h = \nabla y_r/h + \nabla^2 y_r/2h^3. \tag{25}$$

The truncation error in (25) is $h^2 y_r'''/3 + 0(h^3)$. The approximation (25) yields the *implicit* two-step difference approximation

$$y_r = \{4y_{r-1} - y_{r-2} + 2hF(x_r, y_r)\}/3, \tag{26}$$

to the DE $y' = F(x,y)$. In the *linear* case, this implicit second-order ΔE is easily solved recursively for y_r.

EXERCISES D

1. Solve the ΔE $u_{n+1} = 2u_n - u_{n-1}$ for the initial conditions $u_0 = 1$, $u_1 = -1$.
2. The n-th Fibonacci number F_n is the value at n of the solution of the ΔE

$$F_{n+1} = F_n + F_{n-1}$$

for the initial conditions $F_0 = 0$, $F_1 = 1$.

(a) Show that $F_n = (\rho^n - \sigma^n)/\sqrt{5}$, where $\rho = (\sqrt{5} + 1)/2$, $\sigma = (1 - \sqrt{5})/2$.

(b) What is the solution G_n of the Fibonacci ΔE for the initial conditions $G_0 = 2$, $G_1 = 1$?

3. Test the following ΔE's for stability or instability, by calculating the roots of their characteristic equations:

(a) $u_{n+1} = 2u_n - u_{n-1}$, (c) $u_{n+1} - 5u_n + 6u_{n-1} = 0$,
(b) $u_{n+1} = u_n + u_{n-1}$, (d) $u_{n+1} = -u_{n-1}$.

4. Show in detail that $|a + ab| + b^2 < 1$ is a necessary and sufficient condition for the strict stability of the ΔE $y_{n+2} = ay_{n+1} + by_n$.

*5. Derive necessary and sufficient conditions for strict stability of a third-order ΔE.

6. Show that, for small h, the ΔE (26) provides a strictly stable approximation to the strictly stable DE $y' + y = 0$, with truncation error $2h^3 | y_r''' | /3 + 0(h^4)$.

7. Show that, if $y' = F(x,y)$ and $F \in \mathcal{C}^3$, then:

$$y_{r+1} = y_{r-1} + 2hF_r + h^3F_r''/3 + 0(h^4) \qquad \text{(cf. (19))},$$

where $F_r = F(x_r,y_r)$ and $F'' = (d/dx + F\partial/\partial y)^2F$.

8. Show that, under the hypotheses of Ex. 7,

$$y_{r+1} = \{4y_r - y_{r-1} + 2hF_{r+1}\}/3 + 2h^3F_{r+1}''/9 + 0(h^4) \qquad \text{(cf. (26))}.$$

*9. (a) What is the order of accuracy of the explicit three-step Adams formula

$$y_{n+3} = y_{n+2} + h[F_{n+2} + \tfrac{1}{2}\Delta F_{n+1} + \tfrac{5}{12}\Delta^2F_n]$$

for integrating numerically the DE $y' = F(x,y)$?

(b) Show that the resulting ΔE is strictly stable for $y' + y = 0$, provided h is sufficiently small.

9. Simpson's Rule. The results on polynomial interpolation obtained in §§ 3–4 will now be used to derive a truncation error estimate for Simpson's Rule (cf. Ch. VII, (27) and (28)). Since Simpson's Rule approximates the definite integral in the integral equation equivalent to $y' = F(x,y)$, this error estimate applies to *Milne's formula*

$$(27) \qquad y_{r+2} = y_r + \frac{h}{3}[F(x_r,y_r) + 4F(x_{r+1},y_{r+1}) + F(x_{r+2},y_{r+2})]$$

for the numerical integration of $y' = F(x,y)$, see § 11.

The method to be used applies to a wide class of formulas for numerical quadrature. Let $0 \leqq r_0 < r_1 < \cdots < r_n \leqq 1$ be given, and let $x_i = a + r_ih$, $h > 0$. For any function $f \in \mathcal{C}^{n+2}$, let $p(x)$ be the Lagrange interpolation polynomial for the function $f(x)$ associated with the partition

$$a \leqq x_0 < x_1 < \cdots < x_n \leqq a + h = b.$$

Then the formula $f(x) \simeq p(x)$ is associated with a formula for numerical quadrature, namely

$$(28) \qquad \int_a^b f(x)dx \simeq \int_a^b p(x)dx = \sum_{i=0}^n w_iy_i = \sum_{i=0}^n w_if(x_i).$$

The coefficients w_i are the integrals of the polynomials $p_i(x)/p_i(x_i)$ by (11);

$$w_i = \frac{1}{p_i(x_i)}\int_a^b p_i(x)dx, \quad p_i(x) = \prod_{j\neq i}(x-x_i). \tag{28'}$$

Formula (28) is exact for all polynomials of degree $\leqq n$, since then $f(x) = p(x)$. For other functions, the error in (28) is $-\int_a^b e(x)dx$, where $-e(x) = p(x) - f(x)$. Hence, by Theorem 1, the error in (28) for any given n is of the order of h^{n+2} at most.

Setting $n = 1$ and $r_0 = 0$, $r_1 = 1$ in the preceding formulas, we get $p_0(x) = x - x_0$, $p_1(x) = x - x_1$, and so

$$w_0 = \int_{x_0}^{x_1} (x - x_0)dx/(x_1 - x_0) = (x_1 - x_0)/2 = h/2.$$

A similar calculation gives $w_1 = h/2$, so that the formula for *trapezoidal quadrature* (Ch. VII, § 6)

$$\int_a^{a+h} f(x)dx \simeq \frac{h}{2}[f(a) + f(a+h)] = \frac{h}{2}(y_0 + y_1) \tag{29}$$

is obtained as a special case of (28) and (28′). In this special case, the error $e(x)$ satisfies, by Theorem 1,

$$e(x) = L(x) - f(x) = \tfrac{1}{2}(x - x_0)(x_1 - x)f''(\xi),$$

for some $\xi = \xi(x)$ in the interval $x_0 \leqq \xi \leqq x_0 + h = x_1$. Since

$$\int_{x_0}^{x_1} L(x)dx = h(y_0 + y_1)/2,$$

the error $\int_{x_0}^{x_1} e(x)dx = \int_0^h e(x_0 + t)dt$ in trapezoidal quadrature satisfies

$$\tfrac{1}{2}f''_{\min}\int_0^h t(h - t)dt \leqq \int_{x_0}^{x_1} e(x)dx \leqq \tfrac{1}{2}f''_{\max}\int_0^h t(h - t)dt.$$

Since $\frac{1}{2}\int_0^h t(h - t)dt = h^3/12$, we obtain formula (24) of Chapter VII:

$$\frac{h}{2}(y_0 + y_1) - \int_{x_0}^{x_1} f(x)dx = \frac{h^3}{12}f''(\xi), \quad x_0 < \xi < x_1. \tag{30}$$

Applying (30) to each component of any *vector*-valued function $\mathbf{x}(t) \in \mathcal{C}^2$, we have

$$\int_{t_0}^{t_1} x_k(t)dt - \frac{h}{2}[x_k(t_0) + x_k(t_1)] = -\frac{h^3}{12}x_k''(\tau),$$

for some τ in the interval $[t_0, t_0 + h]$, and for each component x_k. By choosing one axis parallel to the error vector $\int_{t_0}^{t_1} \mathbf{x}(t)dt - h(\mathbf{x}_0 + \mathbf{x}_1)/2$, we obtain as a special case of the preceding result the inequality

$$\left| \int_{t_0}^{t_1} x(t)dt - \frac{h}{2}(x_0 + x_1) \right| \leqq \frac{h^3}{12} \sup |x''(\tau)|, \quad t_0 < \tau < t_1.$$

The *relative* truncation error is thus $0(h^2)$, as is to be expected from a formula which neglects quadratic terms.

Note that the vector analogs of the Theorem of the Mean and of (30) are false. For example, let $x(t) = (t^3, t^4)$, $t_0 = 0$ and $t_1 = 1$. Then

$$\int_0^1 x(t)dt - (1/2)(x_0 + x_1) = -(1/4, 3/10)$$

is not equal to $-x''(\tau)/12 = -(6\tau, 12\tau^2)/12 = -(\tau, 2\tau^2)/2$ for any τ in [0,1].

Formula (8) for parabolic interpolation leads similarly to *Simpson's Rule*:

$$(31) \quad \int_{x_0}^{x_2} f(x)dx \simeq \frac{h}{3}[y_0 + 4y_1 + y_2] = \frac{h}{3}[f(x_0) + 4f(x_1) + f(x_2)],$$

$h = x_2 - x_1 = x_1 - x_0$. This formula is exact for quadratic polynomials. Since $\int_{-h}^{h} x^3 dx = 0$, Simpson's Rule is also exact for cubic polynomials; this coincidence makes Simpson's Rule especially practical.

The error estimate for Simpson's Rule (31) will now be derived, for any $f \in \mathcal{C}^4$. Consider the *cubic* polynomial

$$p(x) = a_0 + a_1 x + a_2 x^2 + a_3 x^3,$$

satisfying $p(x_0) = y_0$, $p(x_1) = y_1$, $p'(x_1) = y_1' = f'(x_1)$, $p(x_2) = y_2$ $(x_0 = x_1 - h,\ x_2 = x_1 + h)$. These conditions amount to $a_0 = y_1$, $a_1 = y_1'$, $a_2 = \delta^2 y_1/2h^2$, and $a^3 = -a_1/h^2 + (y_2 - y_0)/2h^3$. Hence they can be satisfied for any y_0, y_1, y_2.†

To estimate the error $e(x) = p(x) - f(x)$, translate coordinates so that $x_0 = -h$, $x_1 = 0$, $x_2 = h$. Consider the function of t for *fixed* x,

$$(32) \qquad \phi(t) = x^2(x^2 - h^2)e(t) - t^2(t^2 - h^2)\, e(x),$$

analogous to the function (13) used in proving Theorem 1. We have $\phi(0) = \phi(\pm h) = \phi(x) = 0$; further, $\phi'(0) = 0$ since $e'(0) = 0$. By Rolle's Theorem, the function $\phi'(t)$ vanishes at three places besides $t = 0$ in the interval $-h < t < h$. Hence $\phi''(t)$ vanishes at least three times in $-h < t < h$, $\phi'''(t)$ vanishes twice, and $\phi^{\text{iv}}(t)$ vanishes once, at some point $t = \xi$. We thus have, much as in (12),

$$(33) \qquad 0 = \phi^{\text{iv}}(\xi) = x^2(x^2 - h^2)e^{\text{iv}}(\xi) - 24e(x).$$

†The resulting interpolation formulas are limiting cases of Lagrangian interpolation, for "infinitely near" points $x_0, x_0 + dx, x_1 - dx, x_1$.

Since $p(x)$ is a cubic polynomial, $p^{\text{iv}}(x) \equiv 0$; hence $-e^{\text{iv}}(\xi) = f^{\text{iv}}(\xi)$. Substituting in (33) and solving for $e(x)$, we get the error estimate

$$e(x) = x^2(h^2 - x^2)f^{\text{iv}}(\xi)/24, \qquad -h \leqq \xi \leqq h. \tag{34}$$

Integrating (34) with respect to x, since $x^2(h^2 - x^2) \geqq 0$, it follows that the truncation error in using Simpson's Rule for quadrature over $-h \leqq x \leqq h$, lies between $m = \min f^{\text{iv}}(\xi)$ and $M = \max f^{\text{iv}}(\xi)$ times the definite integral

$$\int_{-h}^{h} x^2(h^2 - x^2)dx/24 = h^5/90.$$

Since $f(x) \in \mathcal{C}^{\text{iv}}$, $f^{\text{iv}}(\xi)$ assumes every value between m and M. This gives

THEOREM 3. *If $f(x) \in \mathcal{C}^{\text{iv}}$, then the truncation error for Simpson's Rule on the interval $-h \leqq x \leqq h$ is equal to $h^5f^{\text{iv}}(\xi)/90$, for some ξ in the interval $[-h, h]$.*

The *relative* truncation error is therefore $h^4f^{\text{iv}}(\xi)/180$. For example, to achieve five decimal places of accuracy in computing $\ln 2 = \int_1^2 dx/x$, about 10^4 points must be taken if Riemann sums are used, about one hundred with trapezoidal quadrature, while ten are sufficient using Simpson's Rule! See also formula (28) of Chapter VII.

10*. Gaussian quadrature. What is the choice of the numbers

$$r_0 < r_1 < \cdots < r_n$$

which gives the highest order of accuracy in the formulas (28) and (28′) for numerical quadrature? This question was answered by Gauss, using the properties of the *Legendre polynomials* $P_n(x)$ defined in Ch. III, § 2. These properties, to be proved in Ch. XI, § 6, are: (i) $P_n(x)$ has n distinct zeros $x = \xi_1 < \xi_2 < \cdots < \xi_n$ in the open interval $(-1,1)$, and (ii) $P_n(x)$ is orthogonal to any polynomial of lower degree:

$$\int_{-1}^{1} x^m P_n(x)dx = 0 \text{ if } m < n.$$

We shall assume these results, and also the following definition:

DEFINITION. *The Gaussian quadrature formula of order n is the special case of formulas (28)–(28′), in which $r_i = (1 + \xi_i)/2$, $i = 1, \cdots, n$, and ξ_i is the i-th zero of $P_n(x)$.*

THEOREM 4. *Gaussian quadrature is exact if $f(x)$ is a polynomial of degree $2n - 1$ or less.*

Proof. By a translation of the origin and change of scale, we can take the interval of integration to be $[-1,1]$ without loss of generality. Let $f(x)$ be any polynomial of degree $2n-1$ or less. Let $p(x)$ be the polynomial of degree $\leqq n$ satisfying $p(r_i) = f(r_i)$, $i = 1, 2, \cdots, n$.

$$x_i = a + r_i h, = a + (1+\xi_i)h/2 \qquad [i = 1, \cdots, n].$$

Then $e(x) = f(x) - p(x)$ vanishes at $\xi_1, \cdots, \xi_n$. Hence† $e(x)$, which is a polynomial of degree at most $2n-1$ which vanishes at $\xi_1, \cdots, \xi_n$, is of the form $e(x) = (x-\xi_1)\cdots(x-\xi_n)b(x)$, where $b(x)$ is a polynomial of $n-1$ or less. For the same reason, $P_n(x) = c_n(x-\xi_1)\cdots(x-\xi_n)$, where $c_n \neq 0$. Hence $e_n(x) = s(x)P_n(x)$, where $s(x)$ is a polynomial of degree $n-1$ or less. But by (ii), $P_n(x)$ is orthogonal to any polynomial of degree less than n. Hence $\int_{-1}^{1} e(x)dx = \int_{-1}^{1} s(x)P_n(x)dx = 0$, so that (28)–(28′) is exact for $e(\xi)$, by the choice of the ξ_i. But, by the choice of the w_i, the formula is exact for $p(x)$; hence it is exact also for the given $f(x)$, completing the proof.

Now let $f(x) \in \mathfrak{C}^{2n}$, and let $q(x)$ be the polynomial of degree $2n-1$ satisfying $q(x_j) = f(x_j)$ for $x_j = a + jh/(2n+1)$, $j = 1, \cdots, 2n$. Then, by Theorem 1, $e(x) = q(x) - f(x) = 0(h^{2n})$, and so

$$\int_a^{a+h} q(x)dx - \int_a^{a+h} f(x)dx = \int_a^{a+h} e(x)dx = 0(h^{2n+1}).$$

But by Theorem 4,

$$\int_a^{a+h} q(x)dx = \sum_{j=1}^{n} w_j q(a + r_j h) = \sum_{j=1}^{n} w_j f(a + r_j h).$$

Substituting back into the preceding equation, we get

$$\text{(35)} \quad \int_a^{a+h} f(x)dx - \sum_{j=1}^{n} w_j f(a + r_j h) = 0(h^{2n+1}), \quad \text{if} \quad r_j = (1+\xi_j)/2.$$

This proves the following result.

Corollary. *For $f(x) \in \mathfrak{C}^{2n}$, Gaussian quadrature of order $n-1$ has an absolute error $0(h^{2n+1})$, and a relative error $0(h^{2n})$.*

EXERCISES E

1. Using a five-place table of $\sin x$, x in radians (but not tables of $\mathrm{SI}(x)$), evaluate

$$\int_0^x t^{-1} \sin t \, dt \quad \text{for} \quad x = 0.1, 0.2, \cdots, 1.0$$

by Simpson's Rule, with $h = 0.1$.

2. Show that $\int_1^2 dx/x = \ln 2$ is given by various numerical quadrature formulas, with $h = 1/10$, as follows: (a) initial point 0.73654401, (b) trapezoidal 0.69377139, (c) midpoint 0.6928354, (d) Simpson 0.6931474.

†By the Remainder Theorem: see Birkhoff and Mac Lane, p. 70.

3. Use Weddle's Rule (Ex. B3, Ch. VII) with 12 subdivisions to compute the approximation 0.69314935 to $\ln 2 = 0.69314718056$.

4. Use Cotes' Rule (Ex. B2, Ch. VII) with 12 subdivisions, to compute the approximation $\ln 2 \simeq 0.69319535$.

*5. Show that

$$\int_{x_0}^{x_1} f(x)dx = \frac{h}{2}[f_0 + f_1 - \tfrac{1}{12}(\delta^2 f_0 + \delta^2 f_1) + \tfrac{11}{720}(\delta^4 f_0 + \delta^4 f_1)] + 0(h^7).$$

*6. Show that, for $n = 3$, the Gauss quadrature formula on $(-h, h)$ is

$$\frac{h}{9}\left\{8f(0) + 5[f(-h\sqrt{3/5}) + f(h\sqrt{3/5})]\right\},$$

with truncation error $h^6 f^{\mathrm{vi}}(\xi)/15{,}750$, where $-h < \xi < h$.

*7. Show that the error in Hermite's tangent cubic quadrature formula,

$$\int_0^h y\,dx \simeq \frac{h}{2}(y_0 + y_1) - \frac{h^2}{12}(y_0' - y_1'),$$

is $h^5 f^{\mathrm{iv}}(\xi)/720$, where $0 < \xi < h$, if $y = f(x) \in \mathcal{C}^4$.

8. (Simpson's Five-Eight Rule). Show that, if $f \in \mathcal{C}^3$, then

$$\int_0^h f(x)dx = \frac{h}{12}[5f(h) + 8f(0) - f(-h)] + 0(h^4).$$

11. Milne's method. As mentioned in § 9, Simpson's Rule suggests an efficient procedure for calculating approximate function tables for the solutions of any first-order DE

$$y' = F(x,y), \qquad F \in \mathcal{C}^4. \tag{36}$$

Namely, given an initial value $f(a) = c$ and a mesh-length $h > 0$, one first computes $y_1 = f(a + h)$ by a suitable *starting process* (see below) such as expansion in power series. One then solves recursively the *implicit, two-step* ΔE

$$y_{k+2} = y_k + \frac{h}{3}[F(x_k,y_k) + 4F(x_{k+1},y_{k+1}) + F(x_{k+2},y_{k+2})]. \tag{37}$$

The ΔE (37) is obtained from the integral equation form (Ch. V, (11)) of the DE (36), which is

$$y_{k+2} = y_k + \int_{x_k}^{x_{k+2}} F(x,y(x))dx, \tag{38}$$

by approximating the integral in question by Simpson's Rule.

EXAMPLE 2. Consider the linear DE $y' = 1 - 2xy$ of Ch. VII, § 8, with initial value $y(0) = 0$ and mesh-length $h = 0.1$. In this case (37) reduces to

$$y_{k+2} = [15 + x_{k+2}]^{-1}[3 + (15 - x_k)y_k - 4x_{k+1}y_{k+1}]. \tag{39}$$

Evaluating $y(0.1) = 0.09934$ by power series, Milne's formula (39) gives $y(0.2) = 0.19475$. This approximate value agrees to five places with the value of $y(1/5)$ obtained by power series expansion; the comparison suggests that the mesh-length $h = 0.1$ is adequate for four-place accuracy. Repeated use of (39) then gives the following *approximate function table*

x	0.1	0.2	0.3	0.4	0.5
y	0.09934	0.19475	0.28264	0.36000	0.42444

The truncation error is about 10^{-5}, as can be verified by using the power series expansion

$$y = x - \frac{2}{3}x^3 + \frac{4}{15}x^5 + \cdots = \sum_{k=0}^{\infty} a_{2k+1}x^{2k+1}, \quad \frac{a_{2k+1}}{a_{2k-1}} = \frac{-2}{2k+1},$$

which gives $y(1) = 0.538079$. Another check is provided by the four-place table of Ch. VII, § 8.

Having been successfully used on a wide variety of DE's, Milne's method provides an excellent illustration of *implicit, two-step* methods. (An explicit two-step method was briefly discussed in § 7, following formula (19).)

Starting process. Given the initial value $y_0 = c = f(a)$, one must compute y_1 by a *one-step* method before one can begin to apply a *two-step* method. For analytic F, it is usually best to calculate $y_1 = f(a + h)$ by expanding $f(x)$ in a Taylor series as in Ch. III, § 7. When F is not analytic, but fairly smooth (say, if $F \in \mathcal{C}^4$), good approximations to $f(a + h)$ are often obtained by repeated *mesh-halving* of the interval $[a, a + h]$, using a one-step method with a lower order of accuracy. For instance, one might first compute $f(a + h/8)$ by midpoint integration, and then use Milne's formula to get $f(a + h/4) = y_{1/4}$ from y_0 and $y_{1/8}$, next computing $y_{1/2}$ from y_0 and $y_{1/4}$ by a second application of Milne's formula with mesh-length $h/4$, finally getting y_1 from y_0 and $y_{1/2}$ by a third application of the same process.

Iterative solution. To apply Milne's method, one must solve the implicit equation (37) for y_{k+2} at each step. For *linear* DE's, the equation can be solved arithmetically by division as in (39). But for *nonlinear* DE's, one must usually resort to the iterative method of successive approximation† described briefly in Ch. VII, § 10. Namely, one rewrites Milne's equation (37) and defines a function U in the form

$$(40) \qquad y_{k+2} = y_k + \frac{h}{3}[F_k + 4F_{k+1}] + \frac{h}{3}F(x_{k+2}, y_{k+2}) = U(y_{k+2}),$$

where all quantities are known except y_{k+2}. Regarded as an equation in the unknown number y_{k+2}, (40) has the form $y_{k+2} = U(y_{k+2})$, where the function U is computable. For any initial *trial value* $y_{k+2}^{(0)}$, one can hope

†The method is also analogous to Picard's method of successive approximation described in Ch. V, § 7.

that the sequence

$$y_{k+2}^{(1)} = U(y_{k+2}^{(0)}), \quad y_{k+2}^{(2)} = U(y_{k+2}^{(1)}), \quad y_{k+2}^{(3)} = U(y_{k+2}^{(2)}), \cdots$$

will *converge* fairly rapidly to the exact solution.

This hope can be justified if h is small and F satisfies a Lipschitz condition with Lipschitz constant L. More precisely, iteration *converges* if $h < 3/L$, and it converges *rapidly* if $h << 3/L$. For, by (40),

$$\begin{aligned} | y_{k+2}^{(r+1)} - y_{k+2}^{(r)} | &= \frac{h}{3} | F(x_{k+2}, y_{k+2}^{(r)}) - F(x_{k+2}, y_{k+2}^{(r-1)}) | \\ &\leqq (hL/3) | y_{k+2}^{(r)} - y_{k+2}^{(r-1)} |, \end{aligned}$$

by the Lipschitz condition assumed. Hence, if $\theta = hL/3$, induction on r,

$$| y_{k+2}^{(r+1)} - y_{k+2}^{(r)} | \leqq \theta^r | y_{k+2}^{(1)} - y_{k+2}^{(0)} |.$$

For $h < 3/L$, $\theta < 1$ and the sequence of $y_{k+2}^{(r)}$ is a Cauchy sequence. Let y_{k+2} be its limit. Since U satisfies a Lipschitz condition with Lipschitz constant $\theta = hL/3$, it is continuous. Hence, passing to the limit on both sides of the equation $y_{k+2}^{(r+1)} = U(y_{k+2}^{(r)})$, we get (40).

Predictors. One can obtain good initial approximations to y_{k+2} by using numerical quadrature formulas involving equally spaced interior points. The simplest such formula is

(41a) $$y_{k+2}^{(0)} = y_k + 2hF_{k+1},$$

where F_i denotes $F(x_i, y_i)$ as above. The error is $0(h^3)$. For $k \geqq 2$, one can use the more refined formula

(41b) $$y_{k+2}^{(0)} = y_{k-2} + \frac{4h}{3}[2F_{k-1} - F_k + 2F_{k+1}].$$

This would be exact if $F(x, y(x))$ were a cubic polynomial in x. Hence, by Theorem 1, its truncation error is $0(h^5)$.

By analogy with the improved Euler method of Ch. VII, § 10, one can think of the Milne method as combining one of the above *predictor* formulas with the *corrector* formula (40); one or two applications of the corrector formula at each step should give sufficient accuracy.

12. Stability; error analysis. Like the second-order approximation (22) of § 7, Milne's method gives an *unstable* difference approximation to the strictly stable DE $y' + y = 0$. Neglecting roundoff error, the approximate solution satisfies the ΔE, obtained by Milne's method (37)

$$y_{k+2} = y_k - \frac{h}{3}[y_k + 4y_{k+1} + y_{k+2}],$$

or, equivalently, it satisfies the *linear* ΔE

$$y_{k+2} = \frac{3-h}{3+h}y_k - \frac{4h}{3+h}y_{k+1}. \tag{42}$$

The general solution of (42) is, as in § 8, the sequence $x_n = A_1\rho_1{}^n + A_2\rho_2{}^n$, where ρ_1 and ρ_2 are the roots of the characteristic equation of (42), namely

$$\rho^2 + \frac{4h\rho}{3+h} - \frac{3-h}{3+h} = 0.$$

The roots of this equation satisfy the relations

$$\rho_1 = 1 - h + 0(h^2), \qquad \rho_2 = -\left(1 + \frac{h}{3}\right) + 0(h^2).$$

As $h \downarrow 0$, we obtain $\rho_1{}^n = (1-h)^{t/h} + 0(h)$, so that in the limit we get e^{-t}, an exact solution of the DE.

But $\rho_2{}^n = \left[-\left(1+\frac{h}{3}\right)\right]^n + 0(h)$ tends, as $h \to 0$ $(n \to \infty)$, to a *spurious* solution, whose magnitude $e^{t/3}$ grows exponentially and whose sign alternates! As a result, no matter how small the coefficient A_2 of $\rho_2{}^n$ is initially, and how small is subsequent roundoff error, the calculated values of $x_n = x(t_n)$ will ultimately oscillate wildly, if the approximate function table is continued far enough using Milne's method.

Error bound. Since the relative error in Simpson's Rule is $0(h^4)$, one readily guesses that the cumulative truncation error in Milne's method, over any fixed interval $[a, a+T]$, is bounded by Mh^4 for some finite constant M independent of the mesh-length h. This is true provided that both y_0 and y_1 are accurate to $0(h^5)$.

Indeed, let $y(x)$ be any exact solution of the DE $y' = F(x,y)$, and let $\phi(x) = F(x,y(x))$. Then by Theorem 3,

$$y_{k+2} = y_k + \frac{h}{3}[\phi(x_k) + 4\phi(x_{k+1}) + \phi(x_{k+2})] + e_{k+2}, \tag{43}$$

where $|e_{k+2}| = |\phi^{\text{iv}}|_{\max} h^5/90$. From this, a discussion like that of Ch. VII, § 12, yields the bound

$$M = |\phi^{\text{iv}}|_{\max}(e^{LT}-1)\Big/ 90L\left(1 - \frac{hL}{3}\right). \tag{44}$$

Finally, one can express $\phi^{\text{iv}}(x)$ in terms of F and its derivatives, just as in Ch. III, § 8:

$$\phi' = F_x + FF_y, \quad \phi'' = F_{xx} + 2FF_{xy} + F^2F_{yy} + F_xF_y + FF_y{}^2, \tag{45}$$

and so on. Combining these results, one can compute M *a priori* in terms of the values of F and its derivatives, thus getting an explicit error bound.

Practical error analysis. Such *a priori* error bounds are of little use in practice. What one really wants is a (truncation) *error estimate.* Namely, if $y_k = y(x_k)$ is the value of the *exact* solution of a given initial value problem, and $z_k = z(x_k,h)$ is the *approximate* value computed by Milne's method for a given constant mesh-length h, one wants an expression of the form

$$z(x_k,h) = y(x_k) + Ch^4 + 0(h^5), \qquad h = (x_k - a)/n, \tag{46}$$

where the constant C is *known*, at least approximately.

Formulas of this type can be proved to exist; see for example Chapter VII, formulas (19), (26), and (28). To prove this for Milne's method would be very involved, however.

In practice, therefore, one accepts the *order* of accuracy as being given by the error bound, and assumes the validity of a formula like (46). One then estimates the magnitude of the unknown constant C *a posteriori* from approximate function tables, computed for *different* constant mesh-lengths $\theta = h, h/2$, etc. For any fixed x_k and θ, the truncation error $z(x_k,\theta) = Z(\theta)$ can be estimated from these tables and formula (46), using the following elementary result, called Richardson's extrapolation method.

LEMMA. *Given the function* $Z(\theta) = Y + C\theta^n + 0(\theta^{n+1})$, *let* $Z(h) = Z_0$ *and* $Z(h/2) = Z_1$. *Then*

$$Y = Z_1 + (Z_1 - Z_0)/(2^n - 1) + 0(h^{n+1}). \tag{47}$$

Proof. Straightforward substitution into the formulas given, with $\theta = h$ and $\theta = h/2$, yields $Z_1 - Z_0 = (2^{-n} - 1)Ch^n + 0(h^{n+1})$, whence

$$Z_1 + (Z_1 - Z_0)/2^{n-1} = Y + Ch^n + 0(h^{n+1}) - Ch^n + 0(h^{n+1}).$$

Since $Ch^n - Ch^n = 0$ and $0(h^{n+1}) + 0(h^{n+1}) = 0(h^{n+1})$, formula (47) follows immediately.

Note that formula (47) *corrects* the computed value Z_1 by the *extrapolation* term $(Z_1 - Z_0)/(2^n - 1)$. If one computes $Z(h/4) = Z_2$ as well, one gets the improved estimate

$$Y = Z_2 + (Z_2 - Z_1)/(2^n - 1) + 0(h^{n+1}). \tag{48}$$

The internal agreement between (47) and (48) provides the best practical estimate for the unknown terms $0(h^{n+1})$ which are neglected, as well as for the unknown roundoff error. To test the assumption that these are relatively small, one should verify the approximate equation

$$(Z_2 - Z_1)/(Z_1 - Z_0) = 2^{-n} + 0(h),$$

which would hold if there were no roundoff, by a computation like that given above.

EXERCISES F

1. (a) Show that, for the DE $y' = y$ and $h = 0.1$, Milne's method amounts to using the ΔE $y_{k+2} = (31y_k + 4y_{k+1})/29$.

(b) Integrate the DE $y' = y$ from $x = 0$ to $x = 1$ by Milne's method with $h = 0.1$, for the starting values $y_0 = 1$ and $y_1 = 1.1052$.

2. Same question for the DE $y' = 1 + y^2$, using the starting values $y_0 = 0$ and $y_1 = 0.1003$.

3. Same question for the DE $y' = x^2 + y^2$, with the starting values $y_0 = 0$ and $y_1 = 0.00033$.

Ex. 4–6 concern the *two-level midpoint method*, defined by (19).

4. (a) Show that, if $y' = F(x,y)$, where $F \in \mathcal{C}^2$, then $y = f(x)$ satisfies the two-level midpoint formula (19) with discrepancy $O(h^3)$.

(b) Show that, if $F \in \mathcal{C}^4$, and y_{n-1}, y_n are exact, then the truncation error is $Kh^3 + O(h^4)$.

5. (a) Integrate $y' = y$ approximately by the two-level midpoint method, with $h = 0.1$, taking $y_0 = 1$, $y_1 = 1.1052$ as starting values, and integrating to $y_{10} \simeq 2.7145$.

(b) Estimate the discrepancy and the cumulative truncation error in (a), comparing them with the roundoff error.

6. (a) Same as Ex. 5a, but for the system $y' = z - 2y$, $z' = y - 2z$, and the starting values $y_0 = 1$, $z_0 = 0$, $y_1 = 0.8228$, $z_1 = 0.0820$, computed by the method of § 13.

(b) Show that the system in question is stable, but that the approximating ΔE is not. Explain why the computed table is approximately correct, though the method is unstable.

7. (a) For general $h > 0$, set

$$y_0 = 1,\ y_1 = 1 + h + h^2\left(\frac{1}{2} + \frac{h}{6} + \frac{h^2}{24}\right), \quad \text{and} \quad y_{n+1} = y_{n-1} + 2hy_n.$$

Show that $| y_n - e^{nh} | = O(h^2)$, as $h \to 0$ with nh constant.

(b) If $h = 10^{-p}$, and the roundoff error is 10^{-p}, infer that the cumulative *total* error is $O(10^{p-h})$.

8. For the first-order linear system $dx/dt = A(t)x$, show that the trapezoidal, improved Euler, and midpoint integration formulas give respectively:

$$\begin{aligned} x_i &= (I - hA_i/2)^{-1}(I + hA_{i-1}/2)x_{i-1} \\ x_i &= [I + h(A_{i-1} + A_i)/2 + h^2A_iA_{i-1}/2]x_{i-1} \\ x_i &= (I + hA_{i-1/2} + h^2A_{i-1/2}A_i/2)x_{i-1}. \end{aligned}$$

*9. Show that the approximate solution obtained by Milne's method for given initial values converges to the true solution for any $F \in \mathcal{C}^2$. What is the resulting order of accuracy?

13. Local power series. In principle, it is easy to derive formulas of numerical integration for $y' = F(x,y)$ having an arbitrarily high order of accuracy, provided F is sufficiently smooth. One simply evaluates the successive derivatives of y as in Ch. III, § 8, getting $y' = F$, $y'' = F' = F_x + FF_y$,

$$\begin{aligned} y''' &= F_{xx} + 2FF_{xy} + F^2F_{yy} + y''F_y, \\ y^{\text{iv}} &= F_{xxx} + 3FF_{xxy} + 3F^2F_{xyy} + F^3F_{yyy} + y''(3F_{xy} + 3FF_{yy}) + y'''F_y, \end{aligned}$$

and so on. If F is linear or a polynomial of low degree, the preceding formulas may even be practical for computation.

One then evaluates Taylor's formula, valid for $F \in \mathcal{C}^n$,

$$(49) \quad y(x_k + h) = y_k + hy_k' + h^2y_k''/2 + \cdots + h^ny_k^{(n)}/(n!) + 0(h^{n+1}),$$

ignoring the remainder $0(h^{n+1})$. The relative error in the recursion relation so obtained,

$$(49') \qquad y_{k+1} = y_k + hy_k' + h^2y_k''/2 + \cdots + h^ny_k^{(n)}/(n!),$$

is obviously of order n. Hence, by Theorem 9 of Chapter VII, so is the cumulative error. Moreover this *one-step, explicit* method has the advantages of permitting a variable mesh-length, and of being stable for strictly stable DE's.

The calculation of (49'), however, is rather cumbersome, since it involves many terms. Moreover, in some cases the derivatives of F can only be computed approximately by numerical differentiation, which is inexact (§ 6). A one-step method of integration which gives a high order of accuracy and avoids these defects will now be described.

14. Runge-Kutta method. This approach is based on the idea of obtaining as high an order of accuracy as possible, using an *explicit, one-step* method. It consists in extending the approximations of the improved Euler method (Ch. VII, § 10) further, so as to obtain a one-step formula having a higher order of accuracy. One-step methods have the advantage of permitting a change of mesh-length at any step, because no starting process is required.

The most commonly used one-step method with high order of accuracy is the Runge-Kutta† method. We now describe the ΔE used in this method, for the first-order system

$$(50) \qquad d\mathbf{x}/dt = \mathbf{X}(\mathbf{x}, t), \qquad a \leqq t \leqq b,$$

with mesh-points $a = t_0 < t_1 < t_2 < \cdots$. Let $\mathbf{y}_0 = \mathbf{x}(a)$ be the initial value. The approximate function table of values $\mathbf{y}_i$ corresponding to the points t_i is defined by the ΔE

$$(51) \qquad \mathbf{y}_{i+1} = \mathbf{y}_i + \frac{h}{6}(\mathbf{k}_1 + 2\mathbf{k}_2 + 2\mathbf{k}_3 + \mathbf{k}_4),$$
$$\mathbf{k}_1 = \mathbf{X}(\mathbf{y}_i, t_i), \qquad \mathbf{k}_2 = \mathbf{X}(\mathbf{y}_i + h\mathbf{k}_1/2, t_i + h/2)$$
$$\mathbf{k}_3 = \mathbf{X}(\mathbf{y}_i + h\mathbf{k}_2/2, t_i + h/2), \qquad \mathbf{k}_4 = \mathbf{X}(\mathbf{y}_i + h\mathbf{k}_3, t_i + h),$$

where the mesh-length $h = h_i$ may vary with i.

We now show that the preceding Runge-Kutta method has an error of

†*Zeits. Math. Phys.* 46 (1901), 435–453; C. Runge and H. König, *Numerische Rechnung,* 1924, Ch. X.

only $0(h^5)$ per step†. For simplicity, we restrict attention to the first-order DE

$$dx/dt = X(x,t), \quad X \in \mathcal{C}^4, \quad a \leqq t \leqq b, \tag{52}$$

and to the initial condition $x(0) = 0$. Formulas (51)–(51′) reduce in this case to

$$y_{i+1} = y_i + \frac{h}{6}(k_1 + 2k_2 + 2k_3 + k_4), \tag{53}$$

where

$$\begin{aligned} k_1 &= X(y_i, t_i), & k_2 &= X(y_i + hk_1/2, t_i + h/2) \\ k_3 &= X(y_i + hk_2/2, t_i + h/2), & k_4 &= X(y_i + hk_3, t_i + h). \end{aligned} \tag{53′}$$

Let $x(t)$ be the exact solution of the DE satisfying $x(0) = y_0 = 0$. Then k_2 can be written as

$$\begin{aligned} k_2 = X(x_{1/2}, h/2) &+ X_x(x_{1/2}, h/2)[x_0 - x_{1/2} + hk_1/2] \\ &+ X_{xx}(x_{1/2}, h/2)[x_0 - x_{1/2} + hk_1/2] + \cdots, \ x_0 = x(0), \ x_{1/2} = x(h/2), \end{aligned}$$

where subscripts x stand for partial derivatives. Using primes to indicate total derivatives with respect to t, so that $X' = \partial X/\partial t + X\partial X/\partial x$, we get

$$\begin{aligned} x_{1/2} = x_0 + X(0,0)h/2 + X'(0,0)(h/2)^2 &+ X''(0,0)(h/2)^3/6 \\ &+ X'''(0,0)(h/2)^4/24 + 0(h^5). \end{aligned}$$

Since $k_1 = X(0,0)$, it follows that

$$x_0 - x_{1/2} + hk_1/2 = -X'(0,0)(h/2)^2/2 - X''(0,0)(h/2)^3/6 + 0(h^4),$$

so that

$$k_2 = X(x_{1/2}, h/2) - X_x(x_{1/2}, h/2)[X'(0,0)(h/2)^2/2 + X''(0,0)(h/2)^3/6] + 0(h^4).$$

For k_3, we have similarly

$$k_3 = X(x_{1/2}, h/2) + X_x(x_{1/2}, h/2)[x_0 - x_{1/2} + hk_2/2] + \cdots,$$

and since

$$\begin{aligned} x_0 = x_{1/2} &- X(x_{1/2}, h/2)h/2 + X'(x_{1/2}, h/2)(h/2)^2/2 \\ &- X''(x_{1/2}, h/2)(h/2)^3/6 + X'''(x_{1/2}, h/2)(h/2)^4/24 + 0(h^5), \end{aligned}$$

we obtain

$$\begin{aligned} k_3 = X(x_{1/2}, h/2) &+ X_x(x_{1/2}, h/2)X'(x_{1/2}, h/2)(h/2)^2/2 \\ &- X_x(x_{1/2}, h/2)X_x(x_{1/2}, h/2)X'(0, 0)(h/2)^3/2 \\ &- X_x(x_{1/2}, h/2)X''(x_{1/2}, h/2)(h/2)^3/6 + 0(h^4). \end{aligned}$$

†The proof which follows was constructed by Mr. Robert E. Lynch.

Similarly

$$k_4 = X(x_1, h) + X_x(x_1, h)[x_0 - x_1 + hk_3] + \cdots,$$

and

$$x_0 - x_1 = -X(x_{1/2}, h/2)(h) - X''(x_{1/2}, h/2)(h/2)^3/3 + 0(h^4),$$

so that

$$\begin{aligned} k_4 = X(x_1, h) &- X_x(x_1, h)X''(x_{1/2}, h/2)(h/2)^3/3 \\ &+ X_x(x_1, h)X_x(x_{1/2}, h/2)X'(x_{1/2}, h/2)(h/3)^3 + 0(h^4). \end{aligned}$$

Finally, we have the relations

$$\begin{aligned} X(x_{1/2}, h/2) &= X(0,0) + X'(0,0)h/2 + X''(0,0)(h/2)^2/2 \\ &\quad + X'''(0,0)(h/2)^3/6 + 0(h^4), \\ X(x_1, h) &= X(0,0) + X'(0,0)h + X''(0,0)h^2/2 + X'''(0,0)h^3/6 + 0(h^4), \\ X_x(x_1, h) &= X_x(x_{1/2}, h/2) + X_x'(x_{1/2}, h/2)(h/2) + 0(h^2). \end{aligned}$$

Combining these results, we find that

$$\begin{aligned} y_1 = y_0 + \frac{h}{6}[k_1 + 2k_2 + 2k_3 + k_4] &= y_0 + X(0,0)h + X'(0,0)\frac{h^2}{2} \\ &\quad + X''(0,0)\frac{h^3}{6} + X'''(0,0)h^4/24 + 0(h^5), \end{aligned}$$

and $y_0 = x_0$. Since $x(h)$ is given by

$$\begin{aligned} x(h) = x_1 = x_0 &+ X(0,0)h + X'(0,0)h^2/2 + X''(0,0)h^3/6 \\ &+ X'''(0,0)h^4/24 + 0(h^5) \end{aligned}$$

we see that

$$| y_1 - x_1 | = 0(h^5).$$

Hence, the relative error is of order four. Therefore, by Theorem 9 of Chapter VII, so is the cumulative error. The method of proof consists in comparing various Taylor's series.

The main defect of the Runge-Kutta method is the need for evaluating $\mathbf{k}_j = \mathbf{X}(\mathbf{x}_j, t_j)$ for four values of $(\mathbf{x}_j, t_j)$ per time-step. If $\mathbf{X}$ is a complicated function, this may be quite time-consuming.

To avoid this repetitious evaluation, some computer programs use the Runge-Kutta process only to start the computation or in the first few steps after the mesh-length has been changed. At other time-steps Adams-type formulas are used, based on approximate quadrature formulas having a high order of accuracy. For example, one can obtain an absolute error $0(h^4)$ using the *predictor* formula of Adams-Bashforth

$$\tilde{\mathbf{y}}_{i+1} = \mathbf{y}_i + h \sum_{m=0}^{3} \beta_m \nabla^m \mathbf{X}_i \tag{54}$$

where $\beta_0 = 1$, $\beta_1 = \frac{1}{2}$, $\beta_2 = \frac{5}{12}$, and $\beta_3 = \frac{3}{8}$, followed by the *corrector* formula of Adams-Moulton

$$\mathbf{y}_{i+1} = \mathbf{y}_i + h \sum_{m=0}^{3} \gamma_m \nabla^m \tilde{\mathbf{X}}_{i+1}, \tag{55}$$

where $\gamma_0 = 1$, $\gamma_1 = -\frac{1}{2}$, $\gamma_2 = -\frac{1}{12}$, and $\gamma_3 = -\frac{1}{24}$. In (55),

$$\tilde{\mathbf{X}}_{i+1} = \mathbf{X}(\tilde{\mathbf{y}}_{i+1}, t);$$

unless this value is used, the formula is implicit.

EXERCISES G

1. (a) Derive a power series expansion for $f(a + h)$ through terms in h^4, for the solution of $y' = 1 + y^2$ satisfying $f(a) = c$.

(b) Truncating the preceding series after terms in h^3, evaluate approximately in three steps the solution of $y' = 1 + y^2$ satisfying $f(0) = 0$, setting $x_1 = 0.5$, $x_2 = 0.8$, $x_3 = 1$. What is the truncation error? (*Hint:* Consider $\tan x$.)

2. Same question for $y' = x^2 + y^2$. (The exact solution, rounded off to five decimal places, is 0.35023).

3. (a) Apply the Picard process to the DE $y' = x^2 + y^2$ for the initial value $y_0 = 0$ and initial trial function $y^{(0)} \equiv 0$. Calculate the first four iterates.

(b) Using the power series method of the text, calculate the Taylor series of the solution through terms in x^{17}, and check against the answer to (a).

(c) Evaluate $y(1)$ numerically at $x = 1$, using the preceding truncated power series, and compare with the answer of Ex. 2.

4. Apply the Runge-Kutta method to the DE $y' = 1 + y^2$ for the initial value $y(0) = 0$, setting $x_0 = 0$, $x_1 = 0.5$, $x_2 = 0.8$, $x_3 = 1$.

5. Same question for the DE $y' = x^2 + y^2$, with $y(0) = 0$, and the same mesh.

6. For the first-order linear system $d\mathbf{x}/dt = A(t)\mathbf{x}$, show that the Runge-Kutta method is equivalent to:

$$\mathbf{x}_{i+1} = \left[I + \frac{h}{6}(A_0 + 4A_1 + A_2) + \frac{h^2}{6}(A_1A_0 + A_1^2 + A_2A_1) + \frac{h^3}{12}(A_1^2A_0 + A_2A_1^2) + \frac{h^4}{24}(A_2A_1^2A_0) \right] \mathbf{x}_i.$$

where $A_0 = A(t_i)$, $A_1 = A(t_{i+1/2})$, $A_2 = A(t_{i+1})$.

In Exs. 7–11, let $y' = F(x,y) = \sum_{j,k=0}^{\infty} b_{jk}x^jy^k$ and $y(0) = 0$.

7. Show that

$$y'' = F_x + FF_y \text{ and } y''' = F_{xx} + 2FF_{xy} + F^2F_{yy} + F_xF_y + FF_y^2.$$

In Exs. 8–11, let $B = b_{20} + b_{11}b_{00} + b_{02}b_{00}^2$ and $B^* = b_{10}b_{01} + b_{00}b_{01}^2$.

8. Show that, if $y(0) = 0$, then

$$y(h) = hb_{00} + h^2(b_{10} + b_{00}b_{01})/2 + h^3(B/3 + B^*/6) + 0(h^4).$$

9. Show that, with midpoint integration, $y(h)$ is given by the approximate formula

$$y_M(h) = hb_{00} + h^2(b_{10} + b_{00}b_{01})/2 + h^3B/4 + 0(h^4),$$

and that the truncation error is $-h^3(B/12 + B^*/6) + 0(h^4)$.

10. Show that the improved Euler method gives

$$y_E(h) = hb_{00} + h^2(b_{10} + b_{00}b_{01})/2 + h^3B/2 + 0(h^4),$$

with truncation error $h^3(B - B^*)/6 + 0(h^4)$.

11. Show that the trapezoidal approximation to $y(h)$ is

$$y_T(h) = hb_{00} + h^2(b_{10} + b_{00}b_{01})/2 + h^3(B/2 + B^*/4) + 0(h^4),$$

with truncation error $h^3(B/6 + B^*/12) + 0(h^4)$.

12. Check the formulas of Ex. F8 against those of Exs. 9–10 in the special case $t_{i-1} = 0$, $t_i = h$, and $A(t) = p(t) = p_0 + p_1t + p_2t^2 + \cdots$ of a first-order linear DE.

*13. For the linear DE $dx/dt = p(t)x$, $\quad p(t) = \sum_{k=0}^{\infty} p_k(t-a)^k$,

evaluate $x(a + h)$ through terms in h^6 by the Runge-Kutta method. Compare with the Taylor series for the exact solution.

*14. *Adams three-level methods* for integrating $y = F(x,y)$ are:

(A_3) $\quad y_{n+1} = y_n + h[23F_n - 16F_{n-1} + 5F_{n-2}]/12$ (explicit)

(A_3') $\quad y_{n+1} = y_n + h[9F_{n+1} + 19F_n - 5F_{n-1} + F_{n-2}]/24$ (implicit)

Show that the truncation error of (A_3) is $0(h^4)$ per step, while that of the implicit method (A_3') is $0(h^5)$.

CHAPTER IX

Regular Singular Points

1. Continuation Principle. An *analytic*, or *holomorphic*, function $w = f(z)$ of a *complex* variable $z = x + iy$ is one having a complex derivative $f'(z) = dw/dz$ at every point.† This is equivalent to the definition given in Ch. V, § 10, as is proved in books on complex analysis: any complex analytic function can be expanded in a convergent power series. An analytic DE is one in which the functions involved are all analytic. Its solutions are then necessarily also analytic (Ch. V, § 10).

The solutions of analytic DE's are best studied as functions of a complex variable. This is because their isolated singular points are surrounded by connected domains in the complex z-plane. This permits one to continue solutions beyond and around isolated singular points, whereas on the real line solutions terminate abruptly at singular points.

For instance, consider the DE $du/dx = u^2$ for real x and u. The formula $u = -1/x$ defines *two* real solutions of this DE, the one defined for $x > 0$, the other for $x < 0$. As $x \to 0$, one solution tends to $+\infty$, and the other to $-\infty$; the behavior of these two solutions near $x = 0$ seems to be unrelated if x is restricted to real values. On the other hand, consider the same DE $dw/dz = w^2$ for *complex* $z = x + iy$ and $w = u + iv$. The formula $w = -1/z$ defines now a *single* solution of the DE, in a domain D which includes every point of the complex z-plane except the isolated singular point at $z = 0$; hence it includes both real solutions. The general solution of the same DE is the complex-valued analytic function $w = 1/(c - z)$. This function has an isolated singularity at $z = c$.

The DE $dw/dz = w^2$ is defined and analytic for all z and w, real or complex. Each particular solution $w = 1/(c - z)$ of this DE is defined in the punctured z-plane, with the point $z = c$ deleted. Since this domain is connected, the solution can be continued as an analytic function from any region in it to any other. This process of *analytic continuation* is uniquely defined, for any given path of continuation.‡

The solution $u = -1/x$ of $dw/dz = w^2$ on the negative x-axis is obtained by analytic continuation in the complex plane from the solution $u = -1/x$

†Ahlfors, p. 38; Hille, p. 72. Some knowledge of complex function theory is assumed in the present chapter.
‡Ahlfors, p. 209; Hille, p. 184.

of $du/dx = u^2$ for $x > 0$. This is evident if one continues the solution as a complex analytic function $w = (x - iy)/(x^2 + y^2)$ around the origin on either side. The fact that the analytic continuation of a solution of a DE is a solution of the analytic continuation of the DE is valid in general, as we now prove.

Let $F(w_1, \cdots, w_n, z)$ be an analytic complex-valued function of each of its variables. This means that F can be expanded into a convergent power series with complex coefficients in some neighborhood of each point of a given domain D. Then, as shown in Ch. V, § 10, every solution of the n-th order DE

$$\frac{d^n w}{dz^n} = F(w, w', w'', \cdots, w^{(n-1)}, z)$$

is an analytic function. The function $w^{(n)}(z) - F(w(z), w'(z), \cdots, w^{(n-1)}(z), z)$ of the variable z is holomorphic and vanishes identically in the subdomain where the function w is defined. It follows that all analytic continuations beyond D of this function vanish identically. Therefore any analytic continuation of the function w is also a solution of the DE, and we have

THEOREM 1 (Continuation Principle). *The function obtained by analytic continuation of any solution of an analytic DE, along any path in the complex plane, is a solution of the analytic continuation of the DE, along the same path.*

EXAMPLE 1. Consider the first-order Euler DE

$$dw/dz = \gamma w/z, \qquad \gamma = \alpha + i\beta, \qquad \alpha, \beta \text{ real.} \tag{1}$$

By separating variables and writing $z = re^{i\theta}$, we find the solution

$$\begin{aligned} w &= z^\gamma = e^{\gamma \ln z} = e^{(\alpha + i\beta)(\ln r + i\theta)} \\ &= e^{(\alpha \ln r - \beta\theta)}[\cos(\beta \ln r + \alpha\theta) + i \sin(\beta \ln r + \alpha\theta)]. \end{aligned} \tag{1'}$$

When $\beta = 0$ and γ is real, the analytic continuation of the real solution $u = x^\alpha$ on the positive x-axis through the upper half-plane to the negative x-axis, where $\theta = \pi$, is $(\cos \pi\alpha + i \sin \pi\alpha)|x|^\alpha$. Note that this is not equal to the real solution $|x|^\alpha$ on $x < 0$, unless α is an integer.

The preceding example also shows that DE's involving only single-valued functions can have *multiple-valued* solutions in the complex plane. Unless γ is a real integer, the value of $w = z^\gamma$ changes by a factor $e^{2\pi i\gamma} \neq 1$ when z describes a simple closed counterclockwise loop around the origin, making θ increase by 2π and $\ln z$ by $2\pi i$. This example shows that solutions of a linear DE can have *branch points* where the DE has a singular point†, even though the DE has single-valued coefficient-functions.

†One defines a *singular* point of the linear DE

$$p_0(z)w^{(n)} + p_1(z)w^{(n-1)} + \cdots + p_n(z)w = p_{n+1}(z)$$

as a point where some $p_k(z)$ has a singular point, or $p_0(z) = 0$.

EXAMPLE 2. The second-order Euler DE is

(2) $$z^2w'' + pzw' + qw = 0, \qquad p,\ q \ \text{real constants.}$$

For positive $z = x > 0$, a basis of real solutions is provided by the real and imaginary parts of the functions $z^\gamma = e^{\gamma \ln z}$, where γ is either of the roots of the *indicial equation*

(2′) $$\nu^2 + (p-1)\nu + q = 0.$$

For instance, the roots of the indicial equation of the DE

$$z^2w'' + zw' + w = 0$$

are $\nu = \pm i$. A basis of complex solutions, real on the positive x-axis, is therefore provided as in Ch. IV, § 2, by the real and imaginary parts of the functions

$$\begin{aligned} w_1 &= (z^i + z^{-i})/2 = [e^{i(\ln r + i\theta)} + e^{-i(\ln r + i\theta)}]/2 \\ &= \cosh \theta \cos (\ln r) - i \sinh \theta \sin (\ln r) \\ w_2 &= (z^i - z^{-i})/2i = \cosh \theta \sin (\ln r) + i \sinh \theta \cos (\ln r). \end{aligned}$$

The analytic continuation of the solution $\cos (\ln x)$, real on the positive x-axis $\theta = 0$, through the upper half-plane to the negative x-axis $\theta = \pi$, is not the solution $\cos (\ln |x|) = \cos (\ln r)$ given in Ch. IV, § 2, but is the complex-valued function $\cosh \pi \cos (\ln r) - i \sinh \pi \sin (\ln r)$.

2*. Movable singular points. The general solution of the DE $w' = w^2$ considered in § 1 is $1/(c - z)$. This function has a *pole* at the variable point c. Thus, the location of the singular point of a solution depends in this example on the particular solution. This happens for most *nonlinear* DE's; one describes the situation by saying that the "general solution" has a *movable* singular point.

A second example of movable singular points is provided by the DE $w' = z/w$. The general solution of this DE, obtained by separating variables, is the two-valued function $w = (z^2 - c^2)^{1/2}$, which has branch points at $z = \pm c$. Since c is arbitrary, the general solution has a movable branch point.

There is no significant class of nonlinear first-order normal DE's whose solutions have fixed singular points. The solutions of the generalized Riccati DE $w' = p_0(z) + p_1(z)w + p_2(z)w^2$ have *fixed branch points.*† This can be shown by representing $w = v'/p_2v$ as a quotient of solutions v of a linear DE (Ch. II, § 3).

A second-order nonlinear DE having a fixed singular point at $z = 0$ is

$$w'' = (w'^2/w) - (w'/z),$$

whose general solution is $w = Cz^\gamma$, with C, γ arbitrary complex constants.

†The Riccati DE is the *only* first-order DE with fixed branch points.

But nonlinear DE's with fixed singular points are highly exceptional.

It is otherwise for linear DE's, to which this chapter will be largely devoted. An n-th order normal linear DE

$$L[w] = w^{(n)} + p_1(z)w^{(n-1)} + \cdots + p_{n-1}(z)w' + p_n(z)w = f(z),$$

with holomorphic coefficient-functions has holomorphic solutions in any domain where the coefficient-functions are holomorphic. The argument of Ch. V, § 8, can be applied to construct solutions along any path. Moreover as in Ch. V, § 10, all the functions constructed in the Picard iteration process are holomorphic in any *simply connected* domain, say in $0 \leqq |z| < R$. It follows as in Corollary 2 of Theorem 7 of Chapter V that the DE $L[w] = 0$ has a basis of holomorphic solutions in any such domain — and that $L[w] = f(z)$ has a solution for any choice of initial conditions compatible with the order of the DE.

It follows that the only possible singular points of the solutions of a linear DE occur where one or more of the coefficient-functions $p_k(z)$ has a singular point. In short, linear DE's have fixed singular points. In the remainder of this chapter, we will see how the nature of these singular points is determined by the singularities of the coefficient-functions.

3. First-order equations. The study of singular points of linear DE's begins with the first-order linear DE

$$w' + p(z)w = 0. \tag{3}$$

We will treat only *isolated* singular points. For such singular points, one can assume that p is a holomorphic function in the punctured disc Δ: $0 < |z| < \rho$ because any singular point can be put at the origin by a translation of coordinates.

It follows that $p(z)$ can be expanded into a Laurent series†

$$p(z) = \sum_{-\infty}^{\infty} a_k z^k, \qquad 0 < |z| < \rho,$$

convergent in Δ. When all a_k with $k < 0$ vanish, $p(z)$ is said to have a *removable singularity* at $z = 0$; when there is a largest negative integer $k = -m$ for which $a_k \neq 0$, $p(z)$ is said to have a *pole* of *order* m there; if there are an infinite number of nonzero coefficients a_k with $k < 0$, $p(z)$ is said to have an *essential singularity* at the origin.

In all cases, the general solution of (3) is given by the indefinite integral formula of Ch. I, § 5 (Example 2),

$$\begin{aligned} w &= \exp\left[-\int p(z)dz\right] \\ &= C \exp\left[-a_{-1}\ln z - \sum_{k=1}^{\infty} (a_{k-1}/k)z^k + \sum_{k=1}^{\infty} (a_{-k-1}/k)z^{-k}\right]. \end{aligned}$$

†Ahlfors, p. 147; Hille, p. 209.

As a corollary, we obtain the representation of the solution w in the form

(3′) $$w = Cz^{\alpha} g(z), \quad \alpha = -a_{-1}$$

where $g(z)$ is a *holomorphic* function in the domain Δ.

We now describe the fundamental classification of singularities for the DE (3), at any isolated singular point of $p(z)$.

DEFINITION. *If $p(z)$ has a removable singularity, then* (3) *has a* removable singularity; *if $p(z)$ has a pole of order one, then* (3) *has a* regular singular point; *if $p(z)$ has a pole of order $m > 1$ or an essential singularity, then* (3) *has an* irregular singular point.

If (3) has a removable singularity at $z = 0$, then $a_{-1} = 0$ and

$$w = Cg(z), \quad g(z) = \exp\left[-\sum_{1}^{\infty} (a_{k-1}z^{k}/k)\right]$$

also has a removable singularity there. If (3) has a regular singular point, then (3′) still holds and $g(z)$ is given as above by

$$g(z) = 1 - a_0 z + (2a_0^2 - a_1)z^2/2 + \cdots$$

is still regular, and so w has the form

(4) $$w = Cz^{\alpha}(1 + c_1 z + c_2 z^2 + \cdots), \qquad \alpha = -a_{-1}.$$

An analytic function w having an expansion of the form (4) is said to have a *branch pole* of *order* α at $z = 0$. The number $\alpha = -a_{-1}$ can be real or complex.

Finally, if (3) has an irregular singular point, then $g(z)$ has an essential singularity.

From the representation (3′) we obtain

THEOREM 2. *Every solution of the first-order linear DE* (3), *with p holomorphic in Δ, has the form $w = z^{\alpha}g(z)$, where $\alpha = -a_{-1}$ and g is single-valued and analytic in Δ. Removable singularities, regular singular points, and irregular singular points of* (3) *give solutions having removable singularities, branch poles of order $-a_{-1}$, and essential singularities at $z = 0$, respectively.*

Theorem 2 was derived by explicit calculation. To extend it to higher-order linear DE's, which cannot be explicitly solved, more general arguments are needed. These require the notion of a *simple branch point* of an analytic function $w = f(z)$. This is defined as an isolated singular point z_0 near which $f(z)$ can be represented in the form $f(z) = (z - z_0)^{\alpha}g(z)$, where $g(z)$ is a one-valued holomorphic function in the punctured neighborhood of z_0. Expanding $g(z)$ in a Laurent series, we get the following expansion for a function f having a simple branch point at z_0:

$$f(z) = \sum_{-\infty}^{\infty} a_k (z - z_0)^{\alpha+k}.$$

Not all branch points are simple; for example, the functions $\ln (z - z_0)$ and $(z - z_0)^\alpha + (z - z_0)^\beta$ have branch points at $z = z_0$ but do not have simple branch points there, unless $\alpha - \beta$ is an integer. Any branch pole (4) is a simple branch point, but a simple branch point may not be a branch pole; thus consider $z^{1/2}e^{-1/z^2}$ at $z = 0$.

We shall now give another proof of the first result of Theorem 2, namely, that every solution $w(z)$ of (3) which is not a holomorphic function has a simple branch point at $z = 0$.

Starting at a point z_0 in the given punctured disc, we continue the function w analytically counterclockwise around a closed circuit, say the circle $|z| = |z_0|$. Returning to z_0 after a complete circuit around the origin the function $w(e^{2\pi i}z) = \tilde{w}(z)$ obtained in a neighborhood of z_0 is still a solution of the DE, by Theorem 1. But $\tilde{w}$ may differ from the function w in a neighborhood of z_0, because the function w may have a branch point at $z = 0$ even though the coefficient $p(z)$ of the DE does not have a branch point there; the DE $w' = w/2z$ is a case in point.

However the general solution of the DE (2) has the form $cw(z)$; from this it follows that

$$\tilde{w}(z) = w(e^{2\pi i}z) = cw(z), \qquad c \neq 0.$$

Now write $c = e^{2\pi i\alpha}$, where α is a suitable complex number. Consider the analytic continuation of the function

$$g(z) = z^{-\alpha}w(z)$$

around the same circuit. One obtains

$$\begin{aligned} g(ze^{2\pi i}) &= (ze^{2\pi i})^{-\alpha}w(ze^{2\pi i}) = z^{-\alpha}e^{-2\pi i\alpha}w(ze^{2\pi i}) \\ &= z^{-\alpha}e^{-2\pi i\alpha}cw(z) = z^{-\alpha}w(z) = g(z). \end{aligned}$$

This shows that g is a single-valued function in the punctured disc Δ. Thus the function w is the product of z^α and a function without a branch point.

The idea of the preceding alternative proof can be applied to linear DE's of any order, as we now show.

EXERCISES A

1. Show that no solution of $w' = 1/z$ which is real on the positive x-axis can be real on the negative x-axis.

2. (a) Setting $z = re^{i\theta}$, discuss the analytic continuation to the negative x-axis of the solutions z and $z \ln z$ of $z^2w'' - zw' + w = 0$ on the positive x-axis.

(b) Show that no nontrivial solution of $z^2w'' + 3w/8 = 0$ which is real on the positive x-axis can be real on the negative x-axis.

3. Let $w^{(n)} + a_1(z)w^{(n-1)} + \cdots + a_n(z)w = 0$ be any holomorphic linear homogeneous DE satisfied by $\ln z$. Show that $a_n(z) \equiv 0$.

*4. Show that any holomorphic linear homogeneous DE which is satisfied by $z \ln z$ is also satisfied by z.

5. Find the function g of Theorem 2 when:
(a) $p(z) = 1/z^n$ (n an integer), (*b) $p(z) = e^{1/z}$.

6. Solve the DE (2) for $p(z) = \sum_{k=1}^{n} \frac{1}{z - a_k}$.

7. Let $p(z)$ be holomorphic and single-valued in $|z| < \rho$ except at points a and b. Show that any solution w_1 of (3) can be written in the form

$$w_1(z) = (z - a)^\alpha (z - b)^\beta f(z),$$

where f is single-valued and holomorphic in $|z| < \rho$ except at a and b.

8. Generalize the result of the preceding exercise to the case where $p(z)$ is single-valued for $|z| < \rho$ and holomorphic at all points except $a_1, \cdots, a_n$.

9. Prove in detail that solutions of the generalized Riccati equation

$$w' = p_0(z) + p_1(z)w + p_2(z)w^2$$

can only have branch points where the $p_k(z)$ have singular points.

10. Show that if the DE of Ex. 9 has no movable singularities, then $p_2(z) \equiv 0$.

11. Show that for analytic $p_i(z)$, the DE

$$dw/dz = \sum_{k=0}^{n} p_k(z)w^{-k}$$

has a regular solution (*Hint:* Consider the DE satisfied by $1/w$.)

4. Circuit matrix. Let $w_1(z)$ and $w_2(z)$ be a basis of solutions of the second-order DE

$$w'' + p(z)w' + q(z)w = 0, \tag{5}$$

where the functions p and q are single-valued and analytic in the punctured disc Δ: $0 < |z| < \rho$. Analytic continuation of each of these solutions counterclockwise around a circle $|z| = r < \rho$ with center at the origin yields two functions — in general different — $\tilde{w}_1(z) = w_1(ze^{2\pi i})$ and $\tilde{w}_2(z) = w_2(ze^{2\pi i})$. These are, by the Continuation Principle (Theorem 1), also solutions of the DE (5). But every solution of (5) is a linear combination of w_1 and w_2; hence the continued functions $\tilde{w}_j$ can be expressed as linear combinations of the solutions w_1 and w_2:

$$\tilde{w}_1(z) = w_1(e^{2\pi i}z) = a_{11}w_1(z) + a_{12}w_2(z)$$
$$\tilde{w}_2(z) = w_2(e^{2\pi i}z) = a_{21}w_1(z) + a_{22}w_2(z).$$

The two-by-two matrix of complex constants $A = \| a_{ij} \|$ is called the *circuit matrix* of the DE at the singular point $z = 0$, relative to the basis of solutions (w_1, w_2).

For instance, consider the Euler DE $z^2w'' - zw' + 3w/4 = 0$, with indicial equation $(\nu - 1/2)(\nu - 3/2) = 0$. The functions $z^{1/2}$ and $z^{3/2}$ form a basis of solutions; hence the circuit matrix is the diagonal (scalar) matrix $\begin{pmatrix} -1 & 0 \\ 0 & -1 \end{pmatrix}$. A similar calculation shows that the DE $w'' + (2/9z^2)w = 0$

has the solution basis $z^{1/3}$, $z^{2/3}$. Relative to this basis, its circuit matrix is $\begin{pmatrix}\omega & 0\\ 0 & \omega^2\end{pmatrix}$, where $\omega = (-1 + \sqrt{3}\,i)/2$ is a cube root of unity.

Higher-order DE's. This argument can be extended to the n-th order linear DE

$$(6)\qquad L[w] = \frac{d^n w}{dz^n} + p_1(z)\frac{d^{n-1}w}{dz^{n-1}} + \cdots + p_n(z)w = 0,$$

where again all the coefficient-functions $p_k(z)$ are holomorphic in the disc Δ.

If $w_1(z), \cdots, w_n(z)$ are any basis of solutions of (6) in Δ, analytic continuation of these functions once counterclockwise around a circuit $\gamma : |z| = r$ carries them into a new basis of solutions

$$\tilde{w}_j(z) = w_j(e^{2\pi i}z) = a_{j1}w_1(z) + \cdots + a_{jn}w_n(z), \qquad j = 1, 2, \cdots, n.$$

The matrix $A = \| a_{jk} \|$ so defined is the *circuit matrix* of the DE (6) relative to the basis $w_1(z), \cdots, w_n(z)$.

The circuit matrix represents a linear transformation of the vector space of solutions of the n-th order linear analytic DE (6), as follows. If

$$w(z) = c_1w_1(z) + c_2w_2(z) + \cdots + c_nw_n(z)$$

is the general solution of the DE, then analytic continuation of w around the same circuit γ carries it into the solution

$$(6')\qquad \tilde{w}(z) = w(e^{2\pi i}z) = \sum_{j,k=1}^{n} c_j a_{jk} w_k(z).$$

That is, the effect of analytic continuation around γ counterclockwise is to multiply the vector $\boldsymbol{c}$ by the matrix A on the right, so that $\boldsymbol{c} \to \boldsymbol{c}A$.

Recall† that every matrix has at least one (complex) eigenvector (characteristic vector). Hence, for some choice of $\boldsymbol{c} \neq 0$, we can write $\boldsymbol{c}A = \lambda\boldsymbol{c}$, where λ is a complex number, an eigenvalue of the matrix A. Choose $\boldsymbol{c}$ in (6′) to be such an eigenvector, and let $f(z) = z^{-\alpha}w(z)$, where $\alpha = (\ln \lambda)/2\pi i$. Clearly, $\lambda \neq 0$, since otherwise we could retrace backwards the circuit γ, continuing the solution $w = 0$ into a nonzero solution. Continuing the function $f(z) = z^{-\alpha}w(z)$ along the same circuit, we obtain as in the proof of Theorem 2,

THEOREM 3. *The n-th order linear DE* (6) *with coefficients holomorphic in* Δ: $0 < |z| < \rho$ *admits at least one nontrivial solution of the form*

$$(7)\qquad w(z) = z^{\alpha}f(z),$$

where the function f is single-valued in Δ.

†Birkhoff and Mac Lane, p. 313, Corollary. As stated there, λ is a root of the characteristic equation $|A - \lambda I| = 0$.

5. Canonical bases. A solution of a holomorphic DE (6) in Δ has a simple branch point at $z=0$ if and only if it is carried into a constant (scalar) multiple of itself by continuation around the circuit γ. In view of the discussion in the preceding section, we see that a solution $w(z) = \sum_{j=1}^{n} c_j w_j(z)$ of (6) has a simple branch point at $z=0$ if and only if the vector $\boldsymbol{c} = (c_1, c_2, \cdots, c_n)$ and the circuit matrix A satisfy the relation $\boldsymbol{c}A = \lambda \boldsymbol{c}$, where the constant λ will then be necessarily different from zero. In other words, a linear combination $\sum_{j=1}^{n} c_j w_j$ of solutions of (6) has a simple branch point at $z=0$ if and only if the vector $\boldsymbol{c}$ is an eigenvector of the circuit matrix A associated with the basis $(w_1, w_2, \cdots, w_n)$ of solutions. Thus, there are as many linearly independent solutions of (6) with simple branch points as there are linearly independent eigenvectors of the matrix A.

We shall now look for a basis of solutions with simple branch points for any second-order linear DE (5), with coefficients holomorphic in Δ.

Given two linearly independent solutions w_1 and w_2 of (5), we can construct the circuit matrix $A = \| a_{ij} \|$ as in § 4. The linear combination $w = c_1 w_1(z) + c_2 w_2(z)$ will then have a simple branch point if and only if $\Sigma c_j a_{jk} = \lambda c_k$. By the theory of linear equations, this system of equations has a nontrivial solution if and only if the following determinant (the *characteristic equation* of the circuit matrix A) equals zero:

$$|A - \lambda I| = \lambda^2 - (a_{11} + a_{22})\lambda + (a_{11}a_{22} - a_{12}a_{21}) = 0. \tag{8}$$

Ordinarily, this characteristic equation has two distinct roots λ_1, λ_2. These roots give two linearly independent solutions $F(z) = c_1 w_1(z) + c_2 w_2(z)$ and $G(z) = d_1 w_1(z) + d_2 w_2(z)$ having simple branch points: $F(e^{2\pi i}z) = \lambda_1 F(z)$ and $G(e^{2\pi i}z) = \lambda_2 G(z)$. Relative to the canonical basis of solutions F, G, the circuit matrix is thus a *diagonal* matrix $\begin{pmatrix} \lambda_1 & 0 \\ 0 & \lambda_2 \end{pmatrix}$. As in § 4, $F(z) = z^\alpha f(z)$ and $G(z) = z^\beta g(z)$, where $\lambda_1 = e^{2\pi i \alpha}$, $\lambda_2 = e^{2\pi i \beta}$, and f and g are holomorphic in Δ.

When the characteristic equation has a single solution λ, the solutions may still† sometimes have a basis of the form (7). Every solution of the DE is then multiplied by the same nonzero constant $\lambda = e^{2\pi i \alpha}$ when continued around a counterclockwise circuit γ.

Otherwise, one chooses a basis as follows. Let $w_1(z)$ be the solution of the form $z^\alpha f(z)$, where f is one-valued in the punctured disc, whose existence

†This occurs when the matrix A is a multiple of the identity matrix. Otherwise, any 2×2 matrix A with only one eigenvalue is similar to a matrix of the form displayed to the right. This fact is not assumed in the present discussion. $A = \begin{pmatrix} \lambda & 0 \\ 1 & \lambda \end{pmatrix}$

was established in Theorem 3, and let $w_2(z)$ be any other linearly independent solution. Continuation of $w_2(z)$ around the circuit γ gives, as in § 3, $w_2(ze^{2\pi i}) = aw_1(z) + bw_2(z)$. The circuit matrix for this basis of solutions is therefore the matrix $A = \begin{pmatrix} \lambda & 0 \\ a & b \end{pmatrix}$. Since the eigenvalues of such a "triangular" matrix are λ and b, and since the only eigenvalue of A was assumed to be λ, we must have $b = \lambda$, and

$$A = \begin{pmatrix} \lambda & 0 \\ a & \lambda \end{pmatrix}, \qquad a \neq 0.$$

The continuation around the circuit γ of the function $h(z) = w_2(z)/w_1(z)$ is easily computed to be

$$h(ze^{2\pi i}) = \frac{a}{\lambda} + \frac{w_2(z)}{w_1(z)} = \frac{a}{\lambda} + h(z).$$

It follows that the function

$$f_1(z) = h(z) - \frac{a}{2\pi i\lambda} \ln z$$

is single-valued in $0 < |z| < \rho$, and therefore that the function $w_2(z)$ can be written in the form

$$w_2(z) = w_1(z)f_1(z) + \frac{a}{2\pi i\lambda} (\ln z)w_1(z).$$

In each of the two cases above the basis of solutions is called a *canonical basis*. In the exceptional case, since $a \neq 0$, we can make $a/2\pi i\lambda = 1$ by replacing w_2 by $2\pi i\lambda w_2/a$.

This completes the proof of

THEOREM 4. *Under the hypotheses of Theorem 3, the second-order linear DE* (5) *has a basis of solutions in the neighborhood of the singular point* $z = 0$, *having one of the following forms:*

$$w_1(z) = z^\alpha f(z), \qquad w_2(z) = z^\beta g(z), \tag{9a}$$

or exceptionally,

$$\begin{aligned} w_1(z) &= z^\alpha f(z) \\ w_2(z) &= w_1(z)[f_1(z) + \ln z]. \end{aligned} \tag{9b}$$

The functions $f(z)$, $g(z)$, *and* $f_1(z)$ *are holomorphic and single-valued in the punctured disc* $0 < |z| < r$.

Higher-order equations.† The preceding discussion can be extended to n-th order DE's (6). A basis of solutions $w_1, w_2, \cdots, w_n$ is called a canonical

†For a complete discussion see Coddington and Levinson, Ch. IV, § 1.

basis if and only if the associated circuit matrix A is in *Jordan canonical form*. If the eigenvalues of the circuit matrix are $\lambda_1, \lambda_2, \cdots, \lambda_n$, then the continuation of the solution w_j around a small circuit γ is given by one of the two formulas†

$$\tilde{w}_j(z) = w_j(ze^{2\pi i}) = \lambda_j w_j(z) \tag{10a}$$

$$\tilde{w}_j(z) = w_j(ze^{2\pi i}) = \lambda_j w_j(z) + w_{j-1}(z). \tag{10b}$$

By Theorem 3, there always is at least one solution which goes into a multiple of itself. If all the eigenvalues of the circuit matrix are distinct, then the circuit matrix can be reduced to diagonal form by suitable choice of a "canonical basis" of solutions, and the exceptional case of formula (10b) does not arise.

EXAMPLE 3. Consider the n-th order *Euler* DE:

$$L[w] = \frac{d^n w}{dz^n} + \frac{c_1}{z}\frac{d^{n-1}w}{dz^{n-1}} + \frac{c_2}{z^2}\frac{d^{n-2}w}{dz^{n-2}} + \cdots + \frac{c_n}{z^n}w = 0. \tag{11}$$

The trial function z^ν, with unknown exponent ν, satisfies the DE if and only if the exponent ν is a root of the indicial equation of Ch. IV, § 2,

$$I(\nu) = \nu(\nu-1)\cdots(\nu-n+1) + c_1\nu(\nu-1)\cdots(\nu-n+2) + c_{n-1}\nu + c_n = 0. \tag{12}$$

When the roots of the indicial equation are distinct, the z^{ν_i} are a canonical basis of solutions of the Euler DE (11). The circuit matrix is the diagonal matrix with diagonal elements $\lambda_j = e^{2\pi i \nu_j}$, where ν_j is a root of the indicial equation. When ν is a k-tuple root of the indicial equation, then the functions $z^\nu \log z$, $z^\nu (\log z)^2$, etc., form a basis of solutions. When $n = 2$, this is a canonical basis.

EXERCISES B

1. Construct DE's (5) with circuit matrices $\begin{pmatrix} 1 & 0 \\ 0 & 1 \end{pmatrix}$ for which the functions f and g in Theorem 4 have (a) essential and (b) removable singularities at 0.

2. (a) Show that the DE $zw'' + (1 - z)w' + \lambda w = 0$ has a regular singular point at the origin, and that $\nu = 0$ is a double root of the indicial equation.

(b) Find the power series expansion of the solution of this DE which is regular at $z = 0$.

3. Find a DE (5) with circuit matrix $\begin{pmatrix} \lambda & 0 \\ 0 & 1/\lambda \end{pmatrix}$ for which the functions f and g in Theorem 4 have (a) poles and (b) essential singularities. Can f and g have removable singularities?

4. Show that the requirements $\mathrm{Re}\{\alpha\} \geqq 0$, $\mathrm{Re}\{\beta\} < 1$, uniquely determine the exponents α and β in Theorem 4.

5. Show that, in the exceptional case of Theorem 4, the eigenvalues of the circuit matrix are equal.

†Cf. Birkhoff and Mac Lane, pp. 333–334.

6. Construct a second-order holomorphic DE (5) with a singular point at $z=0$ whose circuit matrix has the form $\begin{pmatrix} 0 & 0 \\ 1 & 0 \end{pmatrix}$, such that f in Theorem 4 has an essential singularity at $z=0$.

7. Show that if $w \ln z$ satisfies a (homogeneous) linear DE with holomorphic coefficients, and w is holonomic, then w satisfies the same DE.

6. Regular singular points. The results obtained so far apply to *all* linear analytic DE's near isolated singular points. We now ask the question: When does the canonical basis constructed in Theorem 4 involve functions $f(z)$ and $g(z)$ having, at worst, *poles* at the singular point of interest? Again, when does the function $f(z)$ of Theorem 3 have the form $\sum_{k=r}^{\infty} a_k z^k$, $a_r \neq 0$, for some *finite* integer r? Since this implies

$$w_1(z)/a_r = z^{\alpha+r}\left[1 + \sum_{j=1}^{\infty} (a_{j+r}/a_r) z^j\right],$$

this amounts to asking the following question. What are the conditions on the coefficients of a linear analytic DE having an isolated singular point at the origin, which make it have a basis of solutions of the form $z^{\nu}[1+\sum_{j=1}^{\infty} b_z z^j]$ — that is, of solutions having branch poles?

The answer to the above questions is that the singular point must be *regular* in the following sense.

DEFINITION. *A second-order DE*

$$w'' + p(z)w' + q(z)w = 0 \tag{13}$$

analytic for $0 < |z - z_0| < \rho$ *has a* regular singular point *at* z_0 *when* $p(z)$ *has at worst a simple pole at* $z = z_0$, *and* $q(z)$ *at worst a double pole there.*†

We now show that near the regular singular point $z=0$ there always exists a formal solution of the DE (13), namely, a formal power series of the form

$$\begin{aligned} w &= z^{\nu}(1 + c_1 z + c_2 z^2 + c_3 z^3 + \cdots) \\ &= z^{\nu} + c_1 z^{\nu+1} + c_2 z^{\nu+2} + \cdots, \end{aligned} \tag{14}$$

which, when substituted into (13), satisfies the DE. To calculate the coefficients c_k and the exponent ν of (14) it is convenient to rewrite (13) in the form

$$L[w] = z^2 w'' + zP(z)w' + Q(z)w = 0, \tag{15}$$

where $P(z) = \sum_{k=0}^{\infty} P_k z^k$ and $Q(z) = \sum_{k=0}^{\infty} Q_k z^k$ are convergent for $|z| < \rho$.

†That is, p may either be holomorphic (have a removable singularity) or have a simple pole, and q may be holomorphic or have a pole of first or second order.

Substituting (14) into (15), and equating to zero the coefficient of z^ν, we obtain the *indicial equation*

$$I(\nu) = \nu(\nu - 1) + P_0\nu + Q_0 = 0, \tag{16}$$

for the exponent ν. The roots of this equation are called the *characteristic exponents* of the singular point, and $I(\nu)$ is called its *indicial polynomial.*

Equating to zero the coefficients of the higher powers of z, namely $z^{\nu+1}, \cdots, z^{\nu+n}, \cdots$, one obtains the relation

$$[(\nu + 1)\nu + P_0(\nu + 1) + Q_0]c_1 + P_1\nu + Q_1 = 0,$$

and recursively

$$[(\nu + n)(\nu + n - 1) + (\nu + n)P_0 + Q_0]c_n = - \sum_{k=0}^{n-1} [(\nu + k)P_{n-k} + Q_{n-k}]c_k.$$

Since the left side of the preceding equation is $I(\nu + n)c_n$, the equation can be written in the form

$$I(\nu + n)c_n = - \sum_{k=0}^{n-1} [(\nu + k)P_{n-k} + Q_{n-k}]c_k, \qquad n = 1, 2, 3, \cdots. \tag{17}$$

The above equations for the coefficients c_k can be solved recursively for $c_1, c_2, c_3, \cdots$, except in one case: when for some positive integer n, both ν and $(\nu + n)$ are roots of the indicial equation. By taking a characteristic exponent having the largest real part, we can make sure that $I(\nu + n)$ does not vanish for any positive integer n, even in this case. We therefore obtain

THEOREM 5. *If the DE* (13) *has a regular singular point at* $z = 0$, *then there exists at least one formal power series of the form* (14) *which formally satisfies the DE. Unless the roots of the indicial equation differ by an integer, there are two linearly independent formal power series solutions* (14) *of the DE whose exponents are the two roots of the indicial equation.*

EXAMPLE 4. A remarkable class of special functions having regular singular points at 0, 1, and ∞ (see § 12), and no other singular points, is obtained by applying Theorem 5 to the *hypergeometric* DE

$$z(1 - z)w'' + [\gamma - (\alpha + \beta + 1)z]w' - \alpha\beta w = 0. \tag{18}$$

This DE was first studied by Gauss in 1813.

The hypergeometric DE has regular singular points at $z = 0$ and $z = 1$. The indicial equation at $z = 0$ is $\nu(\nu + \gamma - 1) = 0$, with roots $\nu_1 = 0$ and $\nu_2 = 1 - \gamma$. Unless γ is an integer, by Theorem 5 the hypergeometric DE has two formal power series solutions with exponents 0 and $1 - \gamma$. Unless γ is a negative integer or zero, one such formal power series is obtained from the easily computed recursion relations

$$(19)\qquad (n+1)(\gamma+n)c_{n+1} = (\alpha+n)(\beta+n)c_n, \qquad n \geqq 0.$$

Setting $c_0 = 1$ one obtains the hypergeometric series

$$(20)\quad F(\alpha,\beta,\gamma;z) = 1 + \frac{\alpha\beta}{\gamma}z + \frac{\alpha(\alpha+1)\beta(\beta+1)}{\gamma(\gamma+1)}\frac{z^2}{2!} + \frac{\alpha(\alpha+1)(\alpha+2)\beta(\beta+1)(\beta+2)}{\gamma(\gamma+1)(\gamma+2)}\frac{z^3}{3!} + \cdots.$$

From the Ratio Test it follows that the radius of convergence of the series is at least one, and is exactly one unless α, β or γ is a negative integer. This may also be expected from the existence theorems of Chapter V, since the radius of convergence of a solution extends to the nearest other singular point of the coefficients of the hypergeometric DE, which is at $z = 1$. The function $F(\alpha,\beta,\gamma; z)$ defined by the power series (20) is the *hypergeometric function*, studied in § 10 below.

7. Bessel equation. To illustrate the behavior of solutions of second-order DE's near regular singular points, we consider an example of great importance in applied mathematics. This is the Bessel DE of order n:

$$(21)\qquad z^2w'' + zw' + (z^2 - n^2)w = 0.$$

The Bessel DE has a regular singular point at the origin, with indicial equation $I(\nu) = \nu^2 - n^2 = 0$. In physical applications, n is usually an integer or half-integer. But for theoretical purposes, it is interesting to let n^2 be an arbitrary complex number.

By Theorem 5, one can compute a formal power series solution beginning with z^n, of the form $z^n(1 + c_1z + c_2z^2 + \cdots)$. From the recursion formulas (17), or more simply by direct substitution into the DE, we obtain the recursion relations for the coefficients c_k

$$(2n+1)c_1 = 0; \quad (k+2)(2n+k+2)c_{k+2} + c_k = 0, \quad k = 0, 1, 2, \cdots.$$

Since $\operatorname{Re}(2n) \geqq 0$, the factor $(k+2)(2n+k+2)$ cannot vanish. Solving recursively for c_{k+2}, one obtains the series

$$z^n\left[1 - \frac{1}{n+1}\left(\frac{z}{2}\right)^2 + \frac{1}{(2!)(n+1)(n+2)}\left(\frac{z}{2}\right)^4 - \cdots\right].$$

The series in square brackets is an entire function (convergent for all finite z). Multiplying by the normalizing factor $1/2^n\Gamma(n+1)$, one obtains the *Bessel function of order n*, already discussed in Ch. III, § 4:

$$(22)\qquad J_n(z) = \frac{1}{\Gamma(n+1)}\left(\frac{z}{2}\right)^n\left[1 - \frac{1}{n+1}\left(\frac{z}{2}\right)^2 + \frac{1}{(2!)(n+1)(n+2)}\left(\frac{z}{2}\right)^4 - \cdots\right].$$

The Bessel function J_n is an entire function if n is a nonnegative integer. Using the functional equation for the gamma function $\Gamma(z+1) = z\Gamma(z)$, this formula can be recast in the form

$$J_n(z) = \sum_{k=0}^{\infty} \frac{(-1)^k (z/2)^{n+2k}}{\Gamma(n+k+1)\Gamma(k+1)}.$$

Unless n is an integer, the series (22) defines a second, linearly independent solution of the Bessel DE (21), which can be written

$$J_{-n}(z) = \sum_{k=0}^{\infty} \{(-1)^k (z/2)^{-n+2k}/\Gamma(k+1)\Gamma(-n+k+1)\}.$$

This solution has a branch pole at the origin. If n is not an integer, J_n and J_{-n} form a canonical basis of solutions of the Bessel DE.

Exceptional case. When n is an integer, $J_{-n}(z) = (-1)^n J_n(z)$, so that another method must be used to find a basis of solutions. One can then proceed as follows (cf. Ch. II, (13)).

Consider the Wronskian $W = J_n\phi' - J_n'\phi$ of J_n and any other solution ϕ of the Bessel DE. A straightforward computation gives $W' + (1/z)W = 0$, whence $(zW)' = 0$. Hence for some constant A,

$$J_n(z)\phi'(z) - J_n'(z)\phi(z) = A/z.$$

It follows that, if $g(z)$ is the quotient $\phi(z)/J_n(z)$, then

$$g'(z) = W(z)/J_n^2(z) = A/zJ_n^2(z).$$

Therefore, the general solution of the Bessel DE (21) is

$$(23)\qquad Z_n(z) = J_n(z)\left[B + A\int\frac{dz}{zJ_n^2(z)}\right],$$

for any indefinite integral of $1/zJ_n^2(z)$. One can compute an indefinite integral of $1/zJ_n^2(z)$ by expanding $1/J_n^2(z)$ into a power series of the form $Kz^{-2n}\left\{1 + \sum_{k=1}^{\infty} b_k z^{2k}\right\}$, where K is a suitable constant, having a pole of order $-2n$ at the origin. Hence

$$(23')\qquad \int\frac{dz}{zJ_n^2(z)} = KA\int z^{-1-2n}\left\{1 + \sum_{k=1}^{\infty} b_k z^{2k}\right\}dz,$$

where the circle of convergence of the series in curly brackets extends to the point $z \neq 0$ nearest the origin where $J_n(z)$ vanishes. Within this circle, we can integrate the series term-by-term. Term-by-term integration gives a *logarithmic term* $KAb_n \log z$. This is an instance of the *exceptional case* of formula (9b) in Theorem 4.

When $n = 0$, the logarithmic term dominates the integral (23′). Hence any solution of the Bessel DE of order zero which is not a constant multiple of $J_0(z)$ is logarithmically infinite near $z = 0$.

Thus we obtain the general case (9a) of Theorem 4, with $\alpha = n$ and $\beta = -n$, when the parameter n in the Bessel DE is not an integer, and the exceptional case (9b) when n is an integer. Note that though the Bessel DE of half-integral order $n + 1/2$ has characteristic exponents which differ by an integer, it has a basis of solutions of the form (9a). This is because the recurrence relations for the coefficients in its expansion express c_{k+2} as a multiple of c_k, without involving c_{k+1}.

Modified Bessel functions. The values of $J_n(z)$ on the imaginary axis $z = iy$ define a *real* function of the positive variable y:

$$I_n(y) = (-i)^n J_n(iy) = \left(\frac{y}{2}\right)^n \sum_{k=0}^{\infty} [y^k/2^k\Gamma(k+1)\Gamma(k+n+1)].$$

This function is called the *modified* Bessel function of order n. The function $I_n(y)$ satisfies the modified Bessel DE

$$y^2 \frac{d^2I}{dy^2} + y\frac{dI}{dy} - (y^2 + n^2)I = 0$$

obtained by substituting iy for z in the Bessel DE. The coefficient-functions of the modified Bessel DE are real.

The Neumann function. In the exceptional case that n is an integer, various choices are possible for a canonical basis of solutions of the Bessel equation. The first solution $w_1(z)$ in (9b) must be chosen as a multiple of $J_n(z)$, because only such multiples have branch poles at the origin. Any choice $A \neq 0$ in (23) will give a possible second member of the canonical basis (9b). The most convenient choice for $n = 0$ turns out to be $A = 2/\pi$ and $B = (2\gamma - 2\log 2)/\pi$, where $\gamma = 0.5772\cdots$ is Euler's constant. This defines the *Neumann function* $Y_0(x)$. The choice is convenient because of the asymptotic formulas, valid as $x \to \infty$,

$$\begin{aligned} J_0(x) &= \sqrt{\frac{2}{\pi x}}\left[\cos\left(x - \frac{\pi}{4}\right) + 0\left(\frac{1}{x}\right)\right] \\ Y_0(x) &= \sqrt{\frac{2}{\pi x}}\left[\sin\left(x - \frac{\pi}{4}\right) + 0\left(\frac{1}{x}\right)\right]. \end{aligned} \tag{24}$$

This asymptotic behavior will be explained in Ch. X, § 13.

The Bessel and Neumann functions J_0 and Y_0 are clearly linearly independent; hence they are a canonical basis of solutions of the Bessel DE of order zero. Using these functions, we now derive a canonical basis for the Bessel DE of integral order n.

This can be done as follows. If Z_n is a solution of the Bessel equation of order n, then the function Z_{n+1} defined by the formula

$$Z_{n+1} = -z^n(z^{-n}Z_n(z))'$$

is a solution of the Bessel equation of order $n + 1$. This formula is valid whether n is an integer or not, and is immediately verified by substituting Z_{n+1} into the Bessel DE of order $n + 1$. In particular one easily verifies that $J_{n+1}(z) = -z^n(z^{-n}J_n(z))'$, as in Ch. III, (16).

We now define the Neumann function $Y_n(z)$ for integer n by the recursive formulas

$$Y_{n+1}(z) = -z^n(z^{-n}Y_n(z))', \qquad n = 0, 1, 2, \cdots.$$

Since the function $Y_0(z)$ is of the form $Y_0(z) = J_0(z)[f_0(z) + K_0 \log z]$, where f_0 is holomorphic and one-valued in a punctured disc around $z = 0$, one verifies by straightforward differentiation that

$$Y_1(z) = J_1(z)[f_1(z) + K_1 \log z],$$

where f_1 has the same property as f_0, and successively that

$$Y_n(z) = J_n(z)[f_n(z) + K_n \log z].$$

Thus, all Neumann functions $Y_n(z)$ have a branch point at $z = 0$. From this it follows that Y_n and J_n are linearly independent, and indeed are a canonical basis of solutions for the singular point $z = 0$ of Bessel's DE.

The Neumann function is defined when ν is not an integer by the formula

$$Y_\nu(z) = \frac{J_\nu(z)\cos\nu\pi - J_{-\nu}(z)}{\sin\nu\pi}.$$

When $\nu = n$ is an integer, let $Y_n(z) = \lim_{\nu\to n} Y_\nu(z)$. The limit can be evaluated by l'Hôpital's Rule as

$$Y_n(z) = \frac{1}{\pi}\left[\frac{\partial J_\nu(z)}{\partial\nu} - (-1)^n\frac{\partial J_{-\nu}(z)}{\partial\nu}\right]_{\nu=n}.$$

It can be shown that this definition of the Neumann function for integral n agrees with that given above.

EXERCISES C

1. Show that the self-adjoint form (Ch. II, § 5) of the hypergeometric DE (18) is:

$$\frac{d}{dz}[z^c(1-z)^{a+b+1-c}w'] - [abz^{c-1}(1-z)^{a+b-c}]w = 0.$$

2. State and prove an analog of Theorem 5 for $w' + p(z)w = 0$.

3. (a) Show that if

$$(*) \qquad w'' + p(z)w' + q(z)w = 0$$

has a regular singular point at $z = 0$, and $q(0) \neq 0$, then

$$(**) \qquad w'' + [p - (q'/q)]w' + [p' - (pq'/q) + q]w = 0$$

has a regular singular point at $z = 0$.

(b) Show that, if w_1, w_2 are a basis of solutions of (*), then w_1', w_2' are a basis of solutions of (**).

*4. Show that if the roots of the indicial equation at a regular singular point differ by an integer, then the eigenvalues of any circuit matrix are equal.

5. Let (13) have a regular singular point at $z = 0$, and let α be a root of its indicial equation having largest real part. Show that $v = z^{-\alpha}w$ satisfies a DE of the form (13), with $Q_0 = 0$ and $\text{Re}\{P_0\} \geqq 1$.

6. (a) Given three pairs of complex numbers (λ_1,λ_2), (μ_1,μ_2), (z_1,z_2), construct a holomorphic second-order linear DE (13) having regular singular points at $z = z_1,z_2$, whose circuit matrices at these points have eigenvalues (λ_1,λ_2), (μ_1,μ_2).

(*b) Generalize to n points $z_1, \cdots, z_n$.

7. Show that for n a nonnegative integer, $J_n(z)$ and its complex multiples are the only solutions of the Bessel DE which are holomorphic at the origin.

8. (a) Find the exponents at $z = 0$ of the DE $zw'' + (n + \frac{1}{2})w' + w = 0$, and find formal power series solutions corresponding to each characteristic exponent.

(b) Show that a basis of solutions of this DE is given by the functions

$$d^n[\sin (2\sqrt{z})]/dz^n \qquad \text{and} \qquad d^n[\cos (2\sqrt{z})]/dz^n.$$

*9. Show that, when n is an integer, a solution of Bessel's DE (the Neumann function $Y_n(z)$) is defined by

$$\pi^{-1}[\partial J_n(z)/\partial n - (-1)^n \partial J_{-n}(z)/\partial n].$$

10. Show that if u_1, u_2 and v_1, v_2 are bases of solutions of the Bessel and modified Bessel DE's respectively, then u_1, u_2, v_1, v_2 form a basis of solutions of the DE

$$w^{(4)} + (2/z)w^{(3)} - [(2n^2 + 1)/z^2]w'' + [(2n^2 + 1)/z]w' + [(n^4 - n^2)/z^2 - 1]w = 0.$$

*11. Establish the formula for the generating function of $\{J_n(z)\}$

$$\sum_{n=-\infty}^{\infty} J_n(z)t^n = \exp\left[\frac{z}{2}\left(t - \frac{1}{t}\right)\right].$$

(*Hint:* Expand the right side into a power series in t and show that the coefficients are solutions of (21).)

12. Show that a canonical basis of solutions of the hypergeometric DE (18) is provided by $F(\alpha,\beta,\gamma;\, z)$ and $z^{1-\gamma}F(\alpha - \gamma + 1,\, \beta - \gamma + 1,\, 2 - \gamma;\; z)$, unless γ is an integer.

8. Fundamental Theorem. We now establish the fact that the formal power series solutions obtained in § 6 are convergent. We begin by proving the converse of this result.

THEOREM 6. *Let the analytic functions*

$$(25) \qquad w_1 = z^\alpha\left(1 + \sum_1^\infty a_k z^k\right), \quad w_2 = z^\beta\left(1 + \sum_1^\infty b_k z^k\right), \quad \alpha \neq \beta,$$

have simple branch poles at $z = 0$ of different orders $\alpha \neq \beta$. Then the normal second-order DE satisfied by w_1 and w_2 has a regular singular point at $z = 0$, with characteristic exponents α and β.

Proof. The coefficients of the normal second-order linear DE satisfied by w_1 and w_2 are found by solving the simultaneous linear equations

$$w_j'' + p(z)w_j' + q(z)w_j = 0, \qquad j = 1, 2,$$

for the unknown coefficient-functions p, q. The result is

$$p = -(w_1w_2'' - w_2w_1'')/(w_1w_2' - w_2w_1')$$
$$q = (w_1'w_2'' - w_2'w_1'')/(w_1w_2' - w_2w_1').$$

The Wronskian $W = w_1w_2' - w_2w_1'$ in the denominators is equal to

$$(\beta - \alpha)z^{\alpha+\beta-1}\left(1 + \sum_1^\infty c_k z^k\right),$$

and does not vanish near $z = 0$, since $\alpha \neq \beta$. The numerators are the powers $z^{\alpha+\beta-2}$ and $z^{\alpha+\beta-3}$ multiplied by holomorphic functions of z. Dividing out, we get

$$p(z) = z^{-1}P(z), \quad q(z) = z^{-2}Q(z),$$

where $P(z)$ and $Q(z)$ are holomorphic in some neighborhood of $z = 0$. This completes the proof of the theorem.

THEOREM 7. *Let the second-order linear DE (5) have a regular singular point at the origin, and let α be a root of its indicial equation $I(\nu) = 0$. Then the formal power series $z^\alpha(1 + \Sigma a_k z^k)$ of Theorem 5 converges to a solution of (5) in a domain $0 < |z| < \sigma$, $\sigma > 0$.*

It will be recalled that, in Theorem 5, ν was any root of the indicial equation $I(\nu) = 0$ such that $I(\nu + n) = 0$ for no positive integer n.

Proof. A method similar to the Method of Majorants of Ch. III, § 6 can be used. The functions P and Q are holomorphic in a neighborhood of the origin; thus a closed disc $0 \leqq |z| \leqq \rho$ can be found in which these functions are holomorphic, with $|P(z)| \leqq M$ and $|Q(z)| \leqq N$. It follows from the Cauchy estimates for derivatives† that

$$|P_k| \leqq M/\rho^k, \quad |Q_k| \leqq N/\rho^k, \quad k = 0, 1, 2, \cdots.$$

Hence

$$|P_k||\nu| + |Q_k| \leqq \frac{M|\nu| + N}{\rho^k}, \qquad k \geqq 1.$$

From formula (16) one obtains the bound $|I(\nu + n)| \geqq n^2/K$ for some

†See Hille, pp. 197 and 202.

constant $K \geqq 1$: since $I(\nu + n) \neq 0$ for all nonnegative integers n by hypothesis, the sequence $n^2/|I(\nu + n)|$ is bounded (it tends to 1 as $n \to \infty$). Set $K = 1 + \max(n^2/|I(\nu + n)|)$. Therefore, the recursion formulas (17) give the following bound for the coefficient c_n in the formal power series solution (14):

$$|c_n| \leqq \frac{K}{n}\sum_{k=0}^{n-1}\left(\frac{M|\nu| + N}{n} + \frac{kM}{n}\right)\frac{|c_k|}{\rho^{n-k}}.$$

Now let $A = M|\nu| + N + M + 1$. Clearly $(M|\nu| + N + kM)/n \leqq A$ for all n and for $0 \leqq k \leqq n$, and $AK \geqq K \geqq 1$. Hence we obtain

$$|c_n| \leqq \frac{K}{n}\sum_{k=0}^{n-1} A\frac{|c_k|}{\rho^{n-k}} = \frac{AK}{n}\sum_{k=0}^{n-1}\frac{c_k}{\rho^{n-k}}. \tag{25'}$$

Using this formula, we now prove by induction that

$$|c_n| \leqq \left(\frac{AK}{\rho}\right)^n |c_0|, \qquad n = 1, 2, \cdots.$$

This inequality is immediate for $n = 1$, namely $|c_1| \leqq \dfrac{AK}{\rho}|c_0|$. Now assume it is true for all c_k for $1 \leqq k \leqq n - 1$. Substituting in (25′) the bounds for $c_0, \cdots, c_{n-1}$ given by the induction hypothesis, we obtain

$$\begin{aligned}|c_n| &\leqq \frac{KA}{n}\sum_{k=0}^{n-1}\left(\frac{AK}{\rho}\right)^k \cdot \frac{1}{\rho^{n-k}}|c_0| \\ &= \frac{(AK)|c_0|}{n \cdot \rho^n}[1 + (AK) + (AK)^2 + \cdots + (AK)^{n-1}].\end{aligned}$$

Since $AK \geqq 1$, each term in the brackets above is bounded by $(AK)^{n-1}$; thus

$$|c_n| \leqq \frac{AK|c_0|}{\rho^n} \cdot \frac{n(AK)^{n-1}}{n} = \frac{(AK)^n|c_0|}{\rho^n},$$

and this shows that the formal power series solution (14) has a radius of convergence at least equal to ρ/AK. The proof is therefore complete.

COROLLARY. *In Theorem* 7, *unless the roots* α, β *of the indicial equation differ by an integer, the DE* (5) *has a basis of solutions whose circuit matrix is a diagonal matrix with diagonal entries* $\lambda_1 = \exp(2\pi i\alpha)$ *and* $\lambda_2 = \exp(2\pi i\beta)$.

For this, one only has to choose a canonical basis of the form (25), which exists by Theorem 7.

Exceptional case. The exceptional case, namely when the roots of the indicial equation differ by an integer, can be treated by the following method. Select for α a root of the indicial equation having maximum real part. Then $\beta = \alpha - n$ for some integer $n \geqq 0$, and so, since by the indicial equation $\alpha + \beta = 1 - P_0$, we have that $-2\alpha - P_0 = -n - 1$, where P_0 is the leading coefficient of $p(z) = P_0/z + P_1 + \cdots$ and n is a nonnegative integer.

Moreover, $I(\alpha + n) \neq 0$, for all integers $n > 0$, and so by Theorem 7 the given second-order linear DE (5) has a solution

$$w_1 = z^\alpha f(z) = z^\alpha\left(1 + \sum_{k=1}^{\infty} a_k z^k\right)$$

with a branch pole at $z = 0$, nonvanishing in the punctured disc $0 < |z| < \sigma$ for some $\sigma > 0$. Hence if we set $w = w_1 h = z^\alpha f(z)h(z)$, (5) is equivalent to

$$\begin{aligned} 0 &= w_1 h'' + [2w_1' + p(z)w_1]h' \\ &= z^\alpha f(z)\{h'' + [(2\alpha/z) + 2(f'/f) + p(z)]h'\}. \end{aligned}$$

This first-order DE for the unknown function h' has a regular singular point at $z = 0$, since f'/f is holomorphic there, while $2\alpha/z$ and $p(z)$ have at worst first-order poles. Hence we can write $h'(z) = z^\gamma(1 + \Sigma c_k z^k)$, where $\gamma = -2\alpha - P_0 = -n - 1$, as shown above.

Integrating $h'(z)$ term-by-term in the circle of convergence, we therefore have

$$h(z) = \begin{cases} \ln z + \phi(z) & \text{if } n = 0, \\ c_n \ln z + z^{-n}\phi(z) & \text{if } n \neq 0, \end{cases}$$

where $\phi(z)$ is holomorphic. This shows that the exceptional case of Theorem 4 always occurs when the indicial equation has a double root, and also occurs when the roots differ by an integer n, unless $c_n = 0$.

Collecting results, we have proved (for $C = c_n$)

THEOREM 8. *Suppose that the roots α and $\beta = \alpha - n$ of the indicial equation of a second-order linear DE having a regular singular point at $z = 0$ differ by a nonnegative integer n. Then there exists a canonical basis of solutions of the form*

$$(26) \qquad w_1 = z^\alpha\left(1 + \sum_{k=1}^{\infty} a_k z^k\right), \quad w_2 = z^\beta\left(1 + \sum_{k=1}^{\infty} b_k z^k\right) + C w_1 \ln z,$$

where the power series are convergent in a neighborhood of $z = 0$.

9*. Alternative proof of fundamental theorem. Theorem 7 can also be given a more intrinsic proof, by relying on the following characterization of poles of analytic functions.†

ORDER OF GROWTH THEOREM. *If $f(z)$ is holomorphic in $0 < |z| < R$, then $z = 0$ is a pole of order at most α of $f(z)$, or a removable singularity,*

†Hille, p. 213, Thm. 8.4.1.

if and only if there exists a positive number C such that

$$\sup_{0 \leqq \theta \leqq 2\pi} |f(re^{i\theta})| < Cr^{-\alpha}, \qquad 0 < r < R.$$

Theorem 7 can be deduced quite easily from the following fundamental

LEMMA. *If the DE (5) has a regular singular point at $z = 0$, then the function $f(z)$ in Theorem 3 has at most a pole at $z = 0$.*

Proof. For any solution $w(z)$ of (5), consider the real-valued function

$$U(z) = |w(z)|^2 + |zw'(z)|^2.$$

Setting $z = re^{i\theta}$, we shall majorize the derivative of this function relative to r, for fixed θ; its differentiability follows by the Chain Rule.

For any differentiable complex-valued function $V(r)$ of a real variable r, as in Chapter V, formula (3),

$$\left| \int_a^r V'(t)dt \right| \leqq \int_a^r |V'(t)|\, dt,$$

and hence, differentiating,

$$\left| \frac{d}{dr} |V(r)| \right| \leqq \left| \frac{dV(r)}{dr} \right|.$$

Applying this inequality to $U(re^{i\theta})$ we obtain

$$\tfrac{1}{2} \left| \frac{\partial U}{\partial r} \right| \leqq |ww'| + |z^2w'^2|/r + |z^2w'w''|,$$

where $z = re^{i\theta}$. Using the fact that $w'' = -(P(z)/z)w' - (Q(z)/z^2)w$ we obtain

$$\tfrac{1}{2} \left| \frac{\partial U}{\partial r} \right| \leqq |ww'| + |z^2w'^2|/r + |P(z)||z^2w'^2|/r + |Q(z)||ww'|$$

The functions $P(re^{i\theta})$ and $Q(re^{i\theta})$ are holomorphic in some closed disc $0 \leqq |z| \leqq R$, $R > 0$. Let M be a common upper bound for their absolute values, for $0 \leqq \theta \leqq 2\pi$ and for fixed r. This gives the inequality

$$\tfrac{1}{2} \left| \frac{\partial U}{\partial r} \right| \leqq (M+1)|ww'| + (M+1)|z^2w'^2|/r.$$

By definition of U, we have $|w|^2 \leqq U$, $|w'|^2 \leqq U/r^2$, hence, multiplying, $|ww'| \leqq U/r$. We obtain therefore

$$\left| \frac{\partial U(re^{i\theta})}{\partial r} \right| \leqq (2M+2)U(re^{i\theta})/r = K\frac{U}{r}, \quad K > 0.$$

In particular, for $0 < r \leqq R$ we obtain $\partial U/\partial r + KU/r \geqq 0$, whence, integrating between the limits r and R,

$$R^K U(Re^{i\theta}) - r^K U(re^{i\theta}) \geqq 0.$$

If $N = \max_{0 \leqq \theta \leqq 2\pi} U(Re^{i\theta})$, we obtain

$$U(re^{i\theta}) \leqq N\, R^K r^{-K},$$

and hence, *a fortiori*, that $|\, w(re^{i\theta})\,|^2 \leqq (NR^K)r^{-K}$. By the Order of Growth Theorem, with $C = NR^K$ and $\alpha = K$, the conclusion of the lemma follows.

It follows that, if the DE (5) has a regular singular point at the origin, then it has a solution given by a locally convergent power series of the form described in Theorems 5 and 7. The construction of a second solution can then be achieved as in Theorem 8.

The preceding method of proof can be generalized easily to n-th order linear DE's.

EXERCISES D

1. Find the exponents at $z = 0$ of the DE $w'' + (\mu/z)w' + (1/z)w = 0$. Show that this *DE* has a power series solution $C_\mu(z) = 1 + \sum_{k=1}^{\infty} a_k z^k$, convergent for all $|\, z\,|$. Show that $C_\mu(z) = z^{(1-\mu)/2} J_{\mu-1}(2\sqrt{z})$.

2. Show that $w'' + (n + \frac{1}{2} - z^2/4)w = 0$ has a basis of solutions

$$w_1(z) = 1 - (2n+1)z^2/4 + (4n^2 + 4n + 3)z^4/96 - \cdots, \text{ and}$$
$$w_2(z) = z - (2n+1)z^3/12 + (4n^2 + 4n + 7)z^5/480 - \cdots.$$

For what values of $|\, z\,|$ do these series converge?

3. The Laguerre DE is $zw'' + (1 - z)w' + \alpha w = 0$.
   (a) Find its characteristic exponents.
   (b) Show that a nontrivial solution is given by $\Sigma c_k z^k$, with

$$c_{j+1} = (j - \alpha)c_j/(j+1)^2.$$

4. The associated Laguerre DE is $zw'' + (k + 1 - z)w' + (n - k)w = 0$. Show that this has a polynomial solution $w = L_n^k(z)$ for any positive integers k,n.

5. Show that $e^{-z/2} z^{(k-1)/2} L_n^k(z)$ satisfies the DE

$$(*) \qquad zw'' + 2w' + \left[A + Bz + \frac{C}{z}\right] w = 0,$$

with $A = n - (k-1)/2$, $B = -1/4$, $C = (1 - k^2)/4$.

6. Show that, if $\phi(0) \neq 0$, the substitution $w = \phi(z)v$ carries second-order linear DE's (5) having a regular singular point at the origin into DE's having the same property.

7. Generalize the result of Ex. 6 to n-th order linear DE's.

8. Show that the substitution $w = z^r \phi(z) w_1$, where $\phi(0) \neq 0$ and $\phi(z)$ is regular near $z = 0$, carries a regular singular point at $z = 0$ with indicial polynomial $I(\nu)$ into one with indicial polynomial $I(\nu - r)$.

9. Do the functions $\log z$ and $(\log z)^2$ satisfy a second-order linear DE (3) with a regular singular point at $z = 0$? Do they satisfy a third-order linear DE with regular singular point at $z = 0$? Justify your answer.

*10. (a) The DE $w''' + \sum_{k=1}^{3} p_k(z)w^{(n-k)} = 0$, $p_k(z)$ holomorphic for $0 < |z| < r$, has a regular singular point at $z = 0$ if p_k has at worst a pole of order k. Derive an analog of the indicial equation (16) and generalize Theorem 7 to this DE.

(b) Generalize Theorem 8 for this DE when two exponents coincide.

10*. Hypergeometric functions. So far in this chapter, the behavior of solutions of DE's has been studied only near a single isolated singular point. A fascinating topic of analysis is the relation between the behavior of analytic functions defined by DE's at different singular points. This topic is beautifully illustrated by the hypergeometric functions, defined as solutions of the hypergeometric DE (18). This illustration (Example 4 of § 6) is of especial interest because many common transcendental functions can be expressed in terms of the hypergeometric functions. For example, $(1-z)^{-\alpha} = F(\alpha,\beta,\beta;z)$; $\arcsin z = zF(\frac{1}{2},\frac{1}{2},3/2;z^2)$, $\log(1+z) = zF(1,1,2;-z)$, etc.

According to the program laid out in Chapter III, the properties of the hypergeometric functions can be deduced from the DE (18). For example, let us derive a formula for the derivative of the hypergeometric function $F(\alpha, \beta, \gamma; z)$. Differentiating the hypergeometric DE, one gets

$$z(1-z)w''' + [\gamma+1-(\alpha+1+\beta+1+1)z]w'' - (\alpha+1)(\beta+1)w' = 0,$$

which is again a hypergeometric DE with constants $\alpha_1 = \alpha+1$, $\beta_1 = \beta+1$, $\gamma_1 = \gamma+1$. By Theorems 7 and 8, every solution of this DE holomorphic at the origin is a constant times $F(\alpha+1,\beta+1,\gamma+1;z)$. Hence we obtain $F'(\alpha,\beta,\gamma;z) = kF(\alpha+1,\ \beta+1,\ \gamma+1;z)$. The constant k is determined by evaluating (20) at $z = 0$. This gives the differentiation formula

$$F'(\alpha,\beta,\gamma;z) = \frac{\alpha\beta}{\gamma}F(\alpha+1,\beta+1,\gamma+1;z). \tag{27}$$

The *Jacobi identity*

$$\frac{d^n}{dz^n}[z^{\alpha+n-1}F(\alpha,\beta,\gamma;z)] = \alpha(\alpha+1)\cdots(\alpha+n-1)z^{\alpha-1}F(\alpha+n,\beta,\gamma;z),$$

can be similarly established by multiplying both sides of the identity by $z^{1-\alpha}$, and then verifying that both sides of the resulting identity satisfy the hypergeometric DE with constants $\alpha_1 = \alpha+n$, β, γ.

The study of the hypergeometric DE is greatly facilitated by its *symmetry properties*. Making the substitution $w = z^{1-\gamma}u$, one obtains as a DE equivalent to (18) for the dependent variable u, a second hypergeometric DE with different constants (unless $\gamma = 1$):

(28) $$z(1-z)u''+[\gamma_1-(\alpha_1+\beta_1+1)z]u'-\alpha_1\beta_1 u=0,$$

where $\alpha_1=\alpha-\gamma+1$; $\beta_1=\beta-\gamma+1$; $\gamma_1=2-\gamma$. Since this DE has the solution $w_1(z)=F(\alpha_1,\beta_1,\gamma_1;z)$, we obtain at once a power series solution of (18) corresponding to the exponent $1-\gamma$ in the form

(29) $$w_2(z)=z^{1-\gamma}F(\alpha-\gamma+1,\beta-\gamma+1,2-\gamma;z).$$

The two solutions are a *canonical basis* of solutions of (18) at the regular singular point $z=0$.

The change of dependent variable $w=(1-z)^{\gamma-\alpha-\beta}u$ also gives a DE of the form (18) in the variable u with $\alpha_1=\gamma-\alpha$, $\beta_1=\gamma-\beta$, $\gamma_1=\gamma$. Since the solution of this DE which is holomorphic at $z=0$ and takes the value 1 there is $F(\gamma-\alpha,\gamma-\beta,\gamma;z)$, we obtain the identity

(30) $$F(\alpha,\beta,\gamma;z)=(1-z)^{\gamma-\alpha-\beta}F(\gamma-\alpha,\gamma-\beta,\gamma;z).$$

A change of independent variable which transforms the hypergeometric DE into itself is $t=1-z$. This gives the DE

$$t(1-t)w''+[\gamma_1-(\alpha+\beta+1)t]w'-\alpha\beta w=0$$

where $\gamma_1=\alpha+\beta-\gamma+1$. It follows that the hypergeometric DE has a second regular singular point at $z=1$, and a basis of solutions, $w_3(z)=F(\alpha,\beta,\alpha+\beta+1-\gamma;1-z)$ and $w_4(z)=(1-z)^{\gamma-\alpha-\beta}F(\gamma-\alpha,\gamma-\beta,\gamma-\alpha-\beta+1;1-z)$.† These functions form a *canonical basis* of solutions relative to the singular point $z=1$. Note that the functions w_3 and w_4 are equal to linear combinations of the functions w_1 and w_2, by the Uniqueness Theorem for second-order linear DE's (Ch. II, Theorem 1).

11*. Jacobi polynomials. A classical DE having regular singular points at ±1 (and ∞, cf. § 12) is the *Jacobi* DE

(31) $$(1-z^2)u''+[b-a-(a+b+2)z]u'+n(n+a+b+1)u=0.$$

Multiplying by $(1-z)^a(1+z)^b$, we get the *self-adjoint* form (Ch. II, § 5)

$$\frac{d}{dz}\left[(1-z)^{a+1}(1+z)^{b+1}\frac{du}{dz}\right]+n(n+a+b+1)(1-z)^a(1+z)^b u=0.$$

When $a=b$, this reduces to the *ultraspherical* DE

(32) $$\frac{d}{dz}\left[(1-z^2)^{a+1}\frac{du}{dz}\right]+n(n+2a+1)(1-z^2)^a u=0.$$

This is obtained from the partial DE $\nabla^2[r^n u(\cos\theta)]=0$ in $(2a+3)$-dimensional space by separation of variables; hence its solutions play an important role in potential theory and its generalizations. Familiar special

†Assuming, of course, that the parameters α, β, γ are not chosen in such a way that the solutions coincide: thus $\gamma\neq\alpha+\beta$.

cases of the ultraspherical DE are $a = b = 0$, which gives the Legendre DE $[(1-z^2)u']' + n(n+1)u = 0$ (Ch. II, § 2), and $a = b = -\frac{1}{2}$, which gives the Chebyshev DE $[(1-z^2)^{1/2}u']' + n^2(1-z^2)^{-1/2}u = 0$.

The Jacobi DE can be transformed into the hypergeometric DE (18) by the change of independent variable $z = 1 - 2t$, $t = (1-z)/2$. This change transforms (31) into

$$(33)\quad t(1-t)u_{tt} + [a+1-(a+b+2)t]u_t + n(n+a+b+1)u = 0,$$

which is the hypergeometric equation with parameters $\alpha = -n$, $\beta = n+a+b+1$, and $\gamma = a+1$, as one easily verifies. Hence, as particular solutions of the Jacobi DE, we obtain the hypergeometric functions $F(-n, n+a+b+1, a+1; (1-z)/2)$. Using the results of § 10, one can deduce various important formulas from this relation.

For instance, one can see immediately from the series expansion (20) that if n is a nonnegative integer, then the solution $F(-n, n+a+b+1, a+1; (1-z)/2)$ is a *polynomial* unless also a is a negative integer $-m$, $m \leqq n$. Hence we can define the *Jacobi polynomials*

$$(34)\quad P_n^{(a,b)}(z) = \binom{n+a}{n} F(-n, n+a+b+1, a+1; (1-z)/2),$$

with the normalizing factor $\binom{n+a}{n}$. For $a = b = 0$ we obtain in particular the Legendre polynomials, for $a = b = -\frac{1}{2}$ the Chebyshev polynomials, and for other $a = b$ (with suitable normalizing factors) the Gegenbauer or ultraspherical polynomials. The normalizing factor for the ultraspherical polynomial $P_n^{(\alpha)}$ is given in terms of the Jacobi polynomials (for $a = b$ a half-integer) by the formula

$$P_n^{(\alpha)}(x) = \frac{\Gamma(\alpha+\frac{1}{2})}{\Gamma(n+\alpha+\frac{1}{2})} \cdot \frac{\Gamma(n+2\alpha)}{\Gamma(2\alpha)} P^{(\alpha-\frac{1}{2},\alpha-\frac{1}{2})}(x).$$

From the differentiation formula (27) for the hypergeometric function we infer the differentiation formula for Jacobi polynomials (including Legendre and Chebyshev polynomials)

$$(35)\quad \frac{d^m}{dz^m} P_n^{(a,b)}(z) = C \cdot P_{n-m}^{(a+m,b+m)}(z),$$

$$C = 2^{-m}(n+a+b+1)(n+a+b+2)\cdots(n+a+b+m).$$

An expression for the Jacobi polynomials which is often more convenient than (34) is the *Rodrigues formula*

$$(36)\quad P_n^{(a,b)}(z) = \frac{(-1)^n}{n!2^n}(1-z)^{-a}(1+z)^{-b}\frac{d^n}{dz^n}[(1-z)^{a+n}(1+z)^{b+n}].$$

We shall derive this formula from the identities for the hypergeometric function established in the preceding section. First, since $(1-t)^a = F(a,-b,b;\,t)$, the binomial series is a special case of the hypergeometric series: $(1-t)^{b+n} = F(a+1,-n-b,a+1,t)$. Using also the Jacobi identity, we justify the first two steps of

$$\begin{aligned} t^{-a}(1-t)^{-b}\frac{d^n}{dt^n}&[t^{a+n}(1-t)^{b+n}] \\ &= t^{-a}(1-t)^{-b}\frac{d^n}{dt^n}[t^{a+n}F(a+1,-n-b,a+1;\,t)] \\ &= (a+1)(a+2)\cdots(a+n)(1-t)^{-b}F(a+n+1,\,-n-b,\,a+1;\,t) \\ &= (a+1)(a+2)\cdots(a+n)F(-n,\,n+a+b+1,\,a+1;\,t). \end{aligned}$$

In the last step, identity (30) for the hypergeometric function is used. The Rodrigues formula (36) follows by making the change of variable $t = (1-z)/2$.

EXERCISES E

1. Verify the following identities:

(a) $F(\alpha,\beta,\beta;\,z) = (1-z)^{-\alpha}$,
(b) $F(\tfrac{1}{2},\tfrac{1}{2},\tfrac{3}{2};\,z^2) = (\text{arc sin } z)/z$,
(c) $F(1,1,2;\,z) = -\log(1-z)/z$,
(d) $1 + \binom{a}{1}z + \binom{a}{2}z^2 + \cdots + \binom{a}{m}z^m = \binom{a}{m}z^mF(-m,1,a-m+1;\,-z^{-1})$,
(e) $\cos az = F(a/2,-a/2,1/2;\,(\sin z)^2)$,
(f) $\log[(1+z)/(1-z)] = 2zF(1/2,1,3/2;\,z^2)$.

2. (a) Show that (18) is equivalent to

$$[zd/dz(zd/dz+\gamma-1) - z(zd/dz+\alpha)(zd/dz+\beta)]w = 0.$$

(b) Show that the eigenvalues of the circuit matrix for $z = 0$ are equal if γ is an integer.

(c) Show that the eigenvalues of the circuit matrix for $z = 1$ are equal if $\gamma - \alpha - \beta$ is an integer.

3. (a) Show that if α is zero or a negative integer, then the hypergeometric DE (18) has a polynomial solution unless $\gamma < \alpha$ is a negative integer.

(b) Using (33), express this solution as a Jacobi polynomial.

4. (a) Compute the characteristic exponents at $z = \pm 1$ of the Legendre DE

$$[(1-z^2)w']' + \lambda w = 0.$$

(*b) Describe corresponding circuit matrices, taking as basic solutions an even and an odd solution.

5. (a) Show that setting $t = z^2$ in the Legendre DE gives a hypergeometric DE.

(b) Express the Legendre polynomials as multiples of $F(\alpha,\beta,\gamma;\,z^2)$ for suitable α,β,γ.

6. Find the characteristic exponents at $z = \pm 1$ of the associated Legendre DE:

$$[(1-z^2)w']' + [n(n+1) - m^2/(1-z^2)]w = 0.$$

7. Derive from (31) the self-adjoint form of the Jacobi DE displayed in the text.

*8. Prove that $P_n^{(a,b)}(z) = k_n F(-n,-b-n,1+a\,;\,(z-1)/(z+1))$, where $k_n = \binom{n+a}{n}\left(\frac{z+1}{2}\right)^n$. (*Hint:* Show the right-hand side satisfies (31) using appropriate identities for F.)

9. Find the roots of the indicial equation of the Jacobi DE (31) at $z=1$ and $z=-1$.

10. Show that (34) defines a solution of (32) even when n is not a positive integer. What happens when n is a negative integer?

11. Using (36), show that for $a > b > -1$,

$$\int_{-1}^{1} P_m^{(a,b)}(x)P_n^{(a,b)}(x)(1-x)^a(1+x)^b\,dx = 0 \quad \text{for} \quad m \neq n.$$

12*. Singular points at infinity. Even when the coefficient-functions p and q of the second-order linear DE (5) are regular at infinity, the point at infinity may be neither a removable singularity nor a regular singular point, but an *irregular singular point.* For instance, this is true of $w''=w$, whose solutions $e^{\pm z}$ have essential singularities at infinity.

One defines when the point at infinity is a regular singular point by making the substitution $z = 1/t$. This substitution transforms the second-order linear DE (5) into the DE

$$\frac{d^2v}{dt^2} + \left[\frac{2}{t} - \frac{1}{t^2}\,p\left(\frac{1}{t}\right)\right]\frac{dv}{dt} + \frac{1}{t^4}\,q\left(\frac{1}{t}\right)v(t) = 0, \tag{37}$$

where $v(t) = w(1/t)$. The point at infinity is said to be a regular singular point of the DE (5) when the origin is a regular singular point for the DE (37). This happens when the function $\left[\frac{2}{t} - \left(\frac{1}{t^2}\right)p\left(\frac{1}{t}\right)\right]$ has at worst a pole of the first order at $t=0$, that is, when the first coefficient in the power series expansion of $p(1/t)$ vanishes. Also, the function $t^{-4}q(1/t)$ must have at most a pole of the second order at $t=0$; this happens when the first two coefficients in the power series for $q(1/t)$ vanish. This gives

THEOREM 9. *The point at infinity is a regular singular point for the second-order linear DE (5) if and only if the coefficients p and q have power series expansions, convergent for sufficiently large $|z|$, of the form*

$$p(z) = \frac{p_1}{z} + \frac{p_2}{z^2} + \cdots, \qquad q(z) = \frac{q_2}{z^2} + \frac{q_3}{z^3} + \cdots. \tag{38}$$

That is, it is necessary and sufficient that the function p have a zero of at least the first order and the function q have a zero of at least the second order at infinity. In particular, the solutions of the DE are holomorphic at $z = \infty$, or $t = 0$, if and only if the coefficients $\left[\frac{2}{t} - \left(\frac{1}{t^2}\right)p\left(\frac{1}{t}\right)\right]$ and $\left(\frac{1}{t^4}\right)q\left(\frac{1}{t}\right)$

are regular at $t = 0$. Hence the

COROLLARY. *If the coefficients $p(z)$ and $q(z)$ of the DE* (5) *are holomorphic for sufficiently large z, then all solutions of* (5) *have removable singularities at $z = \infty$ if and only if $p_1 = 2$ and $q_2 = q_3 = 0$ in* (38).

It follows from Theorem 7 that, if $z = \infty$ is a regular singular point, and if the indicial equation of (37) at $t = 0$ has roots α and β not differing by an integer, then the DE (5) has a basis of solutions of the form

$$w_j(z) = z^{-\nu}\left(1 + \frac{a_1}{z} + \frac{a_2}{z^2} + \cdots\right), \qquad \nu = \alpha, \beta.$$

The indicial equation at infinity is defined, because of Theorem 9, to be the following equation for ν:

$$\nu(\nu - 1) + (2 - p_1)\nu + q_2 = 0; \tag{39}$$

its roots are called the *characteristic exponents* at $z = \infty$. If they differ by an integer, then there is still a solution of the form $\left(\frac{1}{z^\nu}\right)\left(1 + \frac{a_1}{z} + \cdots\right)$, but a second linearly independent solution contains a logarithmic term.

EXAMPLE 5. The hypergeometric DE (18) has by Theorem 9 a regular singular point at infinity with characteristic exponents α and β. In order to derive a canonical basis at infinity it is convenient to make the substitution $u(t) = t^{-\alpha}w(1/t)$. This transforms the DE into another hypergeometric DE

$$t(1 - t)u'' + [\gamma_2 - (\alpha_2 + \beta_2 + 1)t]y' - \alpha_2\beta_2 y = 0$$

with $\alpha_2 = \alpha$, $\beta_2 = \alpha - \gamma + 1$, $\gamma_2 = \alpha - \beta + 1$. It follows that the hypergeometric DE has the solution

$$w_5(z) = z^{-\alpha}F(\alpha, \alpha - \gamma + 1, \alpha - \beta + 1; 1/z),$$

convergent when $|z| > 1$. From the symmetry between α and β one obtains a second solution

$$w_6(z) = z^{-\beta}F(\beta, \beta - \gamma + 1, \beta - \alpha + 1; 1/z).$$

The functions w_5 and w_6 form a canonical basis at infinity, provided $\alpha \neq \beta$.

13*. Fuchsian equations. A homogeneous linear DE with single-valued analytic coefficients is called a *Fuchsian DE* when it has at worst regular singular points in the extended complex plane, including the point at infinity. Since functions whose only singular points are poles necessarily are rational functions,† it follows that the coefficients of any Fuchsian

†Hille, p. 217, Theorem 8.5.1.

DE are rational functions. The most general first-order Fuchsian DE has the form (see Ex. F8)

$$w' + \left(\sum_{k=1}^{n} \frac{A_k}{z - z_k}\right) w = 0.$$

The general solution of this DE is the elementary function

$$w(z) = c \prod_{k=1}^{n} (z - z_k)^{-A_k}.$$

Second-order Fuchsian DE's offer much more variety; they are classified according to the number of their singular points. When the number of these is small, their study is greatly simplified by making *linear fractional transformations*† of the independent variable, of the form

$$\zeta = (az + b)/(cz + d), \qquad ad \neq bc.$$

Any such transformation can be obtained by successive changes of variable of the forms $\zeta = z + k$, $\zeta = az$, and $\zeta = 1/z$. Each such change of variable shifts the position of the singular points of a DE, carrying branch poles of solutions into branch poles. Therefore, by Theorems 6, 7, and 8, a general linear fractional transformation transforms regular singular points into regular singular points, and the indicial equations of the transformed DE coincide with those of the original DE at corresponding points.

We first consider second-order Fuchsian DE's having at most two singular points, say at $z = z_1$ and $z = z_2$. By a linear fractional transformation of the form $\zeta = (z - z_1)/(z - z_2)$, we can send these singular points to zero and infinity. It follows from the definition of a regular singular point and from Theorem 9 that $p(z) = p_1/z$ and $q(z) = q_2/z^2$. Hence the most general Fuchsian DE of the second order with two regular singular points is equivalent to the *Euler DE* of Example 1:

$$w'' + \frac{p_1}{z} w' + \frac{q_2}{z^2} w = 0,$$

after a linear fractional transformation.

The simplest Fuchsian DE of the second order whose solutions do not reduce to elementary functions is therefore one having three regular singular points. By a linear fractional transformation of the independent variable we may put these singular points at 0, 1, ∞. From the definition of a regular singular point and from Theorem 9 of § 12, we can determine the coefficient functions of a second-order Fuchsian DE with three regular singular points at 0, 1, ∞ as follows. The coefficient $p(z)$ must have at worst a pole of the first order at $z = 0$ and at $z = 1$, and can therefore be

†See Hille, pp. 46–50, or Ahlfors, pp. 23–35.

written in the form

$$p(z) = \frac{A_1}{z} + \frac{B_1}{z-1} + p_1(z),$$

where the function $p_1(z)$ is regular throughout the plane. However, by Theorem 9 the function $zp(z)$ has a finite limit as $|z|$ tends to infinity. Since $z[(A_1/z) + (B_1/(z-1))]$ is bounded as $|z|$ tends to infinity, it follows that the function $zp_1(z)$ is uniformly bounded. By Liouville's Theorem† it must therefore vanish identically.

Similarly, the coefficient $q(z)$ has at worst poles of the second order at $z = 0$ and $z = 1$, and can therefore be written in the form

$$q(z) = \frac{A_2}{z^2} + \frac{A_3}{z} + \frac{B_2}{(z-1)^2} + \frac{B_3}{z-1} + q_1(z)$$

where the function $q_1(z)$ is holomorphic in the finite complex plane. By Theorem 9 the function $z^2q(z)$ remains bounded as $|z|$ tends to infinity, and hence so does the function

$$z^2\left(\frac{A_3}{z} + \frac{B_3}{z-1} + q_1(z)\right) = z^2\left(\frac{(A_3+B_3)z - A_3 + q_1(z)z(z-1)}{z(z-1)}\right).$$

Therefore $A_3 = -B_3$ and, again by Liouville's Theorem, the function $q_1(z)$ vanishes identically. This completes the proof of

THEOREM 10. *A second-order Fuchsian DE with three regular singular points can be transformed by a linear fractional transformation into the form*

$$(40)\quad w'' + \left(\frac{A_1}{z} + \frac{B_1}{z-1}\right)w' + \left[\frac{A_2}{z^2} + \frac{B_2}{(z-1)^2} - \frac{A_3}{z(z-1)}\right]w = 0,$$

where A_i and B_i are constants.

The DE (40) is called the *Riemann* DE; it evidently depends on five parameters.

With the Riemann DE are associated three pairs of characteristic exponents (λ_1, λ_2), (μ_1, μ_2), (ν_1, ν_2) belonging to the singular points $0, 1, \infty$ respectively. These exponents are the roots of the indicial equations (cf. (16) and (39))

$$\lambda_i(\lambda_i - 1) + A_1\lambda_i + A_2 = 0, \quad \mu_i(\mu_i - 1) + B_1\mu_i + B_2 = 0,$$
$$\nu_i^2 + (1 - A_1 - B_1)\nu_i + A_2 + B_2 - A_3 = 0.$$

By means of these equations we can express the parameters in the DE

†Hille, p. 204, Theorem 8.2.2.

(40) in terms of the (characteristic) exponents:

$$A_1 = 1 - \lambda_1 - \lambda_2; \qquad A_2 = \lambda_1\lambda_2,$$
$$B_1 = 1 - \mu_1 - \mu_2; \qquad B_2 = \mu_1\mu_2,$$
$$A_1 + B_1 = \nu_1 + \nu_2 + 1; \qquad A_2 + B_2 - A_3 = \nu_1\nu_2.$$

From the identities in the first column we obtain the *Riemann identity*

$$\lambda_1 + \lambda_2 + \mu_1 + \mu_2 + \nu_1 + \nu_2 = 1. \tag{41}$$

Substituting into (40) we find the Riemann DE

$$w'' + \left(\frac{1-\lambda_1-\lambda_2}{z} + \frac{1-\mu_1-\mu_2}{z-1}\right)w' + \left(\frac{\lambda_1\lambda_2}{z^2} + \frac{\mu_1\mu_2}{(z-1)^2} + \frac{\nu_1\nu_2 - \lambda_1\lambda_2 - \mu_1\mu_2}{z(z-1)}\right)w = 0. \tag{42}$$

The preceding discussion shows that the Riemann DE (40) is completely determined by assigning the values of the exponents and the location of the singular points:

THEOREM 11. *A Fuchsian DE of the second order with three regular singular points in the extended complex plane is uniquely determined by prescribing the two exponents at each singular point. The exponents satisfy Riemann's identity* (41).

The *hypergeometric DE* of § 6 is a special case of the Riemann DE with three singular points at $0, 1, \infty$. As shown in § 6 and in § 12, the hypergeometric DE has three regular singular points at $0, 1, \infty$ with exponents $0, 1-\gamma; 0, \gamma-\alpha-\beta; \alpha, \beta$ respectively.

From Theorems 6–8 and from the fact that the Riemann DE is the *unique* DE satisfying the conditions of Theorem 11, several identities for the solutions can be derived. If we make the change of dependent variable $v(z) = z^\lambda w(z)$, then the function $v(z)$ has a branch pole at each of the singular points $0, 1, \infty$. Therefore (cf. Theorem 9, Corollary) $v(z)$ satisfies a DE with three regular singular points at $0, 1, \infty$. By Theorem 11, this must be the Riemann DE (42). The exponents of this DE are unchanged at $z = 1$, whereas they are $\alpha_i + \lambda$ at $z = 0$ and $\gamma_i - \lambda$ at infinity. A similar result holds for the more general change of dependent variable

$$v(z) = z^\lambda (z-1)^\mu w(z).$$

Using these identities we can prove the fundamental

THEOREM 12. *Every Riemann DE* (40) *can be reduced to the hypergeometric DE* (18) *by a change of dependent variable of the form* $w = z^\lambda(1-z)^\mu v(z)$.

COROLLARY. *Every second-order Fuchsian DE with three regular singular points can be reduced to the hypergeometric DE by changes of independent and dependent variable.*

Proof. The general solution $w(z)$ of the Riemann DE can be written in the form

$$w(z) = z^{\lambda_1}(1 - z)^{\mu_1}v(z)$$

where v is the general solution of a Riemann DE with exponents $0, \lambda_2 - \lambda_1$; $0, \mu_2 - \mu_1$; $\nu_1 + \lambda_1 + \mu_1, \nu_2 + \lambda_1 + \mu_1$. Thus the function v is a solution of a hypergeometric DE with $\alpha = \nu_1 + \lambda_1 + \mu_1$, $\beta = \nu_2 + \lambda_1 + \mu_1$ and $\gamma = 1 - \lambda_2 + \lambda_1$, q.e.d.

Other identities are obtained by making a change of independent variable. Any linear fractional transformation which permutes the singular points $0, 1, \infty$ transforms the Riemann DE (42) into another DE with the same regular singular points which, again by Theorem 10, is a Riemann DE. For example, make the change of independent variable $t = \dfrac{1}{z}$, which permutes 0 and ∞. If $w(z)$ is a solution of the DE (42) then the function $v(t) = w\left(\dfrac{1}{z}\right)$ satisfies a Riemann DE with singular points at $0, 1, \infty$ for which the exponents at 0 and ∞ are permuted. Similarly, the change of independent variable $t = 1 - z$ permutes the singular points 0 and 1 and leads to the conclusion that $w(1 - z)$ is a solution of a Riemann DE whenever $w(z)$ is a solution. The exponents at the singular points are permuted accordingly.

EXERCISES F

1. Show that the only second-order linear DE which has just two regular singular points, at 0 and ∞, is the Euler DE.
2. Show that no analytic linear DE (5) can have only removable singularities, if the point $z = \infty$ is included.
3. Prove in detail that any linear fractional transformation carries regular singular points into regular singular points.
4. If p and q are constant in (5), is the singular point at ∞ regular? Justify your statement.
5. Show that, unless $B = A^2/4$, the DE $(z^2 + Az + B)w'' + (Cz + D)w' + Ew = 0$ can be reduced to the hypergeometric equation by a linear substitution $z = a\zeta + b$.
6. Show that the Bessel DE has an irregular singular point at $z = \infty$.
7. Find necessary and sufficient conditions on $p(z)$ for $w' + p(z)w = 0$ to have (a) a removable singularity, and (b) a regular singular point at ∞.
8. Show that the most general first-order linear DE with $n + 1$ distinct regular singular points at $z_1, \cdots, z_n$ and ∞ is

$$w' + \left[\sum_{k=1}^{n} q_k/(z - z_k)\right]w = 0.$$

Integrate this DE explicitly.

*9. Find the most general second-order linear DE (5) having regular singular points at $a_1, \cdots, a_n$ and ∞.

*10. Find the most general linear DE having regular singular points at 0, ∞ and no other singular points. Show that any such DE can be integrated in terms of elementary functions.

ADDITIONAL EXERCISES

1. Show that $\int_0^{\pi/2} d\theta/(1 - k^2 \sin^2 \theta)^{1/2} = \frac{1}{2}F(\frac{1}{2}, \frac{1}{2}, 1; k^2)$.

2. Show that the substitution $z = \zeta^m$ (m a nonzero integer) transforms DE's (5) having a regular singular point at $z = 0$ into DE's having a regular singular point at $\zeta = 0$, with characteristic exponents divided by m.

3. Show that the DE $w'' + [(1 - z^2)/4z^2]w = 0$ has a basis of solutions of the form $w_1(z) = z^{1/2}[1 + z^2/16 + z^4/1024 + \cdots]$ and $w_2(z) = w_1 \log z - z^{3/2}/16 + \cdots$.

4. Find an entire function $f(z)$ and constant c for which the functions

$$w_i = f(z)^{1/2} \exp \pm \left\{c \int_c^z dz/[f(z)\sqrt{z(1 - z)}]\right\}$$

are a basis of solutions of $z(1 - z)w'' + (1 - 2z)w'/2 + (az + b)w = 0$.

5. The algebraic form of the Mathieu equation is

$$4\xi(1 - \xi)u_{\xi\xi} + 2(1 - 2\xi)u_\xi + (\lambda - 16k + 32k\xi)u = 0.$$

Show that this has a regular singular point at $\xi = 0$, calculate the exponents, and find a recurrence relation on the coefficients of the power series solutions.

*6. (a) If P and Q are given polynomials without common factors, and if $c_{n+1}/c_n = P(n)/Q(n)$ and $\Sigma c_n z^n$ is convergent, show that $\Sigma c_n z^n$ satisfies the DE $zP(zd/dz)w - Q(zd/dz)w = 0$.

(b) Find all quadratic polynomials P and Q for which the preceding DE has regular singular points only, and express the solutions in terms of hypergeometric functions.

*7. (a) Find the eigenvalues of the circuit matrix of (18) for $z = 0$.

(b) Using the change of variable $t = 1 - z$, solve the same problem for the circuit matrix for $z = 1$.

8. Show that the function $\ln(\ln z)$ satisfies no linear DE of finite order with holomorphic coefficients.

9. Show that, if $f(0) = 0$ but $f'(0) \neq 0$, the substitution $z = f(\zeta)$ carries a regular singular point of (5) at $z = 0$ into one at $\zeta = 0$ having the same indicial equation.

10. Show that, for any nontrivial solution of the Euler DE $z^2w'' + zw' + w = 0$ and any integer n, there exists a spiral path $\theta = h(r)$ approaching the origin, along which $\lim_{z \to 0} |z^n w| = \infty$.

*11. Let the DE $w'' + p_1(z)w' + p_2(z)w = 0$ have an isolated singular point at $z = \infty$. Show that this singular point is regular if and only if, for some $n > 0$, every solution satisfies $\lim_{z \to \infty} z^{-n}w(re^{i\theta}) = 0$ for $0 \leq \theta \leq 2\pi$.

CHAPTER X

Sturm-Liouville Systems

1. Sturm-Liouville systems. A Sturm-Liouville equation is a second-order homogeneous linear DE of the form

$$\frac{d}{dx}\left[p(x)\frac{du}{dx}\right] + [\lambda\rho(x) - q(x)]u = 0. \tag{1}$$

Here λ is a parameter, while p, ρ, and q are real-valued functions of x; the functions p and ρ are positive. In operational notation, with $L = D[p(x)D] - q(x)$, one can rewrite (1) in the abbreviated form

$$L[u] + \lambda\rho(x)u = 0. \tag{1'}$$

Such a DE (1) is *self-adjoint* for real λ; to insure the existence of solutions, the functions q and ρ are assumed to be continuous, and p to be continuously differentiable (of class $\mathcal{C}^1$). For a given value of λ, (1) defines a *linear operator* transforming any function $u \in \mathcal{C}^2$ into $L[u] + \lambda\rho u$. The Sturm-Liouville equation (1) is called *regular* in a *closed* finite interval $a \leqq x \leqq b$, when the functions $p(x)$ and $\rho(x)$ are different from zero for $a \leqq x \leqq b$. The functions p, q, and ρ, being continuous, are bounded in the interval.

For each λ, it follows from the existence theorem of Ch. V, § 8, that a regular Sturm-Liouville equation for $a \leqq x \leqq b$ has a basis of two linearly independent solutions of class $\mathcal{C}^2$.

A *Sturm-Liouville system* (or S-L system) is a Sturm-Liouville equation together with *endpoint* (or boundary) *conditions* to be satisfied by the solutions, for example $u(a) = u(b) = 0$. One type of endpoint condition we shall study is the following.

Definition. *A* regular S-L system *is a regular S-L equation* (1) *on a finite closed interval* $a \leqq x \leqq b$, *together with two* separated *endpoint conditions, of the form*

$$\alpha u(a) + \alpha' u'(a) = 0, \qquad \beta u(b) + \beta' u'(b) = 0. \tag{2}$$

Here α, α', β, β' are given real numbers. We exclude the trivial conditions $\alpha = \alpha' = 0$ and $\beta = \beta' = 0$.

A nontrivial solution of an S-L system is called an *eigenfunction*, and the corresponding λ is called its *eigenvalue*. Each eigenfunction is also said to *belong* to its eigenvalue. The set of all eigenvalues of a regular S-L system is called the *spectrum* of the system.

EXAMPLE 1. The system consisting of the DE $u'' + \lambda u = 0$ in the interval $0 \leqq x \leqq \pi$, with the boundary conditions $u(0) = 0$, $u(\pi) = 0$ has the eigenfunctions $u_n(x) = \sin nx$ and the eigenvalues $\lambda_n = n^2$, $n = 1, 2, 3, \cdots$.

EXAMPLE 2. For fixed n, the Bessel equation

$$\frac{d}{dr}\left[r\frac{du}{dr}\right] + \left(k^2 r - \frac{n^2}{r}\right)u = 0, \qquad a \leqq r \leqq b, \tag{3}$$

is an S-L equation with $p = \rho = r$, $\lambda = k^2$, and $q = n^2/r$. When $0 < a < b$, a regular S-L system is obtained by imposing the endpoint conditions $u(a) = u(b) = 0$, or by imposing any other separated endpoint conditions of the form (2).

With $a = 0$, the DE (3) does not define a regular S-L system, because the coefficient $p(r)$ vanishes at $r = 0$. We then obtain a *singular* S-L system, which is treated in § 4.

For fixed k and variable n, the Bessel equation (3) defines a different S-L equation, because the parameter is different.

Periodic endpoint conditions. For S-L equations whose coefficients are periodic functions of x with period $b - a$, the *periodic* endpoint conditions

$$u(a) = u(b), \qquad u'(a) = u'(b), \tag{4}$$

are sometimes imposed, and give another type of S-L system, a *periodic* S-L system.

EXAMPLE 3. The system consisting of the DE $u'' + \lambda u = 0$, for $-\pi \leqq x \leqq \pi$, with the periodic endpoint conditions $u(-\pi) = u(\pi)$ and $u'(-\pi) = u'(\pi)$ has the eigenfunctions 1, $\cos nx$, $\sin nx$, where n is any positive integer. The corresponding eigenvalues are the squares of integers; if $n > 0$, there are two linearly independent eigenfunctions having the same eigenvalue n^2.

EXAMPLE 4. A regular S-L system is obtained from the *Mathieu equation*

$$u'' + (\lambda + 16d \cos 2x)u = 0, \qquad a \leqq x \leqq b, \tag{5}$$

by imposing separated endpoint conditions. In this example, $p = \rho \equiv 1$, and $q(x) = -16d \cos 2x$. With the periodic endpoint conditions $u(0) = u(\pi)$, $u'(0) = u'(\pi)$, or with $u(0) = -u(\pi)$ and $u'(0) = -u'(\pi)$, S-L systems are obtained which are not regular, but periodic.

2. Sturm-Liouville series. Examples 1 and 3 define two S-L systems from the same S-L equation, $u'' + \lambda u = 0$, but with different endpoint conditions. The eigenfunctions of Example 3 are the functions used in the theory of Fourier series, studied in the advanced calculus. It is shown there that these functions are *orthogonal* on the interval $-\pi \leqq x \leqq \pi$. This means that the following relation holds:†

$$\int_{-\pi}^{\pi} \sin mx \sin nx \, dx = \int_{-\pi}^{\pi} \cos mx \cos nx \, dx = 0 \quad \text{if} \quad m \neq n,$$

$$\int_{-\pi}^{\pi} \sin mx \cos nx \, dx = 0 \quad \text{for all integers} \quad m, n.$$

The eigenfunctions $\sin nx$ of Example 1 are also orthogonal on the interval $0 \leqq x \leqq \pi$ on which the S-L system in question is defined:

$$\int_{0}^{\pi} \sin mx \sin nx \, dx = 0 \quad \text{if} \quad m \neq n.$$

We will now show that analogous orthogonality relations hold for the eigenfunctions of regular S-L systems generally, and for the eigenfunctions of S-L systems with periodic endpoint conditions.

DEFINITION. *Two integrable real-valued functions f and g are orthogonal with weight function $\rho > 0$ on an interval I if and only if*

$$\int_{I} \rho(x) f(x) g(x) dx = 0. \tag{6}$$

The interval I may be finite, open or closed, or infinite.

THEOREM 1. *Eigenfunctions of a regular S-L system* (1)–(2) *having different eigenvalues are* orthogonal *with weight function ρ. Thus, let u and v be eigenfunctions belonging to distinct eigenvalues λ and μ. Then*

$$\int_{a}^{b} \rho(x) u(x) v(x) dx = 0. \tag{7}$$

Proof. We use the operator notation $L[u] = [p(x)u']' - q(x)u$. Then u and v are eigenfunctions of (1) with eigenvalues λ and μ if and only if

$$L[u] + \lambda\rho(x)u = L[v] + \mu\rho(x)v = 0.$$

We now use the *Lagrange identity* of Ch. II, § 6, namely, the identity

$$uL[v] - vL[u] = \frac{d}{dx}\{p(x)[u(x)v'(x) - v(x)u'(x)]\},$$

which is easily verified directly. Integrating this identity between the endpoints $x = a$ and $x = b$, and substituting $-\mu\rho v$ for $L[v]$ and $-\lambda\rho u$ for $L[u]$, we get

$$(\lambda - \mu) \int_{a}^{b} \rho(x) u(x) v(x) dx = -p(x)[u(x)v'(x) - v(x)u'(x)] \Big|_{x=a}^{x=b}. \tag{8}$$

Nothing was assumed about endpoint conditions in deriving identity (8). Therefore we have proved the following result.

†Courant, Vol. 1, p. 438; Widder, p. 395.

LEMMA. *If u and v satisfy an S-L equation* (1) *on a closed interval* $a \leqq x \leqq b$, *for values λ and μ of the parameter, then identity* (8) *holds.*

The right side of (8) is called the *boundary term* of the identity.

To prove Theorem 1, it suffices to show that the boundary term vanishes in the case of separated endpoint conditions. But (2) implies

$$p(a)[u(a)v'(a) - v(a)u'(a)] = [\alpha p(a)/\alpha'][u(a)v(a) - v(a)u(a)] = 0$$

if $\alpha' \neq 0$. If $\alpha \neq 0$, the right side of (8) reduces similarly at $x = a$ to

$$[\alpha' p(a)/\alpha][u'(a)v'(a) - v'(a)u'(a)] = 0.$$

Hence $p(a)[u(a)v'(a) - v(a)u'(a)] = 0$ unless $\alpha = \alpha' = 0$. Similar equations cover the boundary term at $x = b$. Since the possibilities $\alpha = \alpha' = 0$ and $\beta = \beta' = 0$ are excluded, this shows that the right side of (8) vanishes. Formula (7) now follows from identity (8), after dividing through by the nonzero factor $(\lambda - \mu)$.

From the Lemma we also obtain the

COROLLARY. *The result of Theorem* 1 *holds also for S-L systems with periodic endpoint conditions.*

For, in this case, the contributions to the boundary term on the right side of (8) from $x = a$ and $x = b$ are equal in magnitude and opposite in sign; hence they cancel.

The orthogonality relations just proved lead to a theory of expansions of given functions as infinite linear combinations of the eigenfunctions of regular S-L systems, and of the eigenfunctions of S-L systems with periodic endpoint conditions. The resulting infinite series are called *Sturm-Liouville series*. The most important property of Sturm-Liouville series, which will be derived in Chapter XI, is that any reasonably smooth function can be expanded into an infinite linear combination of the eigenfunctions of any regular Sturm-Liouville system. Fourier series are the most familiar example of such an expansion.

In the present chapter, our main objective is to prove that the eigenfunctions of any *regular* S-L system behave like the eigenfunctions of $u'' + \lambda u = 0$ for the same endpoint conditions, in a sense to be made precise.

EXERCISES A

1. (a) Show that every solution of the Airy DE $v'' + xv = 0$ vanishes infinitely often on the positive x-axis, and at most once on the negative x-axis.

(b) Show that if $v(x)$ satisfies the Airy equation, then $u(x) = v(kx)$ satisfies $u'' + k^2xu = 0$.

(c) Show that the S-L system defined for the Airy DE by the endpoint conditions $u(0) = u(1) = 0$ has an infinite sequence of positive eigenvalues and no negative eigenvalue. (*Hint:* See Ch. II, § 4.)

2. For the S-L system defined by $u'' + \lambda u = 0$ and the endpoint conditions $u(0) = u(\pi) + u'(\pi) = 0$, show that there is an infinite sequence of eigenfunctions with distinct eigenvalues. What are its eigenvalues?

3. Determine the eigenvalues of the DE $u'' + \lambda u = 0$, for the endpoint conditions $u(0) = u(\pi)$, $u'(0) = 2u'(\pi)$.

4. (a) Show that $u = U(kr)$ satisfies (3) if and only if $U(x)$, $x = kr$, satisfies the Bessel DE $U'' + (1/x)U' + [1 - (n^2/x^2)]U = 0$.

(b) Show that if $U(x)$ and $V(x)$ satisfy the Bessel DE, and

$$U(ka) = U(kb) = V(k_1a) = V(k_1b) = 0, \qquad k \neq k_1,$$

then $\int_a^b U(kr)V(k_1r)r\,dr = 0$.

5. (a) Show that if $u(x)$ and $v(x)$ are periodic solutions of the Mathieu equation (Example 4) with period π having distinct eigenvalues, then

$$\int_0^\pi u(x)v(x)dx = 0.$$

(b) Show that, for any eigenvalue λ, the Mathieu equation has either an odd eigenfunction or an even eigenfunction.

6. Determine the eigenvalues λ such that $u^{\text{iv}} + \lambda u = 0$ admits a nontrivial eigenfunction satisfying $f(0) = f'(0) = f(\pi) = f'(\pi) = 0$.

7. Show that if $f_1(x)$ and $f_2(x)$ are eigenfunctions of Ex. 6 having distinct eigenvalues, $\lambda_1 \neq \lambda_2$, then $\int_0^\pi f_1(x)f_2(x)dx = 0$.

8. Show that the substitution $\xi = \cos^2 x$ transforms the Mathieu equation into

$$4\xi(1 - \xi)u_{\xi\xi} + (2 - 4\xi)u_\xi + (\lambda - 16\,d + 32\,d\xi)u = 0.$$

*9. Consider the boundary value problem defined by the first-order DE

$$u' + [\lambda + q(x)]u = 0, \quad q \in C, \quad q \text{ real},$$

and one nontrivial side condition $B[u] = \alpha u(a) + \alpha' u'(a) + \beta u(b) + \beta' u'(b) = 0$. Show that this problem admits at most three real eigenvalues.

3*. Physical interpretations. Sturm-Liouville systems arise typically from *vibration* problems in continuum mechanics. In physical language, they describe boundary value problems corresponding to simply harmonic *standing waves.* It is commonly assumed in physics that *any wave motion can be resolved into simply harmonic standing waves,* each of which oscillates with its proper frequency.

Though physicists commonly *assume* this result on the basis of experimental evidence and intuition, it can actually be *deduced* rigorously from the mathematical theory of wave motion as a boundary value problem in differential equations, as will be shown below.

We illustrate the physical interpretation of eigenfunctions of Sturm-Liouville systems by three classic examples.

The partial DE of a vibrating string is†

$$y_{tt} = c^2 y_{xx}, \quad \text{where} \quad c^2 = T/\rho.$$

Here y is the lateral displacement from equilibrium; T is the tension and ρ the density of the string, both assumed constant. Simply harmonic standing waves are defined by the separation of variables

$$y(x,t) = u(x) \cos k(t - t_0).$$

For $y(x,t)$ to satisfy the vibrating string equation $y_{tt} = c^2 y_{xx}$, it is necessary and sufficient that $u'' + \lambda u = 0$, $\lambda = k^2/c^2$.

For the vibrating string, it is natural physically to have *fixed endpoints*, so that $y(a,t) = y(b,t) = 0$. This makes $u(a) = u(b) = 0$, and leads to the S-L problem of Example 1. The eigenvalue belonging to each eigenfunction is proportional to the *squared frequency* $k^2/4\pi^2$. This relation, combined with the analogy between mechanical and electromagnetic waves, has led mathematicians to call the set of eigenvalues the *spectrum* of an S-L system.

Another physical interpretation of S-L systems is furnished by the longitudinal vibrations of an *elastic bar* of local stiffness $p(x)$ and density $\rho(x)$. The mean longitudinal displacement $v(x,t)$ of the section of such a bar from its equilibrium position x satisfies the wave equation

$$\rho(x) \frac{\partial^2 v}{\partial t^2} = \frac{\partial}{\partial x}\left[p(x) \frac{\partial v}{\partial x}\right].$$

The *simple harmonic* vibrations (the *normal modes* of vibration) given by the separation of variables

$$v = u(x) \cos k(t - t_0),$$

are the solutions of the Sturm-Liouville equation

$$\frac{d}{dx}\left[p(x) \frac{du}{dx}\right] + k^2 \rho(x) u = 0.$$

This is the special case $q = 0$ of (1), with $\lambda = k^2$.

For a finite bar, extending over the interval $a \leqq x \leqq b$, various physical boundary conditions arise naturally:

$$\begin{aligned} u(a) = u(b) &= 0 && \text{(rigidly fixed ends)},\\ u'(a) = u'(b) &= 0 && \text{(free ends)},\\ u'(a) + \alpha u(a) = u'(b) + \beta u(b) &= 0 && \text{(elastically held ends)},\\ u(a) = u(b), \quad u'(a) &= u'(b) && \text{(periodic constraints)}. \end{aligned}$$

Each of these endpoint conditions on u implies a corresponding condition on $v(x,t)$, with d/dx replaced by $\partial/\partial x$. The natural frequencies of longi-

†Widder, pp. 344–350. In this section, subscript letters denote differentiation with respect to the variable indicated.

tudinal vibration (musical fundamental tone and overtones) of a bar, whose ends are held in each of the ways described, are thus the solutions of the S-L systems defined by (1) and the appropriate conditions above. Finally, the partial DE of a *vibrating membrane* is

$$w_{tt} = c^2(w_{xx} + w_{yy}) = c^2(w_{rr} + r^{-1}w_r + r^{-2}w_{\theta\theta}),$$

where r, θ denote polar coordinates. A basis of standing wave solutions can be found by trying the separation of variables

$$w(r,\theta,t) = u(r)\begin{Bmatrix}\cos\\ \cdot\\ \sin\end{Bmatrix} n\theta \cos k(t - t_0).$$

For w to satisfy the membrane equation, it is necessary and sufficient that u be a solution of the Bessel equation (3). The singularity at $r = 0$ of the Bessel equation is associated with the singularity in polar coordinates at the origin.

If the membrane is a circular disc of radius a (vibrating drumhead), then the physically natural boundary conditions are $u(a) = 0$, and $u(0)$ nonsingular. The latter condition characterizes the *Bessel functions* among other solutions of the Bessel equation, up to a constant normalizing factor.

EXERCISES B

1. Show that if $U_n(x)$ satisfies the Bessel equation of order n (Ex. A4), then $\phi = U_n(kr) \sin n\theta$ and $U_n(kr) \cos n\theta$ satisfy the Helmholtz equation $\nabla^2\phi + k^2\phi = 0$, for polar coordinates in the plane.

2. The partial DE of a vibrating membrane is $\nabla^2 U + k^2 U = 0$. Using Ex. 1, show that this equation has solutions satisfying $U(x,y) \equiv 0$ on $x^2 + y^2 = 1$, for all numbers k_{mn} such that $J_n(k_{mn}) = 0$.

3. A string of density $\frac{1}{100} + \frac{1}{1000} \cos 2x$ grams/cm is stretched taut between pegs at $x = -\pi/2$ and $x = \pi/2$, under a tension of 2 Kg. Determine its natural frequencies, in cycles per second.

4. For the Bessel DE $(xu')' + \lambda xu = 0$, with the endpoint conditions that $u(1) = 0$ and u is bounded on $0 < x \leqq 1$, show that the first five eigenvalues are approximately $\lambda_1 = 5.78$, $\lambda_2 = 30.5$, $\lambda_3 = 74.9$, $\lambda_4 = 139$, and $\lambda_5 = 223$. (*Hint:* Consult a table of zeros of $J_0(x)$.)

5. A vibrating reed, with one clamped end and one free end, executes simple harmonic vibrations with transverse displacement $y(x,t) = u(x) \cos kt$ if and only if $u^{\text{iv}} = k^2 u$, $u(0) = u'(0) = 0$, and $u''(L) = u'''(L) = 0$. Find the characteristic frequencies $2\pi/k$. (*Hint:* Consider the ultraspherical polynomials of Ch. IX, § 11.)

6. Show that the general solution of the Airy DE is $x^{1/2}U_{1/3}(2x^{3/2}/3)$, where $U_{1/3}$ is the general solution of the Bessel DE of order $\frac{1}{3}$.

7. Show that the function $J_{d/c}(e^{cx}\sqrt{b}/c)$ satisfies the DE $u'' + (be^{2cx} - d^2)u = 0$.

8. Show that the function $xJ_{d/c}(e^{c/x}\sqrt{b}/c)$ satisfies the DE

$$u'' + x^{-4}(be^{2c/x} - d^2) = 0.$$

*9. Show that the general solution of the DE

$$v'' + \left(a^2b^2x^{2a-2} + \frac{1-4n^2a^2}{4x^2}\right)v = 0$$

is the function $v(x) = \sqrt{x}\,U(bx^a)$, where U is the general solution of the Bessel DE of order n.

4. Singular systems. An S-L equation (1) can be given on a finite, semi-infinite, or infinite interval I. In the finite case I may include neither, one, or both endpoints. The exclusion of an endpoint a may be necessary when $\lim_{x\to a} p(x) = 0$, $\lim_{x\to a} \rho(x) = 0$, or when any one of the functions p, q, ρ is singular at a.

Only when I is a closed, finite interval $a \leqq x \leqq b$ can an S-L equation be associated with a *regular* S-L system. When I is semi-infinite or infinite, or if I is finite and p or ρ vanishes at one or both endpoints, or q is discontinuous there, one cannot obtain from (1) any regular S-L system. In any such case, the given S-L equation (1) is called *singular*.

One can obtain *singular S-L systems* from singular S-L equations by imposing suitable homogeneous linear endpoint conditions. These conditions cannot always be described by formulas like (2). For example, the condition that u be bounded near a singular endpoint is a common boundary condition defining a singular S-L system.

EXAMPLE 5. The Legendre DE

$$((1-x^2)u')' + \lambda u = 0, \qquad -1 < x < 1, \tag{9}$$

together with the condition that a solution u be *bounded* in the interval, is an example of a singular S-L system. As shown in Ch. III, § 2, the *Legendre polynomials* $P_n(x)$ are real eigenfunctions of this S-L system belonging to the eigenvalues $\lambda_n = n(n+1)$.

EXAMPLE 6. For fixed n, the Bessel equation of Example 2,

$$\frac{d}{dr}\left[r\frac{du}{dr}\right] + \left(k^2r - \frac{n^2}{r}\right)u = 0, \qquad 0 < r \leqq a,$$

is a singular S-L equation with $p = \rho = r$, $\lambda = k^2$, and $q = n^2/r$. A singular S-L system is obtained for any $a > 0$ by imposing the endpoint conditions $u(a) = 0$, and $u(r)$ bounded as $r \to 0$.

The eigenfunctions of the preceding singular S-L systems are the Bessel functions $J_n(k_jr)$, where k_ja is the j-th zero of the Bessel function $J_n(x)$ of order n. It has been shown in Ch. II, § 4, that $J_n(x)$ has infinitely many zeros; it follows that the singular S-L system just defined has infinitely many eigenvalues.

The eigenfunctions of singular S-L systems are also orthogonal, provided they are *square-integrable*, in the following sense.

DEFINITION. *A real-valued function f is* square-integrable *on the interval I relative to a given weight function* $\rho(x) > 0$ *when*

$$\int_I f^2(x)\rho(x)dx < +\infty. \tag{10}$$

When the weight function ρ is identically equal to 1, one says simply that the function f is *square-integrable* on the interval I.

The *Schwarz inequality* holds† for square-integrable functions:

$$\left(\int_I |f(x)g(x)|\rho(x)dx\right)^2 \leqq \int_I f^2(x)\rho(x)dx \int_I g^2(x)\rho(x)dx. \tag{11}$$

This inequality implies in particular that the product of two square-integrable functions is an integrable function relative to the weight function ρ, that is, the integral on the left of (11) is finite.

The right side of the boundary term in (8) vanishes in the limit, for any endpoint conditions which imply

$$\lim_{\alpha\downarrow a,\beta\uparrow b} p(x)[u(x)v'(x) - v(x)u'(x)]\,|_{x=\alpha}^{\beta} = 0. \tag{12}$$

The conditions $p(a) = p(b) = 0$ and $u'(x)$ bounded on a finite interval have this property, for example.

When (12) holds, one obtains from (8) the identity

$$(\lambda - \mu)\int_a^b \rho(x)u(x)v(x)dx = 0$$

for any two square-integrable eigenfunctions u and v with eigenvalues λ and μ. The integral here may be an improper integral. If $\lambda \neq \mu$, this implies, as in the proof of the lemma of § 2, that u and v are orthogonal. This proves

THEOREM 2. *Square-integrable eigenfunctions u and v belonging to different eigenvalues of a singular S-L system are orthogonal with weight* ρ *whenever the boundary term vanishes, as in* (12).

Applying this result to Example 5, we obtain the orthogonality relation for the Legendre polynomials

$$\int_{-1}^{1} P_m(x)P_n(x)dx = 0, \qquad m \neq n, \tag{13}$$

after verifying that the boundary term vanishes. Applying it to the Bessel equation, we obtain the orthogonality relations for Bessel functions

$$\int_0^a xJ_n(k_i x)J_n(k_j x)dx = 0, \qquad k_i \neq k_j, \tag{14}$$

if $J_n(k_i a) = J_n(k_j a) = 0$.

†Birkhoff and Mac Lane, p. 190.

EXAMPLE 7. The *Hermite DE* is

$$u'' - 2xu' + \lambda u = 0, \qquad -\infty < x < +\infty, \tag{15}$$

as in Ch. III, § 2. Using the recursion formula

$$a_{k+2} = (2k - \lambda)a_k/(k+1)(k+2), \qquad k = 0, 1, 2, \cdots \tag{16}$$

of Ch. III, (9′), one obtains a polynomial solution of degree n for $\lambda = 2n$. These polynomials are commonly normalized by the condition that $a_n = 2^n$ (and $a_{n-1} = 0$); this defines the *Hermite polynomials* $H_n(x)$. For example, $H_0(x) = 1$, $H_1(x) = 2x$, $H_2(x) = 4x^2 - 2$, etc. Evidently, $H_n(x)$ is an even function for even n, and an odd function for odd n.

The Hermite DE is not an S-L equation, because it is not self-adjoint. Making the substitution $y = e^{-x^2/2}u$ in (15), one obtains the following equivalent self-adjoint S-L equation for the *Hermite functions* $y(x)$:

$$y'' + [\lambda - (x^2 - 1)]y = 0, \qquad -\infty < x < \infty, \tag{17}$$

among whose solutions for $\lambda = 2n$ are the functions $e^{-x^2/2}H_n(x)$; these functions are square-integrable and tend to zero as $x \to \pm\infty$.

That is, the functions $\phi_n(x) = e^{-x^2/2}H_n(x)$ are eigenfunctions for the singular S-L system defined by (17) and by the endpoint condition that a solution $y(x)$ shall tend to zero as $x \to \pm\infty$. We shall now derive the orthogonality relations for the Hermite polynomials

$$\int_{-\infty}^{\infty} H_m(x)H_n(x)e^{-x^2}\,dx = 0, \qquad m \neq n. \tag{18}$$

For, substituting into the identity (8), we obtain

$$2(m-n)\int_{-a}^{a} H_m(x)H_n(x)e^{-x^2}dx = [\phi_m(x)\phi_n'(x) - \phi_m'(x)\phi_n(x)]_{x=-a}^{x=a}.$$

Since the boundary terms are e^{-x^2} times a polynomial in x, and

$$\lim_{x\to+\infty} x^n e^{-x^2} = 0 \tag{19}$$

for all n, the boundary term vanishes in the limit, as in (12).

EXERCISES C

1. (a) Prove the orthogonality relations for the Bessel functions

$$\int_0^L xJ_n(\alpha x)J_n(\beta x)dx = 0, \quad \text{if} \quad J_n'(\alpha L) = J_n'(\beta L) = 0 \tag{*}$$

for any nonnegative integer n.

(b) Prove the equality (*), if $\alpha J_n'(\alpha L)J_n(\beta L) = \beta J_n'(\beta L)J_n(\alpha L)$.

(c) For what negative values of n do the relations (*) hold?

2. Show that the Legendre polynomials (and their constant multiples) are the only solutions of the Legendre DE which are bounded on $(-1,1)$.

3. Show that the S-L system $[(x-a)(b-x)u']' + \lambda u = 0$, $a < b$, with $u(x)$ bounded on $a < x < b$ has the eigenvalues $\lambda = 4n(n+1)/(b-a)^2$. Describe the eigenfunctions.

4. (a) (Laguerre polynomials) Consider the singular S-L system

$$(xe^{-x}u')' + \lambda e^{-x}u = 0 \quad \text{on} \quad 0 < x < +\infty,$$

with endpoint conditions that $u(0^+)$ is bounded and that $e^{-x}u(x) \to 0$ as $x \to +\infty$. Show that the values $\lambda = n$ give polynomial eigenfunctions.

(b) Show that the preceding system has no other polynomial eigenfunctions. (*Hint:* Obtain the power series expansion of the general solution of the DE.)

5. Show that the eigenvalues of the singular S-L system defined by

$$\frac{d}{dx}\left[(1 - x^2)^{\alpha+1}\frac{du}{dx}\right] + \lambda(1 - x^2)^{\alpha}u = 0, \qquad \alpha > -1,$$

and the condition of being bounded on $(-1,1)$, are $\lambda_n = n\,(n + 2\alpha)$.

5. Prüfer substitution. We now develop a powerful method for the study of the solutions of a self-adjoint second-order linear DE

$$\frac{d}{dx}\left[P(x)\frac{du}{dx}\right] + Q(x)u = 0, \qquad a < x < b, \tag{20}$$

where $P(x) > 0$ is of class $\mathcal{C}^1$ and Q is continuous. One often wants to find out how much the solutions of (20) *oscillate* on the interval under consideration, that is, the number of zeros they have for $a < x < b$. When $P(x) \equiv 1$, one can apply the Sturm Comparison Theorem of Ch. II, § 4. This theorem will now be extended to more general equations of the form (20).

Prüfer had the idea of replacing (20) by an equivalent system of two first-order DE's for the two unknown functions u and Pu', and then changing to polar coordinates in the (Pu',u)-plane. In other words, he introduced the *Prüfer substitution*

$$P(x)u'(x) = r(x)\cos\theta(x); \qquad u(x) = r(x)\sin\theta(x). \tag{21}$$

The new dependent variables r and θ are defined by the formulas

$$r^2 = u^2 + P^2u'^2, \qquad \theta = \arctan\,(u/Pu'). \tag{21'}$$

r is called the *amplitude* and θ the *phase* variable. When $r \neq 0$, the correspondences $(Pu',u) \rightleftharpoons (r,u)$ defined by (21) are *analytic*, with nonvanishing Jacobian.

For nontrivial solutions, r is always positive, since if $u(x) = u'(x) = 0$ for a given x, then u would be the trivial solution $u \equiv 0$, by the Uniqueness Theorem of Ch. II, § 2.

We now derive an equivalent system of DE's for $r(x)$ and $\theta(x)$. Differentiating the relation† $\cot\theta = Pu'/u$, we get

$$-\csc^2\theta\,\frac{d\theta}{dx} = \frac{(Pu')'}{u} - \frac{Pu'^2}{u^2} = -Q(x) - \frac{1}{P}\cot^2\theta.$$

†When $\theta \equiv 0 \pmod{\pi}$, the relation is not defined. But the final equations (22)–(23) can still be derived by differentiating the relation $\tan\theta = u/Pu'$.

Multiplying through by $-\sin^2\theta$, this expression becomes

$$\frac{d\theta}{dx} = Q(x)\sin^2\theta + \frac{1}{P(x)}\cos^2\theta = F(x,\theta). \tag{22}$$

Differentiating $r^2 = (Pu')^2 + u^2$ and simplifying, we obtain

$$\frac{dr}{dx} = \left[\frac{1}{P(x)} - Q(x)\right] r\sin\theta\cos\theta = \tfrac{1}{2}\left[\frac{1}{P(x)} - Q(x)\right] r\sin 2\theta. \tag{23}$$

The system (22)–(23) is equivalent to the DE (20), in the sense that every nontrivial solution of the system defines a unique solution of the DE by the Prüfer substitution (21), and conversely. This system is called the *Prüfer system* associated with the self-adjoint DE (20).

The DE (22) of the Prüfer system is a first-order DE in θ,x alone, not containing the other dependent variable r, and it satisfies a Lipschitz condition with Lipschitz constant

$$L = \sup_{a<x<b}\left|\frac{\partial F}{\partial\theta}\right| \leqq \sup_{a<x<b}|Q(x)| + \sup_{a<x<b}\frac{1}{|P(x)|}.$$

The constant L is finite in any closed interval in which Q and P are continuous. Hence the existence and uniqueness theorems of Chapter V are applicable, and show that the DE (22) has a unique solution $\theta(x)$ for any initial value $\theta(a) = \gamma$, provided P and Q are continuous at a.

Knowing $\theta(x)$, $r(x)$ is given by (23) after a quadrature:

$$r = K\exp\left\{\tfrac{1}{2}\int_a^x\left[\frac{1}{P(t)} - Q(t)\right]\sin 2\theta\,dt\right\}, \tag{23'}$$

where $K = r(a)$. Each solution of the Prüfer system (22)–(23) depends on two constants: the initial *amplitude* $K = r(a)$, and the initial *phase* $\gamma = \theta(a)$. Changing the constant K just multiplies a solution $u(x)$ by a constant factor; thus the zeros of any solution u of (20) can be located by studying only the DE (22).

6. Sturm Comparison Theorem. The *zeros* of any solution $u(x)$ of the DE (20) occur where the phase function $\theta(x)$ in the Prüfer substitution (21) assumes the values $0, \pm\pi, \pm 2\pi, \cdots$, that is, at all points x where $\sin\theta(x) = 0$. At each of these points $\cos^2\theta = 1$ and $d\theta/dx$ is positive, by (22) (recall that $P(x) > 0$). Geometrically, this means that the curve $(P(x)u'(x), u(x))$ in the (Pu',u)-plane corresponding to a solution u of the DE can only cross the Pu'-axis $\theta = n\pi$ counterclockwise.

Now compare the DE (22) with a DE of the same form $d\theta/dx = F_1(x,\theta)$ with coefficients $Q_1(x) \geqq Q(x)$ and $P_1(x) \leqq P(x)$:

$$\frac{d\theta}{dx} = Q_1(x)\sin^2\theta + \frac{1}{P_1(x)}\cos^2\theta = F_1(x,\theta).$$

If $Q_1(x) \geqq Q(x)$ and $P_1(x) \leqq P(x)$ in an interval I, then $F_1(x,\theta) \geqq F(x,\theta)$ there. By the Comparison Theorem of Ch. I, § 11, we conclude that if $\theta_1(x)$ is a solution of the second DE whose initial value satisfies $\theta_1(a) \geqq \theta(a)$, and $\theta(x)$ is a solution of (22), then $\theta_1(x) \geqq \theta(x)$ for $a \leqq x \leqq b$. Furthermore $\theta_1(x) = \theta(x)$ only when $P(x) \equiv P_1(x)$ and $Q(x) \equiv Q_1(x)$ (cf. Ch. I, § 11, Corollary 1). Therefore, if $\sin \theta(a) = 0$, the number of zeros of $\sin \theta_1(x)$ for $a < x < b$ is greater than the number of zeros of $\sin \theta(x)$, except when $P \equiv P_1$ and $Q \equiv Q_1$, when it is equal. This completes the proof of

THEOREM 3 (Sturm Comparison Theorem). *Let $P(x) \geqq P_1(x) > 0$ and $Q_1(x) \geqq Q(x)$ in the DE's*

$$(24) \quad \frac{d}{dx}\left(P(x)\frac{du}{dx}\right) + Q(x)u = 0, \quad \frac{d}{dx}\left(P_1(x)\frac{du_1}{dx}\right) + Q_1(x)u_1 = 0.$$

Then between any two zeros of a nontrivial solution $u(x)$ of the first DE there lies at least one zero of every solution of the second DE, except in the trivial case when $u(x) \equiv cu_1(x)$, $P(x) \equiv P_1(x)$, and $Q(x) \equiv Q_1(x)$.

Sturm's Separation Theorem of Ch. II, § 4 is obtained as a corollary by comparing two linearly independent solutions of the same DE.

A shortened, if somewhat imprecise, summary which is easily remembered is this: as Q increases and P decreases, the number of zeros of every solution increases.

Maxima and minima. For the self-adjoint DE (20), the inequality $Q(x) > 0$ implies that

$$d\theta/dx > 0 \quad \text{if} \quad \theta = (n + \tfrac{1}{2})\pi.$$

For, in (22), $\cos \theta = 0$ and $\sin \theta = 1$ if $\theta = (n + \frac{1}{2})\pi$. Since $\cos \theta = 0$ if and only if $u' = 0$, it follows that if $Q(x)$ is positive, any nontrivial solution of (20) has exactly one maximum or minimum between successive zeros.

7. Oscillation Theorem. We now consider the variation with λ in the number of zeros of the eigenfunctions of a regular S-L system (1)–(2). Setting $P(x) = p(x)$ and $Q(x) = \lambda\rho(x) - q(x)$ in (1), we obtain (20). Since $u = 0$ if and only if $\sin \theta = 0$ in (21), the zeros of any solution of (1) are the points where $\theta = 0, \pm\pi, \pm 2\pi, \cdots, \pm n\pi, \cdots$, θ being a solution of the associated Prüfer equation

$$(25) \quad \frac{d\theta}{dx} = [\lambda\rho(x) - q(x)]\sin^2\theta + \frac{1}{p(x)}\cos^2\theta, \qquad a \leqq x \leqq b.$$

Here $p(x) > 0$, $\rho(x) > 0$ for $a \leqq x \leqq b$.

We now fix γ, and denote by $\theta(x,\lambda)$ the solution of (25) which satisfies an initial condition $\theta(a,\lambda) = \gamma$ for all λ, where γ is defined by the conditions†

$$(25') \quad \tan \gamma = u(a)/p(a)u'(a) = -\alpha'/p(a)\alpha, \qquad 0 \leqq \gamma < \pi,\ \alpha = 0.$$

†We have assumed $\alpha \neq 0$. When $\alpha = 0$, set $\gamma = \pi/2$.

The constants α and α' come from the initial condition $\alpha u(a) + \alpha' u'(a) = 0$. For fixed γ, the function $\theta(x,\lambda)$ is defined on the domain $a \leqq x \leqq b$, $-\infty < \lambda < \infty$; we will consider its behavior there.

Applying the Comparison Theorem of Ch. I, § 11 (and especially Corollary 1 there) to (25), we obtain

LEMMA 1. *For fixed $x > a$, the function $\theta(x,\lambda)$ is a strictly increasing function of the variable λ.*

LEMMA 2. *Suppose that for some $x_n > a$, $\theta(x_n,\lambda) = n\pi$, where $n \geqq 0$ is an integer. Then $\theta(x,\lambda) > n\pi$ for all $x > x_n$.*

Proof. If x_n is any point where $\theta(x_n,\lambda) = n\pi$, then, by the DE (25), we have $d\theta(x_n,\lambda)/dx_n = 1/p(x_n) > 0$. Thus the function $\theta = \theta(x_n,\lambda)$, considered as a function of x_n, is increasing where it crosses the line $\theta = n\pi$, as shown in Figure X-1. Hence $\theta(x,\lambda)$ stays above this line for $x > x_n$, q.e.d.

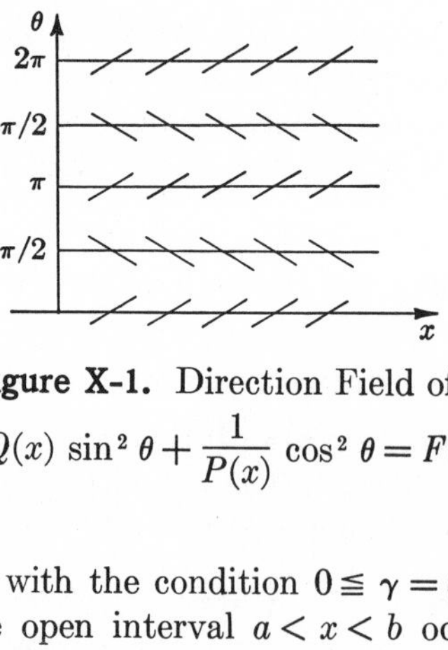

Figure X-1. Direction Field of

$$\frac{d\theta}{dx} = Q(x) \sin^2 \theta + \frac{1}{P(x)} \cos^2 \theta = F(x,\theta)$$

Lemma 2, combined with the condition $0 \leqq \gamma = \theta(a,\lambda) < \pi$, makes the first zero of $u(x)$ in the open interval $a < x < b$ occur where $\theta = \pi$, and the n-th zero where $\theta = n\pi$.

Our next aim is to show that, for fixed x, $\theta(x,\lambda) \to \infty$ as $\lambda \to \infty$.

In view of Lemma 2, we will have shown that $\lim_{\lambda\to\infty} \theta(x,\lambda) = \infty$ for each x if we can show that, for every integer $n > 0$, we can find a number $x_n < x$ such that $\theta(x_n,\lambda) = n\pi$ for sufficiently large λ. Stated in different terms, let $x_n(\lambda)$ be the smallest x such that $\theta(x,\lambda) = n\pi$. Then all we need to show is that $x_n(\lambda)$ exists for large λ and $\lim_{\lambda\to\infty} x_n(\lambda) = a$. This is done in the following lemma.

LEMMA 3. *For a given fixed positive integer n, the function $x_n(\lambda)$ is defined for sufficiently large λ and continuous. It is a decreasing function of λ, and $\lim_{\lambda\to\infty} x_n(\lambda) = a$.*

Proof. By Theorem 3 of Chapter V, the function $\theta(x,\lambda)$ is a continuous function of both variables x and λ for $a \leqq x \leqq b$ and $-\infty < \lambda < \infty$. We shall first prove that if the function $x_n(\lambda)$ is well-defined, that is, if $\theta(x,\lambda) = n\pi$ for some x, then $x_n(\lambda)$ is a monotonic decreasing function of λ. To prove this result, it suffices to prove that $\theta(x,\lambda)$ is an increasing function of λ. But this is the conclusion of Lemma 1.

We now show that, for fixed n, the function $x_n(\lambda)$ is well-defined for large enough λ. This amounts to saying that, for large enough λ, there is an x in the interval $a \leqq x \leqq b$ for which $\theta(x,\lambda) = n\pi$. We can translate this statement into an equivalent statement for the solutions of the DE (1), using (21). It is equivalent to saying that every nontrivial solution of (1) has at least n zeros in the interval $a < x < b$, since $\theta(x,\lambda)$, being a continuous function of x, must take all values between $\theta(a,\lambda) = \gamma < \pi$ and $n\pi$.

Now let q_M and p_M be the maxima of $q(x)$ and $p(x)$, respectively, and ρ_m be the minimum of $\rho(x)$ for $a \leqq x \leqq b$. A solution of the DE

$$p_M u'' + (\lambda\rho_m - q_M)u = 0, \qquad \lambda > q_M/\rho_m, \tag{26}$$

is the function $u_1(x) = \sin kx$, where $k^2 = (\lambda\rho_m - q_M)/p_M$. The successive zeros of this function are spaced at a distance $\pi\sqrt{p_M/(\lambda\rho_m - q_M)}$ apart. By the Sturm Comparison Theorem (Theorem 3 above), any nontrivial solution $u(x)$ of the Sturm-Liouville equation (1) must have at least one zero between any two zeros of the function $u_1(x)$. Since $u_1(x)$ has n zeros on (a,b) when λ is sufficiently large, it follows that $u(x)$ has at least n zeros, and therefore that $\theta(x,\lambda)$ takes the value $n\pi$ for sufficiently large λ, as we wanted to show.

The number $x_n(\lambda)$ falls between the $(n-1)$-st and the n-th zero of $u_1(x)$, and both these zeros tend to a as $\lambda \to \infty$. Therefore $x_n(\lambda) \to a$ as $\lambda \to \infty$, q.e.d.

We are now ready to prove the following result.

THEOREM 4 (Oscillation Theorem). *The solution $\theta(x;\lambda)$ of the DE* (25) *satisfying the initial condition $\theta(a,\lambda) = \gamma < \pi$ for all λ is a continuous and strictly increasing function of λ for fixed x on $a < x \leqq b$. Moreover,*

$$\lim_{\lambda\to\infty} \theta(x;\lambda) = \infty; \qquad \lim_{\lambda\to-\infty} \theta(x;\lambda) = 0, \tag{27}$$

for $a < x \leqq b$.

The first sentence was proved in Lemmas 1–3. The first formula of (27) was proved above.

We shall now prove the second formula of (27). Choose numbers $\gamma < \gamma_1 < \pi$ and $\epsilon > 0$. The slope of the segment in the (x,θ)-plane joining the points (a,γ_1) and (x_1,ϵ), where $a < x_1 \leqq b$, equals $(\epsilon - \gamma_1)/(x_1 - a)$.

For a point (x, θ) on this segment the slope of $\theta(x,\lambda)$, as given by (25), will be less than the slope of the segment for large negative λ. Therefore the function $\theta(x,\lambda)$ will lie below the segment for $a \leqq x \leqq b$, for all sufficiently large negative λ. We conclude that $\theta(x_1,\lambda) < \epsilon$ for sufficiently large negative λ. Since, by Lemma 2, $\theta(x_1,\lambda) > 0$, it follows that $|\theta(x_1,\lambda)| < \epsilon$. Since ϵ and x_1 are arbitrary, the proof is complete.

We now derive an estimate for the position of the zeros of the solutions of a regular S-L equation (1) by comparing it with equation (26) and with

$$p_m u'' + (\lambda \rho_M - q_m)u = 0 \tag{28}$$

where p_m and q_m are the minima of $p(x)$ and $q(x)$, and ρ_M the maximum of $\rho(x)$ for $a \leqq x \leqq b$.

Consider solutions of (26) and (28) for which $u(a)/p(a)u'(a) = \tan \gamma$. The zeros of these solutions can be determined by inspection. They are $(n\pi - \gamma)/\sqrt{(\lambda\rho_m - q_M)/p_M}$ and $(n\pi - \gamma)/\sqrt{(\lambda\rho_M - q_m)/p_m}$, respectively. Applying the Sturm Comparison Theorem, we obtain the

COROLLARY. *Let x_n be the n-th zero of a nontrivial solution of the S-L equation* (1). *Then*

$$\sqrt{\frac{p_m}{\lambda\rho_M - q_m}} \leqq \frac{x_n - a}{n\pi - \gamma} \leqq \sqrt{\frac{p_M}{\lambda\rho_m - q_M}}. \tag{29}$$

The preceding results have been proved under the assumption that $\alpha \neq 0$ in (2). If $\alpha = 0$, one can use the same argument when $\beta \neq 0$, by changing the independent variable to $t = a + b - x$. If $\alpha = \beta = 0$, one can still prove the above results with $\gamma = \pi/2$.

EXERCISES D

1. For $u'' + [\lambda - q(x)]u = 0$, with separated endpoint conditions (2), show that all eigenvalues are positive if $q(x) > 0$, $\alpha\alpha' < 0$, and $\beta\beta' > 0$.

2. Show that the number of negative eigenvalues of a regular S-L system is always finite, and is at most one if $q(x) > 0$.

3. Show that any infinite sequence of eigenvalues of a regular S-L system is unbounded.

4. Find all solutions of the DE $\theta' = A \sin^2 \theta + B \cos^2 \theta$, where A and B are positive constants. (*Hint:* Relate it to a Prüfer system.)

5. Show that at all points x where a solution $u(x)$ of $(Pu')' + Qu = 0$ has a minimum or a maximum, $d\theta/dx = Q(x)$.

6. Extend the Sturm Oscillation Theorem to the case where $\alpha = \beta = 0$ in (2).

7. Derive Theorem 3 from the Sturm Comparison Theorem of Chapter II by introducing the new dependent variables $t = \int_a^x ds/P(s)$ and $t_1 = \int_a^x ds/P_1(s)$.

8. For any solution of $u'' + q(x)u = 0$, $q(x) < 0$, show that the product $u(x)u'(x)$ is an increasing function. Infer that a nontrivial solution can have at most one zero.

9. Show that if $q(x) < 0$ in $u'' + p(x)u' + q(x)u = 0$, then no nontrivial solution of the DE can have more than one zero.

10. (a) Show that $J_n(x)$ is increasing for $0 < x \leqq |n|$. (*Hint:* Use the identity $x(xJ_n')' \equiv (n^2 - x^2)J_n$.)

(b) Prove that, if x_0 is the first positive zero of J_n, and y_0 that of J_n', then

$$|n| \leqq y_0 < x_0.$$

*11. (a) Let $u(x)$ be a solution of $(Pu')' + Qu = 0$, where $P > 0$, $P' > 0$, $Q > 0$, and $(P'/Q)' > 1$. Show that the zeros of u, u', u'' follow one another cyclically.

(b) Infer that the zeros of J_n, J_{n+1}, J_{n+2} follow one another cyclically.

12. (Sturm Convexity Theorem) In $u'' + Q(x)u = 0$, let $Q(x)$ be increasing. Show that $x_n - x_{n-1} < x_{n+1} - x_n$, where $\{x_n\}$ is the sequence of successive zeros of a nontrivial solution u.

13. For the modified Bessel function $I_0(y) = J_0(iy)$, without considering its Taylor series, show that $I_0'(y) > 0$ and $1 < I_0(y) < \cosh y$ for all $y > 0$.

14. Show that, in the Sturm Oscillation Theorem, $\theta(x,\lambda) \to \infty$ as $\lambda \to \infty$, uniformly in any subinterval $a' \leqq x \leqq b$, $a' > a$.

15. Show that $\theta(x,\lambda) \to 0$ as $\lambda \to -\infty$, uniformly in any subinterval $a' \leqq x \leqq b$, $a' > a$.

8. Sequence of eigenfunctions. The existence of an infinite sequence of eigenfunctions of a regular S-L system consisting of the DE (1) together with the separated endpoint conditions (2), that is, the conditions

$$(30) \qquad A[u] = \alpha u(a) + \alpha' u'(a) = 0, \qquad B[u] = \beta u(b) + \beta' u'(b) = 0,$$

will now be proved.

We first transform these endpoint conditions into equivalent endpoint conditions for the phase function $\theta(x,\lambda)$ of the Prüfer system (22)–(23) associated with the DE (1). If $\alpha \neq 0$, then the function $\theta(x,\lambda)$ must satisfy the initial condition $\theta(a,\lambda) = \gamma$, where γ is the smallest positive number $0 \leqq \gamma < \pi$ such that $p(a) \tan \gamma = -\alpha'/\alpha$. When $\alpha = 0$, we choose $\gamma = \pi/2$. Similarly, we choose $0 < \delta \leqq \pi$ so that $\tan \delta = -\beta'/\beta p(b)$.

A solution $u(x)$ of the DE (1) for $a \leqq x \leqq b$ is an eigenfunction of the regular S-L problem obtained by imposing the endpoint conditions (30) if and only if, for the corresponding phase function defined by (21′), we have

$$(31) \quad \theta(a,\lambda) = \gamma, \ \theta(b,\lambda) = \delta + n\pi, \ n = 0, 1, 2, \cdots, \ 0 \leqq \gamma < \pi, \ 0 < \delta \leqq \pi.$$

Clearly, any value of λ for which conditions (31) are satisfied is an eigenvalue of the given regular S-L system, and conversely. Let $\theta(x,\lambda)$ be the solution of (25) for the initial condition $\theta(a,\lambda) = \gamma$. Figure X-2 shows graphs of the function $\theta = \theta(x,\lambda)$ for various values of the parameter λ.

Since $\theta(b,\lambda)$ is an increasing function of λ, and $\theta(b,\lambda) > 0$ by Lemma 2 of § 7, as λ increases from $-\infty$ there is a first value λ_0 for which the second

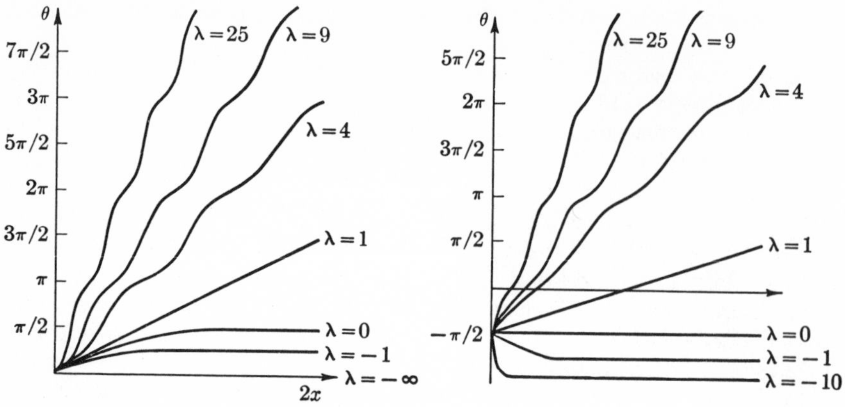

Figure X-2. $\theta(x,\lambda)$ for $u''+\lambda u=0$

of the conditions (31) is satisfied. For this eigenvalue, we have $\theta(b,\lambda_0)=\delta$. As λ increases, there is an infinite sequence of λ_n for which the second boundary condition is satisfied, namely those for which $\theta(b,\lambda_n)=\delta+n\pi$ for some nonnegative integer n. Each of these values gives an eigenfunction

$$u_n(x)=r(x)\sin\theta(x,\lambda_n) \tag{32}$$

of the S-L system. Furthermore, the eigenfunction belonging to λ_n has exactly n zeros in the interval $a\leqq x\leqq b$, by Theorem 4. This proves all but the last statement of the following theorem.

THEOREM 5. *Any regular S-L system has an infinite sequence of real eigenvalues* $\lambda_0<\lambda_1<\lambda_2<\cdots$, *with* $\lim_{n\to\infty}\lambda_n=\infty$. *The eigenfunction* $u_n(x)$ *belonging to the eigenvalue* λ_n *has exactly* n *zeros in the interval* $a<x<b$, *and is uniquely determined up to a constant factor.*

Only the last assertion wants verification. Any two solutions of (1) which satisfy the same initial condition $\alpha u(a)+\alpha' u'(a)=0$ are linearly dependent, by the Uniqueness Theorem of Ch. II, § 2.

EXERCISES E

1. Show that, for a regular S-L system, if $q(x)$ is increased to $q_1(x)>q(x)$, then each n-th eigenvalue of the new system is smaller than that of the old.
2. Show that, for a regular S-L system, if $\rho(x)$ is increased to $\rho_1(x)>\rho(x)$, then all positive eigenvalues decrease and all negative eigenvalues increase.
3. Derive an analog of the Prüfer system for the variables defined by

$$u=R\cos\phi, \qquad Pu'=R\sin\phi.$$

4. For regular S-L systems with two sets of endpoint conditions, (30) and

$$\alpha_1 u(a) + \alpha_1' u'(a) = 0, \qquad \beta u(b) + \beta' u'(b) = 0,$$

show that if $\alpha_1'/\alpha_1 < \alpha'/\alpha$, then the eigenvalues of the second system are smaller than the corresponding eigenvalues of the first.

5. (a) Given $(Pu')' + Qu = 0$ and $(P_1 v')' + Q_1 v = 0$, $P_1(x) > 0$, $Q_1(x)$ continuous, establish *Picone's identity*

$$\int_a^b (Q_1(x) - Q(x))u(x)dx + \int_a^b (P(x) - P_1(x))u'(x)^2\, dx + \int_a^b P_1(x)\left[u'(x) - \frac{u(x)v'(x)}{v(x)}\right]^2 dx = 0,$$

where $u(a) = u(b) = 0$ and $v(x) \neq 0$ in $[a,b]$.

(b) Infer the Sturm Comparison Theorem from Picone's Identity.

*6. (Szegö's Comparison Theorem) Under the hypothesis of the Sturm Comparison Theorem for $a < x < b$, $P \equiv P_1$, $Q \not\equiv Q_1$, let $u(x) > 0$, $u_1(x) > 0$ for $a < x < b$ and $\lim_{x \to a} P(x)[u'u_1 - uu_1'] = 0$. Show that if $u(b) = 0$ then there is an x_2 in (a,b) such that $u_1(x_2) = 0$.

9. Liouville normal form. By changes of dependent and independent variables of the form

$$(33) \qquad u = y(x)w, \qquad t = \int h(x)dx, \qquad y > 0, \qquad h > 0,$$

one can simplify S-L equations (1) considerably. If the functions y and h are positive and continuous in the given interval, the first substitution leaves the location of zeros unchanged, while the second one distorts the range of the independent variable, preserving the order, and leaves the number of zeros of a solution in corresponding intervals unchanged. The equivalent DE in w and t is obtained from the identity $d/dx = h(x)d/dt$, which is obtained from the second of equations (33). When substituted into the S-L equation (1), this identity gives

$$\begin{aligned} 0 &= h(hp(yw)_t)_t + (\lambda\rho - q)yw \\ &= h\{pyh\, w_{tt} + [(hp)_t y + 2hpy_t]w_t + (hpy_t)_t w\} + (\lambda\rho - q)yw. \end{aligned}$$

Dividing through by the coefficient pyh^2 of w_{tt}, we obtain the equivalent DE (for $h,y \in \mathcal{C}^2$),

$$w_{tt} + (pyh)^{-1}[(hp)_t y + 2hpy_t]w_t + [(pyh)^{-1}(hpy_t)_t + h^{-2}p^{-1}(\lambda\rho - q)]w = 0.$$

The term $\lambda(\rho/ph^2)w$ reduces to λw if and only if $h^2 = \rho/p$. The coefficient of w_t vanishes if and only if $(hp)_t/hp = -2y_t/y$, which can be achieved by choosing $y^2 = (hp)^{-1}$. Therefore a simplified equivalent DE in w and t is obtained by choosing

$$(34) \qquad u = w/\sqrt[4]{p(x)\rho(x)}, \qquad t = \int \sqrt{\rho(x)/p(x)}\, dx.$$

This substitution is the *reduction* to *Liouville normal form.* Since p and ρ are positive throughout the interval of definition (cf. § 1), this change of variables makes $h(x)$ and $y(x)$ positive and of class $\mathcal{C}^2$, whenever p and ρ are of class $\mathcal{C}^2$.

THEOREM 6. *Liouville's substitution* (34) *transforms the S-L equation* (1) *with coefficient-functions* $p,\rho \in \mathcal{C}^2$ *and* $q \in \mathcal{C}$ *into the normal form*

$$\frac{d^2w}{dt^2} + [\lambda - \hat{q}(t)]w = 0, \tag{35}$$

where

$$\hat{q} = \frac{q}{\rho} + (p\rho)^{-1/4}\frac{d^2}{dt^2}[(p\rho)^{1/4}]. \tag{36}$$

Evaluating the second derivative in (36) and using the identity $d/dt = (p/\rho)^{1/2}d/dx$, we get the alternative rational form

$$\hat{q} = \frac{q}{\rho} + \frac{p}{4\rho}\left[\left(\frac{p'}{p}\right)' + \left(\frac{\rho'}{\rho}\right)' + \frac{3}{4}\left(\frac{p'}{p}\right)^2 + \frac{1}{2}\left(\frac{p'}{p}\right)\left(\frac{\rho'}{\rho}\right) - \frac{1}{4}\left(\frac{\rho'}{\rho}\right)^2\right]. \tag{36'}$$

If the DE (1) is defined in $a \leqq x < b$, and t is the definite integral $t = \int_a^x \sqrt{\rho(s)/p(s)}\, ds$, then the equivalent DE (35) is defined in the interval $[0,c)$, where $c = \int_a^b \sqrt{\rho(x)/p(x)}\, dx$. An S-L equation (1) with p, $\rho \in \mathcal{C}^2$ and $q \in \mathcal{C}$ is transformed by Liouville's substitution into an S-L equation (35) with $\hat{q} \in \mathcal{C}$, since the denominator in (36) remains bounded away from 0.

COROLLARY 1. *Liouville's reduction* (34) *transforms regular S-L systems into regular S-L systems, separated and periodic boundary conditions into separated and periodic boundary conditions. The transformed system has the same eigenvalues as the original system.*

Let $u(x)$ and $v(x)$ be transformed into the functions $f(t)$ and $g(t)$ by Liouville's reduction (34). From the identity

$$\int_0^c f(t)g(t)dt = \int_a^b u(x)v(x)\sqrt{p(x)\rho(x)}\sqrt{\frac{\rho(x)}{p(x)}}\, dx = \int_a^b u(x)v(x)\rho(x)dx, \tag{37}$$

one infers

COROLLARY 2. *Liouville's reduction* (34) *transforms functions orthogonal with weight* ρ *into orthogonal functions with unit weight.*

The Bessel equation (3) of Example 2, §1,

$$(xu')' + \left(k^2x - \frac{n^2}{x}\right)u = 0$$

is the special case $p=\rho=x$, $q=n^2/x$ of the DE (1). Hence Liouville's reduction (34) is $u=w/\sqrt{x}$ and $x=t$, which leads to the equivalent DE

$$(38) \qquad \frac{d^2w}{dx^2}+\left[k^2-\frac{n^2-1/4}{x^2}\right]w=0, \qquad w=x^{1/2}u.$$

If $n=\frac{1}{2}$, this is the trigonometric DE $w''+k^2w=0$, having a basis of solutions $\cos kx$ and $\sin kx$ $(k=1,2,3,\cdots)$. Since $J_{1/2}(0)=0$, it follows that $J_{1/2}(x)$ is a constant multiple of $(\sin x)/\sqrt{x}$.

EXERCISES F

1. (a) Show that the self-adjoint form of the Hermite DE (15) is the S-L equation

$$[e^{-x^2}u']'+\lambda e^{-x^2}u=0.$$

(b) Show that the Liouville normal form of this is the S-L equation (17) for the Hermite functions.

2. Show that the Liouville normal form of the self-adjoint form of the Jacobi DE is, for $x=\cos t$,

$$w_{tt}+[(\tfrac{1}{4}-\alpha^2)/4\sin^2(t/2)+(\tfrac{1}{4}-\beta^2)/4\cos^2(t/2)+(n+(\alpha+\beta+1)/2)^2]w=0.$$

3. Show that the self-adjoint form of the hypergeometric DE is the singular S-L equation

$$[x^\gamma(1-x)^{\alpha+\beta+1-\gamma}u']'-[\alpha\beta x^{\gamma-1}(1-x)^{\alpha+\beta-\gamma}]u=0.$$

What is the Liouville normal form for this DE?

4. Compute the Liouville normal form for the Legendre DE, setting $x=\cos t$ $(0\leqq t\leqq\pi)$.

*5. Show that every solution of the Legendre DE is square-integrable on $[-1,1]$ and satisfies the endpoint conditions $\lim_{x\to\pm1}(1-x^2)u(x)=0$.

*6. The Laguerre DE is $xu''+(1-x)u'+\lambda u=0$. Show that its self-adjoint form is the S-L equation $[xe^{-x}u']'+\lambda e^{-x}=0$. What is its Liouville normal form?

*7. Show that the Legendre polynomial $P_n(x)$ has exactly n zeros. (*Hint:* Reduce the Legendre DE to Liouville normal form and apply Ex. E6.)

*8. If $x_1=\cos t_1,\cdots,x_n=\cos t_n$ are the zeros of $P_n(x)$, $x_j<x_{j+1}$, show that $2\pi(j-1)/(2n+1)<t_j<2\pi j/(2n+1)$ for $2\leqq j\leqq n$. (*Hint:* Use the Liouville normal form and Ex. E6.)

10. Modified Prüfer substitution. By applying a modification of the Prüfer substitution to the Liouville normal form of an S-L equation, one can obtain asymptotic formulas for the n-th eigenfunction $u_n(x)$, valid for large n.

Using the Liouville substitution of the preceding section, any regular S-L system can be transformed into a regular S-L system consisting of the equation

$$(39) \qquad u''+[\lambda-q(x)]u=u''+Q(x)u=0, \qquad Q(x)=\lambda-q(x),$$

and separated boundary conditions

$$(40) \qquad \alpha u(a)+\alpha'u'(a)=0, \qquad \beta u(b)+\beta'u'(b)=0,$$

where $\alpha^2 + \alpha'^2 \neq 0$ and $\beta^2 + \beta'^2 \neq 0$. By Theorem 6, Corollary 1, the eigenvalues of this system are the same as those of the original system, and the eigenfunctions are obtained from those for the Liouville normal form through the Liouville substitution. To study the distribution of eigenvalues and magnitude of the eigenfunctions, it therefore suffices to treat the system (39), (40).

We shall assume from now on that $Q(x) > 0$ for $a \leqq x \leqq b$, that is, that $\lambda > q(x)$ and $Q \in \mathcal{C}^1$. We now introduce the functions $R(x,\lambda)$ and $\phi(x,\lambda)$, the *modified amplitude* and *modified phase*, which are defined in the terms of a given solution $u(x,\lambda)$ of (39) by the equations

$$u = \frac{R}{\sqrt[4]{Q}} \cos\phi, \qquad u' = R\sqrt[4]{Q}\sin\phi. \tag{41}$$

These equations constitute the *modified Prüfer* system for the DE (39).

We shall now derive a pair of DE's for R and ϕ which are equivalent to (39). We have†

$$\tan\phi = \frac{1}{\sqrt{Q}}\frac{u'}{u}, \qquad R^2 = \sqrt{Q}\,u^2 + \frac{1}{\sqrt{Q}}u'^2. \tag{42}$$

Differentiating the first of these equations, we obtain (using $u'' = -Qu$)

$$(\sec^2\phi)\phi' = -\frac{Qu^2 + u'^2}{Q^{1/2}u^2} - \frac{1}{2}\frac{Q'}{Q^{3/2}}\frac{u'}{u}.$$

Using the second equation, this simplifies to

$$(\sec^2\phi)\phi' = -\frac{R^2}{u^2} - \frac{1}{2}\frac{Q'}{Q}\tan\phi,$$

and, multiplying by $\cos^2\phi$ and simplifying,

$$\phi' = -Q^{1/2} - \frac{1}{4}\frac{Q'}{Q}\sin 2\phi. \tag{43}$$

To derive the DE satisfied by R, differentiate the second equation in (42), obtaining the identity

$$2RR' = 2Q^{-1/2}(Quu' + u'u'') + (Q'/2Q)(Q^{1/2}u^2 - Q^{-1/2}u'^2).$$

The first term vanishes, since $u'' = -Qu$, leaving the DE

$$\frac{R'}{R} = \frac{Q'}{4Q}(\cos^2\phi - \sin^2\phi) = \frac{Q'}{4Q}\cos 2\phi. \tag{44}$$

†When $u \neq 0$. When $u = 0$, set $\cot\phi = \sqrt{Q}u/u'$ and proceed similarly.

In terms of λ and q, the *modified Prüfer system* is

$$\phi' = -\sqrt{\lambda - q} + \frac{q'}{4(\lambda - q)} \sin 2\phi, \tag{45a}$$

$$\frac{R'}{R} = -\frac{q'}{4(\lambda - q)} \cos 2\phi. \tag{45b}$$

Clearly, to every nontrivial solution of (39) there corresponds a solution of the modified Prüfer system, and conversely. Furthermore, $R > 0$, unless R vanishes identically.

Equations (45a) and (45b) determine the asymptotic behavior of the solutions of (39) as $\lambda \to \infty$. The fundamental result is the following:

THEOREM 7. *Let $\phi(x,\lambda)$ and $R(x,\lambda)$ be solutions of the system* (45a) *and* (45b), *where $q(x) \in \mathcal{C}^1$ is bounded. Then, for all sufficiently large λ,*

$$\phi(x,\lambda) = \phi(a,\lambda) - \sqrt{\lambda}\,(x - a) + 0(1)/\sqrt{\lambda}, \tag{46}$$

and

$$R(x,\lambda) = R(a,\lambda) + 0(1)/\lambda. \tag{47}$$

Intuitively, Theorem 8 states that for large λ the modified phase ϕ is approximately a linear function of $\sqrt{\lambda}$, and the modified amplitude function R is approximately constant.

The symbol $0(1)$. The symbol $0(1)$ used here and below signifies a function $f(x,\lambda)$ of x and λ, defined for all sufficiently large λ, which is uniformly bounded for $a \leqq x \leqq b$ as $\lambda \to \infty$. Hence $0(1)/\lambda^s$ signifies a function $f(x,\lambda)$ such that $\lambda^s f(x,\lambda)$ is uniformly bounded. The symbol $0(1)/\lambda^s$ is also often written $0(\lambda^{-s})$, as has been done in analogous contexts in Chapters VII and VIII.

The formula $f(x,\lambda) = 0(1)$, where f is a given function, is not an ordinary equation. Thus to write $0(1) = f(x,\lambda)$ would be meaningless, since $0(1)$ is not a function. The formula means simply that f remains uniformly *bounded* for all x as $\lambda \to \infty$, and that no other property of the function f is needed for the purposes at hand. Using this definition, the following important properties of the symbol $0(1)$ can be easily verified:

$$0(1) + 0(1) = 0(1); \quad 0(1)0(1) = 0(1); \quad \int_a^b 0(1)dx = 0(1)$$

for any finite a,b. Again, if α and β are real numbers with $\alpha \leqq \beta$, then $0(1)/\lambda^\alpha + 0(1)/\lambda^\beta = 0(1)/\lambda^\alpha$. Finally, if $q(x)$ is any bounded function of x, then by Taylor's formula we have, as $\lambda \to \infty$,

$$[\lambda - q(x)]^\alpha = \lambda^\alpha[1 - q(x)/\lambda]^\alpha = \lambda^\alpha - \alpha q(x)\lambda^{\alpha-1} + 0(1)\lambda^{\alpha-2}.$$

The preceding formulas will be used freely in the computations below.

Proof. For all λ for which $|q(x)| < \lambda$ on $[a,b]$, we have as above

$$\frac{q'}{\lambda - q} = \frac{q'}{\lambda}\left(1 + \frac{0(1)}{\lambda}\right) = \frac{q'}{\lambda} + \frac{0(1)}{\lambda^2}$$

$$\sqrt{\lambda - q} = \sqrt{\lambda}\left(1 + \frac{q}{\lambda}\right)^{1/2} = \sqrt{\lambda} - \frac{q}{2\sqrt{\lambda}} + \frac{0(1)}{\lambda^{3/2}}.$$

We now compare the solutions of the DE's (45a) and (45b) with the solutions $\phi_1(a,\lambda) = \phi(a,\lambda) - \sqrt{\lambda}(x - a)$ and $R_1(x,\lambda) \equiv R_1(a)$ of

$$\phi = -\sqrt{\lambda} \quad \text{and} \quad (\log R)' = 0,$$

using Theorem 3 of Chapter V. In making this comparison, we set $\epsilon = 0(1)/\sqrt{\lambda}$, and replace x and y by the functions $\phi(x,\lambda)$ and $\phi_1(x,\lambda)$, respectively. If $\phi_1(a,\lambda) = \phi(a,\lambda)$, then the inequality (7) of Chapter V gives $|\phi(x,\lambda) - \phi_1(x,\lambda)| \leqq 0(1)/\sqrt{\lambda}$, and since $\phi_1(x,\lambda) = \phi(a,\lambda) - \sqrt{\lambda}(x - a)$, equation (46) follows.

Similarly, to derive (47), compare $R(x,\lambda)$ with $R_1(x,\lambda)$, using the identity $e^{0(1)/\lambda} = 1 + 0(1)/\lambda$, obtained from Taylor's formula.

11. Distribution of eigenvalues. The asymptotic distribution of the eigenvalues of a regular S-L system is determined by the boundary conditions; the case of the trigonometric DE $u'' + \lambda u = 0$ is typical. For the boundary conditions $u(a) = u(b) = 0$, the n-th eigenfunction is $\sin [n\pi(x - a)/(b - a)]$ and the n-th eigenvalue is $\lambda_n = n^2\pi^2/(b - a)^2$, $n = 1, 2, 3, \cdots$. For $u(a) = u'(b) = 0$, similarly, $u_n(x) = \sin \sqrt{\lambda_n}(x - a)$, where $\lambda_n = (n + \frac{1}{2})^2\pi^2/(b - a)^2$. For $u'(a) = u'(b) = 0$, the $(n + 1)$-st eigenfunction is $\cos \sqrt{\lambda_n}(x - a)$, where $\lambda_n = n^2\pi^2/(b - a)^2$ and $n = 0, 1, 2, \cdots$.

We will treat below in detail the case of separated endpoint conditions (2) with $\alpha'\beta' \neq 0$. We will show that, in this case, $\sqrt{\lambda_n} = [n\pi/(b - a)] + 0(1)/n$, $n = 0, 1, 2, \cdots$. That is, unless $\alpha' = 0$ or $\beta' = 0$ in (2), the asymptotic behavior of the eigenvalues and eigenfunctions is similar to that for $u'' + \lambda u = 0$, with the endpoint conditions $\alpha = \beta = 0$.

THEOREM 8. *For the regular S-L system* (39)–(40) *let* $\alpha'\beta' \neq 0$. *Then the eigenvalues* λ_n *are given, as* $n \to \infty$, *by the formula*

$$\sqrt{\lambda_n} = \frac{n\pi}{b - a} + \frac{0(1)}{n}, \quad n = 0, 1, 2, \cdots. \tag{48}$$

Here again, $0(1)$ denotes a function of x and n which is uniformly bounded for $a \leqq x \leqq b$ and for all integers $n \geqq 0$.

Proof. Let $A = -\alpha/\alpha'$ and $B = -\beta/\beta'$. By assumption A and B are finite. Choose a solution $\varphi(x,\lambda)$ satisfying for sufficiently large λ the initial condition

$$(49) \qquad \tan \phi(a,\lambda) = -\frac{A}{\sqrt{\lambda - q(a)}}, \qquad -\pi/2 \leqq \phi(a,\lambda) < \pi/2.$$

According to (41), the solution $u(x,\lambda)$ corresponding to ϕ will be an eigenfunction if and only if

$$(50) \qquad \tan \phi(b,\lambda) = -\frac{B}{\sqrt{\lambda - q(b)}}.$$

Condition (49) can be simplified by expanding arctan $(-A/\sqrt{\lambda - q(a)})$ to a first-order approximation in $1/\sqrt{\lambda}$. This gives, as $\lambda \to \infty$,

$$(51) \qquad \phi(a,\lambda) = -\frac{A}{\sqrt{\lambda}} + \frac{0(1)}{\lambda^{3/2}} = \frac{0(1)}{\sqrt{\lambda}}.$$

Condition (50) can be simplified similarly, recalling that for the $(n+1)$-st eigenvalue the modified phase function changes by $n\pi$. This gives

$$\phi(b,\lambda_n) = -n\pi + \frac{0(1)}{\sqrt{\lambda_n}}.$$

Subtracting these two expressions, and comparing with (46) of Theorem 7, we obtain the equation

$$(52) \quad \phi(b,\lambda_n) - \phi(a,\lambda_n) = -n\pi + \frac{0(1)}{\sqrt{\lambda_n}} = -\sqrt{\lambda_n}\,(b-a) + \frac{0(1)}{\sqrt{\lambda_n}}.$$

Letting $\lambda_n \to \infty$ we obtain $\lim_{n\to\infty} n\pi\lambda_n^{-1/2} = (b-a)$, or $\sqrt{\lambda_n} = K_n n$, where K_n is some sequence of numbers tending to $\pi/(b-a)$. Substituting into (52) we obtain

$$\sqrt{\lambda_n} = \frac{n\pi}{b-a} - \frac{0(1)}{\sqrt{\lambda_n}} = \frac{n\pi}{b-a} + \frac{0(1)}{n}, \qquad \text{q.e.d.}$$

COROLLARY. *If λ_n is the sequence of nonzero eigenvalues of a regular S-L system, then* $\sum_{n=0}^{\infty} \lambda_n^{-2} < \infty$.

12. Normalized eigenfunctions. A square-integrable function u on an interval $a < x < b$ is *normalized* relative to a weight function ρ when

$$\int_a^b u^2(x)\rho(x)dx = 1.$$

In the case of the eigenfunctions of (39), $\rho(x) \equiv 1$. Our aim is to show that the normalized eigenfunctions of (39) and (40) behave approximately like cosine functions:

THEOREM 9. *Let $u_n(x)$ $(n = 0, 1, 2, \cdots)$ be the sequence of normalized eigenfunctions of the regular S-L system* (39)–(40), *with $\alpha'\beta' \neq 0$. Then*

$$u_n(x) = \sqrt{\frac{2}{b-a}} \cos \frac{n\pi(x-a)}{b-a} + \frac{0(1)}{n}. \tag{53}$$

The proof of this theorem will be carried out in three steps. For an eigenfunction $u_n(x)$, with eigenvalue λ_n, we have, by (41),

$$u_n(x) = \frac{R(x,\lambda_n)}{\sqrt[4]{\lambda_n - q(x)}} \cos \phi(x,\lambda_n), \qquad a \leqq x \leqq b. \tag{54}$$

In order to obtain formula (53) we obtain asymptotic expressions separately in terms of n for each of the three factors appearing in (54). This is done in the following three lemmas.

LEMMA 1. *Let $\phi(x,\lambda)$ be as in the proof of Theorem* 8. *Then, as $\lambda \to \infty$*

$$\int_a^b \cos^2 \phi(x,\lambda)dx = \frac{b-a}{2} + \frac{0(1)}{\lambda^{1/2}}. \tag{55}$$

Proof. Using $\phi(x,\lambda)$ as the variable of integration in (55), and, recalling from (46) that $dx/d\phi = (d\phi/dx)^{-1} = -\lambda^{-1/2} + 0(1)\lambda^{-3/2}$, we have

$$\begin{aligned}\int_a^b \cos^2\phi(x,\lambda)dx &= \int_{\phi(a,\lambda)}^{\phi(b,\lambda)} \cos^2 \phi \frac{dx}{d\phi}\, d\phi \\ &= (-\lambda^{-1/2} + 0(1)\lambda^{-3/2}) \int_{\phi(a,\lambda)}^{\phi(b,\lambda)} \cos^2 \phi\, d\phi.\end{aligned}$$

The last integral can be evaluated explicitly. Apply Theorem 7, to give

$$\int_{\phi(a,\lambda)}^{\phi(b,\lambda)} \cos^2\phi\, d\phi = \left[\frac{\phi}{2} + \frac{\sin 2\phi}{4}\right]_{\phi(a,\lambda)}^{\phi(b,\lambda)} = -\frac{\lambda^{1/2}(b-a)}{2} + 0(1).$$

Substituting into the previous displayed formula, and simplifying, we obtain (55).

A second step towards our result is the following Lemma.

LEMMA 2. *Let $u(x,\lambda)$ be a solution of* (39). *Then, as $\lambda \to \infty$,*

$$\left(\int_a^b u^2(x)dx\right)^{1/2} = R(a,\lambda)\lambda^{-1/4}\sqrt{\frac{b-a}{2}}\left(1 + \frac{0(1)}{\lambda^{1/2}}\right) + \frac{0(1)}{\lambda^{5/4}}. \tag{56}$$

Proof. Expressing u in terms of R, by (41) and then expanding R as in

Theorem 7, formula (47), we have,

$$\int_a^b u^2(x)dx = \left[R(a,\lambda) + \frac{0(1)}{\lambda}\right]^2 \int_a^b [\lambda - q(x)]^{-1/2} \cos^2 \phi \, dx.$$

Since $(\lambda - q)^{-1/2} = \lambda^{-1/2} + 0(1)\lambda^{-3/2}$, this gives, after simplifying and using (55),

$$\begin{aligned}\int_a^b u^2(x)dx &= \left[R(a,\lambda) + \frac{0(1)}{\lambda}\right]^2 (\lambda^{-1/2} + 0(1)\lambda^{-3/2})\left(\frac{b-a}{2} + 0(1)\lambda^{-1/2}\right)\\ &= \left[R(a,\lambda) + \frac{0(1)}{\lambda}\right]^2 \left(\frac{b-a}{2\lambda^{1/2}} + \frac{0(1)}{\lambda}\right).\end{aligned}$$

Hence, taking square roots,

$$\begin{aligned}\left(\int_a^b u^2(x)dx\right)^{1/2} &= \left(R(a,\lambda) + \frac{0(1)}{\lambda}\right)\left(\frac{b-a}{2\lambda^{1/2}} + \frac{0(1)}{\lambda}\right)^{1/2}\\ &= \frac{R(a,\lambda)}{\lambda^{1/4}}\sqrt{\frac{b-a}{2}}\left(1 + \frac{0(1)}{\lambda^{1/2}}\right) + \frac{0(1)}{\lambda^{5/4}}, \quad \text{q.e.d.}\end{aligned}$$

Corollary. *If in addition* $\int_a^b u^2(x,\lambda)dx = 1$, *then*

$$R(a,\lambda) = \sqrt{\frac{2}{b-a}}\lambda^{1/4}[1 + 0(1)\lambda^{-1/2}]. \tag{57}$$

Proof. Formula (56) gives the following condition to be satisfied by the amplitude function of a normalized solution:

$$1 - \frac{0(1)}{\lambda^{5/4}} = \frac{R(a,\lambda)}{\lambda^{1/4}}\sqrt{\frac{b-a}{2}}\left(1 + \frac{0(1)}{\lambda^{1/2}}\right).$$

Hence, solving for R, and taking the asymptotic form of the quotient, we get (57), q.e.d.

Lemma 3. *Let λ_n be the n-th eigenfunction ($\lambda_0 \leqq \lambda_1 < \lambda_2 < \cdots$) of the S-L system* (39)–(40). *Then, as $n \to \infty$, unless $\alpha'\beta' = 0$,*

$$\cos \phi(x,\lambda_n) = \cos \frac{n\pi(x-a)}{b-a} + 0(1)\lambda_n^{-1/2}. \tag{58}$$

Proof. By the inequality $|\cos a - \cos b| \leqq |a - b|$ and Theorem 7,

$$\begin{aligned}\cos[-\sqrt{\lambda_n}(x-a)] - \cos \phi(x,\lambda_n) &= 0(1)[\sqrt{\lambda_n}(x-a) + \phi(x,\lambda_n)]\\ &= 0(1)\phi(a,\lambda_n) + 0(1)\lambda_n^{-1/2}.\end{aligned}$$

By (51), $\phi(a,\lambda_n) = 0(1)\lambda_n^{-1/2}$. This gives

$$\cos \phi(x,\lambda_n) = \cos[\sqrt{\lambda_n}(x-a)] + 0(1)\lambda_n^{-1/2}. \tag{59}$$

We now apply Theorem 8 to this formula. By formula (48) and the mean value theorem,

$$\cos[\sqrt{\lambda_n}\,(x-a)] - \cos[n\pi(x-a)/(b-a)] = 0(1)n^{-1} = 0(1)\lambda_n^{-1/2}.$$

Substituting into the right side of (59), we obtain (58), q.e.d.

The proof of Theorem 9 can now be completed as follows. Of the three factors in equality (54), the first can be simplified by taking the first-order approximation $(\lambda - q)^{-1/4} = \lambda^{-1/4} + 0(1)\lambda^{-5/4}$. The factor $R(x,\lambda_n)$ is estimated by the Corollary to Lemma 2, and the factor $\cos\phi(x,\lambda_n)$ is estimated by Lemma 3. Substituting all these expressions into (54), and simplifying, we obtain

$$u_n(x) = \sqrt{\frac{2}{b-a}}\cos\left[\frac{n\pi(x-a)}{b-a}\right] + 0(1)\lambda_n^{-1/2}.$$

Since $\lambda_n^{-1/2} = 0(1)n^{-1}$, this gives Theorem 9.

13. Estimates of Bessel functions. We shall now use the modified Prüfer substitution to study the asymptotic behavior of solutions of Bessel's DE as $x \to \infty$. Reducing to Liouville normal form, we can assume that the Bessel DE is in the form

$$u'' + \left[1 - \frac{M}{x^2}\right]u = 0, \qquad 0 < x < \infty, \qquad M = 1 - \frac{n^2}{4} \tag{60}$$

whose solutions are $u(x) = \sqrt{x}\,Z_n(x)$, where Z_n is a solution of the Bessel DE (cf. (38)). The modified Prüfer system equivalent to (60) is obtained by setting $Q(x) = 1 - M/x^2$ in (45a) and (45b). This gives the system

$$\begin{aligned} \phi'(x) &= -\sqrt{1 - \frac{M}{x^2}} - \frac{M\sin 2\phi}{2(x^3 - Mx)} \\ \frac{R'(x)}{R(x)} &= \frac{M\cos 2\phi}{2(x^3 - Mx)}. \end{aligned} \tag{61}$$

Expanding the right sides of these equations for large x, and using $(1 - M/x^2)^{1/2} = 1 - M/x^2 + 0(1)/x^4$, we have, as $x \to \infty$,

$$\phi'(x) = -1 + \frac{1}{2}\frac{M}{x^2} + \frac{0(1)}{x^3}, \qquad \frac{R'(x)}{R(x)} = \frac{0(1)}{x^3}.$$

Here $0(1)$ denotes a function of x which remains bounded as $x \to \infty$. Integrating the first of these equations between $x > \sqrt{M}$ and $y > x$, we obtain

$$\phi(x) - \phi(y) = y - x - M/2x + M/2y + 0(1)/x^2.$$

Keeping x fixed and letting $y \to \infty$, we find that $\phi_\infty = \lim_{y\to\infty}[\phi(y) + y]$ is finite. This gives $\phi(x) = \phi_\infty - x + M/(2x) + 0(1)/x^2$.

If $\sqrt{M} < x < y$, integration of the second equation gives similarly $\log R(x) - \log R(y) = 0(1)/x^2$. Taking exponentials and letting $y \to \infty$, we get

$$R(x) = R_\infty \exp [0(1)/x^2] = R_\infty + 0(1)/x^2,$$

where $R_\infty = \lim_{y\to\infty} R(y)$.

It follows that every solution of the Bessel DE (60) has the aysmptotic form

$$Z_n(x) = x^{-1/2}\left[R_\infty + \frac{0(1)}{x^2}\right] \cos \left(\phi_\infty - x + \frac{M}{2x} + \frac{0(1)}{x^2}\right).$$

Since $\cos (A + 0(1)/x^2) = \cos (-A) + 0(1)/x^2$, the preceding display can be rewritten as

$$Z_n(x) = R_\infty x^{-1/2} \cos (x - \phi_\infty - M/2x) + 0(1)/x^{5/2}.$$

The solution Z_n is uniquely determined by the constants R_∞ and ϕ_∞, for if two solutions had the same asymptotic amplitude R_∞ and phase ϕ_∞, their difference would be a solution with $R(x) = 0(1)/x^{5/2}$. Since

$$R(x) = R_\infty \exp [0(1)/x^2],$$

this would imply $R \equiv u \equiv 0$. This proves

THEOREM 10. *To every nontrivial solution of the Bessel DE* (60) *there correspond a limiting modified phase* ϕ_∞ *and a limiting modified amplitude* R_∞. *The solution is uniquely determined by* ϕ_∞ *and* R_∞. *That is, every solution* $Z_n(x)$ *of Bessel's DE can be expressed as* $x \to \infty$ *in the form*

$$Z_n(x) = \frac{R_\infty}{\sqrt{x}} \cos \left(x - \phi_\infty - \frac{(1 - n^2/4)}{2x}\right) + \frac{0(1)}{x^{5/2}}. \tag{62}$$

For the Bessel function $J_n(x)$ it can be shown that $\phi_\infty = n\pi/2 + \pi/4$ and $R_\infty = \sqrt{2/\pi}$. The Neumann function $Y_n(x)$ is defined by the conditions $\phi_\infty = n\pi/2 + 3\pi/4$ and $R_\infty = \sqrt{2/\pi}$. Thus the Neumann function $Y_n(x)$ is defined by the condition that it has the same asymptotic amplitude as $J_n(x)$, with an asymptotic phase-lag of $\pi/2$ radians.

That is, the asymptotic relation between $J_n(x)$ and $Y_n(x)$ is, for large positive x, the same as that between $\cos x$ and $\sin x$. The *Hankel function* $H_n(x) = J_n(x) + i\,Y_n(x)$ is therefore analogous to $\cos x + i \sin x = e^{ix}$.

EXERCISES G

1. For any DE $u'' + u + \rho(x)u = 0$ with $\rho(x) = 0(x^{-2})$ as $x \to +\infty$, show that for every solution $u(x)$ constants A and x_1 can be found for which

$$u(x) = A \cos (x - x_1) + 0(x^{-1}) \quad \text{as} \quad x \to \infty.$$

*2. Establish the following formula for Legendre polynomials:

$$P_n (\cos \theta) = [A/(\sin \theta)^{1/2}] \cos \left[\left(n + \frac{1}{2}\right)\theta - \frac{\pi}{4}\right] + 0(n^{-3/2}) \quad \text{for} \quad 0 < \theta < \pi,$$

for some constant A. (*Hint:* Find a DE satisfied by $P_n (\cos \theta)$.)

3. Show that the relative maxima of $x^{1/2} \mid J_n(x) \mid$ form an increasing sequence if $0 < n < \frac{1}{2}$ and a decreasing sequence if $n > \frac{1}{2}$.

*4. (Sonin-Polya Theorem) Show that if in $(Pu')' + Qu = 0$, P, $Q \in \mathcal{C}^1[a,b]$, $Q(x) \neq 0$, $P(x)Q(x)$ is nondecreasing, then the successive maxima of $\mid u(x) \mid$ form a nonincreasing sequence, and that equality occurs if and only if $Q(x) = 1/P(x)$. (*Hint:* Show that the derivative of $\phi(x) = u(x)^2 + P(x)u'(x)^2/Q(x)$ is nonpositive.)

*5. Show that the values of $\mid P(x)Q(x) \mid^{1/2} \mid u(x) \mid$ at those points where $u'(x) = 0$ are a monotonic increasing or decreasing sequence, according as the values of $P(x)Q(x)$ are decreasing or increasing. (*Hint:* Consider $\phi(x) = P(x)Q(x)\phi(x)$, ϕ as in Ex. 4.)

14. Inhomogeneous equations. Inhomogeneous second-order linear equations, of the form

$$(63)\qquad L[u] = p_0(x)u'' + p_1(x)u' + p_2(x)u = f(x), \quad p_0(x) \neq 0, \quad p_0(x) \in \mathcal{C}^1,$$

subject to *homogeneous* separated endpoint conditions (30), can be solved using *Green's functions.* The method of solution generalizes that for *two-endpoint* problems described in Ch. II, §§ 9 and 10. The discussion given there, which covers the case $\alpha' = \beta' = 0$ of (30), can now be reviewed to advantage.

Before introducing Green's functions, we first analyze the problem with *inhomogeneous* separated endpoint conditions:

$$(64)\qquad A[u] = \alpha u(a) + \alpha' u'(a) = \alpha_1, \qquad B[u] = \beta u(b) + \beta' u'(b) = \beta_1.$$

Let $U(x)$ be the solution of $L[u] = 0$ satisfying the initial conditions $U(a) = \alpha'$, $U'(a) = -\alpha$; let $V(x)$ be the solution of $L[u] = 0$ satisfying $V(b) = \beta'$, $V'(b) = -\beta$; let $F(x)$ be the solution of $L[u] = f(x)$ satisfying $F(a) = F'(a) = 0$. The existence and uniqueness of these functions follow from Theorem 7, Corollary 2, of Ch. V, § 8. For any constants c, d, the function

$$w(x) = cU(x) + dV(x) + F(x)$$

satisfies the inhomogeneous DE (63). Moreover

$$(65)\qquad \begin{aligned} A[w] &= d(\alpha V(a) + \alpha' V'(a)) = dA[V], \\ B[w] &= c(\beta U(b) + \beta' U'(b)) + B[f] = cB[U] + B[F]. \end{aligned}$$

If U and V are linearly independent, their Wronskian $W = UV' - VU'$ never vanishes. Hence

$$A[V] = \alpha V(a) + \alpha' V'(a) = -U'(a)V(a) + U(a)V'(a) \neq 0;$$

similarly, $B[U] = W(b) \neq 0$. Therefore equations (65) for the unknowns c and d have a unique solution for any values given to $A[w]$ and $B[w]$.

On the other hand, if U and V are linearly dependent, their Wronskian vanishes identically. Hence $U(x)$ satisfies $A[U] = \alpha\alpha' + \alpha'(-\alpha) = 0$

and $B[U]=0$. This proves

THEOREM 11. *Either the DE* (63) *has a solution w satisfying the boundary conditions $A[w]=\alpha_1$ and $B[w]=\beta_1$ for any given constants α_1 and β_1, or else the homogeneous DE $L[u]=0$ has an eigenfunction satisfying the homogeneous conditions $A[u]=0$ and $B[u]=0$.*

15. Green's functions. We now show that, in the first case of the preceding theorem, there exists a *Green's function* $G(x,\xi)$ defined for $a \leqq x, \xi \leqq b$, such that the solution of (63) subject to the boundary conditions (30) is given by

$$u(x) = \int_a^b G(x,\xi)f(\xi)d\xi = \mathcal{G}[f]. \tag{66}$$

Note that $\mathcal{G}$ is an *integral operator* (Ch. II, § 5) whose kernel is the Green's function $G(x,\xi)$.

This result has already been established in Ch. II, § 10, for the endpoint conditions $u(a)=u(b)=0$; it will now be generalized to arbitrary *homogeneous* separated endpoint conditions (30): $A[u]=B[u]=0$.

In this general case, $G(x,\xi)$ can be constructed by the method used in Chapter II. For each fixed ξ, $G(x,\xi)$ is a solution of the homogeneous DE $L[G]=0$ on the intervals $[a,\xi]$ and $[\xi,b]$, satisfying the homogeneous endpoint conditions $A[u]=0$ and $B[u]=0$, respectively. It is continuous across $x=\xi$ (i.e., across the principal diagonal of the square $a \leqq x, \xi \leqq b$), and its derivative $\partial G/\partial x$ jumps by $1/p_0(x)$ across this diagonal. That is,

$$G(x,\xi) = \begin{cases} \epsilon(\xi)U(x)V(\xi), & a \leqq x \leqq \xi, \\ \epsilon(\xi)V(x)U(\xi), & \xi \leqq x \leqq b, \end{cases}$$

where the factor $\epsilon(\xi)$ above is chosen to give $\partial G/\partial x$ a jump of $1/p_0(\xi)$ across $x=\xi$:

$$\frac{\partial G}{\partial x}(\xi^+,\xi) - \frac{\partial G}{\partial x}(\xi^-,\xi) = \epsilon(\xi)\{U(\xi)V'(\xi^+) - V(\xi)U'(\xi^-)\} = 1/p_0(\xi).$$

We are therefore led to try the kernel

$$G(x,\xi) = \begin{cases} U(x)V(\xi)/p_0(\xi)W(\xi), & a \leqq x \leqq \xi \\ U(\xi)V(x)/p_0(\xi)W(\xi), & \xi \leqq x \leqq b, \end{cases} \tag{67}$$

where $W = UV' - VU'$ is the Wronskian of U and V.

THEOREM 12. *Unless $W \equiv 0$, equations* (66)–(67) *yield a solution $u(x)$ of the DE $L[u]=f(x)$ which satisfies the boundary conditions $A[u]=B[u]=0$, for any continuous function f on $[a,b]$.*

That is, unless the homogeneous linear boundary value problem $L[u] = A[u] = B[u] = 0$ admits an eigenfunction, the function defined by (67) is a Green's function for the system $L[u] = f$, $A[u] = B[u] = 0$.

The proof is like that given in Ch. II, § 10. Rewriting (66) in the form

$$u(x) = \int_a^x G(x,\xi)f(\xi)d\xi + \int_x^b G(x,\xi)f(\xi)d\xi,$$

and differentiating, we have by Leibniz' Rule

$$u'(x) = \int_a^x G_x(x,\xi)f(\xi)d\xi + \int_x^b G_x(x,\xi)f(\xi)d\xi.$$

The endpoint contributions give $G(x,x^-)f(x^-) - G(x,x^+)f(x^+) = 0$; they cancel since $G(x,\xi)$ and f are continuous for $x = \xi$. Differentiating again, we have by Leibniz' Rule

$$u''(x) = \int_a^x G_{xx}(x,\xi)f(\xi)d\xi + G_x(x,x^-)f(x^-)$$
$$+ \int_x^b G_{xx}(x,\xi)f(\xi)d\xi - G_x(x,x^+)f(x^+).$$

The two terms corresponding to the contributions from the endpoints come from the sides $x > \xi$ and $x < \xi$ of the diagonal; since f is continuous, their difference is $[G_x(x^+,x) - G_x(x^-,x)]f(x) = f(x)/p_0(x)$. Simplifying, we obtain

$$u''(x) = \int_a^b G_{xx}(x,\xi)f(\xi)d\xi + f(x)/p_0(x).$$

From the above identities we can calculate $L[u]$. It is

$$L[u] = \int_a^b L_x[G(x,\xi)]f(\xi)d\xi + f(x) = f(x),$$

where $L_x[G(x,\xi)]$ stands for the sum $p_0G_{xx} + p_1G_x + p_2G$. This sum is zero except on the diagonal $x = \xi$, where it is undefined. This gives the identity (63).

Since $G(x,\xi)$, as a function of x, satisfies the boundary conditions (30) for all ξ, it follows from (66), by differentiating under the integral sign and using Leibniz' Rule again, that u satisfies the same boundary conditions. This completes the proof of the theorem.

In operator language (cf. Ch. II, § 5), we have shown that the operator $f \to \mathcal{G}[f]$ transforms the space $\mathcal{C}[a,b]$ of continuous functions on the interval $[a,b]$ into the space $\mathcal{C}^2[a,b]$ of functions of class $\mathcal{C}^2$, and that this operator is a *right-inverse* of the operator L. That is, $L[\mathcal{G}[f]] = f$ for all continuous f. In operator notation, we can write $\mathcal{G} = L^{-1}$.

EXERCISES H

In Exs. 1–5 show that the Green's function is as specified.

1. $u'' = f,\ u(0) = u'(1) = 0;\ G(x,\xi) = \begin{cases} x \text{ for } x \leqq \xi \\ \xi - 1 \text{ for } x > \xi. \end{cases}$

2. $u'' = f,\ u(-1) = u(1) = 0;\ G(x,\xi) = -[\,|x-\xi| + x\xi - 1]/2.$

3. $xu'' + u' = f$, $u(x)$ bounded as $x \to 0$, $u(1) = 0$;

$$G(x,\xi) = \begin{cases} -\log \xi \text{ for } x \leqq \xi \\ -\log x \text{ for } x > \xi. \end{cases}$$

4. $u'' - u = f$, $u(x)$ bounded as $|x| \to \infty$; $G(x,\xi) = e^{-|x-\xi|}/2$.

5. $x^2u'' - 2xu' + 2u = f,\ u(1) = u(2) = 0;\ G(x,\xi) = (\xi^2 - 2\xi)(x^2 - x)$ if $x \leqq \xi$; $G(\xi,x) = G(x,\xi)$.

6. Find the Green's function for $u'' - u = f$ with $u(-a) = u(a) = 0$. Show that, as $a \to \infty$, it approaches that of Ex. 4.

*7. Show that the Green's function G of a regular S-L system is a symmetric function of x and ξ.

16*. Schroedinger equation. The *Schroedinger equation* of quantum mechanics in one space dimension is the DE

$$\psi'' + \frac{2m}{\hbar^2}[E - V(x)]\psi = 0. \tag{68}$$

Physically, the function $V(x)$ has the significance of potential energy, the constant m stands for the mass of the particle, the constant E is an energy parameter, $\hbar = h/2\pi$ is a universal constant, whose numerical value depends on the units used. The "wave function" $\psi(x)$ may be real or complex; $\psi\psi^*\,dx = |\psi|^2\,dx$ is the probability that the particle under consideration will be "observed" in the interval $(x, x + dx)$. The *eigenvalues* of (68) for varying E are the *energy levels* of the associated physical system.

The DE (68) is precisely the Liouville normal form

$$u'' + [\lambda - q(x)]u = 0 \tag{69}$$

of a general S-L equation, with $\lambda = 2mE/\hbar^2$ and $q = 2mV/\hbar^2$. But in most physical applications, one is concerned with the *infinite interval* $(-\infty, \infty)$. On this interval, the "endpoint" conditions that a solution shall remain bounded as $x \to \pm\infty$ define a *singular* S-L system (cf. § 4). In problems involving the Schroedinger equation, it is customary among physicists to define the *spectrum* of this S-L system as the set of all eigenvalues for which eigenfunctions exist. The set of isolated points in this spectrum is called the *discrete spectrum*; the part (if any) consisting of entire intervals is called the *continuous spectrum*. We shall adopt this suggestive terminology below, noting however that its logical extension to boundary value problems generally is very technical, even for ordinary DE's.†

†See for example Coddington and Levinson, pp. 252–269.

For regular S-L systems, we have proved that the spectrum is always discrete, and the eigenfunctions are (trivially) square-integrable. We now describe a simple singular S-L system whose spectrum is continuous and whose eigenfunctions are not square-integrable.

EXAMPLE 8. The S-L system of a *free particle* is

$$u'' + \lambda u = 0, \qquad -\infty < x < +\infty. \tag{70}$$

For every positive number $\lambda > 0$ this DE has two linearly independent bounded solutions $\sin(\sqrt{\lambda}\, x)$ and $\cos(\sqrt{\lambda}\, x)$. For $\lambda = 0$, it has the bounded solution $x = 1$, and no other linearly independent eigenfunction. For $\lambda < 0$, it has the linearly independent unbounded solutions $\sinh(\sqrt{\lambda}\, x)$ and $\cosh(\sqrt{\lambda}\, x)$, and no nontrivial bounded solution. Hence the *spectrum* of the free particle is *continuous*: it consists of the half-line $\lambda \geqq 0$.

EXAMPLE 9. In the case of a *harmonic oscillator*, the potential energy $V(x)$ is a constant multiple of x^2. By a change of unit $x \to kx$, one can reduce the resulting Schroedinger DE to the normal form

$$u'' + (\lambda - x^2)u = 0. \tag{71}$$

Comparing with Example 7 of § 4, we see that this has the eigenfunctions $e^{-x^2/2}H_n(x)$ for $\lambda = 2n + 1$ $(n = 0, 1, 2, \cdots)$. These eigenfunctions are even *square-integrable.*

For any value of λ not an odd positive integer, the recurrence relation $a_{k+2} = (2k - \lambda + 1)a_k/(k + 1)(k + 2)$ satisfied by $H_\lambda(x)$ may be compared with that for the Taylor series $e^{\beta x^2} = \Sigma \beta^r x^{2r}/(r!)$, namely $c_{2r+2} = \beta c_{2r}/(r + 1)$. Setting $2r = k$, we see that for all sufficiently large k,

$$a_{k+2}/a_k > c_{k+2}/c_k > 0 \quad \text{if} \quad \beta < 1.$$

Hence $|H_\lambda(x)| > Be^{\beta x^2} - p_\lambda(x)$, where $B > 0$, $p_\lambda(x)$ is a polynomial, and (say) $\beta = 3/4$. It follows that $|e^{-x^2/2}H_\lambda(x)| > Be^{x^2/4} - 0(1)$ is *unbounded* unless λ is an odd positive integer. — Finally, if $u(x)$ is any bounded nontrivial solution of (71), the same is true of $u(-x)$ and of $[u(x) + u(-x)]/2$, $[u(x) - u(-x)]/2$. This shows that if (71) has an eigenfunction, then it must have an odd eigenfunction or an even eigenfunction. Since either of these would be defined up to a constant factor by the relation

$$a_{k+2} = (2k - \lambda + 1)a_k/(k + 1)(k + 2)$$

on its coefficients, we see that the *Hermite functions* $e^{-x^2/2}H_n(x)$ are the *only eigenfunctions* of the harmonic oscillator.

17*. Square well potential. In Example 8, the spectrum is continuous; in Example 9, it is discrete. We now describe a Schroedinger equation whose spectrum is partly continuous and partly discrete.

EXAMPLE 10. A *square well* potential is one satisfying $V(x) = -C^2$ on

$|x| < a$, and $V(x) = 0$ when $|x| > a$. This leads to the Schroedinger DE with *discontinuous* $q(x)$:

$$u'' + \lambda u = \begin{cases} 0 & \text{on} \quad |x| > a \\ -C^2 u & \text{on} \quad |x| < a. \end{cases} \tag{72}$$

The eigenfunctions can again be determined explicitly.†

If $u(x)$ is any eigenfunction, then so is $u(-x)$, and so are the even part $[u(x) + u(-x)]/2$ and the odd part $[u(x) - u(-x)]/2$ of $u(x)$. Hence (72) has a basis of eigenfunctions consisting exclusively of *even* and *odd* eigenfunctions: that is, satisfying $u'(0) = 0$ or $u(0) = 0$.

For $\lambda > 0$, every solution of (72) has the form $A \cos \sqrt{\lambda}\, x + B \sin \sqrt{\lambda}\, x$ for $|x| > a$. Hence every nontrivial solution of (72) is an eigenfunction and, as in Example 8, the spectrum includes the entire half-line $\lambda \geqq 0$.

For $\lambda < -C^2$, on the other hand, the continuation to $|x| > a$ of both the even solution $\cosh(\sqrt{-\lambda - C^2}\, x)$ and the odd solution $\sinh(\sqrt{-\lambda - C^2}\, x)$, from the interval $|x| < a$ can be shown (see Thm. 14 below) to satisfy $u(x) > 0$, $u'(x) > 0$, and $u''(x) > 0$ for all positive x. Hence they are both unbounded. In summary, the spectrum contains no points on $\lambda < -C^2$: there is no bounded solution with eigenvalue $\lambda < -C^2$.

In the interval $-C^2 < \lambda < 0$, one can show that the spectrum is discrete by working out the implications of the Sturm Oscillation Theorem. The solutions bounded for $x > a$ are the functions $A \exp(-\sqrt{-\lambda}\, x)$ which satisfy $u'(a)/u(a) = -\sqrt{-\lambda}$. Writing $\mu = \sqrt{\lambda + C^2}$, we see that the even solutions $A \cos \mu x$ of (72) satisfy the same boundary condition $u'(a)/u(a) = -\sqrt{-\lambda}$ if and only if $\mu \tan \mu a = \sqrt{-\lambda}$; the odd solutions $B \sin \mu x$ satisfy it if and only if $\mu \cot \mu a = -\sqrt{-\lambda}$. Solving the preceding transcendental equations graphically, we see that the number of even eigenfunctions and the number of odd eigenfunctions belonging to the discrete spectrum are both approximately equal to aC/π. Moreover every eigenfunction which corresponds to the discrete spectrum is square-integrable, and conversely.

18*. Mixed spectrum. The preceding example is typical of a wide class of Schroedinger equations — namely, all those having a "potential well" dying out at infinity. We first treat the continuous portion of the spectrum.

LEMMA 1. *In the normalized Schroedinger equation* (69), *let* q *be continuous and satisfy* $q(x) = B/x + 0(1/x^2)$ *as* $x \to \infty$ *for some constant* B. *Then, for* $\lambda > 0$, *every solution has infinitely many zeros and is bounded.*

†With the usual understanding (Ch. II, Ex. A11) that a "solution" of (72) is a function $u \in \mathcal{C}^1$ which satisfies (72), and so is of class $\mathcal{C}^2$ where $q(x)$ is continuous.

Proof. The first statement follows from the Sturm Comparison Theorem, comparing with the DE $u'' + \lambda u/2 = 0$.

To prove the second statement, first change the independent variable to $t = \sqrt{\lambda}\, x$, giving the DE $u_{tt} + Q(t)u = 0$, with $Q(t) = 1 - q(t/\sqrt{\lambda})/\lambda$. Applied to the new DE, the Prüfer substitution (21) gives, by (22),

$$\frac{d\theta}{dt} = Q\,(t) \sin^2\theta + \cos^2\theta = 1 + \frac{A}{t}\sin^2\theta + \frac{0(1)}{t^2};\ A = -B/\sqrt{\lambda}.$$

Moreover $r^2 = u^2 + u_t^2$ is given by (23′), as

$$r^2 = K^2 \exp\left\{\int_a^t \left[\frac{A}{s} + 0\left(\frac{1}{s^2}\right)\right](\sin 2\theta)\frac{ds}{d\theta}d\theta\right\} = K^2 \exp\left\{\int_a^t F(s)ds\right\},$$

where $F(s) = (A/s)(\sin 2\theta) + 0(1)/s^2$, and the limits of integration refer to s. Using the expression $dt/d\theta = 1 - (A/t)\sin^2\theta + 0(1)/t^2$, derivable from the preceding display we have

$$\int_a^t F(s)ds = \int_a^t \left[\frac{A}{s} + 0\left(\frac{1}{s^2}\right)\right] \sin 2\theta\, d\theta.$$

The first term on the right side above can be integrated by parts:

$$(73)\quad \int_a^t F(s)ds = \left[-\frac{A}{2s}\cos 2\theta\right]_a^t - \int_a^t \frac{A}{2s^2}\cos 2\theta\, ds + \int_a^t 0\left(\frac{1}{s^2}\right)\sin 2\theta\, d\theta.$$

The boundedness of the first two terms on the right side of this equation is obvious; the last term is bounded because $d\theta/ds = 1 + 0(1)/s$. Hence u^2 is bounded because $u^2 \leqq r^2 \leqq K^2 \exp\left\{\int_a^t F(s)ds\right\}$.

Combining Lemma 1 with the analogous result for negative x, we obtain

THEOREM 13. *If $q \in \mathcal{C}$ satisfies $q(x) = A/x + 0(1/x^2)$ as $x \to +\infty$ and $q(x) = B/x + 0(1/x^2)$ as $x \to -\infty$, then the spectrum of (69) includes the half-line $\lambda > 0$.*

As regards the discrete portion of the spectrum, the key result is the following lemma, which characterizes the asymptotic behavior for large x of a wide class of DE's having nonoscillatory solutions — such as the modified Bessel equation of Ch. IX, § 7.

LEMMA 2. *In the Schroedinger equation (69), let q be continuous, let $\lim_{x\to+\infty} q(x) = 0$, and let $\lambda = -k^2 < 0$. For any ϵ, $0 < \epsilon < k$, there exist two solutions $u_1(x)$ and $u_2(x)$ of (69) such that, for all sufficiently large x,*

$$(74)\qquad e^{(k-\epsilon)x} \leqq u_1(x) \leqq e^{(k+\epsilon)x}, \qquad e^{(-k-\epsilon)x} \leqq u_2(x) \leqq e^{(-k+\epsilon)x}.$$

Proof. Choose a so large that $(k-\epsilon)^2 < q(x) - \lambda < (k+\epsilon)^2$ for all $x \geqq a$, and let $u_1(x)$ be the solution defined by the initial conditions $u_1(a) = e^{ka}$,

$u_1'(a) = ke^{ka}$. Then $\tau(x) = u_1'/u_1$ satisfies $\tau(a) = k$ and the Riccati equation $\tau' = G(x,\tau) = q(x) - \lambda - \tau^2$. For the DE's

$$\rho' = F(x,\rho) = (k-\epsilon)^2 - \rho^2, \qquad \sigma' = H(x,\sigma) = (k+\epsilon)^2 - \sigma^2,$$

clearly $F(x,\tau) \leqq G(x,\tau) \leqq H(x,\tau)$ on the domain $\tau \geqq k - \epsilon > 0$. Moreover the solutions $\rho(x) = k - \epsilon$ and $\sigma(x) = k + \epsilon$ of the displayed DE's satisfy $\rho(a) < \tau(a) < \sigma(a)$. Hence, by the Comparison Theorem of Chapter I, § 11, $k - \epsilon = \rho(x) \leqq \tau(x) \leqq \sigma(x) = k + \epsilon$. Integrating, we get the first inequality of (74).

We now derive the second inequality. As in Ch. II, § 3, a linearly independent solution of the DE (69) is given by

$$u_2(x) = 2ku_1(x)\int_x^\infty \frac{ds}{u_1^2(s)}.$$

The first inequality of (74), applied to the integral on the right, gives the inequalities

$$\frac{1}{2(k-\epsilon)}\, e^{-2(k-\epsilon)x} \geqq \int_x^\infty \frac{ds}{u_1(s)^2} \geqq \frac{1}{2(k+\epsilon)}\, e^{-2(k+\epsilon)x}.$$

Multiplying through by $2ku_1(x)$, and using (74) again, we get

$$\text{(75)} \qquad \frac{e^{2\epsilon x}}{1-\epsilon/k}\, e^{-(k-\epsilon)x} \geqq u_2(x) \geqq \frac{e^{-2\epsilon x}}{1+\epsilon/k}\, e^{-(k+\epsilon)x}.$$

But for any η such that $0 < 3\epsilon < \eta < k$ we have, for sufficiently large x,

$$e^{-(k-\eta)x} \geqq \frac{e^{2\epsilon x}}{1-\epsilon/k}\, e^{-(k-\epsilon)x}, \quad \text{and} \quad \frac{e^{-2\epsilon x}}{1+\epsilon/k}\, e^{-(k+\epsilon)x} \geqq e^{-(k+\eta)x}.$$

Applying these inequalities to (75), we obtain the second formula of (74) with η in place of ϵ. Since for any η with $0 < \eta < k$ we can find $\epsilon = \eta/6$ with $0 < 3\epsilon < \eta < k$, the proof is complete.

Corollary 1. *On* $(0,\infty)$, *let* $q(x)$ *be continuous and satisfy* $\lim_{x\to\infty} q(x) = q_0$. *Then every solution of the Schroedinger equation with* $\lambda < q_0$ *which is bounded on the interval* $(0,\infty)$ *is square-integrable.*

Corollary 2. *Let* $q(x) \in \mathfrak{C}$ *on the line* $(-\infty,\infty)$, *and let* $q(x)$ *tend to limits* q_0 *and* q_1, *respectively, as* $x \to \pm\infty$. *Then every eigenfunction with eigenvalue* $\lambda <$ *min* (q_0,q_1) *is square-integrable.*

The final conclusions can be summarized in a single theorem.

Theorem 14. *Let* $q(x)$ *be as in Theorem* 13. *Then, for* $\lambda > 0$, *the spectrum is continuous. For* $\lambda < 0$, *the eigenfunctions are square-integrable.*

It can also be shown that, for $\lambda > 0$ the eigenfunctions are not square-integrable, and that for $\lambda < 0$, the spectrum is discrete.

EXERCISES I

1. Show that the S-L system $u'' + \lambda u = 0$, $0 \leqq x < \infty$, $\alpha u(0) + \alpha' u'(0) = 0$, $u(x)$ bounded as $x \to \infty$, has a continuous spectrum $0 < \lambda < \infty$ if $\alpha\alpha' \neq 0$.

2. Show that if $u'' - q(x)u = 0$, $0 \leqq x < \infty$, $q(x)$ bounded, then the DE cannot have two square-integrable linearly independent solutions. (*Hint:* Use the Wronskian.)

3. In $u'' + [\lambda - q(x)]u = 0$, $0 \leqq x < \infty$, if $q(x) \to +\infty$ as $x \to \infty$, show that for any λ the DE has exactly one square-integrable solution up to a constant factor.

*4. Under the assumptions of Ex. 3, show that the S-L system corresponding to the boundary condition $u(0) = 0$, $u(x)$ square-integrable in $[0, \infty)$, has an infinite sequence of eigenvalues.

5. Show that, if the DE $u'' + q(x)u = 0$, $0 \leqq x < \infty$, $q \in \mathcal{C}$ has a solution $u_1(x)$ such that $\lim_{x\to\infty} u_1(x) = 1$, then it also has a solution $u_2(x)$ such that $\lim_{x\to\infty} u_2(x)/x = 1$.

6. In $u'' + q(x)u = 0$, $0 \leqq x < \infty$, suppose that $\int_0^\infty x \mid q(x) \mid dx < \infty$. Show that the DE has a solution such that $\lim_{x\to\infty} u(x) = 1$. (*Hint:* Show by successive approximations that the integral equation $u(x) = 1 - \int_x^\infty (t - x)q(t)u(t)\,dt$ has a solution.)

7. Suppose that all solutions of the DE $u'' + q(x)u = 0$ are bounded as $x \to \infty$ and that $\int_0^\infty \rho(x)\,dx < \infty$, $\rho(x) > 0$. Show that for all λ all solutions of the DE $u'' + (q(x) + \lambda\rho(x))u = 0$ are also bounded as $x \to \infty$. (*Hint:* Consider the inhomogeneous DE $u'' + qu = -\lambda\rho u$, and show that the integral equation obtained by variation of parameters has a bounded solution.)

8. Show that if $k^2 > 0$ and $\int_0^\infty \mid q(x) - k^2 \mid dx < \infty$, all solutions of the DE $u'' + q(x)u = 0$ are bounded as $x \to \infty$.

*9. Show that solutions of the generalized Laguerre DE

$$u'' + \frac{2}{x}u' + \left[\frac{\lambda}{x} - \left(\frac{1}{4} + \frac{\alpha}{x^2}\right)\right]u = 0$$

are $u = e^{-x/2}x^{(k-1)/2}L_n^{(k)}(x)$, where $L_n^{(k)}(x) = d^k[L_n(x)]/dx^k$, for $\alpha = (k^2 - 1)/4$ and $\lambda = n - (k-1)/2$, n, k any nonnegative integers.

ADDITIONAL EXERCISES

1. Show that, if $\alpha, \beta > 0$, the singular S-L system

$$\frac{d}{dx}\left[(1+x)^{\beta+1}(1-x)^{\alpha+1}\frac{du}{dx}\right] + \lambda(1+x)^{\beta}(1-x)^{\alpha}u = 0, \qquad -1 < x < 1,$$

with the endpoint condition that u remain bounded as $x \to \pm 1$ has the eigenvalues $\lambda_n = n(n + \alpha + \beta + 1)$ and eigenfunctions $u_n(x) = P_n^{(\alpha,\beta)}(x)$ (Jacobi polynomials).

2. Obtain orthogonality relations for the Jacobi polynomials.

3. Using Rodrigues' formula, show that between any two zeros of $P_n^{(\alpha,\beta)}$ there is exactly one zero of $P_{n+1}^{(\alpha,\beta)}$, if $\alpha,\beta > -1$.

*4. Derive the following identities for Legendre polynomials:

(a) $\int_{-1}^1 P_n^2(x)dx = 2/(2n+1)$, (b) $\int_{-1}^1 xP_n(x)P_n'(x)dx = 2n/(4n^2 - 1)$.

(*Hint:* Use Rodrigues' formula and integrate by parts.)

*5. Show that the Legendre DE, with the endpoint condition

$$\lim_{x\to\pm 1} [(1 - x^2)u'(x)] = 0,$$

has the Legendre polynomials as eigenfunctions, and no other eigenfunctions.

6. Show that there exists a bounded differentiable function g on $a < x < b$, satisfying the inequality $g' + g^2/P(x) + Q(x) \leqq 0$, if and only if no solution of $(Pu')' + Qu = 0$ has more than one zero on $a \leqq x \leqq b$.

*7. Show that, if $\int_a^b | Q(x) | \, dx \leqq 4/(b - a)$, then no nontrivial solution of $u'' + Q(x)u = 0$ can have more than one zero in $a \leqq x \leqq b$. *Hint:* By Theorem 3, it can be assumed that $Q \geqq 0$. Changing coordinates so that $a = 0$, $b = 1$, use Ex. 6 with

$$g(x) = \int_x^1 Q(t)dt + \begin{cases} (1/x) - 4 & 0 < x \leqq \frac{1}{2} \\ 1/(x-1) & \frac{1}{2} \leqq x < 1. \end{cases}$$

*8. (Fubini) Show that if for $a \leqq x \leqq b$,

$$p'(x) + p(x)^2 - q(x) \leqq p'_1(x) + p_1(x)^2 - q_1(x),$$

then between any two zeros of a solution of $u'' + 2p_1u' + q_1u = 0$ there is at least one zero of $u'' + 2pu' + qu = 0$. (*Hint:* See Ch. II, Ex. B4.)

9. For a regular S-L system with $\alpha\alpha' < 0$, and $\beta\beta' < 0$, and λ less than the smallest eigenvalue, show that the Green's function is negative.

CHAPTER XI

Expansions in Eigenfunctions

1. Fourier series. One of the major mathematical achievements of the nineteenth century was the proof that all sufficiently smooth functions can be *expanded* into infinite series, whose terms are constant multiples of the *eigenfunctions* of any S-L system with discrete spectrum. The present chapter will be devoted to proving this result for regular S-L systems, and to explaining some of its applications.

The most familiar example of such an expansion into eigenfunctions is expansion into Fourier series. We begin by recalling† from the advanced calculus two basic results about Fourier series. The first of these is

FOURIER'S CONVERGENCE THEOREM. *Let $f(x)$ be any continuously differentiable periodic function of period 2π, and let*

$$(1) \qquad a_k = \frac{1}{\pi}\int_{-\pi}^{\pi} f(x)\cos kx\,dx, \quad b_k = \frac{1}{\pi}\int_{-\pi}^{\pi} f(x)\sin kx\,dx.$$

Then the infinite series

$$(2) \qquad a_0/2 + a_1\cos x + b_1\sin x + a_2\cos 2x + b_2\sin 2x + \cdots$$

converges uniformly to $f(x)$.

Though there exist continuous functions whose Fourier series are not convergent, the following sharpened form of Fourier's Convergence Theorem applies to all continuous periodic functions.

FEJÉR'S CONVERGENCE THEOREM. *Let $f(x)$ be any continuous periodic function of period 2π, and let*

$$\begin{aligned}\sigma_N(x) &= \frac{1}{N}\left\{\sum_{n=0}^{N-1}\left[a_0/2 + \sum_{k=1}^{n}(a_k\cos kx + b_k\sin kx)\right]\right\}\\ &= a_0/2 + \sum_{k=1}^{N-1}(\alpha_k^N\cos kx + \beta_k^N\sin kx),\end{aligned}$$

where $\alpha_k^N = (1-(k/N))a_k$, $\beta_k^N = (1-(k/N))b_k$, be the arithmetic mean of the first N partial sums of the Fourier series of $f(x)$. Then the sequence of functions $\sigma_N(x)$ converges uniformly to $f(x)$.

†Fourier's Theorem is proved in Courant, Vol. 1, p. 439; Fejér's Theorem is proved in Widder, p. 353.

The preceding results, which we will assume as known, yield as corollaries the following statements about cosine series and about sine series. Let $f(x)$ be continuous on $0 \leqq x \leqq \pi$; define a function $g(x)$ for $-\pi \leqq x \leqq \pi$ by the equation $g(x) = f(|x|)$. Since $g(-\pi) = g(\pi)$, $g(x)$ can be extended to an even periodic function of period 2π, defined and continuous for all real x. By symmetry, all coefficients b_k are zero in the Fourier series of $g(x)$. Applying Fejér's and Fourier's Convergence Theorems, we have

COROLLARY 1. *Any continuous function on $0 \leqq x \leqq \pi$ can be approximated uniformly arbitrarily closely by linear combinations of cosine functions. If the function is of class $\mathfrak{C}^1$ and $f'(0) = f'(\pi) = 0$, then it can be expanded into a uniformly convergent series of cosine functions:*

$$f(x) = a_{0/2} + a_1 \cos x + a_2 \cos 2x + \cdots. \tag{2'}$$

By a linear transformation of the independent variable, the preceding result can be extended to any closed interval $[a,b]$; the required cosine functions are the functions $\cos [k\pi(x - a)/(b - a)]$.

Similarly, if $f(0) = f(\pi) = 0$, define $h(x)$ as $f(x)$ on $0 \leqq x \leqq \pi$, and as $-f(-x)$ on $-\pi \leqq x \leqq 0$. This gives an odd continuous periodic function of period 2π, in whose Fourier series all a_k vanish.

COROLLARY 2. *Any function of class $\mathfrak{C}^1$ on $0 \leqq x \leqq \pi$ which satisfies $f(0) = f(\pi) = 0$ can be expanded into a uniformly convergent series of sine functions.*

The preceding corollaries are examples of expansions into the eigenfunctions of the two regular S-L systems defined by the DE $u'' + \lambda u = 0$ and the separated endpoint conditions $u'(0) = u'(\pi) = 0$ and $u(0) = u(\pi) = 0$, respectively. We will prove below that analogous expansions are possible into the eigenfunctions of *any* regular S-L system.

2. Orthogonal expansions. Let $\phi_1(x)$, $\phi_2(x)$, $\phi_3(x)$, $\cdots$ be any bounded functions on an interval I: $a < x < b$, square-integrable and orthogonal with respect to a positive weight function $\rho(x)$, so that

$$\int_I \phi_h(x)\phi_k(x)\rho(x)dx = 0 \quad \text{if} \quad h \neq k. \tag{3}$$

Suppose that a given function $f(x)$ can be expressed as the limit of a *uniformly* convergent series of multiples of the ϕ_k, so that

$$f(x) = c_1\phi_1(x) + c_2\phi_2(x) + c_3\phi_3(x) + \cdots = \sum_{h=1}^{\infty} c_h\phi_h(x). \tag{4}$$

Multiplying both sides of (4) by $\phi_k(x)\rho(x)$, and integrating term-by-term over the interval — as is possible for uniformly convergent series — we get from the orthogonality relations (3) the equation

$$\int_I f(x)\phi_k(x)\rho(x)dx = \sum_{h=1}^{\infty} \int_I c_h\phi_h(x)\phi_k(x)\rho(x)dx$$
$$= c_k \int_I \phi_k^2(x)\rho(x)dx.$$

Hence the coefficients c_h in (4) must satisfy the equation

$$c_h = \left\{\int_I f(x)\phi_h(x)\rho(x)dx\right\} \Big/ \left\{\int_I \phi_h^2(x)\rho(x)dx\right\}. \tag{5}$$

When the ϕ_k are the trigonometric functions, from this identity we obtain as a special case the coefficients $c_1 = a_0/2$, $c_2 = a_1$, $c_3 = b_1, \cdots$ of the Fourier series (1)–(2) with $\rho = 1$, using the familiar integrals

$$\int_{-\pi}^{\pi} dx = 2\pi, \qquad \int_{-\pi}^{\pi} \cos^2 kx\, dx = \int_{-\pi}^{\pi} \sin^2 kx\, dx = \pi,$$

for any nonzero integer k.

We can summarize the preceding result as follows.

THEOREM 1. *If a function $f(x)$ is the limit $f(x) = \Sigma c_k\phi_k(x)$ of a uniformly convergent series of constant multiples of bounded square-integrable functions $\phi_k(x)$ which are orthogonal with respect to a weight function $\rho(x)$, then the coefficients c_h are given by* (5).

The preceding conclusion holds provided one can integrate the series $\Sigma c_h\phi_h(x)\phi_k(x)\rho(x)$ term-by-term on the interval I. This holds much more generally than for uniform convergence — e.g., for mean square convergence as defined below.

3. Mean square approximation. So far, we have considered uniformly convergent series, because these can be integrated term-by-term. The notion of convergence which is most appropriate for orthogonal expansions is however not uniform convergence, but *mean square convergence,* which we now define.

DEFINITION. *Let f and the terms of the sequence $\{f_n\}$ $(n = 1, 2, 3, \cdots)$ be square-integrable real functions. The sequence $\{f_n\}$ is said to converge to f in the* mean square *on I, with respect to the positive weight function $\rho(x)$, when*

$$\int_I [f_n(x) - f(x)]^2\rho(x)\, dx \to 0 \quad \text{as} \quad n \to \infty. \tag{6}$$

Now suppose that $\phi_1, \phi_2, \phi_3, \cdots$ form an infinite sequence of square-integrable functions on the interval I, *orthogonal* with respect to the weight function ρ, and let $f_n(x) = \gamma_1\phi_1(x) + \cdots + \gamma_n\phi_n(x)$ be the n-th partial sum of the series $\sum_{k=1}^{\infty} \gamma_k\phi_k(x)$. To make the partial sums f_n converge in the mean square to f as rapidly as possible, we choose the coefficients γ_k so as to minimize the expression

$$(7) \qquad E = E(\gamma_1, \cdots, \gamma_n) = \int_I \left[f(x) - \sum_{k=1}^{n} \gamma_k\phi_k(x)\right]^2 \rho(x)dx.$$

Expanding (7), and using the orthogonality relations (3), the function E of the variables $\gamma_1, \gamma_2, \cdots, \gamma_n$ is given by the expression

$$(7') \qquad E = \int_I f^2\rho\, dx - 2\sum_{k=1}^{n} \gamma_k \int_I f\phi_k\rho\, dx + \sum_{k=1}^{n} \gamma_k^2 \int_I \phi_k^2\rho\, dx.$$

Now consider the numbers $\gamma_1, \gamma_2, \cdots, \gamma_n$, which minimize the function E. Since E is differentiable in each of its variables, the minimum can only be attained by setting $\partial E/\partial\gamma_k = 0$. That is, a necessary condition for a minimum is that the γ_k satisfy the equations

$$0 = -2\int_I f\phi_k\rho\, dx + 2\gamma_k \int_I \phi_k^2\rho\, dx.$$

Solving for γ_k, we get $\gamma_k = \{\int f\phi_k\rho\, dx\}/\{\int \phi_k^2\, \rho\, dx\}$, which is the same as equation (5) for the c_k, in another notation.

We now show that the choice $\gamma_k = c_k$, where

$$(8) \qquad c_k = \left\{\int_I f(x)\phi_k(x)\rho(x)dx\right\} \Big/ \left\{\int_I \phi_k^2(x)\rho(x)dx\right\}$$

does indeed give a minimum for E. A simple calculation, completing the square, gives for E the expression

$$(8') \qquad E = \int_I [f - \sum\gamma_k\phi_k]^2\rho\, dx$$
$$= \int_I f^2\rho\, dx + \sum_{k=1}^{n} [-c_k^2 + (\gamma_k - c_k)^2] \int_I \phi_k^2\rho\, dx.$$

The right side shows that the minimum is attained if and only if $\gamma_k = c_k$. This proves, for any interval I,

THEOREM 2. *Let $\{\phi_k(x)\}$ be a sequence of orthogonal square-integrable functions, and let f be square-integrable. Then, among all possible choices of $\gamma_1, \cdots, \gamma_n$, the integral* (7) *is minimized by selecting $\gamma_k = c_k$, where c_k is defined by* (8).

The coefficients c_k are called the *Fourier coefficients* of f relative to the orthogonal sequence ϕ_k.

The partial sum $c_1\phi_1(x) + \cdots + c_n\phi_n(x)$ in Theorem 1 is thus, for each

n, the *best mean square approximation* to $f(x)$ among all possible sums $\gamma_1\phi_1(x) + \cdots + \gamma_n\phi_n(x)$; it is often called the *least square approximation* to $f(x)$, because it minimizes the mean square difference (7). The remarkable feature of least square approximation by orthogonal functions is that the choice of the coefficients γ_k is independent of n. This is not true, for example, of least square approximation by nonorthogonal functions, of the approximations in Fejér's Theorem, or of best *uniform* approximation minimizing $\sup_{a<x<b} \left| f(x) - \sum_{k=1}^{n} c_k\phi_k(x) \right|$.

Orthonormal functions. The preceding formulas become much simpler when the orthogonal functions ϕ_k are *orthonormal,* in the sense that $\int \phi_k^2\rho\, dx = 1$. For a sequence of orthonormal functions, the formula for the Fourier coefficients is $c_k = \int_I f\phi_k\rho\, dx$. One can easily construct from any sequence ϕ_k of orthogonal functions an orthonormal sequence ψ_k by setting $\psi_k = \phi_k \Big/ \int_I \phi_k^2\rho\, dx$. For example, the functions

$$\frac{1}{\sqrt{2\pi}}, \qquad \frac{1}{\sqrt{\pi}} \cos kx, \qquad \frac{1}{\sqrt{\pi}} \sin kx$$

are orthonormal on $-\pi \leqq x \leqq \pi$ with respect to the weight function $\rho(x) \equiv 1$.

Substituting the condition $\int \phi_k^2\rho\, dx = 1$ into (8′), and remarking that E is nonnegative, we obtain the important

COROLLARY 1. *Let $\sum_1^n c_k\phi_k$ be the least square approximation to f by a linear combination of orthonormal functions ϕ_k. Then*

$$\sum_1^n c_k^2 \leqq \int_I f^2(x)\rho(x)dx. \tag{9}$$

For the right member of (9) to be finite, it is necessary that $f^2\rho$ be integrable — that is, that f be *square-integrable* with respect to the weight function ρ. When this is the case, the integrals (8) are also well-defined by the Schwarz inequality. Under these circumstances, since the right side of (9) is independent of n, if we let n tend to infinity we will still have

$$\sum_1^\infty c_k^2 \leqq \int_I f^2(x)\rho(x)dx < +\infty \qquad \text{(Bessel inequality).} \tag{10}$$

That is, *the Fourier coefficients of any square-integrable function f form a square-summable sequence of numbers, if the ϕ_k are orthonormal.*

4. Completeness. The most important question about a sequence of continuous functions ϕ_k ($k = 1, 2, 3, \cdots$), orthogonal and square-integrable with respect to a weight function ρ, is the following: can *every* square-integrable function f be expanded into an infinite series† $f = \sum_1^\infty c_k\phi_k$ of the ϕ_k? When this is possible for every continuous f,‡ the sequence of orthogonal functions ϕ_k is said to be *complete*.

Using the fundamental equation (8′) on mean square approximation, we can reformulate the definition of completeness as follows. In order that

$$\lim_{n\to\infty} \int_I \left[f(x) - \sum_{k=1}^n \gamma_k\phi_k\right]^2 \rho(x)dx = 0,$$

it is necessary and sufficient that

$$\lim_{n\to\infty} \left\{\left[\int_I f^2\rho\, dx - \sum_1^n c_k^2 \int_I \phi_k^2\rho\, dx\right] + \sum_{k=1}^n (\gamma_k - c_k)^2 \int_I \phi_k^2\rho\, dx\right\} = 0.$$

Since the term in square brackets is nonnegative by the Bessel inequality (10), and since $\int \phi_k^2\rho\, dx > 0$ for any nontrivial ϕ_k, the limit is zero if and only if $\gamma_k = c_k$ for all k, and equality holds in the Bessel inequality (10). This proves

THEOREM 3. *A sequence $\{\phi_k\}$ of functions $\phi_k(x)$, orthogonal and square-integrable with positive weight $\rho(x)$ on an interval I, is* complete *if and only if*

$$\int_I f^2(x)\rho(x)dx = \sum_{k=1}^\infty \left[\int_I f(x)\phi_k(x)\rho(x)dx\right]^2 \Big/ \int_I \phi_k^2(x)\rho(x)dx,$$

for all continuous square-integrable functions f.

COROLLARY 1. *If the $\phi_k(x)$ are orthonormal, then a necessary and sufficient condition for completeness is the validity of the* Parseval equality

$$\int_I f^2(x)\rho(x)dx = \sum_{k=1}^\infty \left[\int_I f(x)\phi_k(x)\rho(x)dx\right]^2, \tag{11}$$

for all continuous square-integrable functions f.

For example, take the case of Fourier series. In the notation of (1), the condition for the completeness of the functions 1, $\cos kx$, $\sin kx$ on $-\pi \leqq x \leqq \pi$ is that for all continuous functions f,

$$\pi\left[a_0^2/2 + \sum_{k=1}^\infty (a_k^2 + b_k^2)\right] = \int_{-\pi}^\pi f^2(x)dx. \tag{12}$$

†Here and below, the equation $f = \sum_1^\infty c_k\phi_k$ is to be interpreted in the sense of mean square convergence, namely, that the partial sums $\sum_{k=1}^n c_k\phi_k$ converge in the mean square to the function f with respect to ρ.

‡If every continuous function can be expanded into a series $\Sigma c_k\phi_k$, then many discontinuous functions also have such an expansion, convergent in the mean square. The class of all such functions is that of all Lebesgue square-integrable functions (see § 11). We are here considering only continuous functions in order to avoid assuming a knowledge of the Lebesgue integral.

It follows from Fourier's Convergence Theorem, integrating the squares of the partial sums of (2), that identity (12) holds if f is a continuously differentiable periodic function.

We shall now prove that identity (12) holds for all continuous periodic functions f. By Fejér's Convergence Theorem, the sums

$$\text{(13)}\quad \sigma_N(x) = \frac{a_0}{2} + \sum_{k=1}^{N-1}\left(1 - \frac{k}{N}\right)a_k \cos kx + \sum_{k=1}^{N-1}\left(1 - \frac{k}{N}\right)b_k \sin kx$$

converge uniformly to a continuous periodic function $f(x)$ for $-\pi \leqq x \leqq \pi$. Therefore $\int_{-\pi}^{\pi} \sigma_N^2\, dx$ converges as $N \to \infty$ to $\int_{-\pi}^{\pi} f^2\, dx$. Evaluating the integral by (13), we find that

$$\text{(14)}\qquad \lim_{N\to\infty} \pi\left[\frac{a_0^2}{2} + \sum_{k=1}^{N-1}\left(1 - \frac{k}{N}\right)^2 (a_k^2 + b_k^2)\right] = \int_{-\pi}^{\pi} f^2(x)dx.$$

Now, by the Bessel inequality,

$$\pi\left[a_0^2/2 + \sum_{k=1}^{\infty} (a_k^2 + b_k^2)\right] \leqq \int_{-\pi}^{\pi} f^2 dx < \infty.$$

Since $[1 - (k/N)]^2 \leqq 1$, it follows that, if we replace the sum in square brackets on the left side of (14) by $a_0^2/2 + \sum_{k=1}^{N} (a_k^2 + b_k^2)$, we will get an increasing sequence whose limit is at least equal to $\int f^2 dx$. But, by Bessel's inequality, this limit is at most equal to $\int f^2 dx$. Hence the limit is exactly $\int f^2 dx$, and (12) is proved. Since any continuous function on $-\pi \leqq x \leqq \pi$ can be given an arbitrarily close mean square approximation by a continuous function satisfying $f(-\pi) = f(\pi)$, this proves

Corollary 2. *The trigonometric functions* $\cos kx$, $\sin kx$ $(k = 0, 1, 2, \cdots)$ *are a complete orthogonal sequence in the interval* $-\pi \leqq x \leqq \pi$.

Using the method of Corollary 2 of § 1 and changing variables, we obtain

Corollary 3. *The functions* $\cos\,[k\pi(x - a)/(b - a)]$ $(k = 0,\ 1,\ 2, \cdots)$ *form a complete orthogonal sequence in the interval* $a \leqq x \leqq b$.

We conclude this section with the following criterion for completeness of a sequence of orthogonal functions, which relates the notion of completeness to that of *approximation* in the sense of mean square convergence.

Theorem 4. *Let* $\{\phi_k\}$ $(k = 1, 2, \cdots)$ *be any sequence of orthogonal square-integrable functions on an interval* I, *relative to a weight function* $\rho > 0$.

The sequence is complete if and only if every continuous square-integrable function can be approximated arbitrarily closely in the mean square by a linear combination of the ϕ_k.

Proof. The condition is clearly necessary. Conversely, suppose that, given $\epsilon > 0$, we can find a linear combination $\sum_{k=1}^{n} \gamma_k\phi_k$ such that

$$\int_I \left(f - \sum_{k=1}^{n} \gamma_k\phi_k\right)^2 \rho\, dx < \epsilon.$$

If we replace each of the γ_k by the Fourier coefficients c_k of f relative to ϕ_k — as given by formula (5) — then, by Theorem 2, the square-integral on the left decreases:

$$\int_I \left(f - \sum_{k=1}^{n} c_k\phi_k\right)^2 \rho\, dx < \epsilon.$$

But this is precisely what we had to prove.

5. Orthogonal polynomials. We will now prove the completeness of the eigenfunctions of some of the singular S-L systems studied in Chapter X. These are the S-L systems on a *finite* interval whose eigenfunctions are polynomials, such as the Legendre polynomials.

One can use any positive *weight function* $\rho(x)$ on an interval (a,b) such that $\int_a^b x^n\rho(x)dx$ is convergent for all $n \geqq 0$ to construct an infinite sequence of polynomial functions $P_0(x)$, $P_1(x)$, $P_2(x)$, $\cdots$, with $P_n(x)$ of degree n, which are orthogonal on (a,b):

$$\int_a^b P_m(x)P_n(x)\rho(x)dx = 0, \qquad m \neq n. \tag{15}$$

Equations (15) define $P_n(x)$ uniquely up to an arbitrary factor of proportionality, the normalization constant.

Given a weight function $\rho(x)$, one can compute the $P_n(x)$ explicitly from (15); the computations will not be described here.† Instead, we shall derive some interesting general properties of orthogonal polynomials.

We shall first establish the fact that, on any *finite* interval, such sequences of orthogonal polynomials are *complete*. To prove this, we will need the following result.

LEMMA. *Every uniformly convergent sequence of continuous functions is mean-square convergent on any interval I, with respect to any integrable positive weight function* $\left(\int_I \rho\, dx < \infty\right)$.

†It is the Gram-Schmidt orthogonalization process applied to the vectors $1, x, x^2, \cdots$. This process can be applied in any Euclidean vector space (Birkhoff and Mac Lane, pp. 192–193).

This follows immediately from the inequality

$$(16)\quad \int_I [f_n(x) - f(x)]^2 \rho(x)dx \leqq \max [(f_n(x) - f(x))^2] \int_I \rho(x)dx,$$

valid when I is any finite or infinite interval. On an infinite interval, however, one must carefully check the integrability of the weight function. For instance, the functions $f_n(x) = n^{-1/2} \exp(-x^2/n^2)$ converge uniformly to the zero function on the interval $-\infty < x < \infty$, but the integrals $\int_{-\infty}^{\infty} f_n^2(x)dx$ do not converge to zero.

Using this lemma, it is easy to prove the completeness of a sequence of *orthogonal polynomials* defined on a *finite* interval I relative to any continuous integrable weight function $\rho(x)$. We shall use the fundamental

WEIERSTRASS APPROXIMATION THEOREM. *Let $f(x)$ be any function continuous on a finite closed interval $a \leqq x \leqq b$, and let $\epsilon > 0$ be any positive number. Then there exists a polynomial $p(x)$, such that $|p(x) - f(x)| \leqq \epsilon$ for all x on $a \leqq x \leqq b$.*†

From this theorem, and the inequality (16), we infer

THEOREM 5. *Let $P_n(x)$ $(n = 0, 1, 2, \cdots)$ be a polynomial function of degree n. For a fixed finite interval I: $a \leqq x \leqq b$, let*

$$\int_a^b P_m(x)P_n(x)\rho(x)dx = 0 \quad \text{if} \quad m \neq n,$$

where $\rho(x)$ is a continuous integrable positive weight function. Then the orthogonal polynomials $P_n(x)$ are complete on I.

Proof. Let $p(x)$ be any polynomial of degree n. We can find c_n such that $p(x) - c_nP_n(x)$ is a polynomial of degree $n - 1$ or less. Hence, by induction on n, we can express $p(x)$ as a finite linear combination of $P_0(x), \cdots, P_n(x)$. By the Weierstrass Approximation Theorem, we can approximate uniformly *any* continuous function arbitrarily closely by a suitable polynomial $p(x)$. By the preceding lemma, every continuous function can therefore be approximated arbitrarily closely in the mean square by a linear combination of the P_k. The result now follows from Theorem 4.

The completeness of Legendre, Chebyshev, Gegenbauer (or ultraspherical) and other Jacobi polynomials (see Ch. IX, § 11) follows as a corollary. But it is harder to prove the completeness of polynomials orthogonal on semi-infinite and infinite intervals, such as the Hermite polynomials and the Laguerre polynomials introduced in the next section.

†See Widder, p. 426, or Courant-Hilbert, Vol. 1, p. 65.

EXERCISES A

1. Show that $a_k \cos kx + b_k \sin kx = (1/\pi) \int_{-\pi}^{\pi} f(t) \cos (k(t-x))dt$.

2. Show that $1/2 + \sum_{k=1}^{n} \cos kx = \sin [(2n+1)x/2]/(2 \sin(x/2))$.

3. Using Ex. 2, infer that

$$a_0/2 + \sum_{k=1}^{n} (a_k \cos kx + b_k \sin kx) = \frac{1}{\pi} \int_{-\pi}^{\pi} f(t) \frac{\sin [(2n+1)(t-x)/2]}{2 \sin [(t-x)/2]}.$$

4. (a) Prove in detail Corollaries 1–2 of Theorem 1, discussing with care the differentiability at 0 and π of the periodic functions constructed.

(b) Find necessary and sufficient conditions for a continuous function on $[0,\pi]$ to be uniformly approximable by a linear combination of functions $\sin kx$.

5. Show that, in Fejér's convergence theorem,

$$\sigma_n(x) = \frac{1}{2\pi n} \int_{-\pi}^{\pi} f(x+t) \left[\frac{\sin (nt/2)}{\sin (t/2)}\right]^2 dt.$$

*6. Prove Fejér's theorem, assuming Ex. 5.

For the following regular S-L systems, (a) find the eigenvalues and eigenfunctions, (b) obtain an expansion formula for a function $f \in \mathcal{C}^1$ into a series of eigenfunctions.

7. $u'' + \lambda u = 0$, $u(0) = 0$, $u'(\pi) = 0$, $0 \leqq x \leqq \pi$,

8. The same DE with $u'(0) = 0$, $u(\pi) = 0$.

9. Show that the trigonometric functions are orthogonal, for any a, in

$$-\pi - a \leqq x \leqq \pi - a.$$

10. Show that if $f_n \to f$ in the mean square, and c_k, $c_k^{(n)}$ are the Fourier coefficients of f, f_n relative to a given orthonormal sequence ϕ_k, then $c_k^{(n)} \to c_k$ uniformly in k.

11. Using expansions into Legendre polynomials, obtain a formula for the best mean square approximation in $|x| \leqq 1$ of a square-integrable function by polynomials of degree $\leqq n$.

*12. Using the Prüfer substitution, obtain from Fourier's Theorem an expansion theorem for functions $f \in \mathcal{C}^2[-1,1]$ into series of Chebyshev polynomials.

*13. Show that, given square-integrable functions $f_1, \cdots, f_n$, a sequence $\phi_1, \cdots, \phi_m$ of orthonormal square-integrable functions can be found for which f_k is a linear combination of $\phi_1, \cdots, \phi_k$, $1 \leqq k \leqq m$.

***6. Properties of orthogonal polynomials.** We shall now develop some of the properties of orthogonal polynomials which depend only upon the fact that they are orthogonal, irrespective of completeness. These properties apply to the classical orthogonal polynomials, which are the Legendre, Gegenbauer (or ultraspherical), Chebyshev, and Jacobi polynomials whose completeness has been proved, and to the Hermite, and Laguerre polynomials. All these polynomials have been met before, except the Laguerre polynomials, which we now define.

EXAMPLE 1. Consider the singular S-L system consisting of the DE

$$(xu')' + [\alpha + (2-x)/4]u = 0, \qquad 0 < x < \infty, \tag{17}$$

with the endpoint conditions that $u(x)$ is bounded as $x \to \infty$ and as $x \to 0$.

Setting $u(x) = v(x)e^{-x/2}$, we get the Laguerre DE

(18) $$xv'' + (1 - x)v' + \alpha v = 0.$$

Trying $v = \sum_{k=0}^{\infty} a_k x^k$, the Method of Undetermined Coefficients (Ch. III, § 2) gives the recurrence relation $a_{k+1} = (k - \alpha)a_k/(k+1)^2$. Hence

(19) $$a_k = (-1)^k \alpha(\alpha - 1)(\alpha - 2) \cdots (\alpha - k + 1)a_0/(k!)^2.$$

The series is a polynomial if and only if $\alpha = n$, a nonnegative integer; otherwise it represents a function which grows exponentially at infinity. Normalizing the polynomial (for $\alpha = n$) by the condition $a_n = (-1)^n/(n!)$, one gets the *Laguerre polynomials*†:

(19′) $$L_n(x) = \sum_{k=0}^{n} (-1)^k \binom{n}{k} \frac{x^k}{k!}.$$

For example, $L_0(x) = 1$, $L_1(x) = 1 - x$, $L_2(x) = 1 - 2x + \frac{1}{2}x^2$,

$$L_3(x) = 1 - 3x + \frac{3}{2}x^2 - \frac{1}{6}x^3, \quad \text{etc.}$$

Thus, the functions $L_n(x)e^{-x}$ are eigenfunctions of a singular S-L system. These functions are certainly square-integrable, together with their derivatives; hence Theorem 2 of Chapter X applies, giving the orthogonality relations

$$\int_0^{\infty} e^{-x} L_m(x) L_n(x)dx = 0, \qquad m \neq n.$$

We shall now consider some of the fundamental properties of an arbitrary sequence of *orthogonal polynomials* (not necessarily solutions of a DE) $P_0(x), \cdots, P_n(x), \cdots$, where P_n is of degree n. As in § 5, we assume that the weight function $\rho(x)$ is such that all products $x^n\rho(x)$ are integrable on I. We do not assume that the interval I is finite.

We first derive a result similar to the Sturm Oscillation Theorem:

THEOREM 6. *Let* $\{P_n\}$ $(n = 0, 1, 2, \cdots)$ *be any sequence of polynomials orthogonal in a given interval* (a,b). *Then the polynomial* $P_n(x)$ *of degree* n *has* n *distinct zeros, all contained in the interval* (a,b).

Proof. Suppose that $P_n(x)$ had fewer than n zeros in (a,b). Let $x_1, \cdots, x_m$ be those zeros at which $P(x)$ changes sign. Then the polynomial $(x - x_1)(x - x_2) \cdots (x - x_m)P(x)$ would be of constant sign. Hence

$$\int_a^b (x - x_1) \cdots (x - x_m)P_n(x)\rho(x)dx \neq 0, \; m < n.$$

†The normalizing condition $a_n = 1$ is also often used, and makes some formulas simpler.

But $(x - x_1) \cdots (x - x_m)$ is a polynomial of degree lower than n. Therefore it can be written as a linear combination of the polynomials $P_0, \cdots, P_m$, say $\sum_{k=0}^{m} C_k P_k(x)$, $m < n$. Hence

$$\int_a^b (x - x_1) \cdots (x - x_m) P_n(x) \rho(x) dx = \int_a^b \sum_{k=0}^{m} C_k P_k(x) P_n(x) \rho(x) dx$$
$$= \sum_{k=0}^{n} C_k \int_a^b P_k P_m \rho \, dx = 0$$

a patent contradiction. Hence $P_n(x)$ has at least n zeros on (a,b). Since a polynomial of degree n has at most n zeros, the proof is complete.

Next, we shall establish a *recursion formula* for an arbitrary system of orthogonal polynomials.

THEOREM 7. *Any three orthogonal polynomials of consecutive degree satisfy a linear relation*

$$P_{n+1}(x) = (A_n x + B_n) P_n(x) + C_n P_{n-1}(x), \tag{20}$$

for suitable constants A_n, B_n, C_n.

Proof. First choose A_n such that $P_{n+1}(x) - xA_nP_n(x)$ is a polynomial of degree n or less, so that

$$P_{n+1}(x) - xA_nP_n(x) = \gamma_0 P_n(x) + \gamma_1 P_{n-1}(x) + \cdots + \gamma_n P_0.$$

Multiplying both sides by $P_k(x)\rho(x)$, integrating from a to b, and using the orthogonality relation, we find that $\gamma_k = 0$ for $k = 2, 3, \cdots, n$. Hence

$$P_{n+1}(x) - xA_nP_n(x) = \gamma_0 P_n(x) + \gamma_1 P_{n-1}(x).$$

Therefore set $\gamma_2 = B_n$ and $\gamma_1 = C_n$, q.e.d.

The numerical values of the constants A_n, B_n, C_n in Theorem 7 depend on the normalizing factors used to define the orthogonal polynomials considered. In Table 1, we have listed for convenience the recursion coefficients for some common polynomials.

Table 1. Recursion Coefficients

Polynomial	A_n	B_n	C_n
Legendre	$\frac{2n+1}{n+1}$	0	$\frac{-n}{n+1}$
Chebyshev	2	0	-1
Gegenbauer	$\frac{2n+\lambda}{n+1}$	0	$\frac{1-n-2\lambda}{n+1}$
Hermite	2	0	$-2n$
Laguerre	$\frac{-1}{n+1}$	$\frac{2n+1}{n+1}$	$\frac{-n}{n+1}$

EXERCISES B

Establish the following formulas for Hermite polynomials (see Ch. III, §2):

1. $H_{n+1}(x) = 2x\, H_n(x) - 2n\, H_{n-1}(x)$,
2. $H_n'(x) = nH_{n-1}(x)$,

*3. $\sum_{k=0}^{\infty} H_k(x)t^k/k! = e^{xt-t^2/2}$. (Generating function)

4. Establish the recursion formula for the Laguerre polynomials

$$L_n(x) = L_n'(x) - L_{n+1}'(x).$$

(*Hint:* Differentiate the recursion formula for L_n.)

5. Show that the functions $\phi_n(x) = e^{x/2} \dfrac{d^n}{dx^n}(e^{-x}x^n)$ are orthogonal in $0 < x < \infty$.

6. Infer from Ex. 5 that $(n!)\ \phi_n(x) = e^{-x/2}\, L_n(x)$, where L_n is the n-th Laguerre polynomial.

7. Show that, if $L_n(x)$ is the Laguerre polynomial of degree n, then $d^k[L_n(x)]/dx^k$ satisfies the DE

$$xv'' + (k + 1 - x)v' + (n - k)v = 0.$$

8. Prove the recursion formula of Table 1:

$$(n + 1)L_{n+1}(x) = (2n + 1 - x)L_n(x) - nL_{n-1}(x).$$

9. Let $P_k(x)$ be a sequence of orthogonal polynomials with weight function ρ in $a < x < b$, and let $c_k = \int_a^b f(x)P_k(x)\rho(x)dx$. Show that the partial sum

$$\sigma_n(x) = \sum_{k=0}^{n} c_kP_k(x)$$

coincides with $f(x)$ in at least $n + 1$ points of the interval. (*Hint:* Use a method similar to the proof of Theorem 6.)

*10. Let P_n be a sequence of orthogonal polynomials in (a,b). Show that between any two zeros of P_n there is exactly one zero of P_{n+1}.

*11. Show that the Legendre polynomials are the only Gegenbauer polynomials for which the maximum of $|\, P_n^\alpha(x)\, |$, namely $P_n^\alpha(1)$, is independent of n.

*12. (a) Expand the function $(1 - 2xh + h^2)^{-1/2}(|\, x\, | < 1)$ into a series of Legendre polynomials, and show that the n-th Fourier coefficient is $2h^n/(2n + 1)$.

(b) Obtain from (a) the formula

$$(1 - 2xh + h^2)^{-1/2} = \sum_{k=0}^{\infty} h^kP_k(x) \quad \text{for} \quad |\, h\, | < \sqrt{2} - 1.$$

*13. Show that the generating function for the Laguerre polynomials is $g(x,t) = (1 - t)^{-1} \exp[-xt/(1 - t)]$, that is, that

$$\sum_{k=0}^{\infty} t^nL_n(x)/n! = g(x,t).$$

In Exs. 14–17, $D = d/dx$, $\rho(x)$ is positive. The method of proof is to find by induction a S-L equation satisfied by the expressions given.

*14. Show that the only orthogonal polynomials of the form

$$p_n(x) = K_n(\rho(x))^{-1}D^n[\rho(x)] \quad \text{for} \quad \rho(x) \in \mathcal{C}^\infty$$

are the Hermite polynomials.

*15. Show that the only orthogonal polynomials of the form

$$p_n(x) = K_n(\rho(x))^{-1}D^n[\rho(x)(ax + b)]$$

are the Laguerre polynomials, after a change of independent variable.

*16. Show that the only system of orthogonal polynomials of the form

$$K_n(\rho(x))^{-1}D^n[\rho(x)(ax^2 + bx + c)]$$

are the Jacobi polynomials, after a change of independent variable.

*17. Show that the only sequences of orthogonal polynomials satisfying a Rodrigues formula $p_n(x) = K_n(\rho(x))^{-1}D^n[\rho(x)p(x)]$, where p is a given polynomial, are the Jacobi, Laguerre, and Hermite polynomials.

***7. Chebyshev polynomials.** The Chebyshev polynomials $T_n(x)$ were introduced in Ch. IX, § 11, as solutions of the self-adjoint DE

$$[(1 - x^2)^{1/2}u']' + \lambda(1 - x^2)^{-1/2}u = 0, \qquad -1 < x < 1. \tag{21}$$

The Liouville normal form of this DE is $u_{\theta\theta} + \lambda u = 0$, obtained by setting $w = u$ and $\theta = \int_{-1}^{x} d\xi/\sqrt{1 - \xi^2}$, or $x = \cos\theta$, $0 < \theta < \pi$. For integral n and $\lambda = n^2$, two linearly independent solutions of this equation are

$$\cos n\theta = T_n\,(\cos\theta) = T_n(x) \tag{21a}$$

and $S_n(x)$ given by the formula

$$S_n(x) = \sin n\theta = \sin\,(n - 1)\theta\,\cos\theta + \sin\theta\,\cos\,(n - 1)\theta. \tag{21b}$$

From the forms of the preceding explicit solutions, one sees that the functions $T_n(x)$ are eigenfunctions of the singular S-L system defined from (21) by the boundary conditions that $u'(-1)$ and $u'(1)$ be finite. All solutions of (21) are bounded at the singular points $x = \pm 1$, as is apparent from inspection of explicit solutions (21a)–(21b), and also from a calculation of the roots $\nu = 0$, $1/2$ of the indicial equation $2\nu^2 - \nu = 0$ of the normal form of (21). But only multiples of the $T_n(x)$ have bounded derivatives at the endpoints.

Minimax property. The most striking property of the Chebyshev polynomials is contained in the following result.

THEOREM 8. *Among all monic polynomials* $P(x) = x^n + \sum_{k=0}^{n-1} a_k x^k$ *of degree* n, $2^{1-n}T_n(x)$ *minimizes* $\max_{-1 \leqq x \leqq 1} |P(x)|$ *(Minimax property).*

Proof. For $n = 0, 1$, the result follows by inspection. For $n \geqq 2$, it follows by induction from the recursion formula

$$T_n(x) = 2x\, T_{n-1}(x) - T_{n-2}(x),$$

which is equivalent to the trigonometric identity

$$\cos(m\theta + \theta) = 2 \cos\theta \cos m\theta + \cos(m\theta - \theta), \quad n = m + 1.$$

Next, since $T_n(\cos\theta) = \cos n\theta$, we have that

$$\max_{-1 \leqq x \leqq 1} | 2^{1-n} T_n(x) | = 2^{1-n}.$$

In order to establish the statement it therefore suffices to show that for any monic polynomial of degree n we have

$$\max_{-1 \leqq x \leqq 1} | x^n + a_{n-1}x^{n-1} + \cdots + a_0 | \geqq 2^{1-n}.$$

Suppose this were not so. Then we could find a monic polynomial $p(x)$ of degree n such that $\max_{-1 \leqq x \leqq 1} | p(x) | < 2^{1-n}$. Now, the polynomial $2^{1-n}T_n(x) - p(x)$ is of degree $n - 1$. We shall reach a contradiction by showing that this polynomial has n distinct zeros.

To see this, notice that the polynomial $2^{1-n}T_n(x)$ takes alternately the values $\pm 2^{1-n}$ at $n + 1$ points $x_0 = -1 < x_1 < \cdots < x_n = 1$, as follows immediately from $T_n(\cos\theta) = \cos n\theta$. Since $| p(x_k) | < 2^{1-n} | T_n(x_k) |$, it follows that the polynomial $2^{1-n}T_n(x) - p(x)$ takes alternately positive and negative values at $n + 1$ points. It follows from Rolle's Theorem that this polynomial of degree $n - 1$ must have at least n distinct zeros, and hence must vanish identically, q.e.d.

The *Chebyshev polynomials of the second kind* are defined by the identity $U_n(\cos\theta) \sin\theta = \sin(n + 1)\theta$. Their theory is parallel to the theory of the Chebyshev polynomials, and is developed in the exercises below.

EXERCISES C

1. Show that the DE $((1 - x^2)^{3/2}u')' + \lambda(1 - x^2)^{1/2}u = 0$ can be reduced to a DE with constant coefficients by setting $v(\theta) = (\sin\theta)u(\cos\theta)$.

2. Show that the endpoint conditions $\lim_{x \to \pm 1} \sqrt{1 - x^2}u(x) = 0$ give an S-L system with eigenvalues $\lambda_n = n(n + 2)$, from the DE of Ex. 1.

3. Show that the eigenfunction belonging to the eigenvalue λ_n is a Chebyshev polynomial of the second kind.

4. Using Ex. 3 obtain an expansion theorem of a smooth function into a series of Chebyshev polynomials of the second kind.

5. Show that $T_n(x) = U_n(x) - xU_{n-1}(x)$.

6. Show that $(1 - x^2)U_{n-1}(x) = xT_n(x) - T_{n+1}(x)$.

7. Express $U_n(x)$ in terms of the hypergeometric function.

8. Expand the function $\arccos x$ into a series of Chebyshev polynomials.

*9. Infer the Weierstrass Approximation Theorem from Fejér's Theorem.

8. Euclidean vector spaces. The concepts of mean square convergence and completeness have suggestive geometric interpretations. These interpretations are based on the properties of inner products.

Consider the set of all real functions f, g, h, $\cdots$, continuous and square-integrable on an interval I, with respect to a fixed positive weight function ρ. The interval I may be open or closed, finite, semi-infinite, or infinite. Define the *inner product* of two such functions f, g as the integral

$$(f,g) = \int_I f(x)g(x)\rho(x)dx, \quad \rho(x) > 0. \tag{22}$$

The following formulas are immediate:

$$(f+g,h) = (f,h) + (g,h), \qquad (cf,g) = c(f,g)$$
$$(f,g) = (g,f), \qquad (f,f) > 0 \quad \text{unless} \quad f \equiv 0.$$

Hence, with respect to the inner product (f,g), this set of functions is a *Euclidean vector space.*†

For real functions, the integral in (6), in the definition of mean square convergence, is the inner product $(f_n - f, f_n - f)$; hence it is the square of the *distance* $\| f_n - f \| = (f_n - f, f_n - f)^{1/2}$ between f_n and f in the Euclidean vector space E. Therefore $f_n \to f$ in the *mean square*, relative to ρ, means that the Euclidean *distance* from f_n to f in E tends to zero.

This distance enjoys the properties of distance in ordinary space, including the *triangle inequality* and the *Schwarz inequality*

$$-\| f \| \cdot \| g \| \leqq (f,g) = \| f \| \cdot \| g \| \cos \angle (f,g) \leqq \| f \| \cdot \| g \|.$$

The Schwarz inequality shows that f and g are *orthogonal* if and only if the angle

$$\theta = \angle (f,g) = \arccos [(f,g)/\| f \| \cdot \| g \|], \qquad 0 \leqq \theta \leqq \pi$$

is 90°; it gives a geometrical interpretation to the definition of orthogonal functions.

We shall now generalize Theorems 1, 2, 3, and 4 to an arbitrary Euclidean vector space E.

If $\{\phi_k\}$ is a sequence of orthogonal vectors in E, and $f \in E$ is given, consider the squared distance

$$E(\gamma_1, \cdots, \gamma_n) = \left\| f - \sum_{k=1}^n \gamma_k \phi_k \right\|^2 = \left(f - \sum_{k=1}^n \gamma_k\phi_k, f - \sum_{k=1}^n \gamma_k \phi_k\right).$$

Defining $c_k = (f,\phi_k)/(\phi_k,\phi_k)$, we obtain, as in § 3,

$$\left\| f - \sum_{k=1}^n \gamma_k \phi_k \right\|^2 = (f,f) - \sum_{k=1}^n [c_k^2(\phi_k,\phi_k)] + \sum_{k=1}^n [(c_k - \gamma_k)^2(\phi_k,\phi_k)].$$

†Birkhoff and Mac Lane, Ch. VII, §§ 10–11. The reader should familiarize himself with this notion.

Geometrically, the *least square* approximation $\sum_{k=1}^{n} c_k\phi_k$ to f appears as the *orthogonal projection* of the vector f onto the *subspace* S of all linear combinations $\gamma_1\phi_1 + \cdots + \gamma_n\phi_n$ of $\phi_1, \cdots, \phi_n$. This is because, in the orthogonal projection onto a subspace S of a vector $\mathbf{c}$ issuing from the origin, the component of $\mathbf{c}$ perpendicular to S is the *shortest* vector from S to $\mathbf{c}$. The coefficients γ_k are given by the direction cosine formulas of analytic geometry.

Completeness of the ϕ_k is defined as in § 4, as the property that

$$\lim_{n\to\infty} \left|\left| f - \sum_{k=1}^{n} c_k\phi_k \right|\right| = 0, \text{ that is, } \sum_{k=1}^{\infty} c_k\phi^k = f,$$

for every f in E. It has a simple geometric interpretation in any Euclidean vector space E. The relation $f = \sum_{1}^{\infty} c_k\phi_k$ holds if and only if the distance $|| f - \sum_{1}^{n} c_k\phi_k ||$ tends to zero as $n \to \infty$. That is, the condition for completeness is, as in the proof of Theorem 3, that one can approximate any f arbitrarily closely by finite linear combinations $c_1\phi_1 + \cdots + c_n\phi_n$ of the orthogonal vectors ϕ_k whose completeness is in question. This idea is most vividly expressed in terms of the concept of a dense subset of a Euclidean vector space.

DEFINITION. *A subset S of a Euclidean vector space E is* dense *in E, if and only if to any f in E and positive number $\delta > 0$, an element s can be found in S such that $|| s - f || < \delta$.*

As in Theorem 4, a set $\{\phi_n\}$ of orthogonal elements of E is *complete* if and only if the set S of all finite linear combinations $\sum_{1}^{n} \gamma_k\phi_k$ of the ϕ_k is dense in E.

The Parseval equality is easily derived in any Euclidean vector space E. Consider the sequence of best mean square approximations

$$f_n = \sum_{k=1}^{n} c_k\phi_k, \qquad c_k = (f,\phi_k)/(\phi_k,\phi_k)$$

to a given vector f in E. If the finite linear combinations $\sum_{1}^{n} \gamma_k\phi_k$ are dense in E, then the squared distance

$$\left|\left| \sum_{k=1}^{n} c_k\phi_k - f \right|\right|^2 = (f,f) - \sum_{k=1}^{n} [(f,\phi_k)^2/(\phi_k,\phi_k)] \geqq 0$$

must tend to zero as $n \to \infty$. Hence, if the sequence $\{\phi_n\}$ is *complete*, then

$$\sum_{k=1}^{\infty} [(f,\phi_k)^2/(\phi_k,\phi_k)] = (f,f) \qquad \text{(Parseval equality).} \tag{23}$$

Applying Parseval's equality to the vector $f + g$, and then expanding and simplifying, we obtain more generally

$$(23') \qquad \sum_{k=1}^{\infty} [(f,\phi_k)(g,\phi_k)/(\phi_k,\phi_k)] = (f,g),$$

valid whenever $\{\phi_k\}$ is complete and f, g are square-integrable. Even if Parseval's equality fails, we still get

$$(24) \qquad \sum_{k=1}^{\infty} [(f,\phi_k)^2/(\phi_k,\phi_k)] \leqq (f,f) \qquad \text{(Bessel inequality).}$$

If Parseval's equality fails, then strict inequality will occur in (24) for some f in E. For such an f we have by Theorem 1

$$\| f - \sum_{k=1}^{n} \gamma_k\phi_k \| \geqq \| f - \sum_{k=1}^{n} c_k\phi_k \| \geqq \sqrt{\delta} > 0,$$

for any choice of γ_k. Since δ is independent of n, this shows that the ϕ_k cannot be a complete set of orthogonal vectors. This gives another proof of Theorem 3, which we now restate for an arbitrary Euclidean vector space as follows:

THEOREM 9. *A sequence $\{\phi_k\}$ of orthogonal vectors of a Euclidean vector space E is* complete *if and only if the Parseval equality* (23) *holds for all f in E.*

9. Completeness of eigenfunctions. The completeness of the eigenfunctions of a regular Sturm-Liouville system is a consequence of the asymptotic formulas of Chapter X, and a geometric property of sets of orthonormal vectors in Euclidean vector spaces. This property is stated in the following theorem.

THEOREM 10. *Let $\{\phi_n\}$ be any* complete *sequence of orthonormal vectors in a Euclidean vector space E, and let $\{\psi_n\}$ be any sequence of orthonormal vectors in E which satisfies the inequality*

$$(25) \qquad \sum_{n=1}^{\infty} \| \psi_n - \phi_n \|^2 < +\infty.$$

Then the ψ_n are complete in E.

This result will be proved in §§ 10–11. It is plausible intuitively, because it asserts that completeness is preserved in passing from a set of orthonormal vectors ϕ_n to any nearby system.

Assuming Theorem 10 provisionally, we can establish the completeness of the eigenfunctions of a regular S-L system as follows.

In Chapter X, consider the asymptotic formula (53):

$$u_n(x) = \sqrt{2/(b-a)} \cos [n\pi(x-a)/(b-a)] + O(1)/n.$$

If $u_n(x)$ is the n-th normalized eigenfunction of a regular S-L system in Liouville normal form, and $\phi_n(x) = \sqrt{2/(b-a)} \cos(n\pi(x-a)/(b-a))$, this gives $|u_n(x) - \phi_n(x)| = 0(1)/n$. Squaring and integrating, we get

$$||u_n - \phi_n||^2 = \int_I [u_n(x) - \phi_n(x)]^2 dx = 0(1)/n^2.$$

Since the series $1 + 1/4 + 1/9 + \cdots + 1/n^2 + \cdots$ converges (to $\pi^2/6$), this implies the following

LEMMA. *Let $u_n(x)$ be the n-th normalized eigenfunction of any regular S-L system in Liouville normal form, and let*

$$\phi_n(x) = \sqrt{2/(b-a)} \cos[n\pi(x-a)/(b-a)].$$

Then the ϕ_n are an orthonormal sequence, and

$$\sum_{n=1}^{\infty} ||u_n - \phi_n||^2 < +\infty. \tag{26}$$

Since the cosine functions are complete (by Corollary 3 of Theorem 3), it follows from this lemma and Theorem 10 that the eigenfunctions of any regular S-L system in Liouville normal form are a complete set of orthonormal functions.

As shown in Ch. X, § 9, the transformation to Liouville normal form, applied to the (normalized) eigenfunctions, carries the inner product

$$(\phi,\psi) = \int_I \phi(x)\psi(x)\rho(x)dx,$$

into the inner product

$$(u,v) = \int_a^b u(x)v(x)dx.$$

Therefore†, the change of variable leading to Liouville normal form carries complete orthonormal sequences relative to a weight function ρ into complete orthonormal sequences. Therefore the eigenfunctions of regular S-L systems not in Liouville normal form are also complete.

THEOREM 11. *The eigenfunctions of any regular S-L system with $\alpha'\beta' \neq 0$ are* complete, *in the Euclidean vector space of square-integrable continuous functions on the interval $a \leqq x \leqq b$, relative to the weight function ρ.*

10*. Hilbert space. The set of real numbers differs from the set of rational numbers by the property that every Cauchy sequence of real numbers is convergent.‡ This property of *completeness* has an analog for Euclidean vector spaces (and, more generally, for metric spaces).

†Since distance and convergence can be defined in terms of inner products in any Euclidean vector space.

‡Courant, Vol. 1, pp. 40, 60; Widder, p. 277.

DEFINITION. *In a Euclidean vector space E, a* Cauchy sequence *is an infinite sequence of vectors* f_n *such that*

$$\|f_m - f_n\| \to 0 \quad as \quad m, n \to \infty. \tag{27}$$

The space E is called complete *when, given any Cauchy sequence* $\{f_n\}$, *there exists a vector f in E such that* $\|f_n - f\| \to 0$ *as* $n \to \infty$. *A complete Euclidean vector space is called a Hilbert space.*

Any finite-dimensional Euclidean vector space is complete; but the Euclidean vector space of continuous square-integrable functions defined in § 8 is not complete, as will appear presently.

EXAMPLE 2. Let (ℓ_2) denote the Euclidean vector space of all infinite sequences $\boldsymbol{a} = \{a_k\} = (a_1, a_2, a_3, \cdots)$ of real numbers which are square-summable, that is, satisfy $\Sigma a_k^2 < +\infty$. The vector operations on these sequences are performed term-by-term, so that $\boldsymbol{a} + \boldsymbol{b}$ is the sequence $(a_1 + b_1, a_2 + b_2, a_3 + b_3, \cdots)$. Inner products are defined by the formula

$$(\boldsymbol{a}, \boldsymbol{b}) = \sum_{k=1}^{\infty} a_k b_k = a_1 b_1 + a_2 b_2 + a_3 b_3 + \cdots \tag{28}$$

LEMMA 1. *The space* (ℓ_2) *is a Hilbert space.*

Proof. The problem is to prove completeness. To this end, let $\{\boldsymbol{a}^n\}$ be any Cauchy sequence of square-summable sequences. That is, let

$$\lim_{m, n \to \infty} \|\boldsymbol{a}^m - \boldsymbol{a}^n\|^2 = \lim_{m, n \to \infty} \left\{ \sum_{k=1}^{\infty} (a_k^m - a_k^n)^2 \right\} = 0.$$

For each fixed k, the sequence of real numbers a_k^n $(n = 1, 2, \cdots)$ (the k-th components of $\boldsymbol{a}^n$) is a Cauchy sequence, and therefore converges towards some real number a_k. Let $\boldsymbol{a} = \{a_k\}$ $(k = 1, 2, 3, \cdots)$. We must prove that the sequence $\boldsymbol{a}$ is square-summable and that $\boldsymbol{a}^n \to \boldsymbol{a}$ in the Euclidean vector space.

Since $|\,\|\boldsymbol{a}^n\| - \|\boldsymbol{a}^m\|\,| \leqq \|\boldsymbol{a}^n - \boldsymbol{a}^m\|$ by the triangle inequality, it follows that the sequence $\|\boldsymbol{a}^n\|$ is bounded. Let $\sqrt{M}$ be an upper bound. Then we have, for all integers N, $\sum_{k=1}^{N} (a_k^n)^2 \leqq M$. Letting $n \to \infty$ in this finite sum, we get $\sum_{k=1}^{N} (a_k)^2 \leqq M$. Since N is arbitrary, it follows that $\|\boldsymbol{a}\|^2 = \sum_{k=1}^{\infty} (a_k)^2 \leqq M$. Hence $\boldsymbol{a}$ is square-summable. Moreover, given $\epsilon > 0$, n can be found so large that $\|\boldsymbol{a}^n - \boldsymbol{a}^m\|^2 < \epsilon$ for all $m > n$. Hence for every integer N we have $\sum_{k=1}^{N} (a_k^n - a_k^m)^2 < \epsilon$. Letting $m \to \infty$, we obtain $\sum_{k=1}^{N} (a_k^n - a_k)^2 < \epsilon$. Since N is arbitrary, this implies $\sum_{k=1}^{\infty} (a_k^n - a_k)^2 < \epsilon$, q.e.d.

The property of Hilbert space which is most useful for establishing the completeness of eigenfunctions is the following.

THEOREM 12. *An orthogonal sequence* $\{\phi_k\}$ *of vectors of a Hilbert space is complete if and only if there is no nonzero vector f orthogonal to all the* ϕ_k.

Proof. Let f be a vector, and let $\{\phi_k\}$ be a sequence of orthogonal vectors in a Hilbert space $\mathfrak{H}$. Let $g_n = \sum_{k=1}^{n} c_k\phi_k$ be the n-th least square approximation to f by a linear combination of $\phi_1, \cdots, \phi_n$; as before $c_k = (f,\phi_k)/(\phi_k,\phi_k)$. For $m > n$,

$$\| g_m - g_n \|^2 = \sum_{n+1}^{m} [(f,\phi_k)^2/(\phi_k,\phi_k)] \leqq \sum_{n+1}^{\infty} [(f,\phi_k)^2/(\phi_k,\phi_k)].$$

By the Bessel inequality (24), the series $\sum_{k=1}^{\infty} [(f,\phi_k)^2/(\phi_k,\phi_k)]$ of positive numbers is convergent; hence the last sum in the preceding display tends to zero as $n \to \infty$. That is, the sequence $\{g_n\}$ is a *Cauchy sequence.*

It follows that $\mathfrak{H}$, being complete, contains a vector g to which the g_n converge; let $h = f - g = \lim_{m\to\infty} (f - g_m)$. Then, since $(f - g_m, \phi_k) = 0$ for all $m \geqq k$, we have in the limit as $m \to \infty$, $(h, \phi_k) = 0$ for all k. By Theorem 9 (Parseval's equality), $h = 0$ for all f if and only if $\{\phi_k\}$ is complete. This completes the proof.

Remark. A complete orthonormal sequence $\{\phi_k\}$ in the space (ℓ_2) is obtained by choosing $\phi_k = e^k$, the k-th unit vector whose k-th component is one, and whose other components are all zero.

The Euclidean vector space $\mathcal{C}[a,b]$ of all continuous functions on a finite interval $a \leqq x \leqq b$ is not complete, that is, it is not a Hilbert space. The following is an example of a mean square Cauchy sequence of continuous functions which does not converge to any continuous function. In $-1 \leqq x \leqq 1$, let $f_n(x) = 0$ for $-1 \leqq x \leqq 0$, $f_n(x) = nx$ for $0 \leqq x \leqq 1/n$ and $f_n(x) = 1$ for $1/n \leqq x \leqq 1$. The limit function $f_\infty(x)$ equals 0 for $-1 \leqq x \leqq 0$ and 1 for $0 < x \leqq 1$.

Though the Euclidean vector space $\mathcal{C}[a,b]$ is not complete, it can be embedded in the (complete) Hilbert space (ℓ_2), as follows. First, make the change of independent variable $t = \pi(x - a)/(b - a)$, to map the interval $[a,b]$ on $[0,\pi]$. Then for each $f(x) \in \mathcal{C}[a,b]$, expand $\tilde{f}(t) = f(a + (b - a)t/\pi)$ into the *cosine series* $\tilde{f}(t) = \Sigma c_k \cos kt$, $k = 1, 2, \cdots$. The vector $\mathbf{f} = (c_0,c_1,c_2,\cdots)$ defines an element of the space (ℓ_2), by the Bessel inequality.

The correspondence $f \to \mathbf{f}$ maps the space $\mathcal{C}[a,b]$ into the space (ℓ_2); moreover it preserves vector operations: $f + g \to \mathbf{f} + \mathbf{g}$ and $\lambda f \to \lambda \mathbf{f}$. By Parseval's generalized equality (23′), which is applicable since the cosine functions are complete (Theorem 3, Corollary 3),

$$(f,g) = [\pi/(b-a)] \int_a^b f(x)g(x)dx = \int_0^\pi \tilde{f}(t)\tilde{g}(t)dt.$$

Hence the correspondence $f \to \tilde{f}$ also preserves *inner products* (up to a constant normalizing factor); therefore it also preserves lengths $(f,f)^{1/2}$. In particular, $f = 0$ implies $\int_0^\pi \tilde{f}^2(t)dt = 0$ — and hence, $\tilde{f}$ being continuous, that $\tilde{f}(t) \equiv 0$. In conclusion, we have proved the following result.

LEMMA 2. *The Euclidean vector space $\mathfrak{C}[a,b]$ $(-\infty < a < b < +\infty)$ can be embedded in the Hilbert space (ℓ_2), with preservation of vector operations and inner products.*

More generally, let ϕ_n be a complete sequence of orthonormal vectors in an arbitrary Euclidean space E. Then the mapping $f \to \mathbf{c} = \{c_k\}$, where $c_k = (f,\phi_k)$ for f in E, defines an embedding of E as a subspace of (ℓ_2). In the same way as above we obtain

LEMMA 3. *Every Euclidean vector space with a complete sequence of orthonormal vectors can be embedded in (ℓ_2), with preservation of vector operations and inner products.*

In view of this Lemma, it suffices to prove Theorem 10 under the assumption that the Euclidean vector space E is complete, that is, that E is a Hilbert space. We shall make this assumption from now on.

11*. Proof of completeness. We are now ready to prove Theorem 10. But to bring out more clearly the idea of the proof, we first treat a special case.

We define a sequence of orthonormal vectors of a Hilbert space to be an *orthonormal basis* if and only if it is complete.

LEMMA. *Let $\{\phi_k\}$ be an orthonormal basis in the Hilbert space $\mathfrak{H}$. Let $\{\psi_k\}$ be an orthonormal sequence in $\mathfrak{H}$ satisfying the conditions*

$$\sum_{k=1}^{\infty} \| \psi_k - \phi_k \|^2 < 1. \tag{29}$$

Then the sequence $\{\psi_k\}$ is also an orthonormal basis in $\mathfrak{H}$.

Proof. If the sequence ψ_k were not a basis, then we could find a nonzero function h orthogonal to every ψ_k, by Theorem 12. The inner product of this function with ϕ_k is given by

$$(h,\phi_k) = (h,\psi_k) + (h,\phi_k - \psi_k) = (h,\phi_k - \psi_k).$$

Squaring and using the Schwarz inequality,

$$(h,\phi_k)^2 = (h,\phi_k - \psi_k)^2 \leqq \| h \|^2 \| \phi_k - \psi_k \|^2. \tag{29'}$$

Summing with respect to k, we get

$$\sum_{k=1}^{\infty} (h,\phi_k)^2 \leqq \| h \|^2 \sum_{k=1}^{\infty} \| \phi_k - \psi_k \|^2 < \| h \|^2,$$

in evident violation of Parseval's equality (Theorem 9), since the ϕ_k are an orthonormal basis.

COROLLARY 1. *Replace condition* (29) *above by the weaker condition*

$$\sum_{k=N+1}^{\infty} \| \psi_k - \phi_k \|^2 < 1 \tag{30}$$

for some integer N. *Then every element of* $\mathfrak{H}$ *orthogonal to* $\phi_1, \cdots, \phi_N$ *and to* $\psi_{N+1}, \psi_{N+2}, \cdots$ *must vanish.*

Proof. Any such element h satisfies the inequality (29′) for $k > N$. Hence, summing over all k, we have, since $(h,\phi_k) = 0$ for $k = 1, 2, \cdots, N$,

$$\| h \|^2 = \sum_{k=1}^{\infty} (h,\phi_k)^2 = \sum_{k=N+1}^{\infty} (h,\phi_k)^2 \leqq \| h \|^2 \sum_{k=N+1}^{\infty} \| \phi_k - \psi_k \|^2 < \| h \|^2,$$

again contradicting Parseval's equality.

COROLLARY 2. *If* φ_k *is an orthonormal basis, and* ψ_k *an orthonormal sequence satisfying* (30), *then every element of* $\mathfrak{H}$ *orthogonal to* $\psi_{N+1}, \psi_{N+2}, \cdots$ *and to the elements*

$$\eta_n = \phi_n - \sum_{k=N+1}^{\infty} (\phi_n,\psi_k)\psi_k, \qquad n = 1, 2, \cdots, N \tag{31}$$

must vanish.

Proof. For any such element h we have

$$(h,\phi_n) = (h,\eta_n) + \sum_{k=N+1}^{\infty} (\phi_n,\psi_k)(h,\psi_k) = 0$$

for $n = 1, 2, \cdots, N$. Thus h also satisfies the conditions of Corollary 1 and therefore vanishes.

The proof of Theorem 10 can now be completed as follows. Choose an integer N so that

$$\sum_{k=N+1}^{\infty} \| \psi_k - \phi_k \|^2 < 1.$$

By Corollary 2 any element h of $\mathfrak{H}$ which is orthogonal to the elements $\psi_{N+1}, \psi_{N+2}, \cdots$ and to the elements η_n ($n = 1, 2, \cdots, N$) defined by formula (31) must vanish. Denote by S the set of all elements of $\mathfrak{H}$ orthogonal to $\psi_{N+1}, \psi_{N+2}, \cdots$. Evidently S is a vector space containing $\eta_1, \cdots, \eta_n$. By virtue of the above remark, the vector space S contains only the linear combinations of these elements. In other words, S is a finite-dimensional vector space whose dimension is at most N.

But the elements $\psi_1, \psi_2, \cdots, \psi_N$ also belong to the vector space S, and they are linearly independent (they are an orthonormal sequence!). Therefore the elements $\psi_1, \psi_2, \cdots, \psi_N$ are a *basis* for the vector space S.† Hence the elements $\eta_1, \eta_2, \cdots, \eta_N$ are linear combinations of $\psi_1, \psi_2, \cdots, \psi_n$. It follows that any element of $\mathfrak{H}$ which is orthogonal to all the ψ_k must vanish, because such an element is also orthogonal to $\eta_1, \cdots, \eta_n$ and to $\psi_{N+1}, \psi_{N+2}, \cdots$. We conclude that the sequence $\{\psi_k\}$ is complete, proving Theorem 10.

Theorem 10 implies Theorem 11, as has already been shown in § 9.

It is natural to ask whether the sums $\Sigma c_k\phi_k$ having square-summable coefficient sequences cannot also be interpreted as functions. This question can also be answered in the affirmative, using the Lebesgue integral. Given any complete family $\{\phi_k\}$ of orthonormal functions on $[a,b]$, the partial sums $\sum_{k=1}^{n} c_k\phi_k$ with *square-summable* coefficient sequence $\{c_k\}$ converge in the mean square to a function $f(x)$ which is *square-integrable* for the *Lebesgue integral.* Conversely, if $f(x)$ is Lebesgue square-integrable, and $c_k = (f,\phi_k)$, then the partial sums $f_n = \sum_{k=1}^{n} c_k\phi_k$ converge to $f(x)$ in the mean square. That is, the metric completion of the space $\mathcal{C}[a,b]$ is precisely the Hilbert space $\mathcal{L}_2[a,b]$ of all functions on $[a,b]$ whose squares are Lebesgue integrable. It is this space which is really appropriate for the theory of expansions in eigenfunctions.

EXERCISES D

1. Show that in a finite-dimensional Euclidean vector space E a set S of elements is dense if and only if, whenever $(\phi,f) = 0$ for all $\phi \in$ S, then $f = 0$.

2. Show that an orthonormal sequence ϕ_k $(k = 1, 2, 3, \cdots)$ in a Euclidean vector space is complete if and only if Parseval's equality (23) holds for all f in a dense subset.

3. (Vitali) Show that an orthonormal sequence $\phi_k(x)$ $(k = 1, 2, \cdots)$ of continuous functions for $a \leqq x \leqq b$ is complete if and only if

$$\sum_{k=1}^{\infty} \left(\int_a^x \phi_k(t)dt \right)^2 = x - a, \qquad a \leqq x \leqq b.$$

(*Hint:* Show that linear combinations of the functions $f(x) = x - c$ form a dense subset, and apply the preceding exercise.)

*4. (Dalzell) Show that a sequence of continuous orthonormal square-integrable functions $\phi_k(x)$, $a \leqq x \leqq b$, is complete if and only if

$$\sum_{k=1}^{\infty} \int_a^b \left(\int_a^x \phi_k(t)dt \right)^2 dx = (b-a)^2/2.$$

(*Hint:* Let $q(x) = x - a - \sum_{k=1}^{\infty} \left(\int_a^x \phi_k(t)dt \right)^2$, and show that $q(x) \equiv 0$ by establishing $q(x) \geqq 0$ and $\int_a^b q(x)dx = 0$, q continuous, applying Ex. 3.)

†As shown in Birkhoff and Mac Lane, pp. 168–169.

5. Assuming the equality $\sum_{k=1}^{\infty} 1/k^2 = \pi^2/6$, infer from Ex. 4 that the trigonometric functions are complete.

6. (Moment problem) Let $f(x)$ be continuous, $a \leqq x \leqq b$, and let

$$m_n = \int_a^b x^n f(x)dx.$$

Show that if all the moments m_n vanish, then $f(x) \equiv 0$. (*Hint:* Use the Weierstrass Approximation Theorem.)

7. Prove the completeness of the eigenfunctions of any regular S-L system with boundary conditions $u'(a) = u'(b) = 0$.

*8. Let $G(f_1,f_2,\cdots,f_n) = \det(a_{ij})$, where $a_{ij} = (f_i,f_j)$. Show that the minimum of $\|f - \Sigma c_k f_k\|$ is equal to $G(f,f_1,f_2,\cdots,f_n)/G(f_1,f_2,\cdots,f_n)$. (*Hint:* Interpret the determinants as volumes.)

9. Show by a counterexample that Theorem 10 does not remain valid unless both the sequences are assumed to be orthogonal.

10. Consider the orthonormal sequence ϕ_k, and let $\psi_k = \phi_k$, $k \geqq 2$, $\psi_1 = 0$. Then $\Sigma \|\phi_k - \psi_k\|^2 < \infty$, but $\{\psi_k\}$ is not complete. Which hypothesis of Theorem 10 is violated?

11. Show that the first-order DE $iu' + (q(x) + \lambda)u = 0$, $a \leqq x \leqq b$, with the boundary condition $u(a) = u(b)$, has a complete sequence of eigenfunctions for any real continuous $q(x)$.

12. Show that linear combinations of the trigonometric functions are dense in $-\pi \leqq x \leqq \pi$ relative to any continuous positive weight function.

BIBLIOGRAPHY

General References

AHLFORS, L. V. *Complex Analysis: An Introduction to the Theory of Analytic Functions of One Complex Variable.* McGraw-Hill Book Company, Inc., New York, 1953.

BIRKHOFF, G., and MAC LANE, S. *A Survey of Modern Algebra,* Second Edition. The Macmillan Company, New York, 1953.

COURANT, R. *Differential and Integral Calculus,* Volumes 1 and 2. Interscience Publishers, Inc., New York, 1937.

———, and HILBERT, D. *Methods of Mathematical Physics,* Volume 1. Interscience Publishers, Inc., New York, 1953.

ERDELYI, A. (Editor). *Higher Transcendental Functions* (three volumes). McGraw-Hill Book Company, Inc., New York, 1953, 1955.

FLETCHER, A., MILLER, J. C. P., and ROSENHEAD, L. *An Index of Mathematical Tables.* McGraw-Hill Book Company, Inc., New York, 1946.

GOURSAT, E. *Cours d'Analyse Mathématique,* Fifth Edition (three volumes). Gauthier-Villars, Paris, 1927.

GRAVES, L. M. *The Theory of Functions of Real Variables,* Second Edition. McGraw-Hill Book Company, Inc., New York, 1956.

HILDEBRAND, F. B. *Introduction to Numerical Analysis.* McGraw-Hill Book Company, Inc., New York, 1956.

HILLE, E. *Analytic Function Theory,* Volume 1. Ginn and Company, Boston, 1959, Volume 2, 1960.

KAPLAN, W. *Advanced Calculus.* Addison-Wesley Publishing Company, Inc., Reading, Massachusetts, 1952.

PEIRCE, B. O., and FOSTER, R. M. *A Short Table of Integrals,* Fourth Edition. Ginn and Company, Boston, 1956.

PICARD, E. *Traité d'Analyse,* Second Edition (three volumes). Gauthier-Villars, Paris, 1922–28.

RUDIN, W. *Principles of Mathemathical Analysis.* McGraw-Hill Book Company, Inc., New York, 1953.

TAYLOR, A. E. *Advanced Calculus.* Ginn and Company, Boston, 1957.

WIDDER, D. V. *Advanced Calculus,* Second Edition. Prentice-Hall, Inc., Englewood Cliffs, New Jersey, 1960.

Works on Ordinary Differential Equations

BELLMAN, R. *Stability Theory of Differential Equations.* McGraw-Hill Book Company, Inc., New York, 1953.

BIEBERBACH, L. *Theorie der Differentialgleichungen.* Springer, Berlin, 1930.

———. *Theorie der gewöhnlichen Differentialgleichungen auf Funktiontheoretischer Grundlage dargestellt.* Springer, Berlin, 1953.

BÔCHER, M. *Leçons sur les méthodes de Sturm.* Gauthier-Villars, Paris, 1917.

CESARI, L. *Asymptotic Behavior and Stability Problems in Ordinary Differential Equations.* Springer, Berlin, 1959.

CODDINGTON, E. A., and LEVINSON, N. *Theory of Ordinary Differential Equations.* McGraw-Hill Book Company, Inc., New York, 1955.

FORD, L. R. *Differential Equations*, Second Edition. McGraw-Hill Book Company, Inc., New York, 1955.

HENRICI, PETER. *Numerical Integration of Ordinary Differential Equations.* John Wiley & Sons, Inc., New York, 1961.

HOCHSTADT, H. *Special Functions of Mathematical Physics.* Holt, New York, 1961.

HUREWICZ, W. *Lectures on Ordinary Differential Equations.* John Wiley & Sons, Inc., New York, 1958.

INCE, E. L. *Ordinary Differential Equations.* Dover Publications, Inc., New York, 1956.

KAMKE, E. *Differentialgleichungen: Lösungsmethoden und Lösungen.* Akademische Verlagsgesellschaft, Leipzig, 1943.

———. *Differentialgleichungen reeller Funktionen.* Akademische Verlagsgesellschaft, Leipzig, 1930.

KAPLAN, W. *Ordinary Differential Equations.* Addison-Wesley Publishing Company, Inc., Reading, Massachusetts, 1958.

LEFSCHETZ, S. *Differential Equations, Geometric Theory.* Interscience Publishers, Inc., New York, 1957.

LIAPOUNOFF, A. M. *Problème Générale de la Stabilité du Mouvement.* Annals of Mathematics Studies, No. 17. Princeton University Press, Princeton, New Jersey, 1947.

MCLACHLAN, N. W. *Ordinary Non-Linear Differential Equations in Engineering and Physical Sciences*, Second Edition. Clarendon Press, Oxford, 1950.

MARTIN, W. T., and REISSNER, E. *Elementary Differential Equations*, Second Edition. Addison-Wesley Publishing Company, Inc., Reading, Massachusetts, 1961.

MINORSKY, N. *Introduction to Non-Linear Mechanics.* Edwards Brothers, Ann Arbor, Michigan, 1947.

NIEMYTSKII, V., and STEPANOV, V. *Qualitative Theory of Differential Equations.* Princeton University Press, Princeton, New Jersey, 1959.

PICARD, E. *Leçons sur Quelques Problèmes aux Limites de la Théorie des Équations Différentielles.* Gauthier-Villars, Paris, 1930.

POINCARÉ, H. *Les Méthodes Nouvelles de la Mécanique Céleste*, Volumes 1–3. Dover Publications, Inc., New York, 1957.

POOLE, E. G. C. *Introduction to the Theory of Linear Differential Equations.* Clarendon Press, Oxford, 1936.

REY PASTOR, J., and BRZEZICKI, A. DE C., *Funciones de Bessel*, Dossat, Madrid, 1958.

SANSONE, G. *Equazioni Differenziali nel Campo Reale*, Volumes 1 and 2. Zanichelli, Bologna, 1948.

———, and CONTI, R. *Equazioni Differenziali Non-Lineari.* Cremonese, Rome, 1956.

STOKER, J. J. *Nonlinear Vibrations in Mechanical and Electrical Systems.* Interscience Publishers, Inc., New York, 1950.

TITCHMARSH, E. C. *Eigenfunction Expansions Associated with Second-Order Differential Equations*, Volume 1. Clarendon Press, Oxford, 1946; Volume 2, 1950.

TRICOMI, F. G. *Equazioni Differenziali*, Second Edition. Einaudi, Turin, 1953.

INDEX

Adams three-level methods, 212
Adams-Bashforth predictor formula, 210
Adams-Moulton corrector formula, 211
adjoint, 37
adjoint equation, 37
adjoint operator, 36
Airy DE, 55, 250, 251, 253
amplitude, 26, 58, 85, 152, 257
amplitude, modified, 268
analytic coefficient-function, 52
analytic continuation, 213
analytic DE's, 119
analytic equations, 119
analytic first-order DE, 65
analytic function, 50, 59, 67, 119, 213
analytic functions of two variables, 67
approximate function table, 162, 185, 203
approximate numerical differentiation, 191
approximate solution, 161, 163
approximation, mean square, 288
approximation, uniform, 290
approximation, Weierstrass Theorem of, 294
Arzelà-Ascoli Theorem, 126
associated Laguerre DE, 235
associated Legendre DE, 239
asymptotic stability, 144
autonomous system, 129, 131, 136
autonomous system, plane, 131

backward difference, 185
basis of solutions, 28, 78, 81
basis of solutions of difference equation, 195
Bernoulli DE, 11
Bessel DE, 26, 34, 56, 226, 230, 245, 248, 253, 254
Bessel function, 34, 56 ff., 226, 253, 274
Bessel function, modified, 228, 263
Bessel inequality, 290, 303
black box, 84
boundary condition, 27, 46, 247
boundary term, 250
branch point, 214
branch point, fixed, 215
branch pole, 217

canonical bases, 221
Cauchy polygon, 162, 177, 183
Cauchy sequence, 305
Cauchy's formula, 59
central difference, 185
change of variable, 38, 265
characteristic equation, 195, 221
characteristic exponent, 225, 241
characteristic polynomial, 73, 137
Chebyshev polynomials, 299
Chebyshev polynomials of second kind, 300
circuit matrix, 219
Clairaut DE, 17
closed domain, 5
Comparison Theorem, 22, 23, 33, 258
Comparison Theorem, Sturm, 33, 259
Comparison Theorem, Szegö's, 265
completeness, 290, 303
completeness, proof of, 307
complex conjugate, 75
complex solutions, 70
confluent hypergeometric function, 58
conjugate point, 44
conservative dynamical system, 145
constant coefficient, 73, 195
Continuation Principle, 214
continuation of solutions, 122
Continuity Theorem, 18, 21, 103, 105
continuous spectrum, 279, 284
contour lines, 132
convergence, mean square, 288
convolution, 95
corrected trapezoidal method, 180
corrector formula, 178, 204, 211
cosine series, 287
Cotes' Rule, 170
critical point, 7, 8, 130, 144
cumulative error, 167, 181

damped linear oscillator, 134
damped nonlinear oscillations, 155
damping factor, 155

degenerate case, 136
degree, 15
dense subset, 302
dependence on initial value, 70, 103, 105
derivative of vector function, 101
determinism, 18
deviation, 161
difference equation, 184, 193, 194
difference equation, constant coefficients, 195
difference operator, backward, 185
difference operator, central, 185
difference operator, forward, 185
difference, second, 186
differential equation, 3
differential inequality, 20, 22, 24, 106
differentiation, numerical, 190
direction field, 13
discrepancy, 175
discrete spectrum, 279
discretization error, 190
discriminant, 142
divided difference, 185
domain, 5
double geometric series, 59
dynamical system, 133, 145
dynamically stable, 155

eigenfunction, 247, 264
eigenfunction, completeness of, 303
eigenfunction, normalized, 271
eigenfunction, sequence of, 263
eigenfunction, square-integrable, 255
eigenvalue, 247, 262, 264, 265
eigenvalue distribution, 270
elastic bar, 252
elastic spring, 152
elliptic function, 143
endpoint conditions, 247
endpoint conditions, inhomogeneous, 276
endpoint conditions, periodic, 248
endpoint conditions, separated, 247, 276
energy function, 145, 150, 151
energy levels, 279
equicontinuous functions, 125
equilibrium point, 145
equivalence, linear, 140
equivalence of autonomous systems, 137
equivalence by transformation, 138
equivalent integral equation, 111
equivalent systems, 138
error, 161
error, cumulative, 181
error analysis, 204
error bounds, 168, 170
error estimate, 168, 172
error function, 5
escape time, 123, 126
essential singularity, 216
Euclidean vector space, 301
Euler-Maclaurin formula, 172
Euler's DE, 43, 60, 75, 223, 242, 245
Euler's quadratic DE, 15
exact differential, 7
existence theorem, 18, 62, 69, 70, 112, 117, 122
exponential substitution, 73
extrapolation method, Richardson's, 206
extremum, 43

feedback, 98
Fejér's Convergence Theorem, 286, 295
first-order DE, 4
first-order DE, analytic, 65
first-order DE, linear, 9
first-order DE, nonlinear, 63
first-order systems, 99
first-order vector DE, 100
Five-Eight Rule, Simpson's, 202
fixed branch points, 215
focal point, 146
forced oscillation, 40
forcing term, 25
formal power series, 68
forward difference, 185
Fourier coefficients, 289
Fourier series, 286
Fourier's Convergence Theorem, 286
Frenet- Serret formula, 110
frequency, 85, 152
function of class $\mathcal{C}^n$, 5
function table, 162
Fuchsian equation, 241
fundamental matrix, 127
Fundamental Theorem of Calculus, 4

gain function, 85
Gaussian quadrature, 200, 202
generating function, 95
global solution, 122
gradient field, 135
graphical integration, 13
Green's function, 39, 41, 44, 45, 89, 95, 276, 277
Gregory-Newton formula, 187

Hankel function, 275
hard and soft springs, 152, 153
harmonic oscillator, 280
harmonic vibrations, simple, 252
Helmholtz equation, 253
Hermite DE, 53, 55, 256, 267
Hermite functions, 256, 280
Hermite polynomial, 53, 256, 298, 299
Hermite quadrature formula, 170, 202
Hilbert space, 304
holomorphic function, 59, 213
homogeneous first-order DE, 9, 14
homogeneous second-order linear DE, 25
hypergeometric DE, 225, 239, 244, 267
hypergeometric DE, self-adjoint form, 229
hypergeometric function, 236
hypergeometric function, confluent, 58

Implicit Function Theorem, 6
improved Euler method, 177, 212
incompressible flows, 132
indicial equation, 60, 225
indicial polynomial, 225
inhomogeneous linear DE, 9, 83
inhomogeneous fractional DE, 14
initial value, dependence on, 70, 103, 105
initial value problem, 18, 27, 109
inner product, 101, 119, 301
input-output operator, 84
integral, 8, 99
integral curve, 8, 129
integral operator, 45
integrating factor, 9, 35
interpolation, 185 ff.
interpolation error, 187
invariant, 38
invariant radii, 12
irregular singular point, 217, 240
iterative solution, 203, 215

Jacobi DE, 237, 267
Jacobi identity, 236
Jacobi polynomial, 237, 238, 284, 299

Kamke's inequality, 24

Lagrange identity, 37, 249
Lagrange interpolation, 187 ff.
Laguerre DE, 235, 267, 296
Laguerre DE, associated, 235
Laguerre DE, generalized, 284
Laguerre polynomials, 257, 296, 298, 299
Laplace transform, 92, 95
Laplacian, 55
least square approximation, 302
Lebesgue integral, 309
Legendre DE, 26, 38, 52, 55, 239, 254, 267
Legendre DE, associated, 239
Legendre polynomial, 53, 200, 254, 256, 267, 275, 284, 295, 298
Leibniz' Rule, 41
Lerch's Theorem, 93
Levinson-Smith Theorem, 158
Liapounov function, 150
Liapounov, Method of, 149
Liénard equation, 157
limit cycle, 156
linear combination, 26
linear DE, 9, 73, 214
linear DE with constant coefficients, 73, 195
linear difference equations with constant coefficients, 195
linear equivalence, 140
linear fractional DE, 14
linear fractional transformation, 242, 245
linear independence, 29, 77
linear interpolation, 163, 186
linear operator, 35
linear oscillator, 134
linear systems, 115, 136
linearly independent, 29, 30, 77
Liouville formula for iterated integrals, 96
Liouville normal form, 265
Liouville reduction, 266
Lipschitz condition, 19, 20, 22, 102
Lipschitz condition, generalized, 22
Lipschitz condition, one-sided, 22, 108
Lipschitz constant, 19, 102
local existence theorem, 117
local solution, 122
locally equivalent systems, 140

Mathieu equation, 246, 248, 251
mean square approximation, 288
mean square convergence, 288
mesh, 184
mesh-halving, 203
Method of Liapounov, 149

Method of Majorants, 60, 63, 68, 231
Method of Undetermined Coefficients, 51, 84
midpoint integration, 179, 212
midpoint quadrature, 167 ff.
Milne's Method, 197, 202
mixed spectrum, 281
modified amplitude, 268
modified Bessel function, 228
modified Euler method, 179
modified phase, 268
modified Prüfer substitution, 267
moment problem, 310
movable singular point, 215
m-step difference equation, 194
multiplicity of root, 73

Nagumo's Theorem, 128
Neumann function, 228, 230, 275
neutrally stable, 144
nodal point, 146, 148
nonlinear DE, first-order, 63
nonlinear oscillations, 151, 155
norm of partition, 163
normal curve family, 6, 18, 70
normal DE, 4, 26, 118
normal form, 25
normal modes of vibration, 252
normal system, 100, 108
normal vector DE, 100
normalized eigenfunction, 271
n-body problem, 109
n-th order DE, 100, 118
numerical differentiation, 190
Nyquist diagram, 86
Nyquist Stability Criterion, 87

one-body problem, 111
one-level formula, 163
one-level method, 181
one-sided Lipschitz condition, 22, 108
one-step method, 181
operator, 35, 84, 112, 185
operational calculus, 74
orbit, 129
order of accuracy, 166
Order of Growth Theorem, 233
orientation, 133
orthogonal expansion, 287
orthogonal polynomials, 293 ff.
orthonormal functions, 249, 290
Oscillation Theorem, 259, 261, 263
oscillations, 151, 152, 155
oscillatory, 75
Osgood's Uniqueness Theorem, 24

parabolic interpolation, 171, 186
Parseval equality, 291, 302
Peano existence theorem, 124
Peano Uniqueness Theorem, 22
Pearson's DE, 63
periodic endpoint conditions, 248
perturbation equation, 123
phase, 26, 152, 257
phase constant, 26, 85
phase lag, 85
phase-plane, Poincaré, 133
phase-space, 145
Picard approximation, 112
Picone's identity, 265
plane autonomous system, 131
Poincaré phase-plane, 133
pole, 216
polynomial, indicial, 225
polynomial interpolation, 186
polynomials of stable type, 82
potential energy integral, 151
power series, 49 ff.
predictor, 178, 204, 210
Prüfer substitution, 257, 295
Prüfer substitution, modified, 267
Prüfer system, 258
punctured plane, 13

quadrature, 11
quartic interpolation, 186

radius of convergence, 59, 63, 66
Rayleigh DE, 156
real analytic DE's, 121
recursive formula, 163
reduced equation, 25
reduced system, 116
regular curve family, 6, 131
regular DE, 26
regular singular point, 217, 224, 230, 235, 246
regular Sturm-Liouville DE, 247
regular Sturm-Liouville system, 247
relative error, 167
relaxation oscillations, 159
removable singularity, 216
resonance, 86
restoring force, 151
Riccati DE, 30, 47, 48, 66, 67
Riccati DE, generalized, 32

Richardson's extrapolation method, 206
Riemann DE, 243
Riemann sum, 162
right-inverse, 84, 278
Rodrigues formula, 238, 284, 299
roundoff error, 189, 191
Routh-Hurwitz conditions, 82
Runge-Kutta method, 208, 211

saddle point, 148
Schroedinger equation, 279
Schwarz inequality, 101, 255, 301
second difference, 186
second-order linear DE, 25
secular equation, 137
self-adjoint DE, 37, 247
separated endpoint conditions, 247
separated endpoint conditions, inhomogeneous, 276
separation of variables, 16
Separation Theorem, Sturm, 32
simple branch point, 217
simple harmonic vibrations, 252
simple pendulum, 135
Simpson's Five-Eight Rule, 202
Simpson's Rule, 169, 173, 183, 197, 200
sine integral function, 5
sine series, 287
singular locus, 15
singular point, 25, 214 ff.
singular point at infinity, 240
singular Sturm-Liouville system, 248, 254, 279
singularity, 25
soft and hard springs, 152, 153
solution, 3, 26, 99
solution base, 78
solution curve, 4, 99, 129
Sonin-Polya Theorem, 276
spectrum, continuous, 279, 284
spectrum, discrete, 248, 279
spectrum, mixed, 281
spring, elastic, 152
square-integrable, 255, 284, 309
square well potential, 280
stable, 81, 88
stable critical point, 143, 146
stability, 81, 143, 196
stability criterion, Nyquist, 87
stability diagram, 83
stability of difference equations, 196
star point, 148
starting process, 202, 203
streamline, 129
strict stability, 143, 149
strictly stable DE, 81, 87, 88
strictly stable critical point, 144
Sturm Comparison Theorem, 33, 258
Sturm Convexity Theorem, 263
Sturm Oscillation Theorem, 263
Sturm Separation Theorem, 32
Sturm-Liouville equation, 247
Sturm-Liouville series, 248
Sturm-Liouville system, 247
subspace, 302
successive approximation, 112 ff.
superposition principle, 26, 36
system, 99
Szegö's Comparison Theorem, 265

third-order DE, 32
three-level method, Adams, 212
time-independent operator, 85
time-independent system, 73, 129
Tonelli's method, 125
trajectory, 129
transfer function, 84, 85
trapezoidal approximation, 212
trapezoidal integration, 174, 182
trapezoidal method, corrected, 180
trapezoidal quadrature, 170, 198
trapezoidal quadrature, error bound, 170
triangle inequality, 101, 301
trigonometric DE, 26, 53
trival solution, 26
truncation error, 177, 190
two-endpoint conditions, 43
two-endpoint problem, 27, 43, 276
two-level midpoint method, 194, 207
two-step difference equation, 194

ultraspherical DE, 237
ultraspherical polynomials, 253
undamped oscillations, 151
undetermined coefficients, method of, 50
uniform approximation, 290
uniform mesh, 184
uniqueness, 5
uniqueness theorem, 18, 19, 20, 22, 24, 27, 70, 103, 104, 120
unstable, 144
unstalbe difference approximation, 204

van der Pol DE, 156
variation of parameters, 41

variational equation, 124
vector, 100
vector field, 129
vector space, Euclidean, 301
vector-valued function, 100
vibrating membrane, 253
vibration problems, 251
vortex points, 146, 151

Weddle's Rule, 170
Weierstrass Approximation Theorem, 294
Weierstrass Convergence Theorem, 120
weight function, 249
well-set problems, 18, 102
Wronskian, 29

zeros of Bessel functions, 57, 58
zeros of solutions, 285

A B C D E F G H I J 0 6 9 8 7 6 5 4 3 2

PRINTED IN THE UNITED STATES OF AMERICA